D1237788

WITHDRAWN

# KINETIC THEORY OF LIQUIDS

# KINETIC THEORY OF LIQUIDS

BY

J. FRENKEL

DOVER PUBLICATIONS, INC.
New York

This new Dover edition,
first published in 1955, is an unabridged and unaltered republication of the first English translation published in 1946. It is published through special arrangement with Oxford University Press.

Manufactured in the United States of America

# PREFACE

THE recent development of the theory of the liquid state, which distinguishes this theory from the older views based on the analogy between the liquid and the gaseous state, is characterized by the reapproximation of the liquid state—at temperatures not too far removed from the crystallization point—to the solid (crystalline) state.

The apparent opposition between these two states has been removed by the disclosure of elements of rigidity and order in liquid bodies on the one hand, and of elements of fluidity and disorder in solid (crystalline) bodies on the other.

The kinetic theory of liquids must accordingly be developed as a generalization and extension of the kinetic theory of solid bodies. As a matter of fact, it would be more correct to unify them under the title of 'condensed bodies'.

In the present book the main stress is laid upon the liquid state; the solid state is considered (in the first two chapters) from the point of view of the amendments which must be introduced in the classical theory of ideal crystal lattices in order to bridge the gap between the solid and liquid states.

I was led to a revision of this classical theory in 1924, in connexion with a study of such processes as the evaporation, diffusion, and conduction of electricity in solid bodies at elevated temperatures.

The introduction into the kinetic theory of real crystals of the conception of a partial dissociation of the crystal lattice (Joffé), of interstitial atoms and movable holes, of the heat motion as an alternation of small vibrations about fixed equilibrium positions with a jerk-like displacement of these positions, has paved the way to a correct understanding of the character of the heat motion of molecules in liquid bodies as a motion of a vibration-diffusion type, with a much more pronounced diffusion component than in the case of solids, i.e. with a much more rapid displacement of the equilibrium positions, in conjunction with the absence of regularity in their spatial distribution.

This conception forms the molecular-kinetic basis for that phenomenological unification of the solid and liquid states of matter from the point of view of their mechanical ('visco-elastic') properties, which was proposed long ago by Maxwell with respect to *amorphous* bodies.

It was believed, however, until the pioneer work of Stewart (1928) on the X-ray analysis of the structure of liquid bodies, that these differ sharply from solid bodies in the thermodynamically stable (crystalline) state by the absence of any regularity in the arrangement and orientation of the atoms or molecules constituting them.

This difference has proved to be rather in the *degree* of order than a qualitative difference, since liquid bodies have been shown to display at low temperatures, lying in the vicinity of the crystallization point, a high degree of local (short-range) order in the relative distribution and orientation of their molecules, of the same type as that characteristic of the corresponding solids.

While the fundamental principles of the kinetic theory of liquids can be regarded as more or less settled, the quantitative development of various general questions of this theory is still in an embryonic stage. This refers, in particular, to such questions as the theory of fusion and the equation of state of liquid bodies. It has further been hardly possible to obtain a satisfactory quantitative theory of various types of liquids, corresponding to different special types of molecular structure and molecular forces, in spite of the considerable number of studies of this subject that have been published in the course of the last few years.

In these conditions the publication of a book on the kinetic theory of liquids may be thought premature. I feel justified, however, in having written it for three reasons. In the first place, because I myself have been interested in this theory for the last twenty years and have made a number of contributions to it (many of which have been published in Russian journals only and have remained unknown to foreign readers). In the second place, because an understanding of the principles of the kinetic theory of liquids seems to have been restricted thus far to a somewhat narrow circle of physicists and chemists, whereas it is of vital importance to all those who have to deal with matter in the condensed state. Finally, a presentation of this new theory, even in a very crude and incomplete form, may serve to attract the attention of other scientists to this subject and accelerate its further development.

The choice of the material incorporated in this book has been determined partly by the author's personal interests and partly by the limitations imposed by its size. Certain topics are treated at a greater length than they may appear to deserve, while other very interesting topics are wholly omitted. I have limited myself to the consideration of ordinary liquids, whose properties can be understood on the basis of classical mechanics and statistical theory, leaving wholly aside a number of interesting questions referring to 'quantum liquids', such as liquid helium II, the free electrons in metals, and the proton-neutron liquid in complex atomic nuclei.

I have written this book at a time ill suited to the pursuit of purely academic tasks. I may be excused for this by the consideration that, when victory had become certain, it seemed advisable to revert to topics of pre-war and post-war interest. In recalling the state of mind and the conditions in which this work has been carried through, I wish to express my debt of deepest gratitude to the men and women of my country who, in the ranks of the Russian Red Army, have heroically and victoriously struggled for the salvation of our life and civilization against the ruthless forces of the Nazi barbarians.

J. F.

ACADEMY OF SCIENCES OF THE
U.S.S.R. PHYSICO-TECHNICAL INSTITUTE
AND UNIVERSITY OF KAZAN, KAZAN—MOSCOW
*July* 1943

## NOTE

The publication of this book, which was written at Kazan in 1942 under rather difficult conditions, has been delayed owing to mailing difficulties connected with the war. I wish to express my warmest thanks to Professor N. F. Mott and to Dr. R. Sack, who undertook the arduous task of reading the proofs and corrected a number of mistakes which had slipped in owing to the impossibility of reading them myself.

J. F.

LENINGRAD, PHYSICO-TECHNICAL INSTITUTE
*March* 1946

# CONTENTS

# I

# REAL CRYSTALS AT ELEVATED TEMPERATURES

## 1. Evaporation of Crystalline Bodies

CRYSTALLINE bodies are usually described as possessing a perfectly regular structure. The only deviation from perfect regularity which is taken into account consists in the vibration of the atoms about their equilibrium positions, which are assumed to constitute an ideal three-dimensional crystal lattice (with a correction for the thermal expansion).

From this point of view, however, such processes as the evaporation of a crystal, its dissolution in a liquid medium, or the mutual diffusion of two different crystalline substances would be utterly unintelligible.

The simplest of these processes—the evaporation of a solid body—obviously consists in the separation of a fraction of the superficial atoms from the rest and their escape into the surrounding space. The possibility—more than that, the necessity—of such an escape directly follows from the general principles of statistical mechanics, in particular from Maxwell's law specifying the velocity distribution (which at elevated temperatures is the same in the solid and liquid as in the gaseous state). If $v_x$, the component of the velocity of a superficial atom along an axis $x$ normal to the surface of the crystal, is directed outwards and is sufficiently large, the attractive force acting on this atom will not be able to prevent it from escaping into the surrounding space. The minimum value of $v_x$ is determined by the equation

$$\tfrac{1}{2}mv_{x\,\min}^2 = U_0,$$

where $m$ is the mass of an atom and $U_0$ is the work necessary to remove it from its (superficial) equilibrium position to infinity, i.e. the evaporation energy referred to a single atom.

Now according to Maxwell's law the relative number of atoms whose velocity in the $x$-direction lies between $v_x$ and $v_x+dv_x$ is equal to

$$f(v_x)\,dv_x = \sqrt{\left(\frac{m}{2\pi kT}\right)}e^{-mv_x^2/2kT}\,dv_x, \tag{1}$$

where $T$ is the absolute temperature of the body.

The number of superficial atoms which during a time $dt$ pass through the respective equilibrium positions in the outward direction with a velocity in the range between $v_x$ and $v_x+dv_x$ referred to unit area of the surface is equal to $nf(v_x)\,dv_x\,v_x\,dt$, where $n$ is the average number of atoms in unit volume of the body. All those atoms for which $v_x \geqslant v_{x\,\min}$

do not return to their equilibrium positions but escape, i.e. are evaporated. Their number referred to unit time is thus equal to

$$G = n \int_{v_{x\,\min}}^{\infty} v_x f(v_x)\, dv_x,$$

that is,
$$G = n\sqrt{\left(\frac{m}{2\pi kT}\right)}\frac{1}{m}\int_{\frac{1}{2}mv_x^2=U_0}^{\infty} e^{-mv_x^2/2kT}\, d\left(\frac{mv_x^2}{2}\right),$$

or
$$G = n\sqrt{\left(\frac{kT}{2\pi m}\right)}e^{-U_0/kT}. \tag{2}$$

This expression is a measure of the rate of evaporation of a solid body as a function of the temperature. So long as $kT \ll U_0$, the rate of evaporation is practically negligible; it must rapidly increase, however, as $kT$ approaches the value $U_0$.

The preceding result can be obtained, without recourse to Maxwell's velocity distribution law, by using Boltzmann's law for the distribution of molecules in space under the influence of given external forces. According to this law the probability that an atom will be found in a position corresponding to a potential energy $U$ is proportional to the expression $e^{-U/kT}$ irrespective of the direction and magnitude of its velocity.

Let us consider a definite atom and let us compare the probability $P'$ of its being bound to a certain equilibrium position on the surface of the body with the probability $P''$ that it will be found in a free state, i.e. in the gas phase.

For the sake of simplicity we shall assume, to begin with, that the potential energy of the atom preserves over the whole surface $S$ of the body up to a certain distance $x = \delta$ (of the order of the interatomic distance) the constant value zero, while for $x > \delta$ it assumes a constant positive value $U_0$.

If $V$ denotes the volume of the gas phase, we get

$$\frac{P''}{P'} = \frac{e^{-U_0/kT}V}{S\delta}. \tag{3}$$

Now, the ratio of the probabilities $P''/P'$ must obviously be equal to the ratio between the number $N''$ of atoms in the gas phase and the number $N'$ of atoms situated on the surface $S$ of the body (i.e. forming its superficial layer). Hence it follows that

$$\frac{N''}{V} = \frac{N'}{S\delta}e^{-U_0/kT},$$

i.e.
$$n'' = \frac{n'}{\delta}e^{-U_0/kT}, \tag{4}$$

where $n''$ is the number of atoms in unit volume of the gas phase and $n'$ is the number of atoms per unit area of the surface of the solid body.

Since $n'$ is practically independent of the temperature, the temperature dependence of the density (concentration) of the saturated vapour is characterized by the Boltzmann factor $e^{-U_0/kT}$.

In order to obtain the equation (2) let us consider the inverse process to the evaporation of a solid, i.e. the condensation of a saturated vapour, and let us take into account the fact that in a state of statistical equilibrium the number of atoms which are evaporated per unit time and area must be equal (on the average) to the number of atoms which are condensed on the same area in unit time. Let us further assume that each atom of the vapour striking the surface of the solid remains attached to the latter (whereas in reality a fraction of the atoms striking the surface are reflected from it, as assumed in the elementary kinetic theory of gases). Under such conditions we get

$$G = n''\bar{v}_x, \tag{5}$$

where $\bar{v}_x$ is the average velocity of the atoms of the vapour moving towards the surface of the solid body.

Using Maxwell's law we get for it the expression

$$\bar{v}_x = \int\limits_0^\infty f(v_x)v_x\,dv_x = \sqrt{\left(\frac{m}{2kT\pi}\right)}\frac{1}{m}\int\limits_0^\infty e^{-mv_x^2/2kT}\,d\left(\frac{mv_x^2}{2}\right),$$

i.e.

$$\bar{v}_x = \sqrt{\left(\frac{kT}{2\pi m}\right)}. \tag{5 a}$$

Hence, according to (5) and (4),

$$G = \frac{n'}{\delta}\sqrt{\left(\frac{kT}{2\pi m}\right)}e^{-U_0/kT}. \tag{6}$$

This formula is identical with (2) if the number of atoms per unit area of the surface layer $n'$ is identified with the product $n\delta$, which fully corresponds to the physical meaning of the quantity $\delta$, namely the thickness of the surface layer.

In reality, of course, the latter has no definite thickness, and a better approximation to the actual conditions, referring to the superficial atoms, is obtained if the potential energy of one of them is represented as a function of its distance $x$ from the surface by a curve of the type shown in Fig. 1. This curve is characterized by a horizontal asymptote $U = U_0$ for $x = \infty$, a vertical asymptote for $x = 0$ (which corresponds to the impenetrability of the following atomic layer), and a minimum $U = 0$ at a point $x = x_0$ corresponding to the equilibrium position.

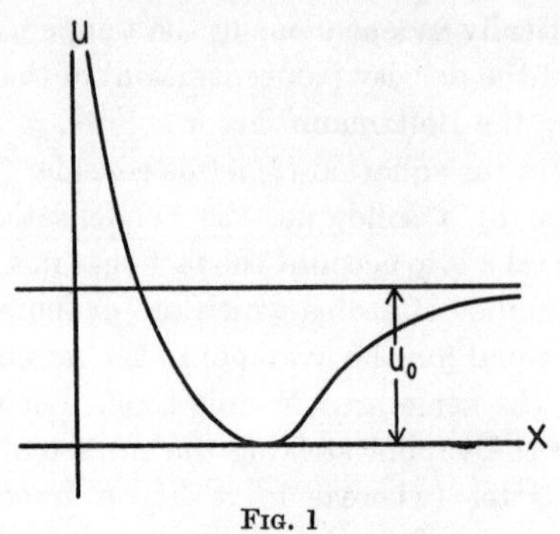


FIG. 1

For small values of the displacement $x - x_0 = \xi$ the potential energy can be represented approximately in the form

$$U(x) = U(x_0) + \tfrac{1}{2}U''(x_0)\xi^2 = \tfrac{1}{2}f\xi^2, \tag{7}$$

where $f$, the value of $d^2U/dx^2$ at the point $x = x_0$, is an essentially positive quantity.

This approximate expression for the potential energy can be used for the description of an atom in a bound state (on the surface of the body), whereas the potential energy of a free atom (in the gas phase) is equal to $U_0$, as before.

Under such conditions equation (3) must be replaced by the following equation:

$$\frac{P''}{P'} = \frac{Ve^{-U_0/kT}}{S\int e^{-f\xi^2/2kT}\,d\xi},$$

where the integration with respect to $\xi$ can be extended from $-\infty$ to $+\infty$ (because of the rapid decrease of the function $e^{-f\xi^2/2kT}$).

We thus come back to the previous equations (4) and (6) with the following expression for the 'effective thickness' of the surface layer:

$$\delta = \sqrt{\left(\frac{2\pi kT}{f}\right)}. \tag{8}$$

Substituting in (6) we get

$$G = n'\frac{1}{2\pi}\sqrt{\left(\frac{f}{m}\right)}e^{-U_0/kT}. \tag{9}$$

Now the quantity $$\nu_0 = \frac{1}{2\pi}\sqrt{\left(\frac{f}{m}\right)}$$

is the frequency of free vibrations performed by the surface atom in the bound state about its equilibrium position (so long as the amplitude of these vibrations is sufficiently small). We thus have

$$G = n'\nu_0 e^{-U_0/kT}. \tag{9a}$$

From the definition of the quantity $G$ it follows that the factor

$$\alpha = \nu_0 e^{-U_0/kT} \tag{10}$$

can be defined as the probability of the evaporation of a superficial atom in unit time. This means that the reciprocal quantity

$$\tau = \tau_0 e^{U_0/kT}, \tag{10a}$$

where $\tau_0 = 1/\nu_0$ is the period of free vibrations, is equal to the mean life of the superficial atom in the bound state reckoned from any given instant up to the instant of its evaporation. The exponential factor $e^{U_0/kT}$ is thus equal to the average number of oscillations about a given equilibrium position performed by a superficial atom before it is torn away from it and escapes into the gas phase.

The actual length of time the atom remains attached to the surface of the body can of course be either greater or smaller than the mean life $\tau$. We meet here the same situation as in the theory of atomic collisions in a gas. According to Clausius's formula the probability that a molecule of a gas will not suffer any collisions along a path with a length exceeding $x$ is equal to $e^{-x/\lambda}$, where $\lambda$ is the mean free path. In a similar way it can be shown that the probability of a superficial atom remaining attached during a time exceeding $t$ is equal to

$$p(t) = e^{-t/\tau}. \tag{11}$$

The preceding theory† is not, of course, quite exact: it does not take into account the forces acting on the atom in a direction parallel to the surface and preventing it from moving freely along the latter; further it does not take into account the fact that different superficial atoms are, in general, characterized by different values of $U_0$, the latent heat of evaporation per atom being equal to the average value of $U_0$.

Along with the ordinary evaporation, which corresponds to a complete removal of a (superficial) atom from the crystal aggregate constituted by the remaining atoms, we must consider the other types of processes, which can be denoted by the term *incomplete evaporation*.

One of them consists in a transition of a superficial atom from a

† Cf. J. Frenkel, *Z. f. Phys.* **26**, 117 (1924); see also Dushman and Langmuir, *Phys. Rev.* **20**, 113 (1922).

regular position in the outermost layer into a regular position *on the top* of the latter, which can be considered as the starting-point for the formation of the next layer of the surface on the one hand, and of a vacant site or 'hole' in the crystal lattice on the other. The second process consists in the transition of a superficial atom from a regular lattice site into an adjacent interstitial position ('inner evaporation'), thus leading to the formation of a hole in the surface layer, which is the starting-point for the 'self-solution' of the external layers of the crystal in its interior. A similar process can, finally, take place not only on the surface of the crystal but equally well inside it; one of the inner atoms jumping from its regular position in a lattice site into an adjacent interstitial position lying between the neighbouring atoms. This type of 'inner evaporation', resulting in the appearance of a dislocated interstitial atom and of a vacant lattice site or hole, will be designated in the sequel as a *dissociation* of the crystal lattice.

These types of 'incomplete' or 'inner' evaporation must play an important role in the behaviour of a real crystal at elevated temperatures; we shall see later on that they are responsible for the processes of self-diffusion (i.e. mixing up of the atoms in a chemically homogeneous crystal) and mutual diffusion in solid solutions. An understanding of these processes can be obtained only if we abandon the idealized picture of the heat motion in a crystal as constituted by small vibrations of the atoms about fixed equilibrium positions, and complete this type of motion by larger displacements of an irreversible character. Just as in the case of an ordinary evaporation, these irreversible displacements are connected with an escape from the original equilibrium position, with the difference that the escaping atom is immediately captured in a new equilibrium position—in a previously vacant lattice site or in an interstice.

The existence of such processes of incomplete and inner evaporation in a crystal at $T > 0$ is a direct corollary from the general principles of statistical mechanics (in conjunction with the character of interatomic forces), just as is the existence of the ordinary evaporation. Hence it follows that at any temperature different from the absolute zero the structure of a real crystal must differ from that described in the usual conception of an ideal crystal lattice by the presence of 'distortions' in the form of holes (vacant lattice sites) and of dislocated (interstitial) atoms, the number of such distortions increasing with the rise of the temperature according to a law of the same type as that determining the pressure (concentration) of a saturated vapour.

## 2. Mechanism of the Processes of Dissociation and Hole Formation in a Crystal

The dislocated atoms and holes can arise in a real crystal lattice in two essentially different ways, namely inside it and on its surface.

(1) In the first case one of the inner atoms escapes from the corresponding regular lattice site and is trapped in one of the adjacent interstitial positions, to which it remains attached for a limited length of time. This process, which was considered for the first time by Joffé in connexion with the electric conductivity of ionic crystals and has been described as a 'dissociation' of the crystal lattice,† is connected with the simultaneous appearance of a vacant site, i.e. of a 'hole'. It is thus quite similar to the dissociation of a diatomic molecule of a gas into two separate atoms, the interstitial atom playing the role of one partner and the hole that of the second partner. From this point of view a regularly located lattice atom corresponds to an undissociated diatomic molecule.‡

It must be noted that this dissociation process cannot be regarded as completed while the dislocated atom is situated in the vicinity of the hole left by it. A configuration of this kind might be described as a state of 'pre-dissociation', which can be followed either by a 'recombination' of the atom with the hole (i.e. by a return of the atom to its original place) or by a complete dissociation, if the dislocated atom quits its initial position and jumps into an interstice further removed from the vacant site, which thereby becomes an actual 'free' hole. This second step, connected with a transition from the pre-dissociated state into a truly dissociated one, requires additional energy, whereas all the subsequent wanderings of the dislocated atom and of the hole correspond to a constant value of the dissociation energy.

The transformation of a pre-dissociated pair into a fully dissociated one can also be realized, not by the dislocated atom, but by a transition of the hole into an adjacent lattice site (farther removed from the occupied interstice) as a result of the transition of an atom, which was initially situated at this site, into the initially vacated site. A dislocated atom and a hole left by it can thus be treated as fully dissociated, i.e. capable of moving through the lattice independently when their distance apart is larger than the lattice constant.

(2) Whereas *inside* the crystal the dislocated atoms and the holes can only arise simultaneously, through processes of pre-dissociation

† A. Joffé, *Ann. d. Phys.* **72**, 461 (1923).
‡ J. Frenkel, *Z. f. Phys.* **35**, 652 (1926).

and dissociation considered above, on the *surface* of the crystal they can arise independently, penetrating afterwards inside the crystal (over interstitial positions or lattice sites). They can form two independent types of 'distortions' with entirely different concentrations (numbers per unit volume).

(*a*) As regards the holes, they can arise on the surface by means of a process which may be described as the dissolution in the crystal of the surrounding vacuum.† The initial preliminary step of this process, corresponding to the process of pre-dissociation, consists in the displacement of a superficial atom outwards, as in the case of an ordinary evaporation, the escaping atom being attached on the top of the original surface layer and starting the formation of a new, still more external, layer. As a result a hole is formed which can be regarded as *adsorbed* on the surface of the crystal.

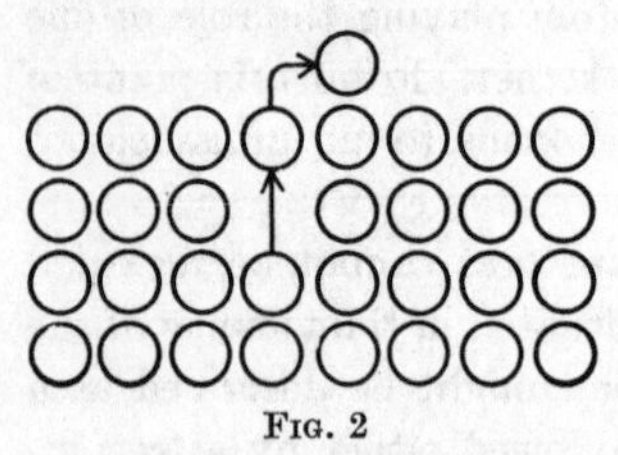

Fig. 2

The next and practically final step consists in the occupation of this superficial hole by an atom which was initially situated underneath it. The lattice site vacated by this atom (see Fig. 2, where the displacements of the two atoms are indicated by arrows) may be treated as a hole *absorbed* by the crystal from the surrounding space.

Let us consider, for the sake of illustration, a simple cubic lattice built up of small cubical atoms, and let us assume that each atom interacts with its nearest neighbours only, with which it has common faces. The energy which is necessary for the separation of two such atoms will be denoted by $U_1$. In this case the 'adsorption' of a hole is connected with an increase of the energy of the crystal by the amount $4U_1$ (for the atom 1 in its original position possessed five neighbours, and in the final position a single neighbour only); for the second step of the process, connected with the transformation of the adsorbed hole into an absorbed one, the additional energy $U$ is required, and the third step proceeds without further increase of energy. In reality the relations are not so simple, but the simplified model gives a correct qualitative picture.

If the atoms displaced on the surface of the crystal by the absorbed holes make a regularly built layer (or several such layers), so that the effective volume of the crystal is increased without any essential change in the shape or structure of its surface, the increase of energy per hole

† Cf. W. Schottky, *Z. phys. Chem.* B, **29**, 335 (1935).

is reduced to $3U_1$, which is equal to the evaporation energy of the crystal referred to one atom. This result follows in the simplest way from the fact that the evaporation of a crystal consists in the subsequent removal of the atoms from its *surface* and requires, on the average, an energy equal to half of the energy which is necessary for removing an atom from an inner lattice site at an infinite distance.† The transition of an atom from the interior of the crystal to its surface, i.e. the formation of a hole by the process of 'incomplete evaporation', thus requires on the average the same amount of energy as the removal of an atom from the surface to infinity, i.e. as its evaporation.

The equality between these two energies must be distorted to some extent by the elastic deformation of the crystal lattice in the region about the hole. So long as this deformation is due to the tendency of the atomic system constituting the crystal to assume a configuration corresponding to a minimum value of the potential energy, it must be accompanied by a certain *decrease* of the energy, so that the energy of hole formation must be somewhat *smaller* than the evaporation energy.

(*b*) The dislocated (interstitial) atoms can also arise independently, i.e. without any holes, by a process similar to the penetration of the holes inside the crystal. This process begins with a transition of a superficial atom into one of the nearest interstitial positions. After this preliminary stage the same atom can jump over to an adjacent interstitial position lying somewhat deeper below the surface of the crystal and become in this way a genuine dislocated atom; its energy undergoes no further change so long as it remains in the interstitial space.

The actual existence of dislocated atoms in simple crystals has often been questioned on the ground that there is no room in an interstitial site for the accommodation of an atom, especially in crystal lattices with a close-packed arrangement of the atoms. This argument would be valid if the 'undislocated' atoms were rigidly bound to the corresponding lattice sites. In reality, however, they can be displaced from their normal positions under the influence of an atom occupying an interstitial position, so as to make enough room for the intruder. The latter must accordingly be surrounded by an elastically strained region whose energy can constitute a considerable fraction of the total dislocation energy.

† The total energy of the crystal (with respect to the gas phase) is equal, if the surface energy is neglected, to $-\frac{1}{2}N6U_1 = -3NU_1$, where $N$ is the number of atoms, i.e. $-3U_1$ per atom.

This energy may be roughly estimated by treating the crystal as an isotropic elastic continuum, strained by the insertion into a spherical cavity with a radius $r_0$ of a rigid sphere with a radius $r_1 > r_0$. In the absence of external volume forces the elastic deformation of the medium is determined by the equation

$$(\lambda+\mu)\nabla\theta+\mu\nabla^2\mathbf{u} = 0, \tag{12}$$

where $\mathbf{u}$ denotes the displacement of a particle and $\theta = \operatorname{div}\mathbf{u}$ the (relative) increase of volume.

In the case under consideration, in virtue of the spherical symmetry, one can put

$$\mathbf{u} = -\nabla\phi, \tag{12a}$$

where $\phi$ is a function of the distance $r$ from the centre of the sphere, representing the dislocated atom (the interstitial position being represented by the spherical cavity in the unstrained elastic medium).

Substituting (12a) in (12) and noting that

$$\nabla\theta = \nabla\operatorname{div}\nabla\phi = \nabla\nabla^2\phi = \nabla^2\nabla\phi,$$

we get $\nabla\nabla^2\phi = 0$. Hence it follows that $\nabla^2\phi = 0$ (since $\nabla^2\phi$ must vanish at infinite distance) and $\phi = \alpha/r$ where $\alpha$ is a constant.

The field of the vector $\mathbf{u}$ is thus identical with the electrical field of a point charge

$$u_x = \frac{\alpha x}{r^3}; \qquad u_y = \frac{\alpha y}{r^3}, \qquad u_z = \frac{\alpha z}{r^3}, \tag{13}$$

i.e. inversely proportional to the square of the distance.

At first sight it may be expected that the region surrounding the intruder (interstitial atom) must suffer a certain compression. In reality, however, the volume deformation $\theta$ vanishes. This means that the volume of the whole body must increase by an amount equal to the difference between the volumes of the rigid sphere and that of the spherical cavity, while its density is not altered.

The components of the strain tensor are

$$u_{xx} = \frac{\partial u_x}{\partial x} = \frac{\alpha}{r^3}\left(1-\frac{3x^2}{r^2}\right)$$

$$u_{xy} = \frac{1}{2}\left(\frac{\partial u_x}{\partial y}+\frac{\partial u_y}{\partial x}\right) = -\frac{3\alpha xy}{r^5}, \quad \text{etc.} \tag{13a}$$

The energy density can be calculated according to the formula

$$\epsilon = \tfrac{1}{2}\lambda\theta^2+\mu(u_{xx}^2+...+2u_{xy}^2+...). \tag{14}$$

Multiplying this expression by $4\pi r^2\,dr$ and integrating from $r_0$ to $\infty$

we obtain the following expression for the total value of the elastic energy:

$$W = 8\pi\mu\frac{\alpha^2}{r_0^3}. \tag{15}$$

The constant $\alpha$ is determined by the condition

$$u = \frac{\alpha}{r^2} = r_1 - r_0 \quad \text{when } r = r_0,$$

i.e.

$$\alpha = r_0^2(r_1 - r_0),$$

so that finally

$$W = 8\pi\mu r_0(r_1 - r_0)^2. \tag{15a}$$

Putting here $r_0 = 10^{-8}$ cm. $r_1 = 2r_0$ (the latter figure is certainly exaggerated) and $\mu = 10^{11}$ dyne/cm.$^2$ we get $W = 2{\cdot}4.10^{-12}$ ergs, which corresponds to 30,000 cal./mole. This energy is of the same order of magnitude as the evaporation energy of metallic substances.

It should be noticed that a hole left by the removal of one of the inner lattice atoms has a tendency to contract; the elastic deformation arising in the surrounding region is of the same type as in the case of a dislocated atom, being described by the equation (13) with a negative value of the coefficient $\alpha$. This deformation corresponds, however, not to an increase but to a decrease of the energy. In fact the equilibrium in a crystal will be disturbed by the removal of one of its atoms, if all the other atoms are supposed to remain fixed (under the condition that the mutual action not only between nearest neighbours but also between more distant atoms is taken into account). The removal of the central atom is equivalent to the introduction of an external field of force acting on the surrounding atoms and tending to shift them in the radial direction. The energy corresponding to this elastic strain is equal to one-half of the work of this external force taken with a negative sign.

## 3. Dependence of the Degree of Dissociation of a Crystal Lattice on Temperature and Pressure

The number of holes ($N'$) and of dislocated atoms ($N''$) in a crystal with a given total number of atoms ($N$) is determined by its temperature $T$ and volume $V$, or pressure $p$, and, so far as equilibrium states are concerned, does not depend on the way these holes and dislocated atoms have arisen (simultaneously—inside the crystal, or separately—on its surface).

It may seem at first sight that if they arise simultaneously, by way of dissociation processes, their numbers $N'$ and $N''$ must be equal. This conclusion is, however, erroneous, for the holes, just as the interstitial atoms, can diffuse independently throughout the crystal up to its surface, where they must vanish if their number exceeds the value corresponding to the condition of statistical equilibrium, or be completed by additional holes and interstitial atoms of surface origin in the contrary case.

A real crystal in a state of statistical equilibrium can thus be considered as a saturated solution of $N'$ holes and $N''$ dislocated atoms in an ideal crystal lattice, constituted by $N-N''$ regularly arranged atoms and containing $N-N''+N'$ sites, among which these atoms and the $N'$ holes can be distributed at random. So long as $N'$ and $N''$ are very small compared with $N$, the numbers $N-N''$ and $N-N''+N'$ can be identified with $N$.

It should be noticed that the holes form in the crystal lattice a solution of the 'substitution' type, in the sense that each hole stands in the place of an absent atom, while the dislocated atoms form a solution of the intrusion type, as in the case of a solid solution of carbon in iron.

If it is taken into account that the formation of holes is connected with an increase of the effective (macroscopic) volume of the crystal, and the formation of dislocated atoms (without any holes) with its contraction, the change of the volume associated with the formation of $N'$ holes and $N''$ interstitial atoms can be represented by the formula

$$\Delta V = N'v'-N''v'', \tag{16}$$

where $v'$ is the volume occupied by an atom in the ideal crystal, diminished by the volume contraction of a hole, and $v''$ the same volume increased by the expansion of an interstitial site when it is filled by an atom.

Further let $U'$ and $U''$ denote the increase of the potential energy connected with the formation of one hole or one interstitial atom (supposed to arise independently by the surface mechanism). The additional energy of a real crystal in the presence of $N'$ holes and $N''$ dislocated atoms can be represented by the sum

$$\Delta W = N'U'+N''U''. \tag{17}$$

This expression, just as the preceding one, corresponds to the assumption that the holes and the dislocated atoms are isolated distortions not interacting with each other. This assumption is justified so long as $N'$ and $N''$ are very small compared with $N$.

In the case of larger concentrations it would be necessary to take into account a mutual repulsion between distortions of the same kind and a mutual attraction between the holes and the dislocated atoms, as a result of which the holes should tend to concentrate about dislocated atoms, and the dislocated atoms about holes, in a way similar to that found in the case of positive and negative ions according to the Debye–Hückel theory of solutions of strong electrolytes. This tendency must result in the formation of a certain number $N'''$ of 'pre-dissociated' atoms.

The number of distortions of each kind can be determined as a function of the temperature from the condition of the minimum of that part of the free energy, or thermodynamic potential, which is due to their presence, the corresponding part of the entropy being proportional to the logarithm of the number of different ways they can be distributed over the respective sites.

In the case of holes this number is equal to

$$\frac{(N+N'-N'')!}{N'!\,(N-N'')!} \approx \frac{N!}{N'!\,(N-N')!}$$

(so long as $N' \ll N$). This gives for the entropy $S = k\log\frac{N!}{N'!\,(N-N')!}$, so that the part of the free energy due to the presence of holes is equal to

$$F' = N'U'-kT[\log N!-\log N'!-\log(N-N')!]. \tag{18}$$

Noting that $$\frac{\partial}{\partial N'}\log N'! = \frac{\partial}{\partial N'}\sum_1^{N'}\log x \approx \log N'$$

and $$\frac{\partial}{\partial N'}\log(N-N')! \approx -\log(N-N'),$$

we see that the minimum of $F'$ as a function of $N'$ corresponds to the value of $N'$ given by the equation

$$\frac{N'}{N-N'} = e^{-U'/kT},$$

or since $N' \ll N$ $$N' = Ne^{-U'/kT}. \tag{19}$$

In order to determine the dependence of $N'$ on the pressure $p$ we must consider, instead of the free energy of the holes, the thermodynamic potential

$$G' = F'+p\Delta V',$$

where $\Delta V' = N'v'$ is the additional volume of the crystal due to the presence of the holes. This gives instead of (19) the equation

$$N' = Ne^{-(U'+pv')/kT}. \tag{19 a}$$

This equation leaves out of account a very important circumstance, namely that the energy $U'$ is itself a function of the volume $V$ of the crystal and consequently of the pressure to which it is subjected. Just as an increase of the interatomic distances involves a decrease of the evaporation energy, it must lead to a decrease of the energy required for the formation of holes (and of interstitial atoms). If $V$ is varied within a sufficiently narrow range the dependence of $U'$ on $V$ can be represented by the linear formula $U' = U'_0 - \beta(v - v_0)$, where $v = V/N$ is the volume of the crystal per atom, and $v_0$ the value of $v$ for $p = 0$. We can put further

$$\frac{v - v_0}{v_0} = -\frac{1}{K}p,$$

where $K$ is the bulk modulus of the crystal. The dependence of $U'$ on $p'$ thus assumes the following form:

$$U' = U'_0 + \frac{\beta}{K}v_0 p. \tag{19b}$$

This expression must be substituted in the formula (19a). It may happen that the influence of the second term in (19b) will prove much more important than that of the term $pv'$ in the exponent of (19a).

It must be noted, further, that owing to the thermal expansion of the crystal the energy $U'$ must vary not only with the pressure but also with the temperature. It seems natural to assume a linear dependence of $v$ on $p$ and $T$ according to the formula

$$\frac{v - v_0}{v_0} = -\frac{1}{K}p + \alpha T,$$

where $v_0$ is the value of $v$ for $p = 0$ and $T = 0$, and $\alpha$ is the thermal expansion coefficient.

This gives according to (19b)

$$U' = U'_0 + v_0 \beta\left(\frac{1}{K}p - \alpha T\right). \tag{19c}$$

Substituting this expression in (19) we get

$$N' = A' e^{-(U'_0 + \omega' p)/kT}, \tag{20}$$

where

$$A' = N e^{v_0 \beta \alpha / k} \tag{20a}$$

and

$$\omega' = \frac{v_0}{K}\beta + v'. \tag{20b}$$

Here $v'$ can be identified with $v'_0$, for the correction term in the product $\omega' p$ can be neglected.

Similar considerations refer to the dependence on the temperature and the pressure of the number of dislocated and of pre-dissociated atoms. The former is given by

$$N'' = Ne^{-(U''+pv'')/kT}$$

and the latter by

$$N''' = zNe^{-(U'''+pv''')/kT},$$

where $z$ is the number of interstices about a regular lattice site.

This factor must be introduced in the expression of $N'''$ on the ground that there are $z$ equivalent interstitial positions for a dislocated atom next to the hole left by it.

The expression (19) is quite similar to the expression (4) for the concentration of the saturated vapour in equilibrium with a crystal. This analogy is a direct corollary from the analogy between the process of ordinary evaporation and that of the 'self-dissolution' or of the 'internal evaporation' of the crystal. In the derivation of (19) we did not allow for a possible change in the vibrational motion of an atom when it comes from a regular lattice site into an interstitial position. This circumstance can easily be accounted for by introducing the corresponding correction into the expression (18) for the free energy.

If the kinetic energy is left aside, the free energy of a linear harmonic oscillator, attracted towards the equilibrium position with a force $f\xi$, where $\xi$ is its distance from this position, is given by $\psi = -kT\log Z$, where

$$Z = \int_{-\infty}^{+\infty} e^{-f\xi^2/2kT}\,d\xi = \sqrt{\left(\frac{2\pi kT}{f}\right)}.$$

In the case of a three-dimensional oscillator, representing in a schematic way an atom vibrating about an equilibrium position in a regular lattice site, the preceding expression of $\psi$ must be multiplied by 3. We thus get

$$\psi = -\tfrac{3}{2}kT\log\frac{2\pi kT}{f}. \tag{21}$$

A similar expression is obtained for the free energy of an atom, vibrating about an interstitial position, the coefficient of the quasi-elastic force $f$ being replaced by a somewhat different coefficient $f''$. A transition of an atom from a regular lattice site to an interstitial position is thus connected with a variation of the thermal part of its free energy by an amount

$$\Delta\psi = \tfrac{3}{2}kT\log\frac{f''}{f} = 3kT\log\frac{\nu''}{\nu}, \tag{21a}$$

where $\nu = \frac{1}{2\pi}\sqrt{\frac{f}{m}}$ and $\nu'' = \frac{1}{2\pi}\sqrt{\frac{f''}{m}}$ are the corresponding vibrational frequencies.

The corrected expression of that part of the free energy of a real crystal which corresponds to its 'self-dissolution' is obtained from (18) by the introduction of the correction term $N''\Delta\psi$. We thus get

$$F'' = N''\left(U''+3kT\log\frac{\nu''}{\nu}\right)-kT[\log N!-\log N'!-\log(N-N')!], \quad (22)$$

which means that the correction under consideration is reduced to a substitution of the expression $U''+3kT\log\frac{\nu''}{\nu}$ for the energy $U''$ of 'dislocating' an atom. The corrected number of dislocated atoms is thus found to be

$$N'' = \left(\frac{\nu}{\nu''}\right)^3 Ne^{-(U''+pv'')/kT}. \quad (23)$$

This expression can be obtained in a straightforward way from Boltzmann's principle (without the introduction of thermodynamic functions) in a form similar to (3).

Let the potential energy of an atom vibrating about a regular lattice site be $\frac{1}{2}f(\xi^2+\eta^2+\zeta^2)$, where $\xi$, $\eta$, $\zeta$ are the components of its displacement, and about an interstitial position $U''+\frac{1}{2}f''(\xi''^2+\eta''^2+\zeta''^2)$, $U''$ being the energy necessary for the corresponding transition for a non-vibrating atom and $\xi''$, etc. the components of its displacement from the new position.

The ratio of the probability that an atom will be found in one of the $N$ vacant interstitial positions to that of finding it in one of the lattice sites is given, according to Boltzmann's principle, by the formula

$$\frac{P''}{P} = \frac{\iiint e^{-\{U''+\frac{1}{2}f''(\xi''^2+\eta''^2+\zeta''^2)\}/kT}\, d\xi''d\eta''d\zeta''}{\iiint e^{-\frac{1}{2}f(\xi^2+\eta^2+\zeta^2)/kT}\, d\xi d\eta d\zeta},$$

the number of interstices being assumed to be equal to the number of the lattice points. Identifying $\frac{P''}{P}$ with the ratio $\frac{N''}{N-N''} \approx \frac{N''}{N}$ we get

$$\frac{N''}{N} \approx \left(\frac{f}{f''}\right)^{\frac{3}{2}} e^{-U''/kT}.$$

In the calculation of the number of holes a similar correction must be introduced corresponding to a transition of an atom from the interior of the crystal to its surface.

Inasmuch as the energy required for the formation of a hole is approximately equal to the evaporation energy, the concentration of the holes (i.e. their number per unit volume) must be, approximately, the same as the concentration of the saturated vapour at the same temperature. As regards the concentration of the dislocated atoms, it must in general be different from it. In the special case $N'' = N'$ corresponding to $U'' = U'$ and $\nu'' = \nu'$ the presence of lattice distortions could be ascribed, in a purely formal way, to dissociation processes alone. The equilibrium condition is expressed accordingly by the same relation as in the case of the dissociative equilibrium of a diatomic gas, namely

$$\frac{N'^2}{N-N'} = K,$$

where $K = Ne^{-U/kT}$; $U = U'+U'' = 2U'$ being the dissociation energy. In the general case the preceding relation can be replaced by the more general one

$$\frac{N'N''}{N-N'} = K = Ne^{-(U'+U'')/kT}.$$

## 4. The Kinetics of Lattice Distortions and their Motion in the Crystal

The holes and the dislocated atoms do not remain fixed at those places where they arise, but now and then jump to one of the equivalent sites situated in the neighbourhood at a distance $\delta$ ($= \delta', \delta''$) equal to or of the same order of magnitude at least as the distance between the nearest neighbours in the ideal crystal lattice. The number of such equivalent sites is equal to the coordination number of the lattice $z$.

A hole or a dislocated atom 'lives' at the same place during a certain time equal, on the average, to $\tau$ ($= \tau', \tau''$). In reality this time can be either longer or shorter than $\tau$. The probability that it will exceed a given value $t$ is given by the formula $p(t) = e^{-t/\tau}$ which has already been considered above (§ 1) for the similar case of evaporation.

The ratio
$$w = \frac{\delta}{\tau} \tag{24}$$

can be defined as the average velocity of the corresponding distortion in its wandering through the crystal lattice. This wandering consists of elementary displacements utterly uncorrelated with each other in respect to their directions and is very similar to the motion of the molecules in a gas, the distance $\delta$ playing the role of the mean free path $\lambda$ and the time $\tau$ that of the corresponding mean time. In the latter case, however, the actual lengths of the free paths are different from $\lambda$ and are distributed about their mean value $\lambda$ according to Clausius's law (the probability of a free path with a length exceeding $x$ being equal to $e^{-x/\lambda}$), whereas in our case all the elementary displacements have exactly the same value $\delta$. Another minor difference consists in the fact that in the case of a gas all the directions of each elementary displacement (free path) are possible and equally probable, while in the case of a crystal a finite number ($z$) of definite possible directions only have to be taken into account.

We thus see that the thermal motion in crystals, at elevated temperatures at least, is not reduced to small vibrations about fixed equilibrium positions, as is usually supposed, but can be described as a combination of such vibrations with a series of elementary displacements of the equilibrium positions over the regular lattice sites (from a filled site to an adjacent vacant one) in the case of the holes, or over the interstices of the lattice in the case of dislocated atoms—to say nothing of an occasional transition from a lattice site into the nearest vacant interstice (in the case of dissociation) or from an interstice into an adjacent vacant site (recombination with a hole). As a result, the atoms move about over the whole crystal, continually mixing up with each other—just as in the case of a gas, but of course more slowly. The presence in the crystalline state of this type of motion, characteristic of the gaseous state, enables one to treat a real crystal as a combination of an ideal crystal with an ideal gas.

The average velocity $w$ with which the atoms are moving about in a crystal is much smaller than their actual thermal velocity $\bar{v} \approx \sqrt{(kT/m)}$ which differs from that in the gaseous state at the same temperature by its vibratory character only. Noting that $\tau = \tau_0 e^{U/kT}$ we have:

$$\frac{w}{\bar{v}} = \frac{\delta}{\tau_0 \sqrt{(kT/m)}} e^{-U/kT}.$$

Putting $\delta = 10^{-8}$ cm. and $\tau_0 = 10^{-13}$ sec. we obtain for the ratio $\delta/\tau_0$ a value of the order $10^5$ cm./sec., which is of the same order of magnitude as $\bar{v}$ at room temperatures. We thus have approximately

$$w \approx \bar{v} e^{-U/kT}.$$

The rate of mixing up of the molecules in a gas is measured by the diffusion or, more exactly, self-diffusion coefficient

$$D = \tfrac{1}{3}\lambda\bar{v}, \tag{25}$$

which can be rewritten in the form

$$D = \tfrac{1}{3}\lambda^2/\tau, \tag{25 a}$$

where $\tau = \lambda/\bar{v}$ is the mean time between two successive collisions.

Let $r$ denote the actual (variable) distance travelled by an atom between two such collisions. According to Clausius's formula the average value of $r$

$$\bar{r} = \int_0^\infty re^{-r/\lambda}\,\frac{dr}{\lambda}$$

is identical with $\lambda$. In a similar way for the mean square of $r$ we obtain the expression

$$\overline{r^2} = \int_0^\infty r^2e^{-r/\lambda}\,\frac{dr}{\lambda} = 2\lambda^2,$$

so that, according to (25 a),

$$D = \frac{1}{6}\frac{\overline{r^2}}{\tau}. \tag{25 b}$$

This expression for the diffusion (or self-diffusion) coefficient has been obtained by Einstein in his theory of the Brownian motion. It is valid for any type of random motion, provided the displacements of a particle in two successive periods of time $\tau$ are wholly independent of each other with respect to their direction. This condition limits the choice of $\tau$ by a certain minimum value which in the case of a gas coincides with the mean duration of a free path. In the case of the motion of lattice distortions in crystals the minimum value of $\tau$ can be identified with the 'mean life' of the corresponding distortion at the same place (in a lattice site, or in an interstitial position), since the successive elementary displacements of this distortion are wholly independent in respect of their direction.

Putting accordingly $\overline{r^2} = \delta^2$ (where $\delta = \delta'$ in the case of holes and $\delta''$ in that of the dislocated atoms) we obtain the following expression for their diffusion coefficient:

$$D = \frac{1}{6}\frac{\delta^2}{\tau}. \tag{26}$$

Since $\delta$ is known and has a constant value, the only quantity which must be determined for a complete description of the 'Brownian' or 'diffusion' motion of lattice distortions in a crystal is their 'mean life', i.e. mean time spent in the same position.

Let us first consider the case of a hole. Each of the $z$ atoms surrounding it has an equal chance to jump into it, which is equivalent to the displacement of the hole to the original site of this atom.

The potential energy of one of these atoms (on the assumption that all the other atoms remain fixed) as it moves from its original equilibrium position (which is the new position of the hole) to its new position (which is the initial one for the hole) must vary with the distance according to a law represented by the full curve of Fig. 3, i.e. by a curve of the type of a potential 'barrier' separating from each other two equivalent potential wells or holes. For the sake of simplicity we shall replace this barrier by a rectangular one with a height $\Delta U'$ with respect to the level of the two adjacent wells. The probability $P_1$ that

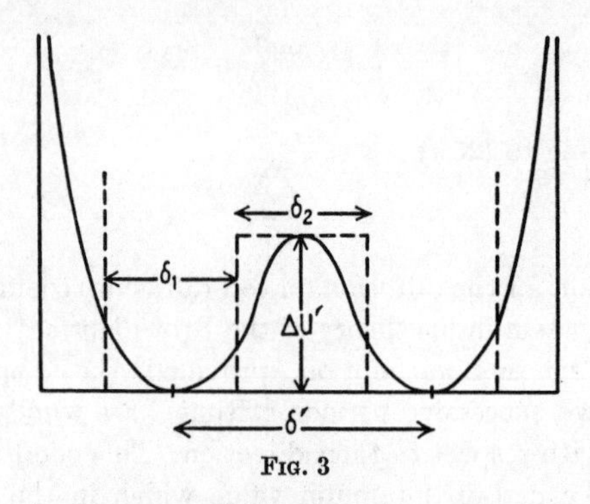


FIG. 3

the atom will be located in one of the latter—the left-hand one, say—must be connected with the probability $P_2$ of finding it in a range corresponding to the flat top of the barrier by Boltzmann's relation

$$\frac{P_2}{P_1} = \frac{\delta_2}{\delta_1} e^{-\Delta U'/kT},$$

where $\delta_1$ and $\delta_2$ denote the widths of the well and of the barrier respectively.

Since the probability of any states of the atom is proportional to the average length of time spent by it in these states, the ratio $P_2/P_1$ can be replaced by the ratio of the corresponding time intervals $t_2/t_1$. We thus get

$$\frac{t_2}{t_1} = \frac{\delta_2}{\delta_1} e^{-\Delta U'/kT}.$$

The atom under consideration can jump across the potential barriers in that case only if, owing to its interaction with the adjacent atoms, it acquires a kinetic energy equal to or larger than the height of the barrier $\Delta U'$, its velocity being directed from left to right. After jumping across the barrier into the right hole the atom would immediately come back if its kinetic energy should be fully restored. We shall assume, however, that in reality all this additional energy ($\geqslant \Delta U'$) or at least a sufficiently large fraction of it is practically immediately transmitted by the atom to its new neighbours, so that it arrives at the right hole with a kinetic energy smaller than $\Delta U'$, which is insufficient for the return into the left hole. This assumption is based on the circumstance that the neighbouring atoms interact very strongly with each other. Its rigorous foundation is a difficult problem which we shall not attempt to solve. It should be mentioned that the excess energy which would enable the atom under consideration to come back to its initial position (in the left hole) must be got rid of within a time interval smaller than the period of free vibrations of this atom, calculated on the assumption that the surrounding atoms remain fixed—an assumption which is in obvious contradiction to the assumption of a rapid energy exchange.

A way out of this contradiction consists in treating the process in question—the transition of an atom from one 'hole' to the next—as a complex process in which along with this atom, which plays the main role, a number of other atoms are involved to a larger or smaller extent. A general method of treating transition processes of this kind through a certain intermediate or 'activated' state of maximum potential or rather *free* energy has been recently devised by Polanyi, Wigner, and Eyring† with special application to chemical kinetics. We shall not discuss it here, for it leads practically to the same result as the simple method considered above, with the only difference that the 'activation energy' $\Delta U'$ introduced by us as the height of the potential barrier between two equilibrium positions is treated as the minimum value of the additional free energy, i.e. the smallest work which must be done at a constant temperature to bring the system into a configuration just intermediate between the initial and the final one. If $\Delta U'$ is defined in this way it can be represented in the form

$$\Delta U' = \Delta W' - T\Delta S',$$

where $\Delta W'$ is the activation energy in the proper sense and $\Delta S'$ the activation entropy of the system in the most advantageous intermediate configuration (with the given atom just on the top of the barrier separating its initial equilibrium position from the final one). Our main point, namely, that a return of the atom from its final position—in the right hole—to the initial one cannot take place immediately, but only after a time of the same order of magnitude as that which is required for the accumulation of the energy $\Delta U'$ necessary for jumping from the

† See, for example, Evans and Polanyi, *Trans. Far. Soc.* **31**, 875 (1935); Stearn and Eyring, *J. Chem. Phys.* **3**, 778 (1935); *Chem. Rev.* **29**, 509 (1941).

left hole into the right one is not established in the Polanyi-Wigner-Eyring theory with any more rigour than in ours.

It is interesting to note that while the activation energy $\Delta U'$ is accumulated rather slowly in a time $t_1$, it is thrown down as a ballast very rapidly in a time $t_2$, which is necessary for the passage over the potential energy barrier with the average thermal velocity $\bar{v} = \sqrt{(kT/m)}$ (the latter being, as well known, independent of the value of the potential energy). We thus have $t_2 \cong \delta_2/\sqrt{(kT/m)}$ and consequently

$$t_1 = t_2 \frac{\delta_1}{\delta_2} e^{\Delta U'/kT} = \frac{\delta_1}{\sqrt{(kT/m)}} e^{\Delta U'/kT}.$$

The ratio $\delta_1/\sqrt{(kT/m)}$ at moderate temperatures is approximately equal to the period $\tau_0'$ of free vibrations of the atom about an equilibrium position, so that the preceding relation can be rewritten as follows:

$$\tau' = \tau_0' e^{\Delta U'/kT}, \tag{27}$$

$\tau'$ standing for $t_1$.

This relation is practically independent of the special shape of the potential barrier which has been used for its derivation. In the case of a barrier represented by the smooth (full) line in Fig. 3 it can be obtained in exactly the same way as the expression (10a) for the mean life of an atom of a solid body on its surface; the evaporation of the atom in the volume $V$ of the gas phase is replaced in the present case by a transition from a hole to the top of the potential barrier. The activation energy $\Delta U'$ plays the role of the evaporation energy and the width of the barrier the role of the volume $V$.

This analogy between the transition of an atom from the bottom of a hole to the top of the barrier separating it from the adjacent hole, on the one hand, and the evaporation process on the other, holds good in so far only as the total energy of the atom remains constant during its motion across the barrier, i.e. if its energy exchange with the other atoms during this short period can be practically neglected. In reality, however, such an energy exchange takes place throughout this short trip; the error introduced by a neglect of this circumstance near the top of the barrier is compensated by an overestimate of the rate of energy dissipation during the descent from the top of the barrier into the new hole.

This descent is analogous to the process of *condensation* of an atom from the vapour phase on the surface of the solid body. As has already been mentioned in § 1, an atom striking this surface does not necessarily adhere to it, but can be reflected. This reflection would correspond in the present case to an immediate return of the atom into the original (left) hole.

If the probability of such a 'reflection', due to an insufficiently rapid dissipation of the activation energy, is denoted by $r$, then the rate of condensation, and accordingly the probability of evaporation per unit time (which is proportional to it), must be diminished in the ratio $(1-r):1$.

Introducing the corresponding reflection coefficient $r'$, equal to the probability of an instantaneous return from the new hole to the initial one, we must decrease the probability of an effective transition from the left hole into the right one by a factor $1-r'$, i.e. replace (27) by the expression

$$\tau' = \frac{\tau_0'}{1-r'} e^{\Delta U'/kT}. \tag{27 a}$$

Practically, however, in the case of most substances $r'$ can be assumed to be equal to zero.

The expressions (27) and (27 a) can be applied with a corresponding change in the notation (two primes instead of one) to the diffusion motion of the dislocated atoms from one interstitial position to the next, the activation energy $\Delta U''$ corresponding to a potential barrier similar to that shown in Fig. 3.

The diffusion motion of the holes alone would be sufficient for a complete mixing up of all the atoms of a given crystal during a sufficiently long lapse of time. As a matter of fact this mixing is realized also by their transition (on the surface of the crystal or inside it) from a lattice site into an interstice (dissociation) and the subsequent wandering over the interstitial space until a dislocated atom either arrives again at the surface of the crystal or meets a hole inside it; after filling the latter it will come back once more to a sedentary condition in a *new* site of the crystal lattice.

The number of such recombination processes in a state of statistical equilibrium must be equal to the number of inverse, i.e. dissociation, processes leading to the formation of a dislocated atom and of a hole.

Let us assume to begin with that the holes remain fixed and let us calculate the mean length of the path $l$, travelled by a dislocated atom from a certain position until it recombines with one of the holes. This length can be determined in the same way as in the case of a gas, from the condition that the volume of a tube with a length $l$ and a cross-section $s = \pi\delta^2$ (where $\delta$ is the effective distance between a dislocated atom and a hole within which their recombination can take place) should be equal to the average volume of the crystal containing one hole, i.e. to the reciprocal of the concentration of the holes $n'$. We thus get

$$l = \frac{1}{sn'}. \tag{28}$$

The path $l$ consists of $l/\delta''$ elementary displacements following each other every $\tau''$ seconds (on the average). Hence it follows that a dislocated atom will meet a hole, with which it will recombine, in a lapse of time equal on the average to

$$t = \tau''\frac{l}{\delta''} = \frac{l}{w''},$$

i.e.

$$t = \frac{1}{sn'w''}, \tag{29}$$

where $w''$ is the mean 'wandering' velocity

$$w'' = \frac{\delta''}{\tau''} = \frac{\delta''}{\tau''_0}e^{-\Delta U''/kT}. \tag{30}$$

The reciprocal of (29) $sn'w''$ can be defined as the probability of 'collision' between a dislocated atom and a hole referred to one second. Since each 'collision' of this kind is tantamount to a recombination, the total number of recombination processes in unit volume of the crystal per unit time is equal to

$$Q = sw''n'n''.$$

In order to account for the mobility of the holes, $w''$ must be replaced by the mean relative velocity $w$ of the dislocated atoms with respect to the holes. Just as in the case of atomic collisions in gases, this relative velocity is given by the formula

$$w = \sqrt{(w'^2+w''^2)}. \tag{30 a}$$

We thus get

$$Q = swn'n''. \tag{31}$$

Substituting here the expressions

$$n' = ne^{-U'/kT}, \qquad n'' = ne^{-U''/kT}$$

for the concentration of the holes and of the dislocated atoms ($n$ total number of lattice points per unit volume), we obtain finally

$$Q = wsn^2e^{-U/kT}, \tag{31 a}$$

where $U = U'+U''$.

In a state of statistical equilibrium the rate of recombinations given by this formula is equal to the number of dissociation processes per unit volume and time. The probability of such a process referred to unit time is therefore equal to

$$p = wsne^{-U/kT}. \tag{32}$$

The reciprocal quantity $\theta = 1/p$ may be defined as the average length of time during which a given atom remains attached to the same lattice site before leaving the site and beginning its wandering through the interstitial space.†

If one of the two velocities $w'$, say, is small compared with the other ($w''$), one can put $w \approx w'' = \frac{\delta''}{\tau_0''}e^{-\Delta U''/kT}$. Since further $s\delta'' = \pi\delta^2\delta''$ is approximately equal to the volume occupied in the crystal by one atom, the product $\delta''sn$ is practically equal to 1, so that the expression for the mean life of a lattice atom can be written in the form

$$\theta = \tau'' e^{U/kT} \tag{32 a}$$

or

$$\theta = \tau_0'' e^{(U+\Delta U'')/kT}, \tag{32 b}$$

where $\tau'' = \tau_0'' e^{\Delta U''/kT}$ is the mean life in one of the interstitial positions.

It should be noticed that the expression for $\tau''$ and $\theta$ are quite similar; the latter differs from the former by a substitution of the sum of the dissociation and activation energy $U+\Delta U''$ for $\Delta U''$.

Along with the simultaneous birth of dislocated atoms and holes by way of dissociation processes, an independent generation of both can take place on the surface of the crystal through the mechanism of 'dissolution of the surrounding vacuum' or 'self-dissolution'. If the intermediate stages (connected with adsorbed holes) are left aside, the probability of these processes can be calculated as follows.

The number of holes crossing per unit time a unit area of the crystal both at its surface and in its interior is equal to $\frac{1}{6}n'w'$. This expression gives accordingly the number of holes emerging on the surface of the crystal (from its interior) per unit time and area. If it is assumed that all these holes vanish (and are not 'reflected' backwards), then in a state of statistical equilibrium the number of fresh holes which arise on the surface of the crystal per unit time and area must be equal to $\frac{1}{6}n'w'$. On the other hand, this number can be represented in the form $n\delta'p'$, where $n\delta'$ is the number of superficial atoms per unit area of the surface layer and $p'$ the probability of an 'incomplete evaporation' of one of them, i.e. of its transition on top of the layer to which it originally

† Formula (32) can be derived directly if we take into account that a transition of an atom from a lattice point into an adjacent interstitial position takes place through an intermediate position with an activation energy $U+\Delta U$, where $\Delta U = U'$ or $U''$.

belonged, the vacant place left by it being 'swallowed' by the crystal and transformed into a genuine hole.

We thus get
$$p' = \frac{1}{6}\frac{n'}{n}\frac{w'}{\delta'}, \tag{33}$$

i.e.
$$p' = \tfrac{1}{6}\alpha' e^{-U'/kT},$$

where
$$\alpha' = \frac{w'}{\delta'} = \frac{1}{\tau'} = \nu_0' e^{-\Delta U'/kT}$$

or
$$p' = \tfrac{1}{6}\nu_0' e^{-(U'+\Delta U')/kT}. \tag{33 a}$$

In a similar way the probability of solution of the surface atoms, referred to unit area and time, is found to be
$$p'' = \tfrac{1}{6}\nu_0'' e^{-(U''+\Delta U'')/kT}. \tag{33 b}$$

Although the preceding expressions for $p$, $p'$, and $p''$ have been derived on the assumption that the crystal is in a state of statistical equilibrium, they remain valid in the absence of such equilibrium. In this case the concentration of the holes and of the dislocated atoms must change with the time, tending to their equilibrium values. The course of these changes can be determined with the help of the following equations:
$$\frac{\partial n'}{\partial t} = D'\nabla^2 n' + np - swn'n''$$

$$\frac{\partial n''}{\partial t} = D''\nabla^2 n'' + np - swn'n'', \tag{34}$$

where the first term on the right-hand side represents the rate of change of the concentration due to the diffusion of the corresponding distortions (from the surface of the crystal or towards this surface); the second, that due to the dissociation; and the third, that due to the recombination processes. In integrating these equations boundary conditions of the type
$$n\delta' p' - \tfrac{1}{6}w'n' = -D'\frac{\partial n'}{\partial z}, \qquad n\delta'' p'' - \tfrac{1}{6}w''n'' = -D''\frac{\partial n''}{\partial z}$$

referring to a surface perpendicular to the $z$ axis (directed inwards) must be introduced; these conditions are formally identical with those which are obtained in a study of the absorption by a solid body of a gas in the atmosphere of which it is placed.

It should be noted that the time which is necessary for the attainment of statistical equilibrium is much larger when the surface processes play an essential role than when the decisive role is played by volume processes (dissociation and recombination); in the former case this time must increase with the size of the body.

If the temperature of the crystal is suddenly lowered, the holes and the dislocated atoms form a kind of supersaturated solution which must gradually approach to the new saturation point by the processes of recombination and diffusion considered above. This picture must, however, be completed in one important point. Instead of diffusing outwards, the extra holes can 'coagulate' with each other, forming small cavities inside the crystal with a considerable 'inner surface'. This coagulation is quite similar to the coagulation of the atoms of an impurity dissolved in a given crystal when the latter is cooled down. It is possible that it is one of the causes of structural defects found in metallic ingots obtained by the usual technological processes, which are connected with a rapid cooling down of the melt.† The microscopic cavities arising through a coagulation of the holes must become more stable when they are filled up by gases dissolved in the metal, and cannot be removed by cold working.

## 5. Self-diffusion and Diffusion of Impurities in Crystals

The mixing up or self-diffusion of the atoms in a crystal can take place in three different ways: firstly, through the wandering of the holes; secondly, through the motion of dislocated atoms arising in one lattice site and ending their career (by recombining with a hole) at some other far distant site; and finally, by a direct interchange of the equilibrium positions of two (or more) neighbouring atoms. The latter mechanism has been considered by Hevesy in connexion with the experimental investigations on diffusion and self-diffusion in solids. For the investigation of self-diffusion Hevesy introduced the method of radioactive isotopes, using the natural radioactive isotopes of lead in his studies on the self-diffusion in this metal in both the liquid and solid state.‡

The possibility of obtaining artificially radioactive isotopes of practically any element (with the help of neutron bombardment) has led in recent years to an extension of Hevesy's method to a number of other metals (silver, gold, copper).

This method is realized as follows. The surface of the crystal under investigation is covered by an extremely thin layer of the corresponding radioactive isotope, and the rate of penetration of the radioactive

† J. Frenkel, *Acta Physicochimica, U.R.S.S.* **4**, 567 (1936).

‡ A review of recent work in this line is found in *Trans. Farad. Soc.* **34**, April 1938.

atoms in the interior of the crystal is measured by determining the radioactivity found at different levels below the surface at different times (the crystal being cut at the corresponding levels or constituted by a number of separate plates pressed against each other).

It has been possible in this way, first of all, to check the validity of the usual equations of the diffusion theory

$$F_x = -D\frac{\partial n^*}{\partial x} \quad \text{and} \quad \frac{\partial n^*}{\partial t} = D\frac{\partial^2 n^*}{\partial x^2}$$

(where $n^*(x)$ is the concentration of the radioactive atoms at a depth $x$ below the surface) in their application to crystalline substances, and, moreover, to determine the self-diffusion coefficient $D$ at different temperatures.

The dependence of $D$ on $T$ has been found to be expressed very exactly by the formula

$$D = Ae^{-W/kT}, \tag{35}$$

where $A$ and $W$ are practically constant quantities. Their numerical values for a number of different metals are given in the following table.

TABLE I

| *Metal* | *A (cm.²/sec.)* | *W (kcal./mole)* | $U_{evap}$ |
|---|---|---|---|
| Pb | 6·4 | 28 | 47 |
| Au | 1·85 | 51 | 92 |
| Cu | 11 | 57·2 | 81 |
| Bi | $10^{-3}$ | 31 | 47 |

For the sake of comparison the values of the evaporation energy are given in the fourth column.

Returning to a theoretical consideration of self-diffusion in a crystalline body, we shall discuss separately the three different mechanisms by which it can take place.

1. *The 'hole' mechanism.* The average length of time required for a hole to move into a lattice site originally occupied by a given atom is determined by formula (29), where $w''$ must be replaced by $w'$ (the mean velocity of the holes) and $s \approx \delta^2$ or $\pi\delta^2$ ($\delta$ = distance between the neighbouring atoms). Hence it follows that the average velocity with which a given lattice atom can move from site to site (by filling an adjacent hole) is equal to

$$w = \frac{\delta}{t} = \delta s n' w',$$

or, since $\delta s \approx \delta^3 \approx 1/n$ ($n$ = total number of atoms in unit volume)

$$w = \frac{n'}{n} w'. \tag{36}$$

We thus see that the ratio $w/w'$ is approximately equal to the ratio $n'/n$, so that under ordinary conditions $w$ is very small compared with $w'$.

Inasmuch as the self-diffusion of the atoms is due to the above mechanism the self-diffusion coefficient $D$ is obtained by multiplying $w$ by $\frac{1}{6}\delta$. Since, on the other hand, the diffusion coefficient of the holes $D'$ is equal to $\frac{1}{6}w'\delta$, we obtain the following relation between $D$ and $D'$:

$$D = \frac{n'}{n} D'. \tag{36a}$$

Putting here $n'/n = e^{-U'/kT}$ and making use of the formulae $D' = \delta^2/6\tau'$ and $\tau' = \tau_0' e^{\Delta U'/kT}$ we get

$$D = \frac{\delta^2}{6\tau_0'} e^{-(U'+\Delta U')/kT}. \tag{37}$$

This expression has the same form as that found experimentally (see (35)), the empirical parameters $A$ and $W$ being defined by

$$A = \frac{\delta^2}{6\tau_0'} \tag{37a}$$

and

$$W = U' + \Delta U'. \tag{37b}$$

2. *Dissociation-recombination mechanism.* The mixing up of the atoms located at different lattice sites through the agency of dislocated (interstitial) atoms can be realized in two different ways: without the participation of holes, if the dislocated atoms arise and disappear at the surface of the crystal, or with the participation of the holes, if they arise and disappear inside the crystal by way of dissociation and recombination processes.

In the absence of holes the process of interatomic mixing would proceed at an extremely slow rate depending on the size of the crystal, so that the self-diffusion coefficient $D$ would be a function of its linear dimensions, which is in contradiction with the experimental facts. We are therefore justified in neglecting surface effects and limiting ourselves to that case only in which the transition of an atom from one lattice site into another takes place by way of its dissociation, a more or less prolonged trip through the interstitial space, and, finally, a recombination with some hole.

The average length of time $\theta$ an atom remains in the same lattice site is equal to the reciprocal value of the probability of dissociation per unit time, given by formula (32), while the duration of the trip through the interstitial space up to a recombination with a hole is determined by formula (29). The total length of time required for an atom to move from one lattice site to another according to the mechanism under consideration is thus equal to

$$t = \frac{1}{wsne^{-U/kT}} + \frac{1}{w''sn'},$$

or since $n' = ne^{-U'/kT}$ and $U = U' + U''$,

$$t = \frac{e^{(U'+U'')/kT}}{swn} + \frac{e^{U'/kT}}{sw''n}.$$

Since the velocities $w$ and $w''$ have the same order of magnitude, the first term is much larger than the second. This means that the trip of an atom from one lattice site to another through the interstitial space is a relatively brief episode compared with the time $\theta$ of a settled life in the initial site.

The ratio of the time $1/sw''n'$ spent in wandering from one interstitial position to another to the mean time $\tau''$ spent in each of them is equal to the number of elementary displacements between a dissociation and a subsequent recombination. Noting that $w'' = \delta''/\tau''$ we obtain for this number the expression $1/s\delta''n'$ which, since $s\delta'' \approx 1/n$, is equal to $n/n'$. Inasmuch as all these elementary displacements are wholly independent in respect of their direction, the mean square of the resulting displacement $r$ is reduced to the sum of their squares, i.e.

$$\overline{r^2} = \delta^2 \frac{n}{n'}.$$

Dividing this expression by $6\theta$ we obtain the value of the self-diffusion coefficient, corresponding to the dissociation-recombination mechanism:

$$D = \frac{\delta^2 n}{6\theta n'}, \tag{38}$$

or, remembering (32 b),

$$D \cong \frac{\delta^2}{6\tau_0''} e^{-(U''+\Delta U'')/kT}. \tag{38a}$$

The expression (32 b) was obtained on the assumption that the dislocated atoms move much faster than the holes. In the contrary case $w$ can be replaced by $w'$ which gives

$$\theta = \tau_0' e^{(U+\Delta U')/kT},$$

and consequently

$$D = \frac{\delta^2}{6\tau_0'} e^{-(U''+\Delta U')/kT}. \tag{38b}$$

It is interesting that the expressions (38 a) and (38 b) are both independent of the energy of hole formation $U'$, that is, of the concentration of the holes. This is explained by the fact that an increase of this concentration leads, on the one hand, to a decrease of the duration of the trip through the interstitial space, and, on the other hand, to an identical decrease in the square of the resulting displacement $r$ (so long as the latter remains small compared with the linear dimensions of the crystal, which excludes the case of excessively small concentrations of the holes, i.e. of excessively large values of $U'$).

The expressions (38 a) and (38 b) for the self-diffusion coefficient are quite similar to the expression (37), corresponding to the hole mechanism, differing from it only by the substitution of $U''$ for $U'$ (and in the case of (38 a) of $\Delta U''$ for $\Delta U'$).

3. *Mechanism of place exchange* (Platzwechsel). According to Hevesy the mixing up of the atoms in a crystal takes place by a simultaneous place exchange between the neighbouring atoms. This process does not involve any permanent distortion of the crystal structure. Of course this 'place exchange' occurs through an intermediate state corresponding to a simultaneous dissociation (or rather pre-dissociation) of two atoms and the formation of two holes, which are practically instantly filled up again. Under such conditions it is, however, meaningless to speak both of holes and of dislocated atoms.

The probability of such a double place exchange (referred to unit time) must be expressed by a formula of the same kind as the probability of a single dissociation (or pre-dissociation) act

$$\alpha = \nu_0 e^{-W/kT}, \tag{39}$$

where $\nu_0$ is the frequency of the atoms in their normal (initial or final) position and $W$ the increase of the potential energy with respect to the initial configuration in the intermediate one, separating it from the final configuration (more exactly, $W$ can be defined as the corresponding smallest maximum value of the additional free energy). $W$ may thus be denoted as the activation energy of the process of place exchange. Since in this process each of the two atoms moves a distance $\delta$, the self-diffusion coefficient corresponding to the mechanism under consideration is given by the formula

$$D = \frac{\delta^2}{6\tau_0} e^{-W/kT} \tag{39 a}$$

of the same type as in the case of the two other mechanisms previously considered.

It should be mentioned that Hevesy's conception of a double 'place exchange' can, in principle, be generalized to the case of a simultaneous place exchange of a set of three or more atoms forming a closed chain (each atom jumping over to the place originally occupied by the next, the resulting process being equivalent to a cyclic substitution). Such multiple permutation processes involving the participation of several atoms are, however, very improbable, for they require a still higher activation energy.

A comparison of the preceding theory with the experimental facts does not allow us to choose between the three mechanisms of self-diffusion considered above or to ascertain which of them is the prevailing one. The theoretical expressions for $D$ have the same form, coinciding with that which is found experimentally; more than that, they all lead to practically the same expression (35 a) for the coefficient $A$ in the empirical formula (35). Putting $\delta = 10^{-8}$ cm. and $\tau_0' \approx 10^{-13}$ sec., we get $A = 10^{-4}$ cm.$^2$/sec., which, as can be seen from Table I, is about $10^4$ times smaller than the experimental figures.

This discrepancy between theory and experiment is probably explained by the fact that both the dissociation energy $U$ $(U', U'')$ and the activation energy $\Delta U$ $(\Delta U', \Delta U'')$ decrease with a rise of the temperature (at constant pressure) owing to the thermal expansion of the crystal. The influence of the latter upon the dissociation energy of the crystal lattice (and, in particular, on the energy of hole formation $U'$) has already been considered in § 3. According to (19) we can put

$$W = W_0 + \beta v_0 \left(\frac{1}{K} p - \alpha T\right). \tag{40}$$

If we limit ourselves to low pressures,† the term with $p$ can be neglected; substituting (40) into (39 a) we thus get

$$D = \frac{\delta^2}{6\tau_0} e^{\gamma} e^{-W_0/kT}, \tag{40'a}$$

where

$$\gamma = \frac{v_0 \alpha \beta}{k}. \tag{40 b}$$

Hence it follows that the coefficient $A$ in Hevesy's empirical formula (35) must be larger than the 'theoretical' value $\delta^2/6\tau_0$ by the factor $e^{\gamma}$. Putting $e^{\gamma} \approx 10^3$ we get $\gamma \approx 7$. This means that the energy $W$, which is usually referred to as the activation energy for diffusion, is decreased by the amount of 14 cal./mole when the temperature is raised by

† Measurements of the diffusion at high pressures are as yet unfortunately lacking.

1 degree. This decrease of $W$ is quite insignificant if it is taken into account that $W$ is of the order of $10^4$ cal./mole; according to (40) $W$ would vanish at a temperature of several thousand degrees, lying far above the melting-point.

Whereas the parameters $\delta$ and $\tau_0$ have approximately the same value for different metals, the parameter $\gamma$ or rather $e^\gamma$ can vary in a marked way as we pass from one metal to another. This explains the variation of the coefficient $A$ for different substances (see Table I).

A numerical estimate of the coefficient $\gamma$ may be obtained in the following way.

The energy $W$ may be defined as a certain function of the interatomic distance $\delta$. In determining its dependence on the temperature we can put accordingly:

$$\frac{dW}{dT} = \frac{dW}{d\delta}\frac{d\delta}{dT} = \delta\frac{dW}{d\delta}\frac{1}{\delta}\frac{d\delta}{dT} = \delta\frac{dW}{d\delta}\frac{\alpha}{3},$$

where $\alpha = \frac{3}{\delta}\frac{d\delta}{dT}$ is the (cubical) thermal expansion coefficient, that is

$$k\gamma = -\frac{1}{3}\alpha\delta\frac{dW}{d\delta}.$$

The exact value of $dW/d\delta$ is unknown; taking, however, into account the extremely rapid falling-off of the interatomic forces with increase of the distance, it can be assumed that $W$ practically vanishes when $\delta$ is, say, doubled. This means that the product $\delta\frac{dW}{d\delta}$ has the same order of magnitude as the energy $W$ (with the opposite sign) for a normal value of $\delta$. We thus get approximately

$$k\gamma \approx \alpha|W|.$$

Putting here $\alpha = 10^{-5}$ and $W/k = 10^4 \div 10^5$ we obtain for $\gamma$ a value of the order of 1 cal./mole deg. which has the same order of magnitude as that found experimentally.†

It should be noticed that a similar decrease with a rise of the temperature is found in the case of the latent heat of evaporation. This decrease is, however, due not only to the thermal expansion of the crystal but also to the difference between the specific heats of the crystal and the vapour.

† If, following Eyring, $W$ is defined as the additional free energy of the activated state, it must be represented as an explicit function of the temperature by the formula $W = \Delta E - T\Delta S$, where $\Delta E$ is the activation energy and $\Delta S$ the activation entropy. Comparing this expression with equation (40) we see that $\Delta E$ corresponds to $W_0$ and $\Delta S$ to $k\gamma$.

It would be interesting to compare the temperature dependence of $D$ measured in the usual way, i.e. at constant pressure, with its dependence on $T$ at constant volume. It would be expected that in the latter case the coefficient $A$ would turn out to be smaller than in the former by a factor of the order $10^{-3}$–$10^{-4}$.

As regards the activation energy $W$ (or $W_0$) there exist at the present time no reliable calculations of its magnitude.† Both the 'hole' and the 'dissociation recombination' mechanism lead to values of the same order of magnitude as the latent heat of evaporation—which is in agreement with the experimental data. In the case of the 'place-exchange' mechanism Chichocki‡ has attempted to compute the energy $W$ from the wholly unwarranted assumption that it can be identified with the energy of the elastic deformation, corresponding to a doubling of the volume occupied by the two atoms in the intermediate configuration. Treating this energy as the compression energy of a continuous elastic medium formed by the surrounding atoms, Chichocki has obtained for it figures of the correct order of magnitude. This agreement can, however, hardly be considered as a justification of his assumptions. In the first place, the assumption that the volume is doubled at the climax of the process of place exchange between two neighbouring atoms is quite arbitrary. In the second place, the corresponding activation energy cannot be ascribed to the mutual action of the surrounding atoms, while the potential energy of the two 'transposed' atoms is regarded as constant. Finally, the resulting elastic deformation of the surrounding medium corresponds not to a compression but to a shear, as has been shown in § 2 in connexion with the computation of the energy of the intrusion of a dislocated atom into an interstitial site.

The preceding conception of self-diffusion in crystals can be extended with a few minor modifications to the process of diffusion of foreign atoms present in a given crystalline substance in the form of an 'impurity' or 'solid solution' with a small concentration.

If this solid solution is of the 'intrusion' type (as a solution of carbon in iron), the diffusion of the dissolved atoms can take place only by the second of the above considered mechanisms, namely by their wandering through the interstitial space. The activation energy $W$ in the expression $D = Ae^{-W/kT}$ reduces in this case to the height $\Delta U$ of the potential barrier separating two equilibrium positions of the dissolved atom in two adjacent interstices. It is clear that under such conditions the

† Cf. Huntington and Seitz, *Phys. Rev.* **61**, 315 (1942).
‡ *Journ. de Phys.* (vii), **9**, 129 (1938).

activation energy $W$ must be much smaller than in the case of self-diffusion, when it is equal to the sum of $\Delta U$ (for an atom of the basic substance) and of $U'$ or $U''$. Since the order of magnitude of the factor $A$ cannot differ very much from $\delta^2/6\tau_0$ it follows that the coefficient of diffusion of impurities, in the case of solid solutions of the intrusion type, must be much larger than the coefficient of self-diffusion (especially in the region of lower temperatures).

This conclusion is supported by the experimental facts, which show that in the case of self-diffusion $W$ is as a rule about twice as large as in the case of the diffusion of foreign atoms.

It is rather surprising, however, that this relation is often verified also in the case of solid solutions which apparently belong to the substitution type. In the latter case the energy $W$ is usually larger the greater the similarity between the atoms of the solvent and of the solute in respect of their physical and chemical properties (such as size and valency), as can be seen from the following table, which refers to a number of substances dissolved in lead.

TABLE II

*Diffusion Constants in Lead*

| *Dissolved substance* | $W$ *(kcal./mole)* | $A$ | *Atomic radius* $\times 10^8$ *cm.* |
|---|---|---|---|
| Pb | 28 | $5{\cdot}8\times10^5$ | 1·75 |
| Sn | 23·7 | $2{\cdot}4\times10^4$ | 1·40 |
| Tl | 20·5 | $2{\cdot}7\times10^3$ | 1·72 |
| Cd | 18 | $7{\cdot}2\times10^2$ | 1·50 |
| Ag | 15·2 | $6{\cdot}5\times10^3$ | 1·46 |
| Au | 14 | $8{\cdot}9\times10^4$ | 1·45 |

This fact is surprising because the mechanism of diffusion must in the present case be the same as in the case of self-diffusion. Whether the dissolved atoms move from one lattice site to another with the help of holes or by way of a temporary wandering through the interstitial space, the activation energy $W$ must be equal to the sum of $\Delta U$ and $U'$ or $U''$, so that no obvious ground can be found for the fact that it is smaller than in the case of self-diffusion, and smaller the greater the difference between the atoms of the impurity and those of the solvent. A possible explanation lies in the fact that the substitution of a foreign atom for an atom of the basic substance causes a distortion of the lattice about the corresponding site, and in this way lowers the energy $U'$ required for the formation of a hole next to this site. According to

Johnson† each substituted atom is accompanied by a hole which revolves about it jumping from one adjacent lattice site to another, and thus gives it permanently a chance of moving to one of the neighbouring sites. It seems, however, improbable that a marked fraction of the foreign atoms should be permanently associated with such 'hole' satellites.

## 6. Lattice Distortions in Ionic Crystals

We have limited ourselves thus far to the consideration of the simplest monatomic crystals, which are found in the case of metallic substances and inert elements only. Essentially new features appear when binary crystals are considered, especially when the latter are built up of oppositely charged atoms. The simplest examples of such ionic or heteropolar crystals are rock salt and other substances of the same type $A^+B^-$.

In this case four different kinds of lattice distortions are possible: dislocated positive ions and the holes left by them, and dislocated negative ions and the corresponding holes. If it is assumed that the dislocated ions of each sort and the corresponding holes arise (and vanish) inside the crystal as a result of dissociation (recombination) processes, then the numbers of holes $N'_A$, $N'_B$ left by the $A^+$ and $A^-$ ions must be equal to the numbers $N''_A$, $N''_B$ of dislocated ions of the corresponding sign. Since a positive hole, i.e. the lack of an $A^+$ ion with a positive charge $+e$, is equivalent in respect of the electrical effects due to it to the presence of a negative charge $-e$, and a negative hole to the presence of a charge $+e$, the conditions $N'_A = N''_A$ and $N'_B = N''_B$ ensure the neutrality of the crystal as a whole, but are not necessary for this neutrality which can be ensured by a single condition

$$N'_A+N''_B = N'_B+N''_A. \tag{41}$$

A similar relation must exist between the concentrations of the distortions (i.e. their number per unit volume $n'_A = N'_A/V$, etc.) in order to guarantee the electrical neutrality of the crystal not only as a whole but also in each of its volume elements separately. If this condition is not fulfilled, then the crystal contains a space charge with a volume density

$$\rho = e(n'_B+n''_A-n'_A-n''_B). \tag{41 a}$$

Let us assume, following Schottky,‡ that the numbers $N'_A$, etc., are connected with each other by the neutrality condition (41). Their

† R. P. Johnson, *Phys. Rev.* **56**, 814 (1939).
‡ W. Schottky, *Z. phys. Chem.* B, **29**, 335 (1935).

determination by the method considered in § 3 for the case of a monatomic substance is impossible, for it would lead us to values incompatible with the neutrality condition.

In order to allow for the latter it is necessary to consider the total free energy of all the four types of distortions:

$$F = F'_A + F'_B + F''_A + F''_B, \tag{42}$$

where $F'_A = N'_A U'_A - kT[\log N_A! - \log N'_A! - \log(N_A - N'_A)!]$, etc.

From the minimum condition of $F$ we get, making use of (41) and putting $N_A = N_B = N$,

$$\left.\begin{aligned} N'_A &= Ne^{\mu-(U'_A/kT)} & N''_A &= Ne^{-\mu-(U''_A/kT)} \\ N'_B &= Ne^{-\mu-(U'_B/kT)} & N''_B &= Ne^{\mu-(U''_B/kT)} \end{aligned}\right\}, \tag{43}$$

where $\mu$ is a Lagrange multiplier; substituting the preceding expression in (41) we obtain for it the following formula:

$$\mu = \frac{1}{2}\log\frac{e^{-U''_A/kT} + e^{-U'_B/kT}}{e^{-U'_A/kT} + e^{-U''_B/kT}}. \tag{43a}$$

Eliminating $\mu$ from (43) we obtain the relation

$$\left.\begin{aligned} N'_A N''_A &= N^2 e^{-(U'_A + U''_A)/kT} \\ N'_B N''_B &= N^2 e^{-(U'_B + U''_B)/kT} \end{aligned}\right\} \tag{44}$$

corresponding to the dissociative equilibrium of each kind of dislocated ion with the corresponding holes, $U'_A + U''_A = U_A$ and $U'_B + U''_B = U_B$ being the respective dissociation energies.

So long as the dislocated atoms and the holes arise and vanish simultaneously, i.e. by way of dissociation or recombination inside the crystal, a separation of the energy $U_A$ or $U_B$ into two parts has no physical meaning. Since in this case $N'_A = N''_A$ and $N'_B = N''_B$, we can put $U'_A = U''_A = \frac{1}{2}U_A$, $U'_B = U''_B = \frac{1}{2}U_B$, and $\mu = 0$.

An independent determination of $U'_A$ and $U''_A$ (or $U'_B$ and $U''_B$) is possible—both in principle and experimentally—only if the holes and the dislocated atoms can arise and vanish independently on the surface of the crystal.

In this case it is necessary to take into account the electrical charges which are left on the surface (in an 'adsorbed' state) by ions or holes migrating inside the crystal. Thus, for example, a positive hole leaves on the surface a charge $+e$, while an $A^+$ ion, wandering through the interstitial space, leaves an uncompensated surface charge $-e$. In the presence inside the crystal of $N'_A$, $N''_A$, $N'_B$, $N''_B$ lattice distortions of all the four possible kinds with a total volume charge

$$Q = e(N''_A+N'_B-N'_A-N''_B),$$

a charge $-Q$ must remain on the surface of the crystal.

The separation of these two charges must give rise to an electrical field tending to restore the neutrality condition. If the potential of this field is denoted by $\phi$, then the total potential energy of a distortion located inside the crystal can be obtained by subtracting the product $e\phi$ from $U'_A$ and $U''_B$ or by adding it to $U''_A$ and $U'_B$.

Under such conditions the volume concentrations of the corresponding distortions are given by the formula:

$$\left.\begin{array}{ll} n'_A = ne^{-(U'_A-e\phi)/kT} & n''_A = ne^{-(U''_A+e\phi)/kT} \\ n'_B = ne^{-(U'_B+e\phi)/kT} & n''_B = ne^{-(U''_B-e\phi)/kT} \end{array}\right\}. \tag{45}$$

The potential $\phi$ is determined as a function of the coordinates by Poisson's equation

$$\nabla^2\phi = -\frac{4\pi}{\epsilon}\rho, \tag{45 a}$$

where $\epsilon$ is the dielectric constant of the crystal, in connexion with the expression (41 a) for the electric density $\rho$ and the equations (45). It should be noticed that these equations are identical with the equations (43) if the parameter $\mu$ is identified with $e\phi/kT$ and the numbers $N$ are replaced by the corresponding concentrations.

Let us suppose, following Schottky, that the interstices of the crystal lattice are too small to accommodate an extra ion (which means that the energies $U''_A$ and $U''_B$ are extremely large compared with $U'_A$ and $U'_B$). In this case the distortions of the crystal lattice will be reduced to the presence of positive and negative holes.

The preceding equation for the potential $\phi$ is then reduced to the form

$$\nabla^2\phi = -\frac{4\pi en}{\epsilon}(e^{-(U'_B+e\phi)/kT}-e^{-(U'_A-e\phi)/kT})$$

or

$$\nabla^2\psi = \frac{4\pi e^2n}{\epsilon kT}e^{-(U'_A+U'_B)/2kT}(e^{\psi}-e^{-\psi});$$

that is

$$\nabla^2\psi = \kappa^2\sinh\psi, \tag{46}$$

where

$$\psi = \frac{e\phi}{kT}-\frac{U'_A-U'_B}{2kT} \tag{46 a}$$

and

$$\kappa^2 = \frac{8\pi e^2n}{\epsilon kT}e^{-(U'_A+U'_B)/2kT}. \tag{46 b}$$

Equation (46) is identical with the well-known equation of the Debye-Hückel theory, which determines the potential distribution in a solution of an electrolyte, the role of the electrode being played in our case by the surface of the crystal. The number

$$ne^{-(U'_A+U'_B)/2kT}$$

represents the concentration of the holes of both signs at a sufficiently great distance from the surface, while the reciprocal of the parameter $\kappa$ is a measure of the thickness of the surface layer where these concentrations are different. We thus see that the neutrality condition $n'_A = n'_B$ is fulfilled at such depths only as are large compared with $1/\kappa$. (If $n'_A$ and $n'_B$ are small, $1/\kappa$ can be of the same order of magnitude as the linear dimensions of the crystal; in this case the neutrality condition is not valid even inside the latter.)

Whereas in Debye's theory the charge of the electrode (per unit area) or its potential with respect to distant points of the solution are arbitrarily fixed, in our case these quantities are determined by the temperature of the crystal and by the condition that the quantity $\psi$ should vanish at a sufficiently great distance from the surface.

Since on the surface of the crystal ($x = 0$) its electric potential, in the absence of external electric fields, must vanish (the volume charge being compensated by the surface one) its intrinsic potential (far away from the surface) must be equal to

$$\phi = \frac{1}{2e}(U'_A - U'_B). \tag{47}$$

This quantity can be treated as the contact drop of potential in the surface layer of the crystal, due to the difference between the absorption energies of positive and negative holes (from the space surrounding the crystal.†

If the surface of the crystal can be treated as a plane, then directing the $x$-axis normally inwards we can rewrite equation (46) as follows:

$$\frac{d^2\psi}{d\xi^2} = \sinh\psi, \tag{48}$$

where $\xi = \kappa x$. Integrating it under the condition $\psi = \psi_0 = \dfrac{U'_B - U'_A}{2kT}$ for $\xi = 0$ and $\psi = 0$ for $\xi = \infty$ we get

$$\frac{1}{2}\left(\frac{d\psi}{d\xi}\right)^2 = \cosh\psi,$$

i.e.

$$\frac{d\psi}{d\xi} = \sqrt{(e^{\psi}+e^{-\psi})}. \tag{48 a}$$

† It should be mentioned that (47) expresses the neutrality condition inside the crystal and is a particular case of the general formula (43 a) for $\mu = e\phi/kT$.

This formula can serve for the determination of the electric field at the surface of the crystal

$$E_0 = -\left(\frac{d\phi}{dx}\right)_{x=0} = -\frac{\kappa kT}{e}\sqrt{(e^{\psi_0}+e^{-\psi_0})},$$

and consequently of the volume charge $Q = e(N'_B - N'_A)$ or the surface charge compensating it; the value of this charge referred to unit area must obviously be equal to $\epsilon E_0/4\pi$.

If $\psi \ll 1$ (this condition is in general unjustified) the equation (48) is reduced to $\frac{d^2\psi}{d\xi^2} = \psi$ and its second integral to

$$\psi = \psi_0 e^{-\xi} = \psi_0 e^{-\kappa x}$$

just as in the approximate form of the Debye-Hückel theory.

The preceding theory can easily be generalized to the case when dislocated atoms are present along with holes. It opens a new electrical method for an experimental solution of the question of the surface or volume origin of the lattice distortions in a crystal lattice. Another more straightforward method is based on the kinetics of the establishment of the equilibrium condition, as defined by the potential $\phi$ or by the electric conductivity of the crystal. Inasmuch as the distortions arise on its surface, the state of equilibrium must be reached by their diffusion (inwards if the temperature is suddenly raised or outwards when it is lowered), which implies a very large relaxation time, increasing with the size of the crystal.

This question has not yet been investigated experimentally, in spite of its obvious interest.

## 7. Electrical Conductivity of Ionic Crystals

Ionic crystals possess, as is well known, an electrical conductivity which is very small at low temperatures, but becomes considerable at elevated ones. In some cases the conductivity has an ionic character, i.e. is due to the mobility of ions, as in solutions of electrolytes. In other cases it is due to the free electrons, as in metals and electronic semiconductors. In a number of cases, finally, a mixed conductivity—partially ionic and partially electronic—is observed.†

A. Joffé was the first to express and establish experimentally the idea that the passage of an electric current through crystals of the

† The electrolytic character of the conductivity of the crystal can be established experimentally by the presence of the Faraday effect (separation of the ions on the electrodes) and by the absence of a Hall effect.

rock-salt type is due to the presence of dissociated (or, according to our terminology, 'dislocated') positive ions in a number rapidly increasing with rise of temperature and possessing a marked mobility.†

This idea has been worked out quantitatively by the present writer and has been completed by the conception of movable holes, which in the case of positive ions behave in an external electric field in the same way as negative ions.‡

In fact, in the presence of an electric field the dislocated positive ions must tend to move in the direction of this field. This refers both to the dislocated ions moving in the interstitial space and to the regularly located ions situated in the neighbourhood of positive holes. In the absence of the electric field such a hole has an equal chance of being filled by a positive ion situated on the left of it and by another ion situated on the right. Under the influence of an electric field directed to the right the former process will be more probable than the latter; in other words, the positive holes will be more frequently displaced to the left than to the right, i.e. they will behave as movable (dislocated) negative ions.

It must be remembered that the mobility of the dislocated ions and of the holes is *not due* to the electric field; in the absence of the latter they perform a random motion, which has been described in the preceding sections, and which leads to a mixing up of similar ions. In the presence of the field this diffusion motion acquires a certain degree of organization in the sense that the dislocated positive ions move preferentially in the direction of the field, while the positive holes move preferentially in the opposite direction. This preferential or drift motion constitutes the electric current.

That part of the diffusion motion which consists in the exchange of places between two neighbouring ions of the same sign (if such place exchange actually exists) is wholly irrelevant for the electric conductivity of the crystal, for a place exchange between two similar ions does not lead to any change in the distribution of the electrical charges in the crystal.§ The existence of an ionic conductivity can therefore be considered as a direct proof of the existence in ionic crystals of lattice distortions in the form of dislocated atoms and of holes capable of moving through all the space occupied by it.

The question to be decided is which of these two kinds of distortion

† A. Joffé, *The Physics of Crystals*, 1931. ‡ J. Frenkel, *Z. f. Phys.* **35**, 652 (1926).

§ An exchange of places between two adjacent ions of the opposite sign is excluded on the ground that it would require a vast increase of energy.

prevails and plays the main role in the phenomena of diffusion and electric conduction. This question probably does not admit of the same solution in all cases.

The electrical conductivity of an ionic crystal is made up of several parts corresponding to the different kinds of movable lattice distortions which are present in it. The mobility of distortions of any given type is measured by the mean velocity $v$ which they acquire under the action of an external force $F$, or rather by the ratio $v/F = q$, which, for not too large values of $F$, is a constant described as the mobility coefficient.

It can easily be shown that this coefficient is connected with the diffusion coefficient of the corresponding particles (or holes) by the relation

$$q = \frac{D}{kT}, \tag{49}$$

which has been established by Einstein in his theory of the Brownian motion and which is applicable to particles of any kind performing a motion of the diffusion type and conforming to the Maxwell-Boltzmann statistics.

The relation (49) can be obtained in the simplest way as follows. Let us suppose that the concentration of the particles under consideration varies in the $x$-direction and that each of them is acted on, in this direction, by a force $F$ (which may be a function of $x$).† The number of particles passing in unit time through unit area of a plane surface normal to $x$ is made up of two parts: the diffusion current, $D\frac{\partial n}{\partial x}$, and the convection current $nv_x = nqF$ due to the action of the external force. In a state of statistical equilibrium the algebraic sum of these two currents must vanish. We thus get

$$-D\frac{\partial n}{\partial x} + qnF = 0.$$

Putting here $F = -\partial U/\partial x$ where $U(x)$ is the potential energy of the particles in the field of force under consideration, and integrating, we obtain

$$n = \text{const.}\, e^{-U/(D/q)}.$$

This relation is similar to Boltzmann's equation and becomes identical with it if $D/q = kT$.

We shall give another derivation of this important relation, and also of the more general relation corresponding to large values of $F$, for the

† In the case of holes $F$ must be identified with the force acting on one of the corresponding ions.

case of particles which require an activation energy for moving from one site to the next.

Let us imagine for the sake of simplicity that the particles under consideration—the dislocated positive ions, for instance—move in one dimension parallel to the $x$-axis, jumping from one potential well to the next through a potential barrier with a height $\Delta U$ (Fig. 4, full line).

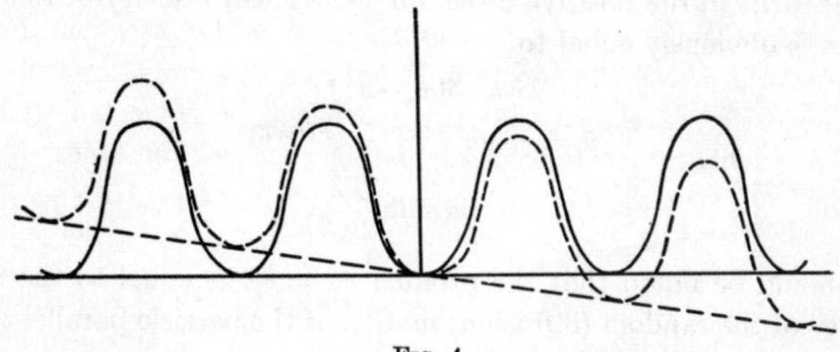

FIG. 4

If to the inner forces which correspond to this 'potential relief' an external force of constant magnitude $F$ in the positive direction of the $x$-axis is added, with a potential energy $U = -Fx$, the resulting potential relief, while preserving its wave-like character, will gradually drop from left to right, as is shown by the dotted line in the figure.

The height of the potential barrier separating each potential well from the next one in the positive direction will now be smaller than $\Delta U$ by the amount $\frac{1}{2}F\delta$, while in the opposite direction it will be larger than $\Delta U$ by this same amount ($\delta$ being the distance between two neighbouring wells, and $\frac{1}{2}\delta$ the distance from the bottom of the well to the point corresponding to the top of the barrier).

The probability that a particle will jump in unit time from a given well into one of the two neighbouring ones, in the case of a symmetrical barrier with a height $\Delta U$, has been shown above (§ 4) to be given by the expression

$$\alpha = \nu_0 e^{-\Delta U/kT},$$

where $\nu_0$ is the vibration frequency of the particle as long as it remains in the well.

Hence it follows that in the presence of an external force $F$ the probability that the particle will jump (in unit time) from the initial well to the next one on the positive side (right) is equal to

$$\alpha_+ = \tfrac{1}{2}\nu_0 e^{-(\Delta U - \frac{1}{2}F\delta)/kT},$$

and on the negative side (left) to

$$\alpha_- = \tfrac{1}{2}\nu_0 e^{-(\Delta U+\frac{1}{2}F\delta)/kT}.$$

The former is thus increased and the latter diminished in the ratio $e^{F\delta/2kT}$.

Under such conditions the positive transitions of the particles must become more frequent than the negative ones, so that they will on the average drift in the positive direction. The mean velocity of this drift motion is obviously equal to

$$\bar{v} = \delta(\alpha_+ - \alpha_-), \tag{50}$$

that is

$$\bar{v} = \tfrac{1}{2}\delta\alpha(e^{F\delta/2kT} - e^{-F\delta/2kT})$$

or

$$\bar{v} = \delta\alpha \sinh\frac{F\delta}{2kT}. \tag{51}$$

It should be noted that the product $\delta\alpha = \delta/\tau$ is equal to the mean velocity of the random (diffusion) motion of the particle parallel to the $x$-axis.

If the force is not too large so that $\frac{1}{2}F\delta \ll kT$, the hyperbolic sine in (51) can be replaced by its argument, which gives

$$\bar{v} = \frac{\delta^2\alpha}{2kT}F, \tag{51 a}$$

i.e. the ordinary linear relation between the drift velocity and the force causing it, corresponding to a constant mobility coefficient

$$q = \frac{\delta^2\alpha}{2kT}.$$

Noting that $\dfrac{\delta^2\alpha}{2} = \dfrac{\delta^2}{2\tau}$ is equal to the diffusion coefficient $D$, we come back to Einstein's relation (49).

In the opposite case of a very strong force whose product with $\delta$ is much larger than $kT$, the relation (51) is practically reduced to the exponential formula

$$v = we^{\delta F/2kT}. \tag{51 b}$$

If $F$ represents the electric force $eE$ acting on an ion in an electric field with a strength $E$, the product $F\delta = eE\delta$ is seen to be small compared with the value of $kT$ at room temperatures for field strengths up to $10^4$ c.g.s. $\approx 10^6$ volt/cm. In the case of weaker fields the current must thus be proportional to the field strength, in agreement with Ohm's law. At higher strengths deviation from this law must be observed. Such deviations have actually been observed by Poole† and

† Poole, *Phil. Mag.* **32,** 112 (1916); **42,** 488 (1921).

are represented with a satisfactory accuracy by the exponential formula (51 b).

The current density due to the drift motion of particles of a given kind ($i$) is equal to

$$s_i = e_i n_i \bar{v}_i.$$

In the case of moderate fields this expression is reduced to

$$s_i = e_i n_i q_i F_i = e_i^2 n_i q_i E = \sigma_i E.$$

The coefficient

$$\sigma_i = e_i^2 n_i q_i = \frac{e_i^2 n_i D_i}{kT} \tag{52}$$

represents that part of the specific electric conductivity of the crystal which is contributed by the particles of the $i$th kind.

In the case of binary ionic crystal of the NaCl type the total value of the electric conductivity $\sigma$ is equal to the sum of four terms corresponding to the positive and negative dislocated ions and to the holes.

Using the expressions

$$D_i = \frac{\delta_i^2}{2\tau_{0i}} e^{-\Delta U_i/kT} \tag{52a}$$

for the diffusion coefficients, and the expressions

$$n_i = ne^{\pm\mu - U_i/kT} \tag{52b}$$

for the concentrations of the various lattice distortions in the region where the space charge vanishes (i.e. at a sufficiently great distance from the surface of the crystal), we obtain for the total conductivity of a binary crystal the following expression:

$$\sigma = C'_{\mathrm{A}} e^{\mu - W'_{\mathrm{A}}/kT} + C''_{\mathrm{A}} e^{-\mu - W''_{\mathrm{A}}/kT} + C'_{\mathrm{B}} e^{-\mu - W'_{\mathrm{B}}/kT} + C''_{\mathrm{B}} e^{\mu - W''_{\mathrm{B}}/kT}, \tag{53}$$

where the coefficients $C$ are given by the formulae

$$C'_{\mathrm{A}} = \frac{e^2 \delta^2 n}{\sigma \tau'_{0\mathrm{A}} kT}, \quad \text{etc.,} \tag{53a}$$

and the energies $W$ by the formulae

$$W'_{\mathrm{A}} = U'_{\mathrm{A}} + \Delta U'_{\mathrm{A}}.$$

The parameter $\mu kT$ is equal to the product of the charge $e$ of one of the positive particles (dislocated positive ion, or a negative hole) with the potential $\phi$ in the interior of the crystal in a state of statistical equilibrium. If there are only two types of lattice distortion actually present, $\mu$ reduces to the difference between the energies $U_i$ for the corresponding particles divided by $2kT$, and the expression for the electric conductivity assumes the following simpler form:

$$\sigma = C'_{\mathrm{A}} e^{-(\frac{1}{2} U_{\mathrm{A}} + \Delta U'_{\mathrm{A}})/kT} + C''_{\mathrm{A}} e^{-(\frac{1}{2} U_{\mathrm{A}} + \Delta U''_{\mathrm{A}})/kT}, \tag{54}$$

if we have to do with dislocated ions of a given kind and the corresponding holes, or

$$\sigma = C'_A e^{-\{\frac{1}{2}(U'_A+U'_B)+\Delta U'_A\}/kT} + C'_B e^{-\{\frac{1}{2}(U'_A+U'_B)+\Delta U'_B\}/kT}, \quad (54\,a)$$

if the conductivity is due to the positive and negative holes only.

Since, according to (53 a), the coefficients $C$ must have approximately the same value for all types of lattice distortions, whereas the activation factors $e^{-\Delta U_i/kT}$ can widely differ from each other (with respect to the order of magnitude),† it is practically always possible in the last two expressions to neglect one of the two terms compared with the other. This means that the electric conductivity of a binary ionic crystal, in the presence of several types of carriers of electric charges, is practically determined by a single type—that with the highest mobility.

As a matter of fact it is found experimentally that the dependence of the electric conductivity of ionic crystals on the temperature is expressed, in very broad limits, by the simple exponential formula

$$\sigma = Ce^{-W/kT} \quad (54\,b)$$

with a practically constant value of the factor $C$.

According to the theoretical formula (53 a) this factor should be inversely proportional to the absolute temperature; this dependence is, however, masked by the much sharper temperature dependence of the exponential factor.

Putting in (53 a) $e = 5\times10^{-10}$, $\delta = 3\times10^{-8}$, $\tau_0 = 10^{-13}$, $n = 10^{22}$, and $T = 300$, we get

$$C \approx 9\times10^{13} \text{ c.g.s.} = 100 \frac{\text{amp./cm.}^2}{\text{volt/cm.}}.$$

This theoretical value of $C$ is in good agreement with the experimental values found in those cases when $\sigma$ can be represented by the formula (54 b) within the whole accessible range of temperatures—from room temperature up to the melting-point of the corresponding crystal. The energy $W$ is usually found to be of the order of 10,000 cal./mole, i.e. of the same order of magnitude as the latent heat of fusion.

The values of $C$ and $W$ for a number of different crystals are given in the second and third columns of the following table.

It must be mentioned that in the case of a number of ionic crystals the electric conductivity is represented by the formula $\sigma = Ce^{-W/kT}$, with a value of $C$ lying close to the theoretical one, in a limited range of moderate temperatures up to a certain temperature $T_0$. Above

† The activation energies $\Delta U_i$ are usually about ten times larger than $kT$ (at room temperatures). Relatively small differences in their values correspond therefore to large differences in the values of the factors $e^{-\Delta U_i/kT}$.

TABLE III

| *Substance* | $C$ | $W$ | $C'$ | $W'$ |
|---|---|---|---|---|
| NaCl | 0·8 | 21,000 | $3{\cdot}5\times 10^6$ | 60,000 |
| NaBr | 0·5 | 18,400 | $1{\cdot}1\times 10^6$ | 44,000 |
| AgCl | $1{\cdot}5\times 10^{-4}$ | 4,320 | $3{\cdot}2\times 10^6$ | 22,100 |
| KI | 0·11 | 9,315 | $0{\cdot}11\times 10^6$ | 39,000 |

the latter the conductivity can be represented by a similar formula $\sigma = C'e^{-W'/kT}$ with a value of $W'$ a few times larger than $W$ and, accordingly, with a value of $C'$ exceeding $C$ by several orders of magnitude (up to $10^9$ times). The latter circumstance directly follows from the equality of the two expressions at $T = T_0$ in conjunction with the fact that $W \gg kT_0$. Taking $1/T$ as the abscissa and $\log\sigma$ as the ordinate we obtain a curve consisting of two straight lines with different slopes intersecting at the point $T = T_0$ (see Fig. 5).

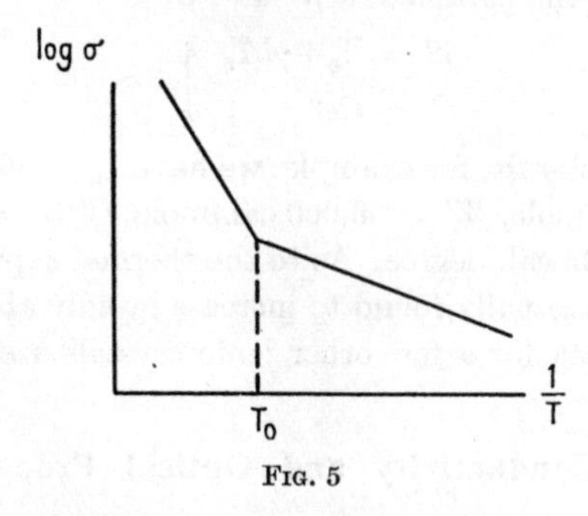

FIG. 5

This dependence of $\sigma$ on $T$ is usually explained by the fact that the electrical conductivity of the crystal is due to charges of two different kinds and is represented by the two-term formula

$$\sigma = Ce^{-W/kT} + C'e^{-W'/kT},$$

one of the terms prevailing at lower and the other at higher temperatures.

This seemingly natural interpretation ignores the fact that the coefficient $C$ in both terms of the theoretical formula (54) or (54 a) must have approximately the same value $\left(\text{of the order of } 100\ \frac{\text{amp./cm.}^2}{\text{volt/cm.}}\right)$.

The above anomaly can, however, be explained in full agreement with our theory if it is taken into account that the energy (or free energy) $W$ decreases with a rise of the temperature owing to the thermal expansion of the crystal (cf. § 5).

If the thermal expansion coefficient has a constant magnitude, the decrease of $W$ with temperature can be described by the linear formula $W = W_0 - k\gamma T$, which leads to an apparent increase of the coefficient $C$ by the factor $e^{\gamma}$ (see eq. (40 a)). In the case of ionic crystals the thermal expansion coefficient is very small in a broad temperature range, while above a certain high temperature $T_0$ it begins to rise sharply up to the melting-point. The corresponding variation of $W$ can be schematically represented as follows:

$$\left.\begin{aligned} W &= W_0 = \text{const. for } T < T_0 \\ W &= W_0 - k\gamma(T - T_0) \text{ for } T > T_0 \end{aligned}\right\}. \tag{55}$$

Substituting these expressions in formula (53 b) we see that above $T_0$ it has the same form $\sigma = C'e^{-W'/kT}$ as below it, with the following altered values of the parameters $W'$ and $C'$:

$$\left.\begin{aligned} W &= W_0 + \gamma k T_0 \\ C' &= Ce^{\gamma} \end{aligned}\right\}. \tag{55 a}$$

In the case of rock-salt, for example, we have $T_0 = 560°$ C. $= 830°$ K., $W = 21{,}000$ cal./mole, $W' = 60{,}000$ cal./mole, $C'/C = 10^6$. This corresponds to $k\gamma = 25$ cal./degree. As to the thermal expansion coefficient of rock-salt, it is actually found to increase rapidly above 500° C. The corresponding data for a few other ionic crystals are collected in the preceding table.

## 8. Electronic Conductivity and Optical Properties of Ionic Crystals

A large number of ionic crystals, especially metallic oxides ($Cu_2O$, CuO, MoO) and sulphides (CaS, PbS, etc.), display an electric conductivity not of an ionic but of an electronic origin. They are denoted, accordingly, as electronic semi-conductors, or simply as semi-conductors. Their conductivity can be due, in the first place, to free or 'collectivized' electrons, i.e. electrons released from a fraction of the ions (usually the negative ones) and capable of moving through the whole volume of the crystal. Along with these electrons an essential role in the conduction of electricity can be played by the vacant places or holes left by these electrons.

Such electron or positive holes, in the form of neutral atoms of the metalloid, for example, surrounded by negative ions of the latter (and of course by the positive ions of the metal), can move throughout the crystal by obtaining an electron initially bound to one of the adjacent negative ions. As a result the positive holes must behave in exactly the same way as electrons with a positive charge.

Inasmuch as the electrons and positive holes arise by a process of dissociation or ionization, their number must increase with a rise of the temperature according to the law const. $e^{-U/2kT}$, where $U$ is the ionization energy. It is conceivable also that they arise independently on the surface of the crystal, leaving there 'adsorbed' electrical charges, just as in the case of crystals with an ionic conductivity. In the case of electronic conductors such processes can, however, play but a minor role.

The free electrons in a crystal are usually treated as a gas in a vacuum. It is possible, however, that in reality they are not quite free, but that after being released from negative ions they become attached to positive ones (converting them into neutral atoms) and move through the crystal lattice by passing from one positive ion to the next—in the same way as the electron holes move by passing from one negative ion to the next.

The factor outside the exponential in the expression

$$N' = N'' = \text{const. } e^{-U/2kT}$$

for the number $N'$ of electrons and $N''$ of holes turns out to be somewhat different in the two cases.

If the electrons and holes are localized in definite lattice sites—the former in those occupied by positive ions, the latter in those occupied by negative ones—this factor is equal to the number $N$ of sites of a given type in the volume $V$ of the lattice.

If, on the other hand, they are treated as particles of two gases capable of moving throughout the whole volume $V$, the energy $U$ in the preceding formula must be completed by the free energy $\psi$ of the electron and hole in the ideal gas state, while the constant must be set equal to 1. Now

$$\psi = -kT \log Z,$$

where

$$Z = \frac{V}{h_3} \iiint e^{-p^2/2mkT}\, dp_x\, dp_y\, dp_z = \frac{V}{h^3}(2\pi mkT)^{\frac{3}{2}} = \frac{V}{\lambda^3},$$

where

$$\lambda = \frac{h}{\sqrt{(2\pi mkT)}} \tag{56}$$

is the de Broglie wave-length corresponding to the average thermal velocity of the particle. We thus have

$$\psi = -kT \log \frac{V}{\lambda^3}. \tag{56a}$$

If the electrons and the holes are assumed to have the same effective mass $m$, then replacing $\frac{1}{2}U$ by $\frac{1}{2}U+\psi$ we get

$$N' = N'' = \frac{V}{\lambda^3}e^{-U/2kT}. \tag{57}$$

At room temperatures $\lambda$ is of the order of $10^{-7}$ cm., so that $\lambda^{-3}$ is of the same order of magnitude as $n = N/V$.

It can seem at first sight that the two conceptions of the motion of the electrons and holes—from one atom to the next, or quite freely throughout the whole volume $V$ of the crystal—must lead to essentially different values of the diffusion coefficient, since in the former case the mean free path must be reduced to the distance $\delta$ between neighbouring ions of the same sign (just as in the case of the motion of dislocated ions and ionic holes), while in the latter it is limited by the linear dimensions of the crystal only.

This difference is, however, only apparent. The coincidence between $l$ and $\delta$ for ions and ionic holes is due to the fact that their transition from one site to the next requires a certain activation energy which is 'dumped' on to the surrounding atoms as soon as the potential barrier separating these two sites has been crossed. In the case of electrons (or electron holes) the transition of an electron from one site to the next can take place, owing to the smallness of the corresponding distance $\delta$, by the mechanism of the tunnel effect which does not require any activation energy.

Under such conditions the electron (or hole) can make a number of subsequent transitions in the same direction, the corresponding set of atoms (ions) playing the role of 'rails' over which the electron is rolling. If the atoms of the crystal were distributed with perfect regularity, this rectilinear motion would proceed unperturbed up to its boundaries only. In reality, however, owing to the thermal vibrations of the atoms, the length of the rectilinear segments laid down by an electron or a hole is limited, being smaller the higher the temperature.

The mean value of the 'free path' can be determined by a formula of the same type as in the case of a gas particle

$$l = \frac{1}{n_a \pi r^2}, \tag{58}$$

if $r$ is used to denote not the radius of an atom (or ion) but its mean displacement from the corresponding equilibrium position (for, as has just been stated, $l$ is limited by these displacements only); $n_a$ denotes the number of atoms in unit volume.

Putting $\frac{1}{2}f\overline{r^2} = \frac{1}{2}kT$, where $f$ is the coefficient of the restoring quasi-elastic force, we get $\overline{r^2} = kT/f$ and consequently

$$l = \frac{f}{\pi n_a kT}. \tag{58a}$$

The mean free path of a 'free' electron or hole is thus seen to be inversely proportional to the temperature. At room temperatures ($T \approx 300°$ K.) the amplitude of the thermal vibrations is of the order of 1/10 of the interatomic distance $\delta$; noting that $n_a \approx 1/\delta^3$ we find in this case, according to (57)

$$l = \delta\left(\frac{\delta}{r}\right)^2 \approx 100\delta.$$

The preceding theory enables one to calculate the diffusion coefficients of the electrons and holes with the help of the usual formula $D = \frac{1}{3}l\bar{v}$, and further to determine the electrical conductivity of the crystal, inasmuch as it is due to them, with the help of the formula

$$\sigma = \frac{e^2n'D'}{kT} + \frac{e^2n''D''}{kT}.$$

Since $n' = n''$ and $D' \approx D''$, $\sigma$ can be represented as a function of the temperature by the simple formula

$$\sigma = \text{const. } T^{-\frac{1}{2}}e^{-U/2kT}, \tag{59}$$

where the factor $T^{-\frac{1}{2}}$ follows from the fact that $\bar{v}$ is proportional to $\sqrt{T}$ in conjunction with $l \sim 1/T$.

Just as in the case of the ionic conductivity, the dependence of the factor outside the exponential on the temperature is masked by the much sharper dependence of the exponential factor, so that with sufficient accuracy one may put $\sigma = \text{const. } e^{-U/2kT}$.

The preceding conception of the character of the motion of the electron and holes requires a number of corrections, the most important of which is the following.

When the electron or hole becomes attached, even for a very short time, to some atom (ion) of the crystal, the surrounding atoms suffer additional forces of attraction or repulsion and tend to be shifted from their normal equilibrium positions in the lattice points. In other words, the lattice tends to get elastically strained and electrically polarized about the centre formed by the 'visiting' electron or hole. If the duration of this visit is long enough for such a strain or polarization actually to take place, the electron or hole will not be able to jump to the following atom (or ion) unless accompanied by the elastic and electric deformation produced by it. The probability of such a transition, implying the participation of heavy particles, is much smaller than in the case when the corresponding deformation does not arise. We thus see that a free electron or hole 'visiting' now one and then another atom can get 'trapped' by it if its visit becomes dangerously prolonged. In the case of slow (thermal) electrons and holes such a spontaneous trapping is very likely and may occur at every step.

The trapped electron or hole can be again released; since, however, this release is connected with an increase of potential energy by a certain amount $\Delta U$ it will have to wait for a certain time $\tau$, increasing as the temperature is lowered according to the usual law $\tau = \text{const. } e^{\Delta U/kT}$. The freedom obtained on release will, on the other hand, be of extremely short duration, being followed by a new trapping near one of the adjacent atoms.

As a result, the thermal electrons and holes with a very small kinetic energy will move through a crystal in approximately the same way as dislocated ions or ionic holes, $\Delta U$ playing the role of the activation energy and $\delta$ of the mean free path.

This circumstance does not alter the character of the dependence of $\sigma$ on $T$, the energy $\frac{1}{2}U$ in equation (59) being simply replaced by $\frac{1}{2}U+\Delta U$.

Summing up, we see that the regularity of the structure of an ionic crystal, especially at high temperatures, must be disturbed in the general case not only by its dissociation—in the sense of the appearance of movable dislocated ions and ionic holes—but also by its ionization, revealed by the appearance of movable electrons and electron holes. The ratio between the concentration of the former and the latter is determined by the relative value of the dissociation and the ionization energy. In the case of ionic conductors, characterized by a relatively high 'ionization' energy, this ionization, i.e. the production of free electrons and holes, can be realized at low temperatures by illumination with ultra-violet light. A very interesting relationship is found between these photo-electrons and electron holes, on the one hand, and the dislocated ions and ionic holes due to the thermal motion on the other.

Theoretically speaking this relationship must be reducible to an additional trapping or 'localization' of the former by the latter. This type of trapping is revealed experimentally by the appearance in the preliminarily irradiated crystal of a specific coloration which is preserved for a certain time after the irradiation has been stopped; this time rapidly decreases as the temperature is raised. This coloration is due to the absorption of visible light by the so-called '$F$-centre', formed by photo-electrons which have become attached to dislocated positive ions or to holes left by the negative ions. The latter conception is due to de Boer and Pohl;† the former has been discussed by the present writer in connexion with the question of the motion of coloured spots in alkali halide crystals under the action of an external electric field.‡

The preservation of the coloration, produced by a preliminary irradiation of the crystal with ultra-violet light, is due to the fact that for the release of the electron from the corresponding centre (e.g. the ionization of a neutral Na atom in an interstice of a NaCl lattice, or the removal of the electron, replacing a Cl ion) a certain energy $W$ is required, so that the loss of coloration accompanying this release must proceed with a finite velocity proportional to $e^{-W/kT}$. At elevated temperatures the coloration is lost practically instantly, while at low temperatures the decoloration of the crystal progresses very slowly.

According to the above conception of the nature of the $F$-centres, they can arise in an irradiated crystal in the presence only of lattice distortions due to dislocated ions or ionic holes. It follows therefrom that a coloration of a crystal in a state of thermodynamic equilibrium at low temperatures is impossible. This conclusion is fully supported by experimental evidence and is of prime importance for the understanding of photography, for the latent photographic image is constituted by a system of $F$-centres created by preliminary illumination. An apparent violation of it is found when the crystal exposed to illumination has been preliminarily heated and thereafter rapidly cooled (quenched), so that the degree of dissociation of the lattice has remained at the initial high level.

It should be mentioned, in conclusion, that the coloration centres can arise in crystals at arbitrarily low temperatures in the presence of impurities. The latter play an important role in the electric conductivity of the crystal when the atoms of the impurity are easily ionized, being thus a source of free electrons, or have a large electron affinity and capture electrons from the atoms of the bulk substance, thus giving rise to free electron holes in the latter.

† See discussion in *Proc. Phys. Soc.* **49** (1937).

‡ J. Frenkel, *Phys. Z. d. Sowjetunion*, **5**, 911 (1934). It is also possible to treat the $F$-centres as positive electron holes attached to negative ionic holes.

# II

# PERTURBATION OF ALTERNATION AND ORIENTATION ORDER IN MIXED AND MOLECULAR CRYSTALS

## 1. Order and Disorder in the Distribution of Atoms in Binary Alloys (Inter-metallic Compounds)

THE disturbances of regularity in the structure of crystals which we have considered heretofore were limited to the presence, in relatively small numbers, of dislocated atoms, ions, or electrons, and of the corresponding holes, dissolved, as it were, in the crystal lattice and distorting the latter in the same way as foreign impurities.

Along with such disturbances (which are characteristic of monatomic substances and binary *ionic* crystals), binary non-ionic crystals and, in particular, intermetallic compounds of the type AB (or more generally $A_mB_n$) display at elevated temperatures much more important structural disturbances consisting in the lack of regularity in the *alternation* of the atoms of different kinds between the successive crystal sites.

Thus, for example, in a 50 per cent. ZnCu alloy ($\beta$-brass) the Zn and Cu atoms form a volume-centred cubic lattice, alternating between the neighbouring sites in a chainlike order, with complete regularity at low temperatures, just as do the Cs and Cl ions in a CsCl crystal. This regular alternation becomes, however, more and more disturbed as the temperature is raised, until at and above a certain 'critical' temperature $T_0$ the distribution of the atoms of the two kinds between the lattice points becomes wholly irregular.

This decrease of 'alternation order' in a binary alloy is to a certain extent similar to ordinary melting and may be denoted by the term 'alternation melting', especially when the degree of order, gradually decreasing with the approach to a certain temperature $T_0$, suddenly drops to zero when this temperature is reached. Such a transition, which is connected with absorption of latent heat, is referred to as a transition of the first order. It can be exemplified by the case of the $Cu_3Au$ alloy. In other cases such as that of CuAu the alternation order decreases continuously, though at an ever-increasing rate, until it vanishes completely at a certain temperature $T_0$. This transition is characterized by an abnormal rise of the specific heat at constant pressure $C_p$, reaching a finite or infinite peak value at $T = T_0$ and rapidly dropping to its normal value as the temperature is raised beyond the point $T_0$. The latter is referred to in such cases as a 'Curie point' because of its analogy to the ordinary Curie point of ferromagnetic substances, while the transition is denoted as a transition of the second kind. This type of transition is illustrated by Fig. 6, the dotted line

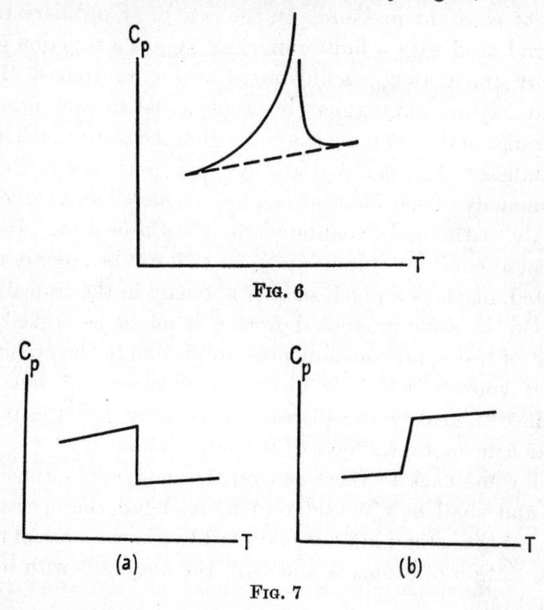


FIG. 6

FIG. 7

indicating the normal course of the specific heat. It has often been confused with a type of transition introduced under the same title by Ehrenfest, and characterized by a discontinuous change of the specific heat, illustrated by Fig. 7 *a* and *b*. As a matter of actual fact, such transitions have never been observed and cannot correspond to a stable equilibrium between the corresponding phases.

On the other hand, transitions of the second kind typified by Fig. 6 are actually found not only in the case of ordinary Curie points or of alternation melting but in a number of other cases, some of which will be considered later on. They may be treated, from a purely thermodynamical point of view, as a generalization of transitions of the first kind, with the transition point $T_0$ replaced by a certain temperature range $\Delta T$ about $T_0$. The latent heat of fusion is replaced accordingly by the integral $\int \Delta C\, dT$, where $\Delta C$ denotes the excess of the specific heat over its 'normal value' (dotted line in Fig. 6). As a matter of fact, a transition of the first kind may be described, in a formal way, as a limiting case of a transition of the second kind with a specific heat anomaly $\Delta C_p$ represented by a delta function. The accompanying change of volume $V_2 - V_1$ may likewise be represented by the integral $v_0 \int \alpha_p \, dT$, where $\alpha_p$ is the additional value of the thermal expansion coefficient at constant pressure. In the case of an ordinary transition of the second kind with a finite range $\Delta T$, $\alpha_p$, as a function of $T$, has a form quite similar to $C_p$, as illustrated by Fig. 6. Indeed, the values of $\Delta C_p$ and $\Delta \alpha_p$ are approximately proportional to each other within the whole range of the anomaly characterizing the transition in question.

This parallelism between $\Delta C_p$ and $\Delta \alpha_p$ has given rise to the opinion that the anomaly of specific heat can be considered as a *consequence* of the anomaly of thermal expansion near the Curie point. In fact the specific heat at constant volume $C_v$, so far as it can be directly measured or calculated, displays a much smaller anomaly in the transition range than $C_p$. On the same grounds, however, it might be argued that the latent heat of fusion (at constant pressure) is due to the accompanying increase of volume, which is obviously incorrect, or but partially correct, since in reality the increase of entropy and the increase of volume are concomitant effects of the same cause.

We shall come back to these general thermodynamic considerations later on, and shall now consider in more detail the special case of transitions of the second kind, constituted by the decrease of regularity in the alternation of atoms A and B in the alloy AB with increase of the temperature.

In the case of an ionic crystal $A^+B^-$ the alternation of the ions of opposite sign follows from the fact that unlike ions attract each other while similar ions are mutually repelled. A similar distribution of neutral atoms A, B found at low temperatures implies that unlike atoms attract each other more strongly than similar ones. The tendency towards such a distribution is thus characterized by a positive value of the energy

$$U = \frac{U_{AA} + U_{BB}}{2} - U_{AB}, \tag{1}$$

where $U_{AA}$, $U_{BB}$, $U_{AB}$ denote the mutual potential energies of two atoms of the corresponding kind situated in neighbouring lattice sites (at the same average distance $\delta$ from each other).

Since the forces between neutral atoms decrease very rapidly with increase of their distance apart (in contradistinction to the ions), the potential energy of the whole crystal $E$ can be represented with sufficient approximation as the sum of the potential energies $U_{AA}$, $U_{BB}$, $U_{AB}$

between the nearest neighbours only. A regular alternation corresponding to the minimum value of $E$ must be realized at low temperatures only. At higher temperatures it is necessary to take into account not only the energy of the crystal but also its entropy, which has a tendency to increase by irregular interchanges of place between neighbouring atoms of different kind. In the case of ionic crystals such interchanges are ruled out by the resulting very large increase of energy. In the case of binary alloys, on the other hand, the corresponding increase of potential energy is relatively small, that is, of the order of or smaller than the value of $kT$ for the temperature of melting. Hence alternation melting can occur at a temperature $T_0$ lying below the melting-point, the atoms A and B preserving a regular distribution between the points of a crystal lattice, with loss of regular alternation, corresponding to lower temperatures.

If the coordination number of the lattice (i.e. the number of nearest neighbours) is equal to $z$, then the interchange of two adjacent atoms A and B in a crystal with complete alternation order requires an amount of energy

$$W = 2(z-1)U, \tag{1 a}$$

where $U$ is given by (1). As, however, the number of such irregular pairs is increased, the energy required from the interchange of one more pair of adjacent atoms from a regular position to an irregular one gradually decreases, vanishing in the limiting case when the number of atoms of each kind remaining in their proper sites becomes equal to the number of atoms which have moved to foreign sites.

Strictly speaking, the notion of 'proper' and 'foreign' sites becomes meaningless in this case. If, after this limiting form of disorder has been reached, the B atom moves to such places as were originally occupied by A atoms, and vice versa, we shall come back again to a completely regular distribution, with a reversed definition of proper and foreign sites.

Let us denote those sites which were originally occupied by the A atoms as 'even', and those which were originally occupied by the B atoms as 'odd'. Further, let $N_1$ denote the number of A atoms remaining in the even sites and $N_2$ the number of such atoms that have moved to odd sites; these numbers must obviously be equal to the number of B atoms remaining in the odd sites or situated in the even sites respectively.

The fraction

$$\xi = \frac{N_1-N_2}{N}, \tag{2}$$

where $N = N_1+N_2$, can be treated as a measure of the degree of order in the relative distribution of the atoms. It would be more correct, perhaps, to define the degree of this order by the square of $\xi$, or its absolute value, which remains the same when *all* the A and B atoms are interchanged.

According to Bragg and Williams† the energy increment $U$ due to interchange of two atoms A, B from regular positions to irregular ones is proportional to the existing degree of order $\xi$

$$U = W\xi = W\frac{N_1-N_2}{N} = W\frac{N-2N_2}{N},$$

where $W$ is given by (1 a).

If $N_2$ pairs of atoms are interchanged consecutively, the energy of the crystal is increased by

$$E = \frac{W}{N}\sum_{x=0}^{N_2}(N-2x),$$

that is,

$$E = N_2\left(1-\frac{N_2}{N}\right)W = \frac{N_1 N_2}{N}W. \tag{3}$$

The same result may be obtained on the assumption that the distribution of atoms around a given (even or odd) site remains on the average the same whether this site is occupied by an A atom or by a B atom.

Let us consider an even site. Since it is surrounded by odd ones, then the number of adjacent A and B atoms is equal respectively to

$$z_A = z\frac{N_2}{N}, \qquad z_B = z\frac{N_1}{N}.$$

Now out of the $N$ even sites under consideration $N_1$ are occupied by A atoms and $N_2$ by B atoms. Their potential energy with respect to the surrounding atoms is thus equal to

$$N_1\left(\frac{N_2}{N}zU_{AA}+\frac{N_1}{N}zU_{AB}\right)+N_2\left(\frac{N_2}{N}zU_{BA}+\frac{N_1}{N}zU_{BB}\right).$$

For the odd sites we obtain in the same way

$$N_1\left(\frac{N_2}{N}zU_{BB}+\frac{N_1}{N}zU_{BA}\right)+N_2\left(\frac{N_2}{N}zU_{AB}+\frac{N_1}{N}zU_{AA}\right).$$

The total potential energy of the crystal is equal to one-half of the sum

† W. L. Bragg and E. J. Williams, *Proc. Roy. Soc.* A, **145**, 699 (1934).

of these two expressions. Subtracting from it the smallest value of the potential energy, corresponding to $N_2 = 0$, we get

$$E = 2Uz\frac{N_1 N_2}{N}, \tag{3 a}$$

which is identical with (3) if $W$ is defined as $2zU$ instead of $2(z-1)U$.

Since by the definition of $\xi$

$$N_1 = \tfrac{1}{2}N(1+\xi), \qquad N_2 = \tfrac{1}{2}N(1-\xi),$$

we have

$$N_1 N_2 = \frac{N^2}{4}(1-\xi^2),$$

and consequently

$$E = \tfrac{1}{4}NW(1-\xi^2). \tag{3 b}$$

The interchange of $N_2$ atoms A, B from regular to irregular positions can be carried out in $N!/N_1!\,N_2!$ different ways, corresponding to different ways of choosing $N_2$ odd places for accommodating A atoms instead of B atoms. The resulting increase of the entropy of the crystal is thus given by

$$S = k(\log N! - \log N_1! - \log N_2!). \tag{4}$$

The equilibrium values of $N_1$ and $N_2$ corresponding to the minimum of the free energy $F = E - TS$ under the condition $N_1 + N_2 = N$ are thus determined by the equation

$$\frac{N_1 - N_2}{N}W = kT\log\frac{N_1}{N_2},$$

that is,

$$\frac{N_2}{N_1} = e^{-W\xi/kT}. \tag{5}$$

It should be remarked that this result is a direct corollary of Boltzmann's principle, in conjunction with the Bragg-Williams assumption as to the linear dependence of the interchange energy on the degree of order $\xi$.

Since

$$\xi = \frac{N_1 - N_2}{N} = \frac{1 - N_2/N_1}{1 + N_2/N_1},$$

it follows from (5) that

$$\xi = \frac{1 - e^{-W\xi/kT}}{1 + e^{-W\xi/kT}} = \frac{e^{\frac{1}{2}W\xi/kT} - e^{-\frac{1}{2}W\xi/kT}}{e^{\frac{1}{2}W\xi/kT} + e^{-\frac{1}{2}W\xi/kT}},$$

that is,

$$\xi = \tanh\frac{W\xi}{2kT}. \tag{5 a}$$

This equation, derived by Bragg and Williams in their original paper on order and disorder in crystal lattices, has solutions different from zero for such temperatures only as lie below a certain 'critical' or Curie temperature

$$T_0 = \frac{W}{2k}. \tag{5 b}$$

This follows from the fact that the initial slope of the tangent to the curve $y = \tanh \alpha x$ which is equal to $\alpha$ must be larger than 1 in order that this curve should meet the straight line $y = x$.

The dependence of $\xi$ on $T$ is illustrated by the curve, Fig. 8, which

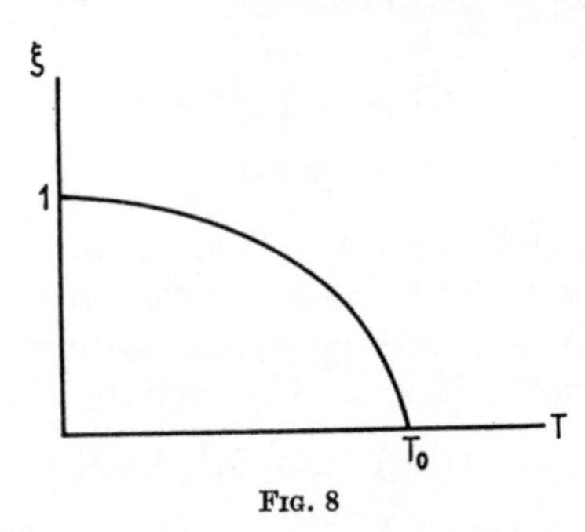


FIG. 8

has a horizontal tangent at $T = 0$ and a vertical one at $T = T_0$. In view of the smallness of $\xi$ in the neighbourhood of this point, the function (5 a) can be approximated by the expression $\alpha\xi[1-\frac{1}{3}(\alpha\xi)^2]$.

Equating it to $\xi$ we get $\qquad \xi^2 = \frac{3}{\alpha^2}\left(1-\frac{1}{\alpha}\right),$

or since $\alpha = \frac{W}{2kT} = \frac{T_0}{T}$ lies close to 1,

$$\xi^2 = 3\frac{T_0-T}{T_0}. \tag{6}$$

This equation represents a parabola the axis of which coincides with the negative direction of the $T$-axis.

The rapid decrease of the degree of order near the Curie point $T_0$ is connected with an abnormal increase of the specific heat. The additional value of the latter can be defined by the formula $\Delta C = T\frac{dS}{dT}$, where the entropy $S$ is given by (4). Noting that

$$dS = -k\log N_1\, dN_1 - k\log N_2\, dN_2$$

$$= -k(\log N_1 - \log N_2)\frac{N}{2}\,d\xi = -\frac{Nk}{2}\log\frac{N_1}{N_2}\,d\xi,$$

we get, in virtue of (5),

$$\Delta C = -\frac{NW}{2}\xi\frac{d\xi}{dT},$$

which, according to (3 b), coincides with $dE/dT$, i.e. with the rate of increase of the energy due to the decrease of the degree of order.†

Substituting in the preceding formula the expression (6) for $\xi$ we get

$$(\Delta C)_0 = \frac{3NW}{4T_0},$$

or, since $T_0 = W/2k$, $\qquad (\Delta C)_0 = \tfrac{3}{2}kN = \tfrac{3}{2}R. \qquad$ (6 a)

Thus, according to the preceding theory, the additional specific heat

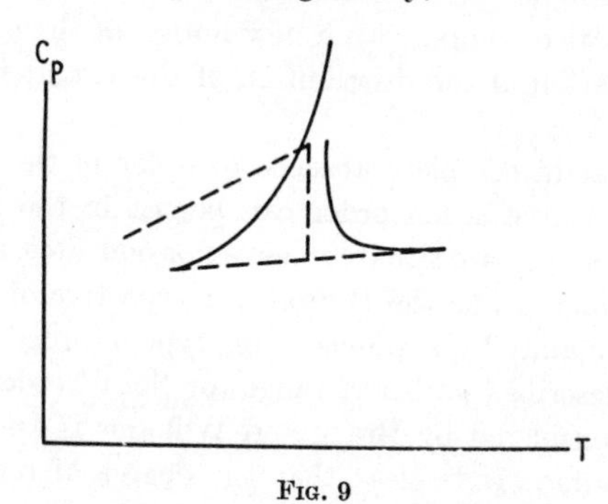


FIG. 9

due to the progress of alternation disorder with elevation of the temperature increases smoothly until the limiting value $\frac{3}{2}R$ is reached at $T = T_0$, after which it suddenly drops to zero.

This behaviour roughly corresponds to Ehrenfest's conception of a transition of the second kind, and can be illustrated by Fig. 7 *a*, provided the slope of the curve $(c, T)$ is somewhat larger for $T < T_0$ than for $T > T_0$.

In reality, however, the curve $c$, $T$ has an entirely different shape, more or less similar to that shown in Fig. 9.

It seems thus more appropriate to speak not of a *jump*, but of a *peak* of the specific heat with a somewhat asymmetrical form, the slope of the ascending branch being more gradual than that of the descending one. Fig. 9 gives a comparison between the actual course of the specific

† This follows from the general thermodynamical relation $C_p = T\frac{\partial S}{\partial T} = \frac{\partial E}{\partial T}+p\frac{\partial V}{\partial T}$ if $p = 0$ or if $p\frac{dV}{dT}$ is small compared with $\frac{\partial E}{\partial T}$.

heat of the alloy near the Curie temperature $T_0$ (full line) and that following from the Bragg-Williams theory (dotted line).

## 2. Distant and Local Alternation Order

This discrepancy between theory and experiment is obviously due to the fallacy of the assumption that the energy which is necessary for the interchange of two atoms A, B from regular to irregular positions is proportional to the existing degree of regularity.

The preceding derivation of this result from a consideration of the distribution of A and B atoms about even and odd sites is likewise incorrect, because it erroneously identifies the notion of order as defined above, i.e. referring to the distribution of the A and B atoms between even and odd lattice points, with a new notion of the order, emerging from a consideration of the distribution of the A and B atoms about one of them.

It is clear that in complete absence of order in the above sense a certain degree of alternation order can persist in the sense that the A atoms, whether they are situated in even or odd sites, are surrounded *mainly* by B atoms, while the B atoms, irrespective of their position, are surrounded mainly by A atoms. This type of order, first discussed by Bethe,† is described as 'short-range' or 'local' order, whereas the type of order considered by Bragg and Williams is known as distant or long-range order. It is clear that the degree of regularity in the alternation of A and B atoms between neighbouring lattice sites is more adequately specified by the degree of short-range order than by that of long-range order.

Let $z'$ and $z''$ denote the average numbers of different and similar neighbours of any one atom (either A or B). The degree of local order can be defined by the ratio

$$\eta = \frac{z'-z''}{z'+z''} = \frac{z'-z''}{z}. \tag{7}$$

If $\eta = 1$, then all the A atoms are distributed between sites of one parity (even only, or odd only), and the B atoms between the sites of the opposite parity. This corresponds to a degree of distant order $\xi = +1$ or $-1$.

We thus see that for small disturbances of the alternation order $\eta \cong \xi^2$. With further decrease of order, however, $\eta$ falls off more slowly than $\xi^2$, preserving a finite value above the Curie point where $\xi = 0$, and vanishing only in the limiting case $T \to \infty$.

† H. Bethe, *Proc. Roy. Soc.* A, **150**, 552 (1935).

The dependence of $\eta$ on $T$ can be obtained in a roughly approximate form as follows. Let us first consider the A atoms along with their $z$ neighbours. Let $P_{AA}$ and $P_{AB}$ denote the probabilities that one of these neighbours will be an A or a B atom respectively. If the mutual potential energy between these neighbours and more distant atoms is neglected, then, according to Boltzmann's principle,

$$\frac{P_{AA}}{P_{AB}} = \frac{e^{-U_{AA}/kT}}{e^{-U_{AB}/kT}} = e^{-(U_{AA}-U_{AB})/kT}.$$

Identifying this ratio with the average value of the ratio between the numbers of B atoms ($z'_A$) and A atoms ($z''_A$) about an A atom, we might define the degree of local order with respect to A atoms by the expression

$$\eta_A = \frac{z'_A - z''_A}{z} = \frac{P_{AB}-P_{AA}}{P_{AB}+P_{AA}},$$

that is,
$$\eta_A = \tanh\frac{U_{AA}-U_{AB}}{2kT},$$

while the degree of local order with respect to a B atom would be given by the expression

$$\eta_B = \tanh\frac{U_{BB}-U_{AB}}{2kT}.$$

The two expressions coincide in the special case $U_{AA} = U_{BB}$ only. It seems natural to replace them in the general case by the single expression

$$\eta = \tanh\frac{\frac{1}{2}[(U_{AA}-U_{AB})+(U_{BB}-U_{AB})]}{2kT},$$

that is,
$$\eta = \tanh\frac{U}{2kT}. \tag{8}$$

This result is obviously incorrect, since for very low temperatures $\eta$ must coincide with $\xi^2$, that is, approximately, with $\tanh^2(W/2kT)$, according to (5 a). It gives, however, a fair idea of the variation of $\eta$ at elevated temperatures when $\xi = 0$.

We shall not stop here to consider various attempts which have been made by Bethe, Kirkwood, and a number of other authors to obtain a more exact expression for $\eta$ as a function of the temperature and to derive $\xi$—the degree of distant order—in conjunction with $\eta$. It may suffice to note that this problem has not hitherto been solved satisfactorily. The approximate relation $\eta = \xi^2$, holding in the limiting case of low temperatures, can be established as follows. Since the energy of disorder $E$ depends on the mutual action of adjacent atoms only, it can be expressed as a function of the local order $\eta$ and not of the distant one as has previously been assumed. By the definition of $\eta$ according to (7) we have $z' = \frac{1}{2}(1+\eta)$, $z'' = \frac{1}{2}(1-\eta)$, so that

$$E = \tfrac{1}{2}N[(U_{AA}-U_{AB})z''+(U_{BB}-U_{AB})z''] = NUz'',$$

that is,
$$E = \tfrac{1}{2}NzU(1-\eta). \tag{9}$$

Comparing this with the expression (3 b) of the Bragg-Williams theory and noting that $2zU = W$, we see that $\eta$ can be identified with $\xi^2$.

As a matter of fact, however, the equation (3 b) has been derived under the erroneous assumption that the arrangement of A and B atoms about one of them is determined by the degree of distant order, so that equation (3 b) is wrong while equation (9) is correct.

While the energy $E$ is a function of local order, the entropy $S$ seems to have been correctly defined by equation (4) as a function of the distant order (or of the numbers $N_1$, $N_2$, which serve to determine it). If this were so, the distant order could never vanish, since for $\xi = 0$ the free energy $F = E(\eta)-TS(\xi)$ would become a function of $\eta$ only, which would yield $\eta = 1$ from the condition $\partial F/\partial\eta = 0$. We thus see that in the exact theory $S$ must be defined as a certain function both of $\xi$ and $\eta$.

The notion of local order can be considered as an extension of that of distant order applied not to the whole crystal as that of distant order, but to a limited portion of it. Under such conditions there is no need to introduce two different parameters for the specification of the degree of alternation order, the latter being defined by a certain *function* $\xi$ of the coordinates $x$, $y$, $z$, assuming all values in the range between $-1$ and $+1$ (with the convention that opposite values of $\xi$ are equivalent with respect to the degree of order specified by them).

This function can be introduced by considering each lattice point as the centre of a sphere (or cube) with a radius (or edge) $L$ which is much larger than the lattice constant $a$, but very small compared with the linear dimensions of the whole crystal. The degree of order $\xi$ is thus defined according to equation (2) for the corresponding portion of the crystal. The subdivision of the lattice points into even and odd ones being the same for the whole crystal, $N_1$ can be either larger or smaller than $N_2$. The degree of the order $\xi$ defined in this way and referred to the central point will be in general a continuous function of its coordinates $x$, $y$, $z$. This generalized and unified definition of the alternation order is especially convenient in the case of a non-uniformly heated crystal, $\xi^2$ varying from point to point along with the temperature.

But even in the case when the crystal is under the same macroscopic conditions, it is necessary to distinguish the average value of the degree of order for the whole crystal $\bar{\xi}$ from its local value $\xi(x,y,z)$. The difference $\xi-\bar{\xi} = \Delta\xi$ will be denoted as the *fluctuation* of order. The average value of the square of this fluctuation $\overline{(\Delta\xi)^2}$ is just as important for the specification of the state of the crystal as $\bar{\xi}$. Above the Curie point, when $\bar{\xi}$ vanishes, $\overline{(\Delta\xi)^2}$ can be identified with the degree of local order $\eta$ previously introduced. In the general case the latter can be defined as the average value of $\xi^2$

$$\eta = \overline{\xi^2} = (\bar{\xi})^2+\overline{(\Delta\xi)^2}. \tag{10}$$

When $|\xi|$ lies close to 1 this formula is reduced to the relation $\eta = (\bar{\xi})^2$, which has been used before, when no distinction was made between $\xi$ and $\bar{\xi}$.

The degree of regularity in the whole crystal can be specified by a more general parameter, namely by the average value of the products of the values of the function $\xi$ for two different points $(x_i, y_i, z_i)$ and $(x_k, y_k, z_k)$ at a given distance $R$ from each other

$$\zeta(R) = \overline{\xi_i\,\xi_k}.$$

This parameter reduces to $\eta$ when $R = 0$ and to $(\bar{\xi})^2$ when $R = \infty$. That value of $R$ for which the function $\zeta(R)$ reduces to a certain fraction, one-half, say, of its maximum value can be defined as the 'range' of order. This 'range' determined by the equation

$$\zeta(R) = \tfrac{1}{2}\eta$$

must be a few times, at least, larger than the lattice constant; in the contrary case the above definition of $\xi$, as a function of the coordinates, becomes meaningless.

If the distance $R_{ik}$ is sufficiently small we can put

$$\xi_k = \xi_i+\left(\frac{\partial\xi}{\partial x}\right)_i(x_k-x_i)+...+\frac{1}{2}\left(\frac{\partial^2\xi}{\partial x^2}\right)_i(x_k-x_i)^2+...$$

and consequently

$$\overline{\xi_i\,\xi_k} = \overline{\xi^2}+\frac{R^2}{6}\overline{\xi\left(\frac{\partial^2\xi}{\partial x^2}+\frac{\partial^2\xi}{\partial y^2}+\frac{\partial^2\xi}{\partial z^2}\right)}=\overline{\xi^2}+\tfrac{1}{6}R^2\overline{\xi\nabla^2\xi},$$

since the average values of the differences $(x_k-x_i)$,... and of the products $(x_k-x_i)(y_k-y_i)$ vanish for all directions of the vector $\mathbf{R}$. Using the transformation

$$\overline{\xi\nabla^2\xi} = \frac{1}{V}\int \xi\nabla^2\xi\,dV = \frac{1}{V}\int [\operatorname{div}(\xi\nabla\xi)-(\nabla\xi)^2]\,dV$$

$$= -\frac{1}{V}\int (\nabla\xi)^2\,dV = -\overline{(\nabla\xi)^2},$$

we find
$$\zeta(R) = \eta-\tfrac{1}{6}R^2\overline{(\nabla\xi)^2}.$$

Hence it follows that the 'range' of the order can be defined approximately by the formula

$$R^2 = \frac{3\eta}{(\nabla\xi)^2}.$$

We have hitherto assumed that the free energy of the crystal is a function of the parameters $\bar{\xi}$ or $(\bar{\xi})^2$ and $\overline{\xi^2} = \eta$. In reality, as has been pointed out by L. Landau in a paper on the scattering of X-rays by binary alloys in the neighbourhood of the Curie point,† it must also depend on $\overline{(\nabla\xi)^2}$. Assuming this dependence to be of the simplest form $\frac{1}{2}\gamma(\nabla\xi)^2$ per unit volume, it is possible to determine the order of magnitude of the coefficient $\gamma$ from the fact that in the limiting case of the contact of two regions with sharply different values of $\xi$, $\xi = 1$, and $\xi = 0$, or $\xi = -1$, for example, the quantity $(\nabla\xi)^2$ reaches a maximum value of the order $1/a^2$, where $a$ is the lattice constant, to which the thickness of the transition layer is reduced in this case. The quantity $\frac{1}{2}\gamma(\nabla\xi)^2 a$ can then be treated as the surface energy per unit area of this layer. On the other hand, it must be of the same order of magnitude as the interchange energy $W = 2(z-1)U$ multiplied by the number of atoms $1/a^2$ per unit area. We thus get $\gamma \cong W/a$.

Surfaces of discontinuity of $\xi$ actually arise in the process of quenching, i.e. of rapid cooling of the alloys under consideration. Starting independently at different points the process of 'ordering' can lead to the formation of contiguous regions characterized by opposite sign of $\xi$ ('antiphase' regions of Sykes and Jones).

In a state of thermodynamical equilibrium such discontinuities are, of course, absent and the variations of $\xi$ due to thermal fluctuations are sufficiently smooth.

## 3. Improvement and Extension of the Bragg-Williams Theory

The preceding considerations, among other things, give a clue to the explanation of an essential feature of the curve of Fig. 6, representing the temperature dependence of the additional specific heat $\Delta C$, namely, the preservation of the excess value of $C$ *above* the Curie point, with a gradual decrease of $\Delta C$ to zero. This circumstance is obviously due to the preservation of a certain degree of local order $\eta$ (or in other words, to the fluctuations of the order function $\xi$ about the mean value $\bar{\xi} = 0$) gradually decreasing with elevation of the temperature.

Making use of the equation (9) and of the expression (8) for $\eta$, we

† L. Landau, *Phys. Z. d. Sowjetunion*, **12**, 123 (1937).

obtain the following formula for the energy of disorder as a function of the temperature

$$E = \frac{2zUN}{e^{U/kT}-1},$$

whence

$$\Delta C = \frac{dE}{dT} = \frac{2zNU^2}{(e^{U/kT}-1)^2}\frac{e^{U/kT}}{kT^2} = \frac{zNU^2}{2kT^2}\frac{1}{\sinh^2(U/2kT)}.$$

This expression describes correctly—from a qualitative point of view at least—the 'tail' of the specific heat curve above the Curie point.

It must be noted, however, that an extrapolation of the expression (8) for the degree of local order in the region of lower temperatures would give no indication of the existence of a Curie point, i.e. of a discontinuity of the derivative $dC/dT$.

As has been stated, however, this discontinuity is found experimentally to be much sharper (both with respect to the slope of the $C$–$T$ curve and to the value of the maximum) than would be expected from the Bragg-Williams theory. This circumstance appears especially surprising because the latter makes use of an expression for the energy based upon an extrapolation to higher temperature of the approximate relation between local and distant order ($\eta = \xi^2$) which is valid for low temperatures only, making no allowance for the smoothing influence of the temperature on the course of the local order, which is so conspicuously displayed above the Curie point.

In the theories of Bethe, Kirkwood, and of a number of other authors† this difficulty is overcome by a more exact calculation of the entropy, associated with a given value of the energy, determined as a function of local order, according to (9). The expression (4) for the entropy, previously used, is inadequate for small values of $\xi$, for in this case different arrangements of $N_2 = \frac{1}{2}N(1-\xi)$ atoms over 'wrong' sites of the lattice (belonging to atoms of a different kind) correspond, generally speaking, to widely different values of the energy $E$, depending upon the resulting number of pairs of like or unlike nearest neighbours. The number $P(E)$ of distributions, consistent with a given value of the energy (which is determined by the degree of local order, according to equation (9)) must thus in the case $N_2 \approx N_1$ be greatly reduced compared with the expression $N!/N_1!\,N_2!$ of the Bragg-Williams theory. This corresponds to a decrease of the entropy $S = k\log P$ and to a slower rate of its increase with a decrease of the degree of (local) order.

† H. Bethe, *Proc. Roy. Soc.* A, **150**, 552 (1935); R. Peierls, ibid. A, **154**, 207 (1936); J. Kirkwood, *J. Chem. Phys.* **6**, 70 (1938). See also the review of Nix and Shockley, *Rev. Mod. Phys.* **10**, 1 (1938).

Let us consider the expression of the free energy $F$ as a function of $\xi$ for small values of $\xi$.

Putting in (4) $N_1 = \frac{1}{2}N(1+\xi)$ and $N_2 = \frac{1}{2}N(1-\xi)$ and using Stirling's formula $x! \approx (x/e)^x$ we get

$$S = -\frac{kN}{2}[(1+\xi)\log(1+\xi)+(1-\xi)\log(1-\xi)], \tag{11}$$

which for $\xi \ll 1$ reduces with sufficient accuracy to

$$S = -kN(\tfrac{1}{2}\xi^2+\tfrac{1}{12}\xi^4+\tfrac{1}{30}\xi^6). \tag{11a}$$

The free energy in the corresponding region thus assumes the following approximate form:

$$\begin{aligned} F &= \tfrac{1}{4}NW(1-\xi^2)+NkT(\tfrac{1}{2}\xi^2+\tfrac{1}{12}\xi^4+\tfrac{1}{30}\xi^6) \\ &= \tfrac{1}{4}NW-N(\tfrac{1}{4}W-\tfrac{1}{2}kT)\xi^2+\tfrac{1}{12}NkT\xi^4+\tfrac{1}{30}NkT\xi^6, \end{aligned}$$

i.e.

$$F = A+B\zeta+\tfrac{1}{2}C\zeta^2+\tfrac{1}{3}D\zeta^3, \tag{12}$$

where $\xi^2 = \zeta$ (this quantity must not be identified with the degree of local order) and

$$A = \tfrac{1}{4}NW, \qquad B = -N(\tfrac{1}{4}W-\tfrac{1}{2}kT), \qquad C = \tfrac{1}{6}NkT, \qquad D = \tfrac{1}{10}NkT. \tag{12a}$$

The decrease of the value of $S$ and of the rate of its increase with a fall of $\xi$ and the corresponding more correct expression of the energy as a function of the distant order (as a matter of fact it must be treated as a function of local order) can be accounted for by an adequate definition of the coefficients $A$, $B$, $C$, $D$ in (12) as functions of the temperature.

This question has been considered from a purely phenomenological point of view, without allowing for fluctuation effects, by L. Landau.†

Let us assume, to begin with, that because of the smallness of $\zeta$ the last term in (12) can be neglected (this implies that the coefficient $C$ should remain finite in the limit $\eta \to 0$). From the minimum condition for $F$ as a function of $\zeta$ we get

$$\zeta = -\frac{B}{C}, \tag{13}$$

which coincides with equation (6) of the preceding section if the coefficients $B$ and $C$ are defined according to (12a).

In the vicinity of the Curie point $T = T_0$, defined by the condition $\eta = 0$, the coefficients $B$ and $C$ can be represented as functions of the temperature by the expressions

$$B = B_1(T-T_0), \qquad C = C_0+C_1(T-T_0),$$

† *Phys. Z. d. Sowjetunion*, **8**, 113 (1935).

where $C_0 > 0$, since (12) corresponds to a minimum of $F$. The fact that $\eta$ must remain zero above the Curie point means that the function $F = A+B\zeta+\frac{1}{2}C\zeta^2$ has no minimum for $T > T_0$, whence it follows that the coefficient $B$ must be positive. We thus obtain from general thermodynamic considerations the same results as those following from the Bragg-Williams theory, and, in particular, the same course of the additional specific heat.

In order to obtain a sharper increase of the latter with approach to the Curie point it can be assumed, following Landau, that at $T = T_0$ not only $B$ but also $C$ vanishes ($C_0 = 0$). Under such conditions the cubic term in (12) must be retained and we can put

$$B = B_1(T-T_0), \qquad C = C_1(T-T_0), \qquad D = D_0+D_1(T-T_0),$$

where $D_0 \neq 0$. The condition $\partial F/\partial\zeta = U$ yields the equation

$$B+C\zeta+D\zeta^2 = 0,$$

whence

$$\zeta = \frac{-C\pm\sqrt{(C^2-4BD)}}{2D}. \tag{14}$$

Substituting this expression in the second derivative of $F$ with respect to $\zeta$ we get

$$\frac{\partial^2 F}{\partial\zeta^2} = C+2D\zeta = \pm\sqrt{(C^2-4BD)}. \tag{14 a}$$

Hence it is seen that one of the roots, namely

$$\zeta = \frac{-C+\sqrt{(C^2-4BD)}}{2D},$$

corresponds to a minimum of $F$ and the other to a maximum. In the vicinity of the Curie point this expression reduces to

$$\zeta = \sqrt{\left\{\frac{B_1(T_0-T)}{D_0}\right\}}, \tag{15}$$

since $(T-T_0)$ can be treated in this case as small compared with $\sqrt{(|T-T_0|)}$. In order to obtain real values for $\eta$ below $T_0$ we must have $B/D > 0$, i.e. $B_1/D_0 < 0$.

Whereas in the previous case ($C_0 > 0$) the quantity $\eta$ vanished near $T_0$ as $T_0-T$, in the present case ($C_0 = 0$) it is seen to be proportional to the square root of this difference. This circumstance leads to an essentially different course of the curve $C(T)$ near the Curie point.

Using the general expression $S = -\partial F/\partial T$ for the entropy, we get in the first approximation

$$S = -\frac{\partial A}{\partial T}+B_1\zeta,$$

and consequently $\qquad \Delta C = T\frac{\partial S}{\partial \zeta}\frac{d\zeta}{dT} \cong B_1 T_0 \frac{d\zeta}{dT},$

that is, according to (14a),

$$\Delta C = \frac{\text{const.}}{\sqrt{(T_0-T)}} \qquad \left(\text{const.} = -\frac{B_1^{\frac{3}{2}} T_0}{2D_0^{\frac{1}{2}}}\right). \tag{15a}$$

This result, obtained by Landau, is in much better agreement with the experimental data about the rise of the specific heat with approach to the Curie point from the side of lower temperatures than the Bragg-Williams theory. In order to explain the 'tail' of the $C$, $T$ curve above this point it is necessary to take into account either the local order as a parameter independent of the distant order (see the beginning of this section) or the thermal fluctuations of the order function $\xi$. The latter procedure is in principle equivalent to the former; it has, however, the important advantage of enabling one to use the accurate expression for the free energy as a function of $\xi$ near the Curie point. If $C_0 > 0$, then just above this point the increase of the free energy of a small volume $v$ due to a deviation of $\xi$ from the value zero can be approximated by the expression $\Delta F = \frac{1}{2}vC_0\xi^4$. Since the probability that this deviation will be enclosed between $\xi$ and $\xi+d\xi$ is proportional to $e^{-\Delta F/kT}\,d\xi$, the average value of $\Delta F$

$$\overline{\Delta F} = \int e^{-\Delta F/kT}\,\Delta F d\xi \Big/ \int e^{-\Delta F/kT}\,d\xi$$

is found to be equal to

$$\overline{\Delta F} = -\frac{vC_0}{2}\frac{\partial}{\partial \alpha}\log z(\alpha),$$

where

$$z = \int_{-\infty}^{+\infty} e^{-\alpha\xi^4}\,d\xi = \frac{1}{\alpha^{\frac{1}{4}}}\int_{-\infty}^{+\infty} e^{-u^4}\,du = \text{const. } \alpha^{-\frac{1}{4}} \quad \text{and} \quad \alpha = \frac{vC_0}{2kT},$$

that is,
$$\overline{\Delta F} = \frac{vC_0}{8\alpha} = \frac{kT}{4}.$$

The corresponding value of the entropy of the volume element $v$, $\Delta S = -\frac{\partial}{\partial T}\overline{\Delta F} = -\frac{k}{4}$, turns out to be independent of $T$, so that the preceding approximation is insufficient for the interpretation of the tail of the $C$, $T$ curve. In order to obtain a non-vanishing value of $\Delta C$ above $T_0$ it is necessary to take into account both the coefficient $B$ and the temperature-dependent part of the coefficient $C$. According to Landau it is necessary also in this case to introduce the additional free energy $\frac{1}{2}\gamma(\nabla\xi)^2$ (per unit volume), which is due to a variation of $\xi$ from one point of the crystal to another.†

We shall not enter on a more detailed investigation of this question. It should be mentioned that if in the expansion of $F$ in a series of powers of $\xi$, the coefficients of all the terms up to the $n$th were supposed to vanish for $T = T_0$, then we should obtain, instead of (15) and (15a),

$$\zeta \sim (T_0-T)^{1/n} \quad \text{and} \quad \Delta C \sim (T_0-T)^{-(n-2)/(n-1)},$$

i.e. a still sharper increase of $C$ near $T_0$, tending in the limit $n = \infty$ to an inverse proportionality to $T_0-T$.

If the expression (12) is assumed to hold exactly for all values of $\zeta$ up to $\zeta = 1$, then it can happen that above a certain temperature $T^*$ the derivative of the free energy with regard to $\zeta$ does not vanish anywhere. This requires that for $T \geqslant T^*$, $D \geqslant C^2/4B$. With this condition, the *continuous* drop in the degree of order of $\zeta$ $(= \xi^2)$ with increase in temperature does not extend to zero, but ceases at a finite value reached at $T = T^*$, and corresponding to $D = D^* = C^{*2}/4B^*$, i.e. at $\zeta^* = -C^*/2D^*$.

The simplest assumption about the coefficients $C$ and $D$ which satisfies the preceding requirements and the condition $\zeta = 1$ for $T = 0$ consists in $-D = C > 0$ and $B = B_0 T > 0$.

The expression (12) for the free energy is reduced in this case to

$$F = A+B_0 T\zeta-\tfrac{1}{2}C\zeta^2+\tfrac{1}{3}C\zeta^3, \tag{16}$$

and the equation $\partial F/\partial\zeta = 0$ to

$$\zeta(1-\zeta) = \frac{B_0 T}{C}. \tag{16a}$$

The smallest possible value of $\zeta$ turns out to be equal to $\frac{1}{2}$. It should be mentioned that this equation has two roots, one of which lies between 1 and $\frac{1}{2}$ and the other between $\frac{1}{2}$ and 0. Since

$$\frac{\partial^2 F}{\partial\zeta^2} = -C(1-2\zeta)$$

and $C > 0$, the former corresponds to a stable equilibrium ($F$ = minimum) and the latter to an unstable equilibrium ($F$ = maximum). The

† In order to account for this term in the free energy it is necessary to expand $\xi$ into a Fourier series $\xi = \sum A_n e^{i\boldsymbol{\alpha}_n\cdot\mathbf{z}}$ which gives $\nabla\xi = \sum \boldsymbol{\alpha}_n A_n e^{i\boldsymbol{\alpha}_n\cdot\mathbf{z}}$ and consequently $\int \frac{1}{2}\gamma(\nabla\xi)^2 dV = \frac{1}{4}\gamma\sum\alpha_n^2(A_n)^2$. If $\Delta F$ is assumed to be quadratic in $\xi$, it can easily be calculated; since $\int \overline{\xi^2}dV = \frac{1}{2}\sum(A_n)^2$ (the integration being extended over the whole volume of the body) we get $\overline{\Delta F} = \int \frac{1}{2}B_1\xi^2 dV + \int \frac{1}{2}\gamma(\nabla\xi)^2 dV = \frac{1}{4}\sum|A_n|^2(B_1+\gamma\alpha_n^2)$, whence

$$\overline{(A_n)^2} = kT/(B_1+\gamma\alpha_n^2).$$

dependence of $\zeta$ on $T$ is shown graphically in Fig. 10, the upper branch of the curve (which is an ordinary parabola) corresponding to physically realizable states.

In the case under consideration the transition from a partially ordered state (for which $\zeta > \frac{1}{2}$) to a completely disordered one (with $\zeta = 0$) must be discontinuous if equilibrium states only are taken into

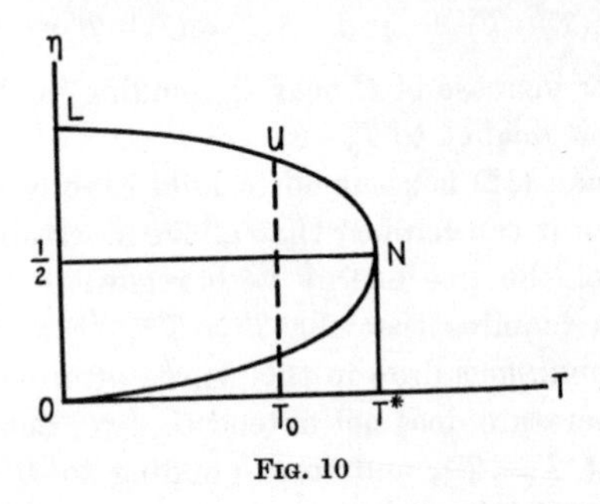


FIG. 10

account, and must be associated with the absorption of latent heat. The transition point $T_e$ corresponding to an equilibrium between the initial and the final state must lie somewhat lower than $T^*$, being determined by the condition

$$F_1(T,\zeta_e) = F_2(T).$$

Here $\zeta_e$ is the limiting value of the degree of order at the transition point ($> \frac{1}{2}$). States with a lower value of $\zeta$ ($\geqslant \frac{1}{2}$) must be treated as metastable, corresponding to a 'superheating' of the body. The disordered phase can, on the other hand, be supercooled below the temperature $T_e$.

We thus see that the behaviour of a body with a free energy of the type (16) is qualitatively similar to that of an ordinary 'condensed' body, with a stable crystalline structure below $T_e$ and a stable amorphous structure above this temperature. The latter can thus be identified (approximately) with the melting-point.

It is interesting to note that the approach to this 'fusion point' from the side of lower temperatures must be accompanied by an abnormal increase of the specific heat. This abnormal rise of $C$ is actually observed near the melting-point of all solid bodies and has been denoted by Ubbelohde as 'pre-melting' (see Ch. VII, § 3).

In order to obtain an expression for $C$ we must note that with $\eta = \bar{\eta}(T)$ as determined from the condition $\partial F/\partial \eta = 0$, the entropy can be defined by either of the formulae

$$S = -\left(\frac{\partial F}{\partial T}\right)_{\zeta=\bar{\zeta}} \quad \text{or} \quad S = -\frac{d}{dT}F[T,\bar{\zeta}(T)].$$

In fact the latter reduces itself to the former, since $(\partial F/\partial\zeta)_{\zeta=\bar{\zeta}} = 0$. Turning to the determination of the specific heat we obtain, however, two different values for it, using the expressions

$$C_{\bar{\zeta}} = T\left(\frac{\partial S}{\partial T}\right)_{\zeta=\bar{\zeta}} \quad \text{and} \quad \bar{C} = T\frac{dS}{dT} = T\left[\left(\frac{\partial S}{\partial T}\right)_{\zeta=\bar{\zeta}} + \frac{\partial S}{\partial\bar{\zeta}}\frac{d\bar{\zeta}}{dT}\right].$$

The latter can be defined as the equilibrium value of the specific heat corresponding to the variation of $\zeta$ with the temperature according to the condition $\partial F/\partial\zeta = 0$, while the former corresponds to a fixed value of $\zeta$ characteristic of the temperature under consideration. While $C_{\bar{\zeta}}$ is a smooth function of $T$ of the usual type, the difference $\bar{C}-C_{\bar{\zeta}} = \Delta C$, representing the additional specific heat due to a variation of the structure, shows a sharp increase with approach to the point $T^*$ or $T_e$.

To see this let us differentiate the equation $(\partial F/\partial\zeta) = 0$ with respect to $T$. This gives

$$\frac{d}{dT}\left(\frac{\partial F}{\partial\zeta}\right)_{\zeta=\bar{\zeta}} = \left(\frac{\partial^2 F}{\partial T\partial\zeta}\right)_{\zeta=\bar{\zeta}} + \left(\frac{\partial^2 F}{\partial\zeta^2}\right)_{\zeta=\bar{\zeta}}\frac{d\bar{\zeta}}{dT} = 0, \tag{17}$$

that is, since

$$\left(\frac{\partial^2 F}{\partial T\partial\zeta}\right)_{\zeta=\bar{\zeta}} = \left(\frac{\partial}{\partial\zeta}\frac{\partial F}{\partial T}\right)_{\zeta=\bar{\zeta}} = -\left(\frac{\partial S}{\partial\zeta}\right)_{\zeta=\bar{\zeta}},$$

$$\left(\frac{\partial S}{\partial\zeta}\right)_{\zeta=\bar{\zeta}} = \left(\frac{\partial^2 F}{\partial\zeta^2}\right)_{\zeta=\bar{\zeta}}\frac{d\bar{\zeta}}{dT}. \tag{17 a}$$

Substituting this expression in the formula

$$\Delta C = T\left(\frac{\partial S}{\partial\zeta}\right)_{\zeta=\bar{\zeta}}\frac{d\bar{\zeta}}{dT},$$

we get

$$\Delta C = T\left(\frac{\partial^2 F}{\partial\zeta^2}\right)_{\zeta=\bar{\zeta}}\left(\frac{d\bar{\zeta}}{dT}\right)^2. \tag{17 b}$$

Since $F$ has a minimum for $\zeta = \bar{\zeta}$, the second derivative of $F$ with respect to $\zeta$ must have for $\zeta = \bar{\zeta}$ a positive value, which in the present case is equal to $-C(1-2\bar{\zeta})$. We have further, according to (16 a),

$$(1-2\bar{\zeta})\frac{d\bar{\zeta}}{dT} = \frac{B_0}{C},$$

and consequently

$$\Delta C = \frac{T}{2\bar{\zeta}-1}\frac{B_0^2}{C},$$

or, according to the definition of $T^*$ as that temperature for which $\zeta = \frac{1}{2}$,

$$\Delta C = \frac{1}{4} B_0 \frac{T}{\sqrt{\{T^*(T^*-T)\}}}.$$

Thus $\Delta C$ is found to depend on $T$ in exactly the same way as in the case of Landau's theory of the Curie point, examined above.

## 4. General Thermodynamic Theory of Phenomena connected with a Variation of the Degree of Order

We have limited ourselves thus far to the investigation of the dependence of the degree of order on the temperature, leaving aside the second parameter specifying the state of any material body, namely its volume $V$ or pressure $p$. In reality, however, the degree of order must depend upon the (specific) volume or the pressure—in a very marked way, falling off with increase of $v$. This dependence can be calculated if the expression of the energy $W$ in the equation giving the dependence of $\xi$ (or $\eta$) on the temperature is itself known as a function of the volume. If the variations of the latter are not too large this function can be approximated by the linear expression

$$W = W_0 - \beta(V - V_0),$$

where $V_0$ is the volume at $T = 0$ and $p = 0$, say, and $\beta$ a certain positive coefficient (see Ch. I, p. 14, l. 6). Under such conditions the Curie temperature must fall off with increase of the volume according to a linear law, i.e. rise according to a similar law with increase of the pressure.

Without giving an explicit expression for $W$ as a function of $V$ and without expanding $F$ into a series of powers of $\xi$ or $\eta$† with coefficients $A$, $B$, $C$, etc., defined as certain functions of $T$ and $V$ (or $p$), it is possible to obtain by the application of general thermodynamic equations a number of interesting relationships which characterize the abnormal behaviour in the vicinity of the Curie point not only of the specific heat of a crystal but also of other properties connected with its volume or the pressure to which it is subjected, viz. the thermal expansion coefficient at constant pressure $\bar{\alpha} = \frac{1}{V}\left(\frac{dV}{dT}\right)_p$, the thermal coefficient of the pressure at constant volume $\bar{\beta} = \frac{1}{p}\left(\frac{dp}{dT}\right)_V$, and the modulus of compressibility at a constant temperature $\bar{K} = -V\left(\frac{dp}{dV}\right)_T$.

† In the sequel we shall use the notation $\zeta$ to indicate either one of the quantities $\xi$ or $\eta$ (not to be confused with the $\zeta$ used in §§ 2 and 3).

We are using here the notation for total and not partial derivatives in order to indicate the fact that in performing the differentiation account must be taken of the dependence of the corresponding function on the equilibrium degree of order $\zeta = \bar{\zeta}(T, V)$ or $\bar{\zeta}(T, p)$ as determined by the condition $\partial F/\partial\zeta = 0$ or $\partial\phi/\partial\zeta = 0$ (where $\phi = F+pV$ is the thermodynamic potential).

Just as in the case of the specific heat, it is interesting to compare the 'complete' or equilibrium values of the quantities $\alpha$, $\beta$, and $K$ ($\bar{\alpha}, \bar{\beta}, \bar{K}$) and those values $\alpha_{\bar{\zeta}}$, $\beta_{\bar{\zeta}}$, $K_{\bar{\zeta}}$ which are obtained if the degree of order is kept constant while the temperature is changed in the vicinity of a given value $T$. The differences $\bar{\alpha}-\alpha_{\bar{\zeta}} = \Delta\alpha$, etc., can be treated as the additional values of the corresponding parameters, due to change of the degree of order with a variation of the temperature or of the volume.

If the expression of $F$ as a function of $\zeta$, $T$, and $V$ is known, the pressure can be calculated by means of the general formula

$$p = -\left(\frac{\partial F}{\partial V}\right)_{T,\zeta},$$

which for $\zeta = \bar{\zeta}$ yields the same equilibrium value of $p = \bar{p}$ as the formula

$$p = -\left[\frac{d}{dV}F(V,T,\zeta)\right]_T = -\left(\frac{\partial F}{\partial V}\right)_{T,\zeta=\bar{\zeta}} - \left(\frac{\partial F}{\partial \zeta}\right)_{V,T,\zeta=\bar{\zeta}}\left(\frac{\partial\bar{\zeta}}{\partial V}\right)_T,$$

because of the minimum condition for $F$, i.e. $\partial F/\partial\zeta = 0$ serving to determine $\bar{\zeta}$.

An entirely different situation is met with when the derivatives of $p$ with respect to $V$ and $T$ are compared with each other. We have thus,

$$\left(\frac{d\bar{p}}{dT}\right)_V = \left(\frac{\partial p}{\partial T}\right)_{V,\bar{\zeta}} + \left(\frac{\partial p}{\partial \zeta}\right)_{V,T,\zeta=\bar{\zeta}}\left(\frac{\partial\bar{\zeta}}{\partial T}\right)_V,$$

and further, in the same way as in the derivation of (17 a):

$$\left(\frac{dp}{d\zeta}\right)_{\zeta=\bar{\zeta}} = -\left(\frac{\partial^2 F}{\partial\zeta\partial V}\right)_{\zeta=\bar{\zeta}} = \left(\frac{\partial^2 F}{\partial\zeta^2}\right)_{\zeta=\bar{\zeta}}\frac{d\bar{\zeta}}{dV},$$

and consequently
$$\Delta\beta = \frac{1}{p}\left(\frac{\partial^2 F}{\partial\zeta^2}\right)_{\zeta=\bar{\zeta}}\frac{\partial\bar{\zeta}}{\partial V}\frac{\partial\bar{\zeta}}{\partial T}. \tag{18}$$

Since $\partial\bar{\zeta}/\partial V < 0$ and $\partial\bar{\zeta}/\partial T < 0$ while $(\partial^2 F/\partial\zeta^2)_{\zeta=\bar{\zeta}} > 0$, $\Delta\beta$ must have an essentially positive value with a temperature course of a similar type to that of the additional specific heat $\Delta C$.

We obtain in a similar way

$$\left(\frac{d\bar{p}}{dV}\right)_T - \left(\frac{\partial p}{\partial V}\right)_{\zeta=\bar{\zeta},T} = \left(\frac{\partial p}{\partial \zeta}\right)_{\zeta=\bar{\zeta}} \frac{\partial \bar{\zeta}}{\partial V} = \left(\frac{\partial^2 F}{\partial \zeta^2}\right)_{\zeta=\bar{\zeta}} \left(\frac{\partial \bar{\zeta}}{\partial V}\right)^2,$$

i.e.

$$\Delta K = -V\left(\frac{\partial^2 F}{\partial \zeta^2}\right)_{\zeta=\bar{\zeta}} \left(\frac{\partial \bar{\zeta}}{\partial V}\right)_T^2. \tag{18a}$$

For the calculation of the thermal expansion coefficient (at constant pressure) it is more convenient to use the thermodynamic potential $\phi(T, p, \zeta)$. We then get for the determination of $\bar{\zeta}(T, p)$ the equation $\partial\phi/\partial\zeta = 0$, and further,

$$V = \left(\frac{d\phi}{dp}\right)_T = \left(\frac{\partial \phi}{\partial p}\right)_{T,\zeta=\bar{\zeta}} + \left(\frac{\partial \phi}{\partial \zeta}\right)_{\zeta=\bar{\zeta}} \frac{\partial \bar{\zeta}}{\partial p} = \left(\frac{\partial \phi}{\partial p}\right)_{T,\zeta=\bar{\zeta}}.$$

Differentiating this expression with respect to $T$ with $p =$ const. we obtain, as before,

$$\left(\frac{dV}{dT}\right)_p = \left(\frac{\partial V}{\partial T}\right)_{p,\zeta=\bar{\zeta}} + \left(\frac{\partial V}{\partial \zeta}\right)_{p,T,\zeta=\bar{\zeta}} \frac{\partial \bar{\zeta}}{\partial T},$$

and further,

$$\left(\frac{\partial V}{\partial \zeta}\right)_{\zeta=\bar{\zeta}} = \left(\frac{\partial^2 \phi}{\partial p \partial \zeta}\right)_{\zeta=\bar{\zeta}} = -\left(\frac{\partial^2 \phi}{\partial \zeta^2}\right)_{\zeta=\bar{\zeta}} \frac{\partial \bar{\zeta}}{\partial p},$$

whence

$$\Delta\alpha = -\frac{1}{V}\left(\frac{\partial^2 \phi}{\partial \zeta^2}\right)_{\zeta=\bar{\zeta}} \frac{\partial \bar{\zeta}}{\partial p} \frac{\partial \bar{\zeta}}{\partial T}. \tag{18b}$$

Formula (18a) shows that the bulk modulus must display an abnormal drop with elevation of the temperature, sharply increasing

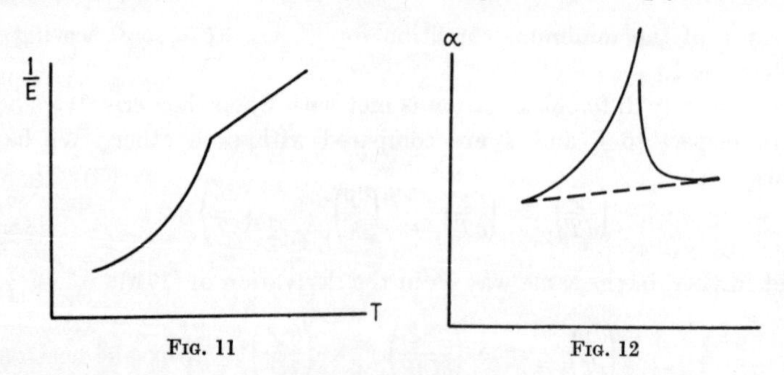


FIG. 11 FIG. 12

in the vicinity of the Curie point. Since $\partial\bar{\zeta}/\partial p > 0$, it follows that the thermal expansion coefficient must abnormally rise in a way similar to the specific heat.

These thermodynamical deductions are in full agreement with the experimental facts, as can be seen, for example, from Figs. 11 and 12 illustrating the dependence of the reciprocal of Young's modulus in the case of $\beta$-brass, according to Rinehardt,† and of the thermal expansion coefficient.

The parallelism in the course of $\alpha$ and $C$ near $T = T_0$ (which follows from their proportionality to the first and second powers of $d\zeta/dT$ respectively) has led some authors to regard the anomaly of thermal expansion near the Curie point as the *cause* of the anomaly of the specific heat, as usually measured (i.e. at a constant pressure).‡ It should be noted that equation (17 b) refers to the specific heat at constant volume $C_v$, since it has been derived from the expression of the free energy $F$. The corresponding formula for $C_p$ is obtained from (17) if $F$ is replaced by $\phi$ and may be written in the form

$$\Delta C_p = T\left(\frac{\partial^2\phi}{\partial\zeta^2}\right)_{\zeta=\bar{\zeta}}\left(\frac{\partial\zeta}{\partial T}\right)_p^2.$$

If in a transition through the Curie point the specific heat is changed by a finite amount, as required by the Bragg-Williams theory, all the other quantities $\alpha$, $\beta$, $K$ must also suffer finite jumps only. Under such conditions the dependence of the Curie point on the pressure can be determined with the help of Ehrenfest's equation referring to all transitions of this kind (i.e. transitions of the second kind in Ehrenfest's sense, cf. § 1).

This equation is obtained from the continuity condition for the entropy $S_1 = S_2$ at the transition point. Differentiating both sides of the latter for equation we get

$$dS_1 = \left(\frac{dS_1}{dp}\right)_T dp + \left(\frac{dS_1}{dT}\right)_p dT = dS_2 = \left(\frac{dS_2}{dp}\right)_T dp + \left(\frac{dS_2}{dT}\right)_p dT,$$

whence, according to the relations $\left(\frac{dS}{dT}\right)_p = \frac{\bar{C}_p}{T}$ and

$$\left(\frac{dS}{dp}\right)_T = -\frac{dV}{dT} = -V\alpha,$$

there follows
$$\frac{dT_0}{dp} = T_0 V \frac{\bar{\alpha}_2 - \bar{\alpha}_1}{\bar{C}_{p_2} - \bar{C}_{p_1}}. \tag{19}$$

If, however, with approach to the Curie point the specific heat and the thermal expansion coefficient tend to infinity, the transition is more adequately treated as similar to an ordinary transition of the first kind, taking place, however, not at a definite point but within a finite (sometimes exceedingly narrow) range, as has already been pointed out in § 1.

† J. S. Rinehardt, *Phys. Rev.* **58**, 365 (1940).

‡ See, for instance, Eisenschitz, *Proc. Roy. Soc.* A, **168**, 546 (1938).

The dependence of the transition temperature $T_0$ corresponding to the peak values of $c$, $\alpha$, and other quantities of this type (second derivatives of the thermodynamic potential with respect to $T$ and $p$) on the pressure can be determined, at least approximately, with the help of the ordinary Clausius-Clapeyron equation

$$\frac{dT_0}{dp} = \frac{T_0(V_2-V_1)}{Q_{1,2}},$$

where

$$V_2-V_1 = \int V_0 \Delta\alpha \, dT \quad \text{and} \quad Q_{1,2} = T_0(S_2-S_1) = \int \Delta C \, dT$$

are the additional increase of volume and the additional heat absorbed in a transition from a state of complete order ($\zeta = 1$) to that of complete disorder ($\zeta = 0$) at a constant value of the pressure.

Transitions, both of the first and of the second kind, can take place not only at constant pressure but also at constant volume. In this case Ehrenfest's equation is replaced by

$$\frac{dT_0}{dV} = \frac{T_0[(dp_1/dT)_v-(dp_2/dT)_v]}{C_{v_2}-C_{v_1}}, \tag{20}$$

and that of Clausius-Clapeyron by

$$\frac{dT_0}{dV} = -\frac{T_0(p_2-p_1)}{Q_{1,2}}, \tag{20a}$$

the latter following from the continuity of the free energy. It is not used in practice for the reason that the maintenance of a constant volume in phase transitions is inconsistent with a mechanical equilibrium between the two phases, which requires the equality between their pressures.

It should be noted, in conclusion, that transitions of both kinds can be caused not only by a change of the temperature at a constant pressure or volume but equally well, in principle, by a variation of the volume or pressure at a constant temperature. Thus, for example, if it were possible to increase the volume of an alloy of the type $AB$ by the application of a sufficiently large negative pressure, the degree of order could be reduced to zero at any temperature $T$, which could be regarded as the result of lowering the transition point $T_0$, according to equation (19a) or (20a), down to the given value $T$. The actual realization of such a procedure is handicapped, however, by the difficulty of obtaining experimentally negative pressures.

It can easily be shown that with approach of the volume to the limiting value $v_0$ corresponding, at a given temperature $T$, to $\bar{\zeta} = 0$

(i.e. to the lowering of the Curie temperature down to $T$) the fall of $\bar{\zeta}$ must proceed more and more rapidly, just as in the case when it is due to heating at constant volume or constant pressure.

Putting, for instance, $W = W_0 - \beta(V - V_0)$ and making use of the equation $\xi = \tanh(W/2kT)\xi$, following from the Bragg-Williams theory, we see that with approach to a critical value of $V = V_c$ for which $W/2kT = 1$ this equation reduces approximately to

$$\xi^2 = 3\,\frac{V_c - V}{V_c}$$

(cf. the derivation of equation (6), which corresponds to $d\xi/dV = -\infty$ for $\xi \to 0$).

Since opposite values of $\xi$ are physically equivalent, the free energy (or the potential $\phi$) must be even functions of $\xi$, i.e. they must depend on its square $\xi^2 = \zeta$. Using the expression (18 a) for the bulk modulus, and the approximate expression (12) for the free energy in the neighbourhood of the Curie point, we get, since $d\bar{\zeta}/dV = -3/V_c$,

$$(\Delta K)_{T \to T_0} \cong -\frac{3N}{2V_c}\,kT_0.$$

We thus see from the point of view of the Bragg-Williams theory that the decrease of the degree of order with increase of the volume

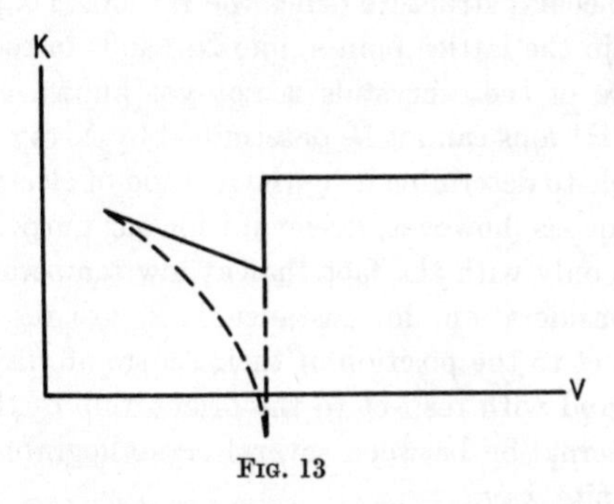


FIG. 13

must lead to a finite drop of the compressibility modulus with approach to the Curie point, the normal value of $K$ being restored just above the latter (Fig. 13, full line). If the free energy near the Curie point is approximated by the expression (12) of Landau's theory and if the linear relation between the energy $W$ or, what amounts to the same thing, between the Curie temperature $T$ and the volume $V$ is preserved, the compressibility modulus must tend with approach to the Curie point to a negatively infinite value (dotted line in Fig. 13). This means that states lying in the neighbourhood of this point are mechanically and thermodynamically unstable.

A more detailed discussion of the consequences of such an instability will be given in the next chapter in connexion with the theory of ordinary melting.

## 5. Orientation Order in Dipolar Crystals†

We have dwelt at such length on the 'alternation order' in binary alloys not so much because of the interest presented by this question itself but because the results obtained can be applied with only insignificant modifications to a number of similar questions connected with the presence in the structure of material bodies of various types of order, realized to a certain limited extent.

One of the simplest and most important types of order in chemically homogeneous bodies, constituted by diatomic or more complicated molecules, is the order in the *orientation* of the molecules (their centres of gravity being assumed to be regularly arranged in the points of a crystal lattice).

This type of order is found, for example, in the case of halogen hydrides, HF, HCl, HBr, HI, which form crystal lattices with a pronounced molecular structure (since the $H^+$ ions, i.e. protons, cannot remain at rest in the lattice points, like $Na^+$ ions in rock-salt crystal).

The structure of these crystals is not yet known exactly (for the position of the $H^+$ ions cannot be determined by X-ray methods; it has not been possible to determine it by the method of electron diffraction). This circumstance is, however, irrelevant for our purpose. We shall be concerned here only with the fact that at low temperatures the molecules under consideration, for instance HCl, are regularly arranged both with respect to the position of their centre of gravity (in definite lattice points) and with respect to the orientation of their axes, these orientations alternating between several crystallographic directions in a perfectly definite way.

Following a (probably wrong) scheme, proposed long ago by Bonn and Kornfeld, we can imagine, for example, that the centres of gravity of the HCl molecules constitute a simple cubic lattice, while their axes are parallel to the four diagonals of each elementary cubic cell, so that the axes of each pair of molecules situated at the end points of each diagonal have the same direction, the orientations of the nearest

† J. Frenkel, *Acta Physicochimica U.R.S.S.* 3, 23 (1935).

neighbours, situated at the four corners of each face alternating between an inward and outward direction.

This arrangement of the molecules need not be actually true; the important point is that it corresponds to a stable equilibrium of the whole system with respect to the orientations of the molecules, the axis of each molecule, as defined by its electric moment $\mathbf{p}$, being directed along the electric field $\mathbf{E}_0$ due to the dipole moments of all the other molecules.

Such a condition can be realized at the temperature of absolute zero only, with neglect of the 'zero-point energy' required by quantum mechanics, and realized in the form of small vibrations of the centres of gravity of the molecules about their equilibrium positions and rotational oscillations about the corresponding equilibrium orientations. The frequency of these oscillations $\nu_0$ is given by the (approximate) formula

$$\nu_0 = \frac{1}{2\pi}\sqrt{\left(\frac{E_0 p}{J}\right)}, \tag{21}$$

where $J$ is the moment of inertia of a molecule,† while the lowest value of their energy (at $T = 0$) is equal to $\frac{1}{2}h\nu_0$.

At sufficiently high temperatures for which the condition $kT > h\nu_0$ is satisfied, the average energy of these rotation-oscillations must be approximately equal to the value $kT$ per degree of freedom, required by the classical theory (a molecule of this type possessing two rotational degrees of freedom).

Since a deviation of a molecule by a (small) angle $\theta$ from the equilibrium direction involves an increase of the potential energy by the amount $E_0 p(1-\cos\theta) \approx \frac{1}{2}E_0 p\theta^2$, and since in the case of harmonic vibrations the average value of the potential energy is equal to that of the kinetic energy, we get

$$\overline{\theta^2} = \frac{kT}{E_0 p}. \tag{22}$$

The condition that the angle $\sqrt{(\overline{\theta^2})}$ determined by this formula should be small (compared with $\frac{1}{2}\pi$, for example) is practically satisfied up to the highest temperatures available in the laboratory. In fact, as regards its order of magnitude, $E_0$ is equal to $p/a^3$, where $a$ is the distance between nearest neighbours (i.e. the lattice constant). Putting $p = 10^{-18}$ and $a = 3.10^{-8}$ we get $pE_0 = \dfrac{10^{-36}}{2{\cdot}7\times 10^{-23}} = 3.10^{-12}$ ergs,

† This formula is obtained on the assumption that the axis of the molecule under consideration deviates from the equilibrium direction by a small angle $\theta$, while the remainder are held fixed in their equilibrium position and orientations.

whereas at room temperature $kT = 3.10^{-14}$ ergs, i.e. 100 times smaller. The corresponding average deviation $\sqrt{(\overline{\theta^2})}$ is equal approximately to 1/10. We thus see that the assumption of the smallness of $\theta$ is justified for temperatures up to a few thousand degrees.

The preceding considerations need, however, one important correction. We have assumed thus far that in spite of the (rotational) oscillations of *all* the molecules the electric field $E$, acting on one of them, has the same value $E_0$ as if all the other molecules did not participate in the thermal motion.

In order to account for the latter we must, in the determination of the average field $\bar{E}$ acting on a given molecule in the direction of its equilibrium orientation, replace the actual electric moments by the corresponding (i.e. referring to the respective equilibrium orientation) components of these moments. Since all the molecules are oscillating under exactly the same conditions, we get

$$\bar{E} = E_0 \overline{\cos\theta}. \tag{23}$$

Since with a rise of the temperature $\overline{\cos\theta}$ decreases, the increase of the average deviation $\theta$ or its square must take place more rapidly than according to (22), owing to the increase of the average energy of the thermal oscillations on the one hand, and to the accompanying decrease of the orientating forces on the other. At sufficiently low temperatures the corresponding correction can be introduced if $E_0$ in (22) is replaced by $E_0 \overline{\cos\theta} \approx E_0(1-\overline{\theta^2}/2)$. We thus get the following equation for the quantity $\zeta = \overline{\cos\theta} \approx 1-\frac{1}{2}\overline{\theta^2}$ which can be treated as a measure of the degree of orientation order

$$\zeta(1-\zeta) = \frac{kT}{2pE_0}. \tag{24}$$

According to this equation $\zeta$ can fall continuously down to a value $\frac{1}{2}$ reached for a temperature $T^* = pE_0/8k$ and jump to zero above it (cf. (16 a), § 3).

An apparently more exact calculation yields a somewhat different result. If the effective (average) field $E$, tending to orientate each molecule in the corresponding equilibrium direction, is treated as constant (with respect to the time) the average value of the component of its electric moment in this direction can be calculated by means of the well-known equation of Langevin-Debye

$$p\,\overline{\cos\theta} = pL\left(\frac{p\bar{E}}{kT}\right),$$

where $L(x) = \coth x - 1/x$ is Langevin's function. Putting here $\bar{E} = E_0\zeta$ we obtain the following equation for $\zeta$

$$\zeta = L(x_0\zeta), \tag{25}$$

where
$$x_0 = \frac{E_0 p}{kT}.$$

This equation is quite similar to the equation (5a) which determines the degree of long-range alternation order in a binary alloy, according to the Bragg-Williams theory.

In fact Langevin's function $L(x)$ has a shape similar to that of the function $\tanh x$; with increase of $x$ it increases in a monotonic way tending to the value 1. The initial slope of the tangent to it at the point $x = 0$ is equal to $\frac{1}{3}$. This means that equation (25) has a non-vanishing solution only if $\frac{1}{3}x_0 > 1$. The quantity $\zeta$ thus falls continuously from 1 to 0 as the temperature is raised from 0 to the 'Curie point'

$$T_c = \frac{E_0 p}{3k}. \tag{25a}$$

In the neighbourhood of this temperature we have approximately

$$L = \frac{x_0\zeta}{3}\left[1 - \frac{1}{15}x_0^2\zeta^2\right],$$

so that equation (25) is reduced to

$$\zeta^2 \cong \frac{15}{x_0^2}\left(1 - \frac{3}{x_0}\right),$$

or since, $x_0/3 = T_c/T$,
$$\zeta^2 = \frac{5}{2}\frac{T_c - T}{T_c}. \tag{25b}$$

This formula differs from (6) by a numerical factor only.

We thus see that the theory of orientation order in a crystal lattice formed by dipole molecules is practically identical with the Bragg-Williams theory of alternation order in a binary alloy, the role of the degree of distant order being played by the quantity $\zeta = \overline{\cos\theta}$.

The above method for the determination of $\zeta$ as a function of $T$ is open to the objection that it makes use of the Boltzmann expression for the probability of a given orientation of a dipole molecule in a *constant* electric field, whereas the $\bar{E}$ is but the average value of a rapidly and irregularly oscillating field.

This circumstance may be accounted for by a method similar to that which is used in the Debye or rather the Born-Karman theory of the transitional heat motion of the atoms in a solid body (crystal). The drawback of this method lies in the necessity of limiting oneself to vibrations of a small amplitude, i.e. to the case of low temperatures, so that the mutual potential energy of the dipole molecules can be represented, with a sufficient degree of accuracy, as a quadratic function of the angles $\theta_1$, $\theta_2$,... of their axes with respect to the corresponding normal directions. The rotation part of the heat motion can thus be described as a superposition of 'rotation-oscillation' waves, which are quite analogous to the 'optical' waves of the Born-Karman theory in the case of an ionic crystal lattice.

For the sake of simplicity we shall limit ourselves to the case of a one-dimensional dipole lattice, i.e. an endless linear chain; we shall assume further that all the dipole moments are normally directed along the line connecting their centres of gravity. The distance between the latter will be denoted by $a$, and the oscillations will be assumed to take place in a definite plane.

The mutual potential energy of two neighbouring dipoles, as a function of the angles $\theta_1$, $\theta_2$, is equal to

$$U_{1,2} = \frac{p^2}{a^3}[-2\cos\theta_1\cos\theta_2+\sin\theta_1\sin\theta_2].$$

If the angles are sufficiently small it can be replaced by

$$U_{1,2} = -\frac{2p^2}{a^3}+\frac{p^2}{a^3}(\theta_1^2+\theta_2^2+\theta_1\theta_2).$$

The oscillations of the dipoles under the action of forces (torques) acting on each of them on the part of the two neighbours are determined by the system of linear equations

$$J\frac{d^2\theta_n}{dt^2} = -\frac{\partial U_{n,n+1}}{\partial\theta_n}-\frac{\partial U_{n,n-1}}{\partial\theta_n},$$

that is

$$J\frac{d^2\theta_n}{dt^2} = -\frac{p^2}{a^3}(4\theta_n+\theta_{n+1}+\theta_{n-1}). \tag{26}$$

It should be mentioned that the quantity

$$\omega_0^2 = \frac{4p^2}{a^3 J}$$

is the square of the angular frequency due to an external field $E_0 = 4p/a^3$ which is created at the centre of each molecule by its two nearest neighbours.

We shall solve the system of equations (26) by taking for $\theta_n$ the usual expression for progressive waves

$$\theta_n = Ae^{i(\omega t-\alpha n)}. \tag{26 a}$$

Substituting this expression in the equation (26) we get

$$\omega^2 e^{i\alpha n} = \omega_0^2[e^{ikn}+\tfrac{1}{4}(e^{i\alpha(n+1)}+e^{i\alpha(n-1)})],$$

that is

$$\omega^2 = \omega_0^2(1+\tfrac{1}{2}\cos\alpha). \tag{26 b}$$

This formula defines the angular frequency as a function of the wave number $k = \alpha/a = 2\pi/\lambda$, where $\lambda$ is the wave-length. The maximum value of $\omega$=$(\sqrt{\frac{3}{2}}\omega_0)$ corresponds to the case $\lambda = \infty$; the minimum value $\omega_0/\sqrt{2}$ to the case $\lambda = 2a$; the shortest wave-length is thus equal to twice the spacing between neighbouring atoms.

The formulae (26) and (26 a) remain valid in the case of a dipolar chain of finite length if complications due to end effects are avoided by connecting the two ends with each other and thus closing the chain. If the number of dipoles is $g$, the coefficient $\alpha$ can assume discrete values $\alpha = (2\pi/g)r$, where $r$ is an integer lying between $\frac{1}{2}g$ and $-\frac{1}{2}g$ (this corresponds to waves propagated to the left or to the right with a length $\lambda_r = ag/r = L/r$, where $L$ is the length of the chain).

The general solution of equation (26) can be represented by a sum of particular solutions

$$\theta_n = \sum_r A_r e^{i(\omega_r t-\alpha_r n)}, \tag{27}$$

where the coefficients $A_r$ or rather the products of those coefficients and $e^{i\omega_r t}$ play the role of normal coordinates.

The potential energy of the chain referred to the equilibrium orientation of all the dipoles ($\theta_1 = \theta_2 = ... = 0$) is given by the formula

$$U = \frac{p^2}{a^3}[\sum 2\theta_n^2+\tfrac{1}{2}\sum \theta_n(\theta_{n-1}+\theta_{n+1})].$$

In order to determine its mean value (with respect to the time) the products $\theta_n\theta_n$ and $\theta_n(\theta_{n-1}+\theta_{n+1})$ must be replaced by $\frac{1}{2}\theta_n^*\theta_n$ and $\frac{1}{2}\theta_n^*(\theta_{n-1}+\theta_{n+1})$, where $\theta_n^*$ is the complex conjugate of $\theta_n$. A simple calculation gives us

$$U = \frac{p^2}{a^3}g\sum_r A_r A_r^*(1+\tfrac{1}{2}\cos\alpha_r),$$

that is, according to (26 b),

$$U = \tfrac{1}{4}Jg\sum_r \omega_r^2 A_r A_r^*. \tag{27 a}$$

The doubled value of each term of the sum is equal to the total (potential+kinetic) energy of the corresponding normal vibration of the chain. Equating its average (statistical) value to $kT$ we get

$$\tfrac{1}{2}Jg\sum_r \omega_r^2|A_r|^2 = kT,$$

whence

$$\overline{\theta_n^2} = \tfrac{1}{2}\overline{\theta_n\theta_n^*} = \tfrac{1}{2}\sum_r |A_r|^2 = \frac{kT}{Jg}\sum_{r=1}^{g}\frac{1}{\omega_r^2}.$$

If the mean value of $1/\omega_r^2$ is replaced by $\dfrac{1}{\omega_0^2} = \dfrac{a^3J}{4p^2} = \dfrac{J}{pE_0}$, we come back to the formula

$$\overline{\theta^2} = \frac{kT}{pE_0}$$

derived previously, starting from the assumption that each molecule vibrates in a constant field $E_0$, its neighbours being supposed to remain fixed in their equilibrium orientations.

We thus see that a rise of the temperature is accompanied by a decrease of the degree of orientation of the molecules $\zeta = \overline{\cos\theta}$ at a gradually increasing rate, until at a certain temperature $T_c = pE_0/3k$ it vanishes (continuously or with a discontinuous drop from the value $\frac{1}{2}$ to zero).

We must now clear up the physical meaning of the notion of the 'degree of orientation' and, in particular, of a vanishing degree of orientation ($\zeta = 0$).

It may seem at first sight that the latter means a transition of the molecules from a state of rotational oscillations about equilibrium orientations with gradually increasing amplitudes to a free rotation. In fact an electric field $E$ can orientate a molecule with a moment $p$ only if its total energy $W$ does not exceed the value $2pE$ which is required for a transition from an equilibrium orientation $\theta = 0$ to the opposite orientation $\theta = \pi$, corresponding to a maximum of the potential energy. Since according to the Maxwell-Boltzmann law the energy $W$ can reach values exceeding $2pE$ even at temperatures for which $kT \ll pE$, we are forced to the conclusion that when $T$ approaches the value $pE_0/k$ or even $pE_0/3k$, a more or less considerable fraction of the molecules, constituting the dipole crystal, must pass from rotational oscillations to a practically free rotation, differing from that in a gas by a certain lack of uniformity (the electrical field furthering the rotation during one half period and hindering it during the other).

The idea that the molecules of a crystalline body can rotate freely or nearly freely was expressed for the first time by Pauling in 1930, in application to the case of solid hydrogen at very low temperatures.† This idea has been subsequently applied to the explanation of the anomalies of specific heats and of thermal expansion coefficients of the λ-type (i.e. of the same type as in a CuZn alloy), which have been found in the case of a very large number of chemically homogeneous sub-

† L. Pauling, *Phys. Rev.* **22**, 480 (1930). See also Simon, *Ann. d. Phys.* **68**, 241 (1922); Simon, Simpson, and Ruhemann, *Z. f. phys. Chem.* **129**, 339 (1927).

stances, constituted by undissociated molecules ($HCl$, $CH_4$, etc.) or radicals (such as $NH_4$, $NO_3$, and so forth).

Fowler† has given a quantitative development of this idea, starting from the simplified conception that at any given temperature the molecules can be divided into two groups: the orientated (i.e. performing rotational oscillations about equilibrium orientations) and the rotating. To the first group all those molecules are referred whose kinetic rotational energy $W$ is smaller than $\gamma pE$, where $\gamma$ is a numerical coefficient of the order of 1; the second group consists of all those molecules for which $W > \gamma pE$. The orientating field $E$ is determined on the assumption that it is produced by non-rotating molecules only which, for the sake of simplicity, are supposed to remain fixed in their equilibrium orientations. The field $E$ must, accordingly, be proportional to the degree of orientation $s$, defined as the ratio of the number of non-rotating molecules $N_1$ to their total number $N = N_1+N_2$. Using Maxwell's law of the distribution of rotational velocities, it can easily be shown that the ratio $N_2/N = 1-N_1/N$ must, under such conditions, be equal to $e^{-\gamma pE/kT}$. Replacing $N_1/N$ by $s$ and putting $E = E_0 s$, where $E_0$ is the value of $E$ for $s = 1$, we obtain the following implicit equation for the determination of $s$:

$$s = 1-e^{-(\gamma pE_0/kT)s}.$$

The function given by $s = 1-e^{-\alpha s}$, where $\alpha = \gamma pE_0/kT$, is of the same type as the functions $\tanh \alpha s$ or $L(\alpha s)$, previously considered; with increase of $s$ it tends to the saturation value 1. Taking into account the fact that the slope of its tangent at the origin $s \to 0$ is equal to $\gamma pE_0/kT$, we see that the preceding equation has a solution different from zero (and $< 1$) only if $\gamma pE_0/kT < 1$. Fowler's theory thus also leads to the existence of a Curie point $T_c = \gamma pE_0/k$. With a value $\frac{1}{3}$ for $\gamma$ this expression exactly coincides with that derived above from a consideration of the degree of orientation of the molecules according to the Langevin-Debye theory. The latter derivation has, with respect to that of Fowler, the advantage of being free from any arbitrary coefficients like $\gamma$.‡ Although it does not involve explicitly the conception of a free rotation

† R. H. Fowler, *Proc. Roy. Soc.* A, **149**, 1 (1935).

‡ Fowler's derivation is similar to that given by Pauli for the Langevin-Debye law. Considering the orientation of the molecules in a dipole gas, Pauli likewise divides them into 'orientated' with a kinetic energy of rotation $< \gamma pE$ and 'rotating' with an energy $> \gamma pE$. The electric moment of the gas $P$, due to the orientating influence of the field $E$, is reduced under such conditions to $pN_1 = pNs = pN(1-e^{-\gamma pE/kT})$ or to $\frac{\gamma p^2 N}{kT}E$ in the case $pE \ll kT$. This expression is identical with that derived in the usual way from a consideration of the potential (and not the kinetic) energy if $\gamma = \frac{1}{3}$.

of the molecules, it is nevertheless clear that at sufficiently high temperatures in the vicinity of $pE_0/k$ practically all the molecules would be found in a state of free rotation.

With approach of the temperature to the critical value $T_c$ the specific heat of the crystal must increase in the same way as in the case of binary alloys. In fact, the average value of the potential energy of a molecule with respect to the other molecules is equal to

$$-p\overline{E\cos\theta} = -pE_0(\overline{\cos\theta})^2,$$

i.e.

$$\overline{U} = -pE_0\zeta^2. \tag{28}$$

Multiplying it by $\frac{1}{2}N$ and differentiating with respect to $T$ we obtain the additional value of the specific heat, due to the decrease of orientation order,

$$\Delta C = -\tfrac{1}{2}NpE_0\frac{d}{dT}\zeta^2. \tag{28 a}$$

Substituting here the expression (25 b) for $\zeta$ in the neighbourhood of the Curie point we get a value

$$(\Delta C)_{\max} = \frac{5}{2}\frac{1}{2}\frac{NpE_0}{T_c} = \tfrac{15}{4}Nk = \tfrac{15}{4}R \tag{28 b}$$

which is independent of $T_c$ (cf. equation (6 a) of § 1).

The specific heat of freely rotating molecules with two degrees of freedom of rotational motion, is one-half the specific heat of orientated molecules, performing rotational oscillations, since in the latter case they possess, besides a kinetic energy $kT$, a potential energy of the same average value.

If the Curie point corresponded, as assumed by Pauling, to a transition from rotational oscillations to free rotation, then just above this point the specific heat would drop not to its original value, corresponding to $T \ll T_c$, but to a value lying by $R$ units (i.e. by 2 cal./mole) lower.

As a matter of fact, such an additional drop of the specific heat has never been observed, the final value of $C$ (for $T > T_c$) being even slightly larger than the initial one (for $T < T_c$). Hence it must be concluded that the thermal motion of the molecules preserves above the Curie point the same character of rotational oscillations as below it. In the case of HCl, $NH_4Cl$, and a number of other substances this conclusion is supported by the fact that the Curie temperature is much lower (by a factor of 10 approximately) than that calculated according to the formula $T_c = pE_0/3k$. Thus near the true Curie temperature only a negligible fraction of the molecules are actually capable of free rotation. The $\lambda$ transition taking place (or rather coming to an end) at this Curie temperature must therefore be treated, not as a transition from rotational oscillations to free rotation, but as a *disorientation* in the sense that the equilibrium orientations about which the rotational oscillations take place above the Curie point no longer display a regular alternation from one lattice point to the others, as they do below it. In other words, the transition under consideration must be described as a loss of *distant order* in the orientation of the molecules, both with respect to each other and to the crystal axes. This is the actual implication of the fact that the average value of $\cos\theta$, i.e. the component along the normal direction of a molecule of the electric field created by other molecules, vanishes. This does not, however, mean that the molecules do not altogether interact with each other. It means only that the electrical field $E'$ which is produced at the centre of each molecule by the surrounding molecules has no correlation whatever with the crystal axes, displaying with respect to the distribution of its direction (which determines the corresponding equilibrium orientation of the molecules) a certain (limited) degree of local order only. As to the magnitude of this 'local' orientating field, it must be comparable with, though probably smaller than, the magnitude of the field $E_0$ associated with the long-range order in a crystal at low temperatures.

The difference between $E'$ and $E_0$ is not reduced to a difference of direction and magnitude. Whereas $E_0$ preserves at each lattice point a fixed direction, the local field $E'$ must change its direction in a more or less irregular way not only from point to point (with preservation of local order), but also from time to time. In other words, in a disorientated crystal a constant equilibrium orientation of the dipole molecules is preserved for a limited time only. The average value of this time $\tau'$ must be large compared with the period of rotational oscillations $\tau_0' = 2\pi\sqrt{(J/pE')}$ performed by a molecule under the influence of the local field, and must increase when the temperature is lowered according to the usual law $\tau' = \tau_0' e^{U'/kT}$, where $U'$ is a certain activation energy which is required for a reorientation of a small group of molecules.

The rotational motion of the molecules above the Curie point is thus not at all free, but consists in rotational oscillations about irregularly distributed equilibrium orientations of a limited duration. It should be mentioned that the limited duration cannot be considered as a direct corollary of the random orientation. At very low temperatures the irregular orientations can become frozen up, as it were, just as the irregular positions of the molecules in a solid amorphous body (glass).

It seems, however, improbable that they would remain frozen at sufficiently elevated temperatures. The rate of their change can be investigated experimentally by measuring the electrical properties of the corresponding crystals in rapidly alternating fields (see Ch. V).

We thus see that the parameter $\zeta = \overline{\cos\theta}$ defines the long-range orientation order with respect to fixed crystallographic directions, the equation $\zeta = 0$ meaning that the average value of the component of the orientating field in the corresponding crystallographical direction vanishes, which does not imply that under such conditions the molecules do not tend to orientate each other. On the contrary, as follows from specific heat data, this tendency persists above the Curie point, and can be specified by a local field $E'$ with a direction sharply variable both in space and in time and a magnitude comparable with $E_0$.

The transformation taking place with a transition through the Curie point, which has been denoted above as a disorientation of the crystal, is therefore quite similar to an ordinary melting process, characterized by the disappearance of long-range order in the distribution of the centres of gravity of the molecule. We shall accordingly refer to it, in the sequel, as an 'orientation fusion'. It should be mentioned that in the case of many substances, such as HBr and HI for example, not a single $\lambda$ point, but two and even three of them are sometimes observed at a relatively small distance from each other. It is clear that only one of them can be connected with the process of orientation melting in the above sense; the mechanism responsible for the other $\lambda$ points is still obscure.

The theory of orientation melting based on the application of the Langevin-Debye equation is, of course, very inexact. One important source of error consists, as has been indicated above, in using the average value of a variable field $E$, instead of considering the coupled rotational oscillation of a number of dipole molecules (without limitation to the case of small amplitudes). A second error is due to the neglect of quantum effects which can be very important at such low temperatures as those of the actual Curie point. In the case of HCl, for example, the latter corresponds to $T_c = 98°$ K. (at atmospheric pressure). Now the characteristic temperature $T_0$ for which $kT_0 = h\nu_0$, where

$$\nu_0 = \frac{1}{2\pi}\sqrt{\frac{pE_0}{J}},$$

is equal in this case to 100° K. The evaluation of the average value of $\theta^2$ with the help of the classical formula $\overline{\theta^2} = kT/pE_0$ for $T < T_c$ is therefore absolutely inadmissible. Using the quantum formula for the average value of the energy of a harmonic oscillator with a frequency $\nu_0$ and equating it to $2pE_0\overline{(1-\cos\theta)} \cong pE_0\overline{\theta^2}$ we get

$$\overline{\theta^2} = \frac{h\nu_0}{pE_0}\frac{1}{e^{h\nu_0/kT}-1} = \frac{kT_0}{pE_0}\frac{1}{e^{T_0/T}-1}.$$

The increase of $\overline{\theta^2}$ given by this formula is much more rapid than that determined by the classical one. It becomes still more accentuated if $\nu_0 = 1/2\pi\sqrt{(pE_0/J)}$ is replaced by $\nu = 1/2\pi\sqrt{(pE/J)} = \nu_0\sqrt{\zeta}$ and $pE_0$ by $pE_0\zeta$, which gives

$$\sqrt{\zeta}(1-\zeta) = \frac{kT_0}{2pE_0}\frac{1}{e^{T_0/T}-1}.$$

The maximum value of this expression corresponds to $\zeta = \frac{1}{3}$. Noting that $pE_0 = 3kT_c'$ where $T_c' \cong 300$ is the classical value of the Curie temperature, mentioned above, we get for 'quantum' value $T_c$ the equation

$$\frac{1}{e^{T_0/T_c}-1} = \frac{2}{3\sqrt{3}}\frac{1800}{160} \cong 4,$$

which corresponds approximately to $T_c \approx 4T_0 = 640$. This result is still more remote from the truth than the preceding one. This means that in the case of HCl orientational fusion takes place for a value of $\zeta$ much smaller than $\frac{1}{3}$.

A more exact determination of $T_c$ can probably be reached by treating orientation fusion in the same way as ordinary fusion, i.e. as a transformation of the first kind, and applying to it the thermodynamical equilibrium condition (equality of thermodynamic potentials). This procedure has been applied in an early paper, based on the application of Pauling's hypothesis of free rotation.† The modification of the theory, corresponding to the modified 'disorientation' conception, is impracticable, for it requires a knowledge of the disorientation entropy which it has not yet been possible to determine theoretically (see Ch. III).

As has been stated above, a Curie point differs from an ordinary melting-point by the fact that the corresponding transition takes place not at a definite temperature but within a certain temperature range, which can sometimes be extremely narrow. The factors which influence its width have not been elucidated yet. It should be mentioned in this connexion that, according to Eucken,‡ the introduction of a few

† Frenkel, Ismailov, and Todes, *Acta Physicochimica U.R.S.S.* **2**, 97 (1934).
‡ Eucken, *Phys. Z.* **35**, 954 (1934); cf. also Eucken and Veith, *Z. f. phys. Chem.* B, **34**, 275 (1936).

per cent. of argon into crystalline $CH_4$ lowers and widens the specific heat maximum in such a way that it practically vanishes when the argon concentration reaches 18 per cent.

Of special interest are the observations of Müller concerning the $\lambda$ points of paraffins, which are found close to the corresponding melting-points.†

These $\lambda$ points are usually interpreted as Curie points corresponding to a transition from rotational oscillations to a free rotation of the molecules about their longitudinal axes. On our view, however, we have to do in this case, just as in the case of HCl, $CH_4$, etc., with a disorientation of the paraffin molecules in the planes normal to their longitudinal axes, with preservation of the vibrational character of the rotational motion about these axes and of a certain degree of local order in the distribution of the transverse axes; a transition to a free rotation would imply a decrease of the specific heat by the amount of 1 cal./mole, which is contrary to observation.

Our conception of the temporary character of the orientations of the axes of the molecules in the disorientated state is supported, in the case of dipole substances like HCl, by the fact that the dielectric constant is sharply increased from a value of 2·5 for $T < 98°$ K. to a value of 14 for $T > 98°$ K. This increased value of the dielectric constant, however, which is due to a partial reorientation of the molecules in the direction of the applied electric field, vanishes in alternating electric fields of a sufficiently high frequency. It seems natural to identify the critical frequency for which this decrease becomes marked with the reciprocal of the mean duration of a fixed orientation.

The problem of this electric relaxation time will be discussed in more detail in Ch. V.

† Müller, *Proc. Roy. Soc.* **154,** 624 (1936). It should be remembered that the paraffin molecules do not possess a rotation symmetry about their longitudinal axis, and may be pictured rather as narrow belts with a symmetry plane defined by the carbon links than as cylindrical rods.

III

# PROPERTIES OF LIQUIDS AND MECHANISM OF FUSION

## 1. Relation between the Solid and Liquid States

FUSION is accompanied, as a rule, by a relatively small increase of volume amounting to 10 per cent. This fact alone serves to show that the arrangement of molecules in a liquid—in the neighbourhood of the crystallization point, at least—must be more or less similar to their arrangement in the corresponding solid bodies, in spite of the fundamental difference existing between the amorphous structure of the liquids and the crystalline structure of the solids (in a state of thermodynamic equilibrium).

We must further note the well-known experimental fact that the latent heat of fusion is much smaller than the latent heat of vaporization. In the case of sodium, zinc, lead, and mercury, for example, the former is equal to 630, 1,800, 1,170, and 560 cal./mole, while the latter amounts to 23,300, 27,700, 46,000, and 14,200 respectively, exceeding thus the heat of fusion by a factor of 30–40.

This means that the cohesive forces between the molecules decrease only very slightly in the process of fusion, in agreement with the fact that their distance apart is increased by a very small figure of the order of 3–4 per cent.

We must finally stress the well-known fact that the specific heat of condensed bodies is only very slightly affected by fusion, being somewhat greater just above the melting-point than just below it.

This means that the character of the heat motion in liquid bodies, at least near the crystallization point, remains fundamentally the same as in solid bodies, reducing mainly to small vibrations about certain equilibrium positions and, in the case of diatomic and more complex molecules, to rotational oscillations about certain equilibrium orientations.† The corresponding figures for a few monatomic, diatomic, and more complex substances are collected in the following table:—

| *Substance* | Na | Hg | Pb | Zn | Al | $N_2$ | $Cl_2$ | $Br_2$ | $CH_4$ | HCl | $NH_3$ | $C_6H_6$ |
|---|---|---|---|---|---|---|---|---|---|---|---|---|
| $C_p$ solid | 7·6 | 6·7 | 7·2 | 7·2 | 6·8 | 11·3 | 14 | 14·1 | 10·6 | 12·27 | 12·2 | 26·6 |
| $C_p$ liquid | 8 | 6·7 | 7·7 | 7·9 | 6·25 | 13·10 | 16·2 | 17·1 | 13·5 | 14·73 | 18·4 | 30·1 |

† Cf. Eucken, *Handbuch der Experimentalphysik*, B, **12**, 344. Eucken gives no references, as if he was the first to state clearly this principle.

This result is in full agreement with those preceding, since the slight increase of the distance between the molecules on fusion can affect materially neither their cohesive forces nor the character of their heat motion.†

To the above three facts one more should be added, namely, that liquids, just as well as solids, can suffer, without rupture, very high extension forces inasmuch as they reduce to a negative pressure, excluding the possibility of flow. Such negative pressures can be realized, for example, by cooling a liquid—for instance, mercury—along with the vessel containing it and completely filled by it at the initial high temperature, if the former has a larger coefficient of thermal expansion than the substance of the latter (glass).

An experiment of this kind was carried out for the first time in 1911 by Mayer,‡ who has shown in this way that liquid mercury can be extended by an amount corresponding to a negative pressure of 100 atmospheres, this limit being set not by the strength of the mercury itself, which probably can suffer without rupture much higher tensions (of the order of a few thousand atmospheres), but by the force of its adhesion to the walls of the glass vessel (see Ch. VI).

The last-named fact is not so important for our purpose—the establishment of a close similarity between the solid and the liquid state—as the preceding three, although it is logically connected with them. The fact that liquids can withstand or exert a negative pressure is implied by van der Waals's theory, which is based on the assumption of a close similarity between the liquid and the gaseous state (and not the solid one); according to this theory both states represent two extreme forms of a single 'amorphous' state, one of which can be obtained from the other by isothermal compression or expansion in a continuous way, leading through intermediate states possessing a mechanically unstable character. Owing to this instability, the actual transition from the liquid state to the gaseous one and vice versa takes place not along the theoretical isotherm (full line of Fig. 14) but along a horizontal isotherm, corresponding to the splitting up of the original homogeneous substance into two different coexisting phases, one of which gradually grows at the cost of the other (dotted line of Fig. 14). This discontinuity of the transition from the liquid to the gaseous state

† It must be mentioned that the increase of the specific heat at constant pressure on fusion is often due to the accompanying increase of the thermal expansion coefficient. Thus, for example, in the case of mercury the specific heat at constant volume is slightly decreased on fusion—from 5·95 to 5·90; the corresponding figures for solid and liquid sodium are 6·71 and 6·62.

‡ *Abh. d. Deutsch. Bunsengesellschaft*, No. 6, 1911.

vanishes, as is well known, only above the critical temperature, when the theoretical isotherms assume a monotonic course and become actually realizable.

It can hardly be contested that liquids are more similar to compressed gases than to solid crystalline bodies at high temperatures lying close

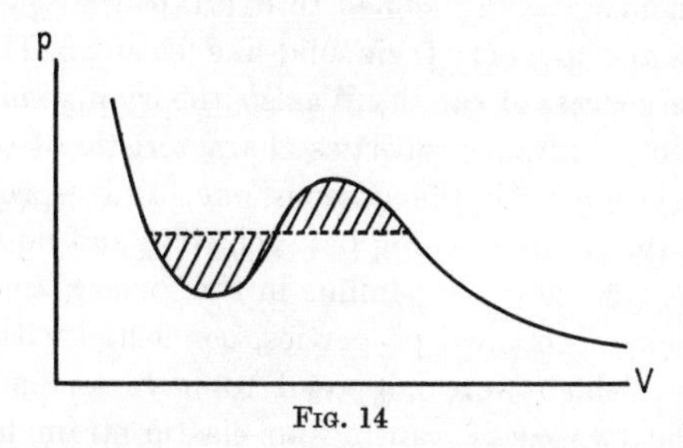


FIG. 14

to the critical point and at moderate pressures, that is, when their density is much smaller than that of the corresponding solid. It must, however, be kept in mind that by application of a sufficiently high pressure a liquid can be crystallized whatever its temperature. In principle such a crystallization, due to high compression, must take place even above the critical temperature. The pressures required for this cannot, as a rule, be realized in the laboratory—except in the case of such substances as hydrogen or neon, which are characterized by an extremely small cohesion, and which under ordinary conditions, i.e. atmospheric pressure, crystallize at very low temperatures. F. Simon was able in 1929 to crystallize them under a pressure of a few hundred atmospheres above their critical temperature.†

The crystalline state obtained at supercritical temperatures under high pressures is, of course, very different—from the point of view of its mechanical properties—from that corresponding to low temperatures, when the crystalline body requires no external pressure for its existence and, moreover, resists all external forces tending to change its size or shape.

Although the close similarity between liquids and gases at high temperatures and moderate pressures, that is at relatively large specific volumes, is an incontestable fact, yet at temperatures lying near the crystallization point, when the specific volume of a liquid is but slightly larger than that of the corresponding crystalline body, the liquid must

† F. Simon, Report delivered at the Physical Congress, Odessa, 1930.

be more nearly similar to a solid crystalline body than to a compressed gas—with respect to its structure (i.e. arrangement of the molecules), character of heat motion, and as will be shown later, a number of mechanical properties.

It must be acknowledged, however, that until recently physicists and physico-chemists were inclined to overrate the 'gas-like' features of liquid bodies and to ignore their solid-like features. This is explained partially by the success of van der Waals's theory in explaining, though only qualitatively, certain properties characteristic of the liquid state and its interrelation with the gaseous one; and especially by over-estimating the difference existing between solid and liquid bodies with respect to their structure—crystalline in the former, amorphous in the latter—and their mechanical properties, connected with the action of shearing forces, which were supposed to have an entirely different influence in the two cases, causing an elastic strain in solids and a viscous flow in liquids.

A closer scrutiny shows, however, that these distinctions are far less drastic and fundamental than they have hitherto been believed to be.

In the first place we must recall the firmly established though often forgotten fact that solid bodies under high shearing stress display a phenomenon of plastic flow which is more or less similar to the viscous flow of liquids, and that, on the other hand, liquid bodies display a shearing elasticity which is usually masked by their high fluidity. This fact is especially obvious in the case of such substances as under the influence of cooling pass from the liquid into the solid amorphous (glass-like) state without crystallization, that is in a continuous manner. It is clear that in this case the fluidity which is characteristic of the liquid state does not vanish at a definite temperature, being suddenly replaced by rigidity (i.e. resistance to shear), but falls off gradually, while the rigidity which was coexistent with but masked by it becomes gradually revealed.

In the second place, the application of the methods of X-ray structure analysis to liquid bodies has disclosed the fact that the arrangement of molecules in a liquid, especially near the crystallization point, is quite different from the wholly disordered arrangement found in the gaseous state, displaying at small distances a close similarity with that completely regular arrangement into which it is transformed when the liquid is crystallized. This fundamental fact, established by the pioneer work of G. W. Stewart on organic substances with rod-like molecules,†

† Stewart, *Phys. Rev.* **30**, 232 (1927); **31**, 174 (1928); **35**, 726 (1930); **37**, 9 (1931).

can be interpreted, with the help of the notions of distant and *local* order introduced in the preceding chapter, as the preservation of a certain limited degree of local (short-range) order in the arrangement of molecules following the process of fusion, which consists in a discontinuous loss of distant (long-range) order, characteristic of the crystalline structure. From this point of view the change of structure, from crystalline to amorphous, on fusion is much less drastic than has previously been pictured. Of course the loss of distant order makes a liquid *isotropic* or amorphous, that is similar in this respect to a gas. It must be remembered, however, that solid bodies are usually found, not in the form of single crystals, but as polycrystalline aggregates, consisting of a large number of very small crystals with random orientations. From a roughly macroscopic point of view such bodies are just as isotropic as liquids. X-ray diagrams of liquids are similar to those of the corresponding polycrystalline bodies and could be interpreted, in their broad features, on the assumption that a liquid consists of a very large number of randomly orientated crystals of submicroscopic size. A conception of this kind has actually been introduced by Stewart, who proposed to denote these submicroscopic crystals consisting of a few tens of molecules, at most, by the term 'cybotactic groups' (or regions) and assumed them to be connected with each other by thin layers of a wholly amorphous phase.

From the point of view of the conception of distant and local order, introduced in the preceding chapter, Stewart's cybotactic groups must be considered as indefinitely delineated regions within which the relative arrangement of the molecules preserved a certain degree of regularity, the variation of this arrangement about each point being, as a rule, continuous.

With the help of an adequately introduced function $\xi(x,y,z)$, specifying the degree of order in the relative distribution of the centres of gravity of the molecules near a point $x, y, z$, the effective size of Stewart's cybotactic groups could be determined by the equation $\zeta(R) = \frac{1}{2}\eta$ of Ch. II (§ 2), i.e. by the reciprocal value of $|\text{grad}\,\xi|$.

It should be mentioned that the degree of order in the relative distribution of the orientations of the molecules must be specified by an independent parameter $\xi'$, so that the size of the cybotactic groups may prove entirely different from the point of view of the relative positions and relative orientations of the molecules. An example of this distinction has been considered in the preceding chapter, in the case of 'orientation fusion'. A second equally instructive example is afforded by 'liquid crystals' or 'anisotropic liquids', which are characterized by a small degree of order in the arrangement of the centres of gravity of the molecules, but by a large degree of order in the distribution of their mutual orientations. Regions containing more or less regularly orientated molecules are called in this case 'swarms'. When the substances under consideration are heated starting from low temperatures, they first pass from the ordinary state to the liquid-crystalline one, which entails a loss of distant order in the distribution of the centres of gravity, just as in the case of ordinary fusion, while a large degree of order in their mutual orientation persists; with further heating of the 'anisotropic melt' this orientation order is gradually decreased, until the large swarms are suddenly replaced by small cybotactic groups forming an ordinary amorphous liquid. This second fusion can be treated as orientation fusion.

## 2. Estimate of the Influence of Volume and Temperature Changes on the Properties of Solid and Liquid Bodies. Mechanism of Melting

It follows from what has been said in the preceding section that the difference between the liquid and the solid state—not only amorphous but even crystalline—is of a rather quantitative than qualitative nature. In certain respects—with regard to density (specific volume), cohesive forces (heat of vaporization), and character of the heat motion—this difference must be considered as insignificant. In certain other respects, viz. the degree and character of fluidity and the degree of order in the arrangement of the molecules, this difference is so striking that it is usually considered as a qualitative and not merely quantitative one.

The main problem of the kinetic theory of liquids consists in explaining the apparent lack of correspondence between these two types of differences and in elucidating the causes and mechanisms of the processes of fusion and crystallization whereby these differences suddenly (i.e. discontinuously) arise.

The next problem consists in explaining those continuous variations of different properties of liquids which take place with increase of volume and temperature, and which gradually shift the liquid state from the solid-like to the gas-like type.

It should be mentioned that in the consideration of all these variations, both continuous and discontinuous, the role of the volume as a factor determining, along with the temperature, the state of a given molecular system was usually underrated, for the simple reason that from the experimental point of view, it is much easier to realize a variation of the temperature in a very broad range under constant pressure than a variation of the volume, under constant temperature, by varying the pressure. Leaving aside the fact that it has been practically impossible hitherto to realize high negative pressures and investigate the properties of liquids under such conditions, the realization of high positive pressures and the investigation of solid and liquid bodies under such pressures has also been no easy task. The largest pressures obtained hitherto by Bridgman and his co-workers do not exceed $10^5$ atmospheres. It should be mentioned that the volume contraction of various liquids under such pressures (if they are not forced to crystallize) amounts roughly to 25 per cent. This is a rather high figure, since the volume expansion of solid bodies on heating from the zero point of temperature up to the melting-point, including the increase of volume on melting, is of the order of 10 per cent. (at ordinary pressures). Such an increase of the volume at constant temperature would require the application of a negative pressure of the order of a few thousand atmospheres.

If it were not for the experimental difficulties besetting the application of high positive and especially negative pressures, we could, by varying the specific volume of liquids at a constant temperature, influence their properties, and, in particular, cause their crystallization, just as effectively as this is usually done by varying the temperature.

In order to illustrate the influence of volume and temperature changes on the properties of liquids we shall give below a few very rough calculations based on the order of magnitude of the cohesive forces between the molecules, the range of these forces, and the effective size ('radius' of the molecules). As regards the latter, in the case of simple molecules it amounts to a few Angstrom units, i.e. $10^{-8}$ cm. This is also the order of magnitude of the range of the attractive forces between the molecules. The magnitude of these forces can be estimated from the tensile strength of the solid (or liquid) body constituted by them, that is by the maximum value of the negative pressure the body is capable of sustaining without splitting into separate molecules, or by the latent heat of evaporation (sublimation), that is, by the increase of mutual potential energy of the molecules accompanying such a splitting. The fact that the cohesive forces between the molecules practically vanish when their distance apart is doubled (with respect to the value corresponding to their arrangement in a solid body at $T = 0$) means that the volume of a solid or liquid body cannot be increased without its disintegration into separate molecules several times over. It should be mentioned in this connexion that according to the van der Waals theory the critical volume of a substance is only 12 times larger than the total volume of the molecules treated as rigid spheres. A more exact consideration of the dependence of the mutual potential energy of two molecules $U$ on their distance apart $r$ (see Fig. 1, Ch. I) shows that the maximum value of their attractive force $F = -dU/dz$ as defined by the condition $d^2U/dr^2 = 0$ is reached at a distance $r = r_1$, which is but 10–20 per cent. larger than the normal distance $r = r_0$ corresponding to the equilibrium condition $dU/dr = 0$. Hence it follows that the 'internal pressure' due to an extension of a solid body by the application of a negative pressure and balancing the latter reaches its largest value for a linear extension of the order of 10–20 per cent., that is a volume expansion of the order of 30–60 per cent.

The magnitude of this largest negative pressure the body is capable of sustaining without disintegrating can be estimated with the help of the usual equation $p = -K(\Delta V/V_0)$, which, strictly speaking, is valid for small values of $\Delta V/V_0$ only, but cannot lead to a serious error with respect to the order of magnitude if we put $\Delta V/V_0 = \frac{1}{3}$, preserving the normal value of the compressibility modulus $K$. The latter is, both for solids and liquids, of the order of $10^{11}$–$10^{12}$ dyne/cm.$^2$ (in the case of liquids it is usually a few times smaller than in that of the corresponding solids). Hence it follows that the tensile strength of solid and liquids does not exceed $10^5$–$10^6$ negative atmospheres.

The tensile strength of solid bodies under ordinary tensile stress is usually smaller by a factor of 100 than this theoretical figure. This circumstance is explained by the fact that under such conditions the rupture of the body does not take place simultaneously over the whole area of a cross-section perpendicular to the direction of the extension, but starts on a relatively small area near the edge of a surface or inner crack which is highly overstrained, and is propagated thence over the rest of the corresponding cross-section by a process which can be considered as a gradual spreading of the original crack.

If it were not for this circumstance, that is, if it were possible to strain a body by the application of so large a negative pressure that its rupture would take place simultaneously over the whole of its volume, then this rupture would be entirely equivalent to the disintegration constituting ordinary evaporation at an arbitrarily low temperature.

It is quite clear that under such conditions the maximum value of the elastic energy stored in the body which is extended to the critical volume $V_0+\Delta V$, that is $\frac{1}{2}K(\Delta V)^2/V_0 = \frac{1}{2}|p|\Delta V$, must be (approximately) equal to the latent heat of vaporization. Referring the latter to unit volume ($V_0 = 1$) and putting $\Delta V = \frac{1}{3}V_0 = \frac{1}{3}$ we see that it must be by one order of magnitude smaller than the corresponding compressibility modulus, i.e. of the order of $10^{10}$–$10^{11}$ ergs/cm.$^3$, or $10^2$–$10^3$ calories per c.c., which is in agreement with the experimental data.†

It should be noted that a second quantity characteristic of each substance, namely its critical temperature $T_c$, can be defined approximately as that temperature for which the average value of the energy of heat motion of a molecule $kT_c$ becomes of the same order of magnitude as the energy which is required in order to tear one molecule from the rest, i.e. as the latent heat of evaporation referred to a single molecule. If $V_0$ denotes the volume occupied by one mole of a given substance, i.e. $N = 6.10^{23}$ molecules (in the solid state), we can thus put

$$NkT_c = \gamma K V_0,$$

where $\gamma$ is a numerical coefficient of the order of $\frac{1}{5}$–$\frac{1}{10}$. Putting $V_0 = 10$ and $K = 10^{11}$–$10^{12}$, we obtain $T_c \approx 10^2$–$10^4$. The critical temperatures of most substances actually lie within this range.

Coming back to the main problem of the kinetic theory of liquids stated at the beginning of this section, we must, to begin with, answer the following questions (which have already been stated in a somewhat different form):

(1) To what is due the sharp decrease of the degree of order in the arrangement of the molecules of a body and the sharp increase of its fluidity on melting, in spite of the relatively small increase of volume at constant temperature?

† Raschevsky, *Z. f. Phys.* **40**, 214 (1927), has attempted to identify this quantity with the latent heat of fusion. If $\Delta V$ represents the increase of volume on fusion, then the quantity $\frac{1}{2}K\frac{(\Delta V)^2}{V_0}$ turns out to be about three times smaller than the experimental value of the latent heat of fusion. R. Fürth, *Proc. Roy. Soc.* A, **177**, 217 (1941), has recently attempted to calculate the practical tensile strength of solids subjected to a one-sided extension, on the assumption that the body is ruptured by a process which can be described as the melting of the additional volume $\Delta V$ due to the extension. This assumption implies that the elastic energy spared by the body at the instant of rupture, $\frac{1}{2}E\frac{(\Delta V)^2}{V_0}$, where $E$ is Young's elasticity modulus, is equal to $Q\Delta V$, $Q$ being the latent heat of fusion per unit volume. Although this equation yields results which are in good agreement with the experimental data, yet the basic idea of Fürth's theory seems to be wholly devoid of physical meaning, its success being quite accidental. As has been explained above and proved experimentally by A. Joffé, the low value of the tensile strength observed experimentally compared with the theoretical figure is due to superficial (or internal) cracks.

(2) What is the immediate cause of melting, isobaric heating or isothermal expansion?

(3) Why is melting associated with a discontinuous increase of volume and entropy, and why does it thus form a transition of the first order, and not of the second order, like processes of loss of alternation order in binary alloys?

On the basis of the results obtained in the preceding chapter in the study of order-disorder phenomena in crystals, we can give the following preliminary answers to the above questions:

(1) The regularity in the arrangement and orientation of the molecules in the crystal begins to fall with rise of the temperature long before the melting-point is reached; as the latter is approached this process is gradually accelerated, acquiring a more pronounced 'co-operative' character in the sense that a further decrease of the degree of order requires less and less energy. The thermal expansion of the crystal, taking place when it is heated at a constant pressure, is a factor furthering and accelerating the loss of order, the increase of volume associated with fusion being simultaneously the direct cause and effect of this loss.

The sharp increase of fluidity on fusion can be explained in broad outline as follows. The fluidity of a body, that is its complete yielding to shearing stress, implies the possibility of the individual displacement of its molecules, which, in its turn, requires a certain amount of free space or 'free volume'. In the case of crystalline bodies this free volume is relatively small, being realized in the form of a number of separate 'holes' and of a general thermal expansion. The 10 per cent. increase of volume on fusion is sufficient to make room for the individual displacements of the molecules, which constitute what is described macroscopically as the flow of a liquid. This can be illustrated by the rapid flow of a crowd initially squeezed in a closed room through a door suddenly opened as soon as the crowd becomes slightly less dense.

The current view that the fluidity of liquids is due to an absence of shearing elasticity, i.e. to a disappearance of the rigidity modulus $G$, is wholly erroneous, as has already been indicated (with the exception, perhaps, of the case of liquid helium II). The fluidity of liquids does not exclude the existence of an elastic resistance to shearing stress, but only *masks* it. This conclusion follows, firstly, from the fact of the existence, in the case of many substances, of a continuous transition from the liquid to the solid amorphous ('glassy') state, in which, while preserving a certain minute amount of fluidity, they display a sharply pronounced elasticity of shape (i.e. 'rigidity'). It follows, secondly, from the fact that in the vicinity of the melting-point the cohesion between the molecules above it remains nearly the same as below. Under such conditions the disappearance of the rigidity modulus on melting is obviously excluded, although it must be expected to suffer a sharp decrease. A similar, though probably smaller, decrease is found experimentally in the compressibility modulus on melting when the latter takes place at moderate pressures; at very high pressures it remains practically constant.

The possibility of combining rigidity with fluidity will be considered in detail in the next chapter; it may suffice here to note that this combination implies a more or less rapid disappearance or 'relaxation' of the elastic shearing stress due to a given strain when the latter is kept constant, and that the sharp increase of fluidity on melting is due to a decrease of the corresponding 'relaxation time'.

(2) If fusion is considered as a process of loss of long-range order, the fact that it must take place, sooner or later, with elevation of the temperature or increase of the volume (at a constant temperature) follows from the same type of argument as the loss of long-range order in the alternation of the atoms of different kind in binary alloys, or in the orientation of molecules in crystals of the type HCl and $CH_4$. In all these cases the decrease and finally loss of distant order is primarily due to the heat motion; the concomitant increase of volume enhances the disorganizing influence of heat motion by decreasing the forces which resist it. In other words, the crystal lattice becomes unstable at high temperatures, this instability being accelerated by the increase of specific volume.

The process of fusion can be considered from a different angle, and, in particular, from the point of view of the concomitant appearance or rather increase of fluidity. Inasmuch as the latter is connected with the lower and less regular structure of the liquid, this 'mechanical' point of view is practically equivalent to the preceding 'structural' point of view.

(3) Finally, the discontinuous character of fusion, as a transition of the first order, can also be explained in a few—formally different but substantially equivalent—ways, depending on the point of view regarding the nature of this transition. From the 'structural' point of view the discontinuity of fusion is due to the 'co-operative effect' characteristic of all processes of loss of regularity, and specified by the accompanying decrease of the corresponding energy. It has been shown in § 3 of the preceding chapter by a simple example that the process of decrease of

distant order can assume a discontinuous course characteristic of first-order transition. This type of behaviour must obviously take place in the case of fusion. If the degree of order in a state of thermodynamic equilibrium is determined as a function of the temperature and specific volume $\xi = \xi(T, V)$, minimizing the free energy of the body, then the cause of the discontinuous character of fusion can be looked for in the dependence of the pressure $p$ on $T$ and $V$, or of the volume on $p$ and $T$, in the same way as this is done in van der Waals's theory of the transition between the liquid and the gaseous state. In doing this it is necessary, firstly, to admit the virtual possibility of a continuous transformation from the solid crystalline to the liquid amorphous state (corresponding to a continuous variation of $\xi$ from 1 to 0), and secondly to show that such a continuous transition is connected with a series of mechanically or thermodynamically *unstable intermediate states*. Such a virtually possible but actually unrealizable continuous transition is typified by the liquid-vapour transition along one of the van der Waals's isotherms below the critical temperature (cf. Fig. 14). It has been shown in the preceding chapter that the isotherms $p(v)$ can have a similar character, inconsistent with a continuous isothermal transition from the ordered to the disordered state, for such bodies as can be brought continuously from one state to the other by isobaric heating up to and above a Curie point.

It should be noted that van der Waals's theory excludes the possibility of a continuous transition from the liquid to the gaseous state not only along an isotherm $(p, v)$ below the critical point but also along the isobars $(v, T)$ for pressures lying below the critical one. In fact, these have a shape shown in Fig. 15. One of them (on the right) corresponds to a pressure $p$ lying above the critical one $p_k$, while the other two correspond to smaller ('subcritical') pressures. The portion $OA$ of the left curve corresponds to the usual thermal expansion of a liquid; the portion $AB$, corresponding to superheated states, can be realized only partially, as also the portion $ED$, corresponding to the supercooled (or oversaturated) vapour. These two portions can be denoted as thermodynamically metastable (with a more or less extended lifetime). Those states, which are represented by the portion $BCD$ of the curve $(v, T)$ and which are characterized by negative values of the thermal expansion coefficient, are apparently wholly unstable.†

† Negative values of the thermal expansion coefficient are by no means connected with a thermodynamical instability of the corresponding states, as is illustrated by the example of water in the temperature range between 0° C. and 4° C.

The actual transition from the liquid into the gaseous state proceeds accordingly discontinuously, the original phase being split up into two distinct phases—liquid and saturated vapour, and the temperature remaining constant until the liquid has been wholly evaporated. This evaporation or rather boiling temperature is shown by a dotted vertical line in Fig. 15. The position of this line cannot be determined by the

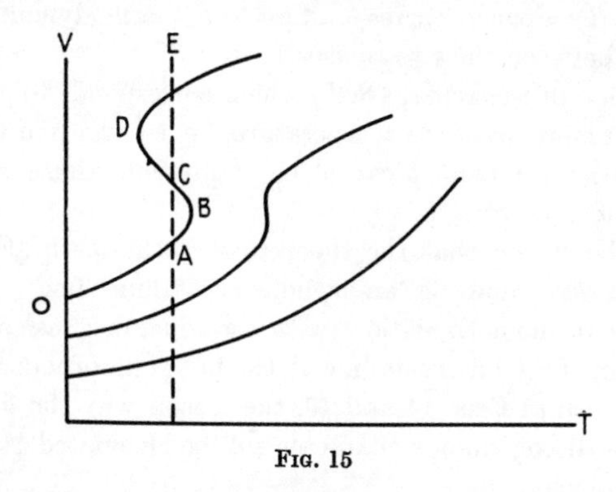


FIG. 15

help of simple thermodynamic considerations similar to those which refer to isothermal transitions described by the $(p, v)$ diagram.

Simpler and indeed more instructive results are obtained if the volume of the body is replaced by its entropy $S$. The isobars $S(T)$, corresponding to van der Waals's theory, are very similar in shape to the isobars $V(T)$. In fact, substituting in the equation $T\,dS = dE+p\,dV$ the expressions

$$E = -\frac{a}{V}+C_v T \quad \text{and} \quad p = \frac{RT}{V-b}-\frac{a}{V^2}$$

following from this theory, we get

$$dS = C_v\frac{dT}{T}+\frac{R}{V-b}dV,$$

that is, $$S = C_v \log T+R\log(V-b)+\text{const.}$$

Hence it is clear that at a constant pressure the entropy must change as a function of the temperature in a way similar to that of the volume, displaying in the $S(T)$ diagram, for sub-critical values of the pressure, similarly shaped curved portions. The vertical straight line, representing the boiling temperature, must, however, cut the S-shaped portion of the theoretical isotherm into two exactly equal parts, just as the straight line representing the pressure of the saturated vapour cuts into two equal parts the wave-like portion of van der Waals's isotherm. This conclusion follows from the fact that when $p =$ const. the integral $\int_{S_A}^{S_E} T\,dS$, representing the change of the total heat $J = E+pV$ in a virtual transition from the liquid to the gaseous state along a theoretical $(S, T)$ curve, must have the same value as for a transition along the straight line $T =$ const. corresponding to a thermodynamically stable equilibrium between the two phases.†

That portion of the isobar $(S, T)$ which corresponds to a decrease of entropy with increase of the temperature, i.e. to negative values of the specific heat at constant pressure $C_p$, represents thermodynamically unstable states.

If it can be shown that the theoretical isotherms $(p, V)$ or isobars $(S, T)$ of a 'rigid-liquid' or 'amorphous-crystalline' body, capable virtually of a continuous transition (with a gradual decrease of the degree of order) from the solid crystalline to the liquid amorphous state, have the shape shown in Figs. 14 and 15, the reason why the actual fusion process has a discontinuous character will be elucidated.‡

## 3. Application to the Process of Fusion of the 'Hole' and 'Dissociation' Schemes

Turning to a quantitative investigation of the nature of the liquid state and of the mechanism of melting, we shall consider, to begin with, a few theories based on structure arguments, i.e. on the introduction of a certain parameter, specifying the degree of order in the arrangement of the particles of the body. The problem then consists in determining the dependence of this parameter on the temperature (and also on the volume or the pressure), assuming that it can be varied in a continuous way from the maximum value, say 1, to a certain lowest value, which may be equal to zero (though this need not necessarily be the case, as will be seen below).

The simplest theory of this kind was proposed by the present writer in 1932. It was based on the idea that the perturbations of order in a monatomic crystal can be reduced to the formation of holes, i.e. vacant sites of the crystal lattice, and that melting takes place when the relative

† A still closer analogy between the isotherms $(p, V)$ and the isobars $(T, S)$ is obtained if the entropy is plotted along the abscissa and the temperature along the ordinate axis.

‡ L. Landau (*Phys. Z. d. Sowjetunion* **11**, 545, 1937) obtains the same result from a consideration of the variation of the symmetry of the structure of a crystalline body on melting. By the very nature of the method used he confines himself *a priori* to thermodynamically stable states only, wholly ignoring such actually realizable 'metastable' states as correspond to a superheated liquid or to a supercooled vapour.

number of such holes reaches a certain limiting value defined in a more or less arbitrary way. In 1939 this theory was independently developed and extended by S. Bresler† and by Frank, who removed this arbitrariness by introducing certain assumptions similar to those used in the theory of Bragg and Williams.

Let us consider a crystal lattice constituted by $N$ atoms and containing $N'$ (inner) holes. The number of ways these holes can be distributed between the $N+N'$ lattice sites is equal to

$$\frac{(N+N')!}{N!\,N'!}.$$

If the energy which is necessary for the creation of these holes is a function $W(N')$ of their number only and does not depend upon their distribution, then the free energy of the system is given by the expression

$$F = W(N') - kT\log\frac{(N+N')!}{N!\,N'!}.$$

From the condition $F$ = minimum the following equation is obtained for $N'$:

$$\frac{N'}{N+N'} = e^{-U'_{N'}/kT}, \tag{1}$$

where $U'_{N'} = dW/dN'$ is the energy required for increasing the number of holes ($N'$) by 1.

Solving (1) for $N'$ we get

$$N' = \frac{N}{e^{U'_{N'}/kT}-1}. \tag{1a}$$

The ratio $N/(N+N')$ is obviously equal to the probability of any site of the lattice being occupied. It could be used accordingly as a measure of the degree of order of the lattice. Bresler prefers to define the degree of order $\eta$ as the probability that all the $z$ sites surrounding an arbitrarily chosen atom ($z$ coordination number of the lattice) should be occupied, putting thus

$$\eta = \left(\frac{N}{N+N'}\right)^z = (1-e^{-U'_{N'}/kT})^z. \tag{2}$$

A choice between the two definitions would be only a matter of taste if the energy $U'_{N'}$ were supposed to be independent of $N'$, i.e. of $\eta$. Actually, however, Bresler assumes it to be a linear function of $\eta$, as defined by (2),

$$U'_{N'} = U_0 + U_1\eta. \tag{2a}$$

The equations (2) and (2a) determine $\eta$ implicitly as a function of

† S. Bresler, *Acta Physicochimica U.R.S.S.* **10**, 491 (1939).

the temperature. In the case $z = 1$ this function coincides with that considered by Fowler in his theory of the rotation of molecules in a crystal (Ch. II, § 5).

Putting $U'_{N'}/kT = x$ we can find $\eta$ graphically by considering the intersection of the curve $\eta = (1-e^{-x})^z$ with the straight line

$$\eta = \frac{kT}{U_1}x - \frac{U_0}{U_1}.$$

These lines are shown in Fig. 16, the straight line being drawn for two

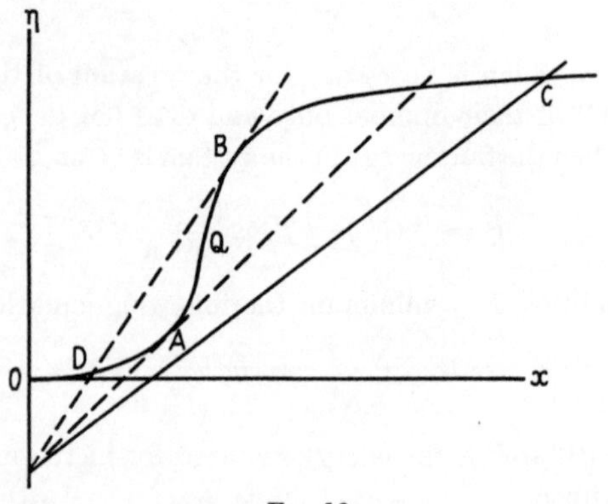


FIG. 16

different temperatures (its slope being proportional to $T$). The curve has an inflexion point $Q$ for $x = \log z$ (where $d^2\eta/dx^2 = 0$). At low temperatures the straight line intersects the curve in a point $C$, which corresponds to values of $\eta$ lying close to 1. At elevated temperatures the intersection point $D$ corresponds to $\eta \approx 0$; the value $\eta = 0$ is reached, however, in the limiting case $T = \infty$ only, so that a Curie point does not exist. In the range between two temperatures $T_1$ and $T_2$ for which the straight line is tangent to the curve at the points $A$ and $B$, three intersection points are obtained corresponding to a small, moderate, and high degree of order ($\eta_1 < \eta_2 < \eta_3$).

Hence it is clear that the dependence of $\eta$ on $T$ can be represented by the curve shown in Fig. 17. As the temperature is raised the degree of order decreases gradually until a certain value is reached corresponding to the point $B$, when it must suddenly drop to a lower value corresponding to the point $B'$, thereafter approaching asymptotically the value $\eta = 0$. If the temperature is gradually lowered, the degree of order can be raised to a value corresponding to the point $A$, whereafter it must suffer a discontinuous increase, jumping to the point $A'$. We thus obtain a hysteresis loop, embracing thermodynamically unstable states, which are characterized by an increase of the degree of order with increase of the temperature.

The region to the left of the loop ($\eta \approx 1$) corresponds to the crystalline state, the right half of the arc $A'B$ to a superheated crystal, the left half of $B'A$ to a supercooled liquid. A thermodynamical equilibrium between the crystalline and the liquid phase corresponds to a

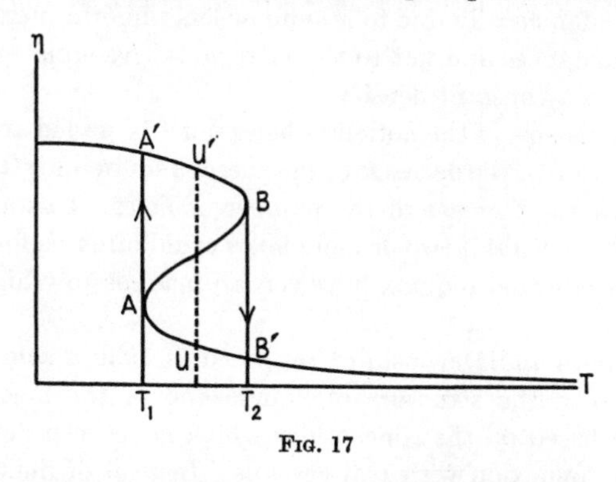


FIG. 17

certain intermediate temperature $T_{1,2}$, determined by the condition of the equality between the values of the specific free energies (if the volume changes are neglected), and shown in Fig. 17 by the dotted line. This temperature $T_{1,2}$ must be considered as the true temperature of fusion or crystallization.

Bresler has not attempted to calculate this temperature and has confined himself to a consideration of the kinetics of crystallization from the point of view of the above theory.

Although the latter, by a suitable choice of the parameters $U_0$ and $U$, can yield a satisfactory agreement with the experimental data, its basic conception that the perturbation of order in a crystal, leading finally to its transformation into a liquid, can be reduced to the formation of holes is open to serious criticism.

(1) The notion of holes, i.e. vacant sites of a crystal lattice, implies the existence of such a lattice, i.e. the existence of long-range order; accordingly, the latter must subsist so long as we are speaking of holes, however large their number may be. Its disappearance implies a breakdown of the crystal lattice with its regularly distributed sites, and not a partial vacation of these sites.

(2) The concentration of the holes in crystalline bodies must remain very small up to the fusion point—of the same order of magnitude as the concentration of the atoms in the saturated vapour; this can hardly be harmonized with Bresler's scheme.

From the point of view of this scheme the increase of volume on melting, just as the thermal expansion of the crystal and of the liquid, should be explained by an increase of the number of holes, while the lattice constant should remain unaltered. In reality, the thermal expansion is fundamentally due to a more or less uniform increase of the interatomic distances and not to the intrusion of vacuum quanta into a medium with a constant density.

To these criticisms of the notion of holes must be added an objection to the assumption of the decrease of the energy required for the creation of a hole with the increase of the number of holes. This assumption would be quite natural if two or more holes could often be found beside each other; this would require, however, an inadmissibly high concentration of holes.

Lennard-Jones and Devonshire† proposed in 1939 a somewhat different scheme of the structure of liquids and of the mechanism of melting, also based on the conceptions which have been developed in Chapter I in connexion with real crystals. Instead of limiting themselves to holes, these authors have also made use of dislocated atoms, reducing the increase of disorder in a crystal to a gradual *dissociation* of the crystal lattice, as a result of a transition of a fraction of the atoms from the regular lattice sites into the corresponding interlattice holes. This dissociative scheme has been subjected to a purely verbal modification consisting in treating the interlattice holes of the crystal under consideration as the regular sites of a second lattice, a monatomic crystal being described as a binary alloy of atoms $A$ and holes $B$. At low temperatures they regularly alternate, each atom being surrounded by $z$ holes and each hole by $z$ atoms; as the temperature is raised this alternation order must gradually decrease and finally vanish. If the degree of order is defined by the same formula

$$\xi = 1 - \frac{2N'}{N}$$

as the degree of distant order in the case of actual binary alloys, then the crystalline state must be specified by values of $\xi$ only slightly smaller than 1, while the liquid state corresponds to $\xi = 0$.

† *Proc. Roy. Soc.* A, **169**, 317 (1939).

Practically the same objections can be raised to this scheme as to the previous one, dealing with holes only.

The dissociative scheme has, however, the advantage of enabling one to introduce the notion of local order, which is of prime importance for the structure of liquid bodies.

Leaving aside this question, Lennard-Jones and Devonshire develop with the help of the above scheme a quantitative theory of the solid and liquid states and the process of melting. Instead of assuming, following Bragg and Williams, that the dissociation energy decreases with increase of the degree of dissociation (disorder), they attempt to obtain the same result by taking into account the accompanying increase of the volume (at a constant pressure) and by defining the dissociation energy as a certain decreasing function of the volume.

With the help of these assumptions they are led to results quite similar to those which we have already obtained in a much simpler way for binary alloys (Ch. II, § 4). In particular the isotherms $p(V)$ assume the shape shown in Fig. 14, i.e. similar to that of the isotherms of van der Waals's theory, which they claim explains the discontinuous character of the process of melting. They overlook, however, the fact that the isobars $S(T)$, following from their theory, display a monotonic rise instead of being S-shaped, as required for the explanation of the discontinuous character of melting caused by heating at constant pressure (and not by isothermal expansion).

In calculating the pressure as a function of the volume (and the temperature) Lennard-Jones and Devonshire take into account, along with the additional pressure due to decrease of order (which in § 4 of Ch. II we have denoted by $\Delta p = \bar{p}-p_T$), the elastic and the thermal part, starting from rather arbitrary assumptions as to the dependence of the potential energy of two atoms on their distance apart; it should be mentioned that these assumptions are hardly necessary for the consideration of such phenomena as melting, which are associated with an increase of the interatomic distances by a few per cent. only.

The considerable quantitative agreement between the calculated and the observed positions of the melting-points and of the volume and entropy increases in the case of argon and nitrogen can hardly be considered as a convincing confirmation of the underlying dissociative scheme, such a numerical agreement being easily obtained by a proper choice of the parameters involved.

Both conceptions of melting—by an increase of the number of holes in a crystal lattice or by an increase of the degree of its dissociation—

are nothing but crude schemes which can claim to represent more or less adequately the qualitative relationships only and cannot serve as a basis for a quantitative theory.

## 4. Local Order in Liquids and 'Structure Diffusion' in a Crystal Lattice (Prins)

As has already been stated in § 1, the structure of liquids can be denoted by the term 'quasi-crystalline' in the sense that they display a certain degree of local order of the same type as that characteristic of the corresponding crystals. In the case of simple liquids (such as fused metals) the degree of local order can be judged from the average distribution of the atoms about one of them; this 'relative' distribution must obviously be independent of the choice of the central atoms and must be spherically symmetrical with respect to it. It can be specified, accordingly, by a certain function $\rho(r)$ equal to the average number of atoms (or rather nuclei) per unit volume at a distance $r$ from the central atom. The product

$$\rho(r)4\pi r^2\,dr = g(r)\,dr$$

gives the average number of atoms (nuclei) situated at a distance between $r$ and $r+dr$ from the central atom.

Such a description of the relative arrangement of the atoms can be applied not only to liquids but also to crystalline bodies. If in the latter case the atoms are supposed to remain fixed in their equilibrium positions, the functions $\rho(r)$ and $g(r)$ will be discontinuous (of the type of Dirac's $\delta$-function), vanishing for all values of $r$ with the exception of a certain set of values

$$r_1 < r_2 < r_3 < \dots$$

for which they become infinite in such a way that the integrals

$$\int\limits_{r_s-\epsilon}^{r_s+\epsilon} g(r)\,dr \quad (\epsilon \to 0)$$

are equal to the number $n_s$ of atoms, situated at a distance $r_s$ from the central one.

A crystal with a perfectly regular structure can thus be described by specifying a set of values of the distance $r_s$ and the associated numbers of atoms $n_s$.

The corresponding data for a few lattices of different types—cubic close-packed ($A$), hexagonal ($A'$), cubic volume-centred ($B$), simple cubic ($C$), and tetrahedral (diamond-like) $D$, are collected in the following table;† $n_1$ is the number of nearest neighbours, which is identical

| $A$ | | $A'$ | | $B$ | | $C$ | | $D$ | |
|---|---|---|---|---|---|---|---|---|---|
| $(r_s/a)^2$ | $n_s$ | $(r_s/a)^2$ | $n_s$ | $(r_s/a)^2$ | $n_s$ | $(r_s/a)^2$ | $n_s$ | $(r_s/a)^2$ | $n_s$ |
| 1 | 12 | 1 | 12 | 1 | 8 | 1 | 6 | 1 | 4 |
| 2 | 6 | 2 | 6 | $1\frac{1}{3}$ | 6 | 2 | 12 | $2\frac{2}{3}$ | 12 |
| 3 | 24 | $2\frac{2}{3}$ | 2 | $2\frac{2}{3}$ | 12 | 3 | 8 | $3\frac{2}{3}$ | 12 |
| 4 | 12 | 3 | 18 | $3\frac{2}{3}$ | 24 | 4 | 6 | $5\frac{1}{3}$ | 6 |
| 5 | 24 | $3\frac{2}{3}$ | 12 | 4 | 8 | 5 | 24 | $6\frac{1}{3}$ | 12 |
| 6 | 8 | 4 | 6 | $5\frac{1}{3}$ | 6 | 6 | 24 | 8 | 24 |

with the coordination number of the lattice $z$; the distance between nearest neighbours is denoted by $a$ ($= r_1$). It should be mentioned that the type of crystal structure is unambiguously defined by the quantities $r_s$, $n_s$; the figures referring to the first few values of $s$ are probably sufficient for this purpose, all the others following from them in a certain way.‡

In reality the atoms of a crystal do not remain fixed, but vibrate about their equilibrium positions. If they are assumed to be attached to these positions by isotropic quasi-elastic forces, the probability of finding an atom at a distance between $\xi$ and $\xi+d\xi$ from its equilibrium position in the radial direction will be given by the expression

$$dP = e^{-f\xi^2/2kT}\,d\xi \Big/ \int\limits_{-\infty}^{+\infty} e^{-f\xi^2/2kT}\,d\xi,$$

that is,

$$dP = \frac{1}{\sqrt{(2\pi\overline{\xi^2})}} e^{-\xi^2/2\overline{\xi^2}}\,d\xi, \tag{3}$$

where

$$\overline{\xi^2} = \frac{kT}{f} \tag{3a}$$

is the average value of $\xi^2$ at a temperature $T$ while $f$ is the coefficient of the quasi-elastic force.

Under such conditions the function $g(r)$ introduced above can be defined as a sum of Gaussian functions

$$g_s(r) = n_s \frac{1}{\sqrt{(2\pi\overline{\xi_s^2})}} e^{-(r-r_s)^2/2\overline{\xi^2}}, \tag{4}$$

corresponding to different spherical layers surrounding the central atom (or more exactly, its equilibrium position). Fig. 18 shows the function ('relative density')

$$\rho(r) = \frac{1}{4\pi r^2} \sum_s g_s(r)$$

† Taken from a paper by Prins and Petersen, *Physica*, **3**, 147 (1936).

‡ This question deserves a more detailed investigation.

for the case of a simple cubical lattice. It should be noted that as the distance $r$ is increased the spacing between successive maxima decreases, whereas their width, equal, roughly speaking, to the amplitude of the thermal vibrations of the atoms in the radial direction, remains constant. In the limit $r \to \infty$, $\rho$ tends to a constant value equal to the average number of atoms in a unit volume of the crystal.

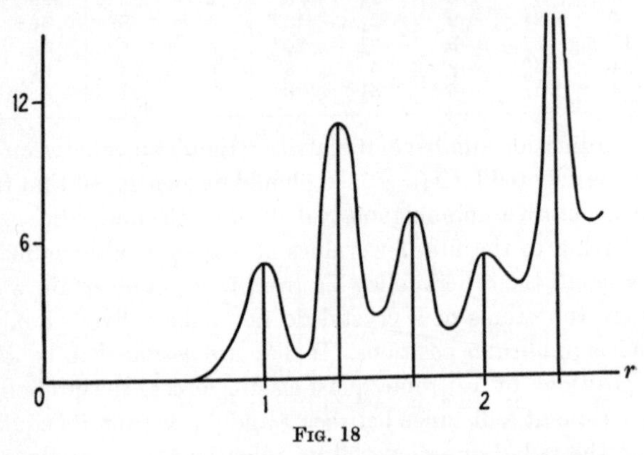


Fig. 18

Prins was the first to express the view that in the case of simple (monatomic) liquids with a quasi-crystalline structure the relative density function can be found in a similar way, i.e. starting with the values $r_s$, $n_s$ which characterize the corresponding crystal, if the width of the successive Gaussian curves (4) is increased *as the square root of the distance* $r_s$.† This increase in degree of indeterminacy of the position of more distant atoms is due, of course, not to an increase of the amplitude of thermal vibrations about the equilibrium positions, but to an increase of indeterminacy in the location of these positions, connected with the absence of long-range order in liquids, but with a partial preservation of the same type of short-range order as in the corresponding crystals.

The fact that the width of the successive maxima must increase as the square root of the distance, i.e. according to the law

$$\overline{\xi_s^2} = 2Dr_s, \tag{4a}$$

where $D$ is a certain constant, follows from very general statistical considerations. In fact, let us imagine a linear chain of atoms, the

† J. A. Prins, *Naturwissenschaften*, **19**, 435 (1931); see also Zernicke, *Z. f. Phys.* **41**, 184 (1927) and Kratki, *Phys. Z.* **34**, 482 (1933); the latter author replaced Gaussian functions by triangles.

position of each atom with respect to the preceding one being determined with a certain degree of indeterminacy $q_i$. This means that the actual distance of the $i$th atom from the $(i-1)$th is known to lie between $a_i+\frac{1}{2}q_i$ and $a_i-\frac{1}{2}q_i$, where $a_i$ is their average distance. The distance of the $s$th atom from the initial one ($s = 0$) must be equal under such conditions to $r_s+\xi_s$, where $r_s = a_1+a_2+...+a_s$ is the average value of this distance, while the 'error' $\xi_s$ is enclosed between the limits $-\frac{1}{2}(q_1+q_2+...+q_s)$ and $\frac{1}{2}(q_1+q_2+...+q_s)$. The average value of this error, just as the average of the individual errors $\Delta a_i$, vanishes. Squaring it we have

$$\overline{\xi_s^2} = \overline{(\Delta a_1)^2}+\overline{(\Delta a_2)^2}+...+2\overline{\Delta a_1\,\Delta a_2}+...,$$

or, since the individual errors are independent of each other,

$$\overline{\xi_s^2} = \overline{(\Delta a_1)^2}+\overline{(\Delta a_2)^2}+...+\overline{(\Delta a_s)^2}. \tag{4 b}$$

Comparing this equation with the equation $r_s = a_1+a_2+...+a_s$ we see that a correlation between $\xi_s^2$ and $r_s$, if it exists, must be of the form (4 a). This result follows with especial simplicity if the average distances between nearest neighbours are equal ($a_1 = a_2 = ... = a$) as well as the individual errors. In this case (4 b) is reduced to $\overline{\xi_s^2} = s\overline{(\Delta a)^2}$, i.e.

$$\frac{\overline{\xi_s^2}}{r_s} = \frac{\overline{(\Delta a)^2}}{a}.$$

It should be noted that similar results are obtained in the theory of the Brownian diffusion motion for the resultant displacement of a particle $\xi_s$ during a time $t_s$, constituted by $s$ elementary displacements $\Delta a_i$ performed during time intervals $\tau_i$. The ratio $\dfrac{\overline{\xi_s^2}}{2t_s} = \dfrac{\overline{(\Delta a_i)^2}}{2\tau_i}$ is equal in this case to the diffusion coefficient. The quantity obtained when the time $t_s$ is replaced by the average value $r_s$ of the distance can be conveniently denoted as the 'structure diffusion coefficient'. This is the quantity $D$ appearing in equation (4 a).

In the case of a crystal, i.e. in the presence of distant order, it is equal to zero; an identical broadening of all the maxima, due to the thermal vibrations about regularly distributed equilibrium positions, implies no structure diffusion. The structure diffusion coefficient specifies the degree of disorder in the distribution of the equilibrium positions of the atoms arising after a breakdown of distant order, i.e. after melting. The degree of local order in the resulting liquid is smaller the larger the structure diffusion coefficient $D$.

Theoretically speaking this coefficient can be arbitrarily small (so that it can be used for the definition of the degree of local order not only in liquids but also in crystals). It cannot, however, be arbitrarily large. In the case of a chain of atoms with an average equal spacing $a$, we obtain the largest possible degree of disorder when $\sqrt{\{(\overline{\Delta a^2})\}}$ is comparable with $a$, i.e. when $D \approx a$. The degree of local order can accordingly be defined by the formula $\eta = 1 - D/D_{\text{max}}$.

Prins, Kratki, and other investigators have shown that the notion of 'structure diffusion' in the relative distribution of the atoms of

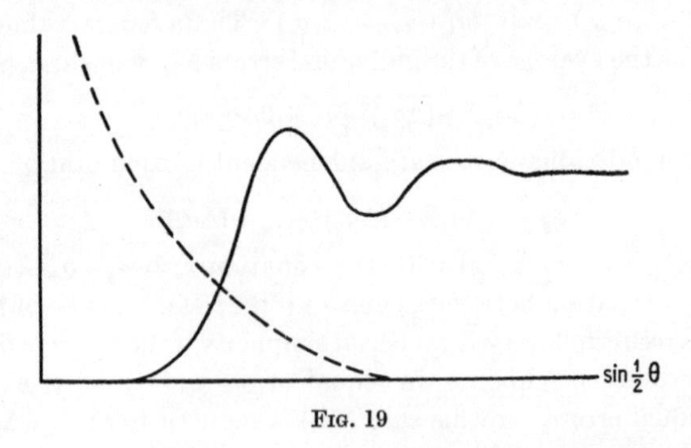


FIG. 19

simple liquids (with respect to the corresponding crystals) is in good agreement with the experimental data obtained from an X-ray analysis of the structure of liquid bodies.

A characteristic feature of the corresponding X-ray diagrams is the absence of rays scattered at small angles (as in the case of gases) and the presence of one or several intensity maxima in the form of diffuse diffraction rings (see Fig. 19, where the full line represents the distribution of intensity of rays scattered in a liquid, while the dotted line refers to a gas). The intensity distribution of the rays scattered by an isotropic system of like atoms (constituting a gas, liquid, or a polycrystalline body) can easily be calculated if the function $g(r)$, characterizing the relative distribution of the atoms with respect to one of them, is known.

Let $A_k e^{i\phi_k}$ denote the complex amplitude of the rays scattered by a certain ($k$th) atom in a given direction. The total intensity of scattered rays is equal to

$$I = \sum_k \sum_l A_k A_l e^{i(\phi_k - \phi_l)}$$

or

$$I = A^2 \sum_k \sum_l e^{i(\phi_k - \phi_l)}$$

if the elementary amplitudes $A_k$ are identical. Since (with neglect of surface effects) all the atoms can be assumed to be distributed with respect to each of them in the same way, this expression is reduced to the form

$$I = A^2N[1+2\sum_{s\neq 0}\cos(\phi_s-\phi_0)],$$

where $N$ is the number of atoms and $\phi_0$ the phase corresponding to an arbitrarily chosen 'central' atom. Denoting the radius vector of the $s$th atom with respect to the central one by $\mathbf{r}_s$ we have

$$\phi_s-\phi_0 = \mathbf{k}.\mathbf{r}_s,$$

where $\mathbf{k}$ is the vector difference of the wave vectors $\mathbf{k}_1 = (2\pi/\lambda)\mathbf{n}_1$ and $\mathbf{k}_2 = (2\pi/\lambda)\mathbf{n}_2$ of the incident and scattered rays ($\mathbf{n}_1$ and $\mathbf{n}_2$ are unit vectors specifying the corresponding directions). The absolute value of the vector $\mathbf{k}$ is equal to $k = (4\pi/\lambda)\sin\frac{1}{2}\theta$, where $\theta$ is the angle of scattering.

The sum $\sum_s \cos(\phi_s-\phi_0)$ can be replaced by the integral

$$\int\limits_0^\infty \overline{\cos(\phi_s-\phi_0)}g(r)\,dr,$$

where $\overline{\cos(\phi_s-\phi_0)}$ denotes the average value of $\cos(\phi_s-\phi_0)$ for all the directions of the vector $\mathbf{r}_s$ (of a fixed magnitude), i.e.

$$\overline{\cos(\phi_s-\phi_0)} = \frac{1}{4\pi}\int\limits_0^\pi \cos(kr\cos\vartheta)2\pi\sin\vartheta\,d\vartheta = \frac{\sin kr}{kr}.$$

The relative intensity of the scattered rays $E = I/NA^2$ is thus given by the following formula

$$\tfrac{1}{2}(E-1) = \int\limits_0^\infty \frac{\sin kr}{kr}g(r)\,dr = \frac{4\pi}{k}\int\limits_0^\infty \sin(kr)\rho r\,dr,$$

where $\rho = g(r)/4\pi r^2$ is the relative density.

If this function is replaced by its mean value $\rho_0$ the integral vanishes, which corresponds to the absence of diffraction effects in a practically homogeneous continuous medium. Hence it follows that $\rho$ can be replaced by the difference $\rho-\rho_0$ which tends to zero as $r$ is increased. We thus get

$$\frac{1}{8\pi\rho_0}(E-1)k = \int\limits_0^\infty \left(\frac{\rho}{\rho_0}-1\right)r\sin(kr)\,dr. \quad (5)$$

This formula has been obtained by Zernicke and Prins, who noticed that it can be considered as the expansion into a Fourier integral of the quantity $(E-1)k/8\pi\rho_0$ as a function of the parameter $k$ (or of the angle of scattering $\theta$), the factor $(\rho/\rho_0)-1$ playing the role of the corresponding Fourier amplitude. This factor can accordingly be determined from the experimental data, referring to the function $E(k)$ with the help of the Fourier transformation

$$\left(\frac{\rho}{\rho_0}-1\right)r = \frac{1}{16\pi^2\rho_0}\int\limits_0^\infty (E-1)k\sin(kr)\,dk. \qquad (5\,\text{a})$$

The results obtained by applying this formula to a number of simple liquids are in fair agreement with the theoretical formula obtained by summing up the expressions (4) for the partial distribution functions of the atomic layers of the corresponding crystalline bodies, if the broadening $\sqrt{(\overline{\xi^2})}$ is increased as the square root of the mean radius $r_s$ of these layers, in accordance with (4 a). The structure diffusion coefficient, specifying the amount of this broadening, increases with elevation of the temperature of the liquid, in agreement with the theoretical conception about the resulting decrease of the degree of local order. This circumstance is revealed by a lowering and broadening of the maxima both on the curve $E(\theta)$, describing the distribution of intensity on the X-ray diagram of a liquid, and on the curve $\rho(r)$, specifying the relative distribution of the atoms.†

The relative distribution of the atoms in various liquids at temperatures lying sufficiently close to the corresponding crystallization points has been shown in this way to maintain the same type as in the corresponding crystalline bodies. In other words the melting of a (simple) crystal is accompanied by a slackening and diffusion of its structure, its fundamental features being preserved. A further rise of temperature leads, however, to a gradual variation of this structure, and, in particular, of the coordination number (i.e. the average number of nearest neighbours). Thus, for example, in the case of water the distribution of the molecules near the melting-point has a tetrahedral character, both below and above it, the structure of ice being similar to that of tridimyte and of liquid water to that of quartz (which explains, according to Bernal and Fowler,‡ the decrease of volume on melting). Near the boiling temperature, however, this structure, connected with a large degree of order in the mutual orientation of the $H_2O$ molecules, is

† As has been noted by V. I. Danilov (unpublished), the correspondence between the two curves in the sense of the equations (5) and (5 a) is incomplete, since the parameter $k$ increases from zero to a finite value $4\pi/\lambda$ and not to infinity, as required by equation (5 a), when the scattering angle $\theta$ is increased from 0 to $\pi$. This circumstance (which seems to have been overlooked hitherto) leads to an apparent broadening of the maxima on the curve $\rho(r)$, that is to an apparent increase of $D$.

‡ J. Bernal and R. H. Fowler, *Journ. Chem. Phys.* **1**, 515 (1933).

replaced by a structure characteristic of spherically symmetrical particles, each molecule being surrounded by twelve neighbours. Such structure might be called 'close-packed' if the molecules were represented by spheres in contact with each other. In reality, however, such a contact is out of the question, since the volume of water at high temperatures is larger than near the freezing-point.

Water is a characteristic example of a substance the melting of which is connected with a change of the *type* of structure (i.e. transition from a tridimyte-like to a quartz-like structure). A similar situation is met with in the case of certain simple substances like Bi and Sb; just as in the case of water the melting of these substances is characterized by a decrease of volume.

As a rule, however, the type of structure remains unaltered on melting, which corresponds only to a decrease of local order (and to a loss of distant order).

Prins† has attempted to derive a theoretical expression for the structure diffusion coefficient as a function of the temperature with the help of the following argument (which, as will be shown below, is wholly fallacious).

Let us consider a linear model of a crystal, i.e. an atomic chain with equally spaced equilibrium positions. Let their distance apart be $a$, and the displacement of the $s$th atom from its equilibrium position $x_s = sa$ be $\xi_s$. At the beginning of this section we have assumed the atoms to be attached by quasi-elastic forces $f\xi_s$ to the corresponding 'absolute' equilibrium positions $x_s$. In reality, however, they are attached not to these equilibrium positions (which have a purely geometrical meaning) but to each other, so that the $s$th atom is acted on by the $(s-1)$th, with a force $-fq_s$, proportional to their *relative* displacement $q_s = \xi_s - \xi_{s-1}$. Accordingly, the potential energy of the chain is equal to the sum of terms $\frac{1}{2}fq_s^2$, referring not to individual atoms but to the individual *links* of the chain formed by pairs of neighbours. In calculating the average values we must therefore start not with absolute displacements $\xi_s$ but with relative ones $q_s$. In particular, the probability that the relative displacement of the $s$th and $(s-1)$th atoms, i.e. the length of the link formed by them, is increased by an amount lying between $q$ and $q+dq$, is given by the expression

$$dP = \frac{1}{\sqrt{(2\pi\overline{q^2})}} e^{-q^2/2\overline{q^2}}\, dq,$$

† Prins and Petersen, *Physica*, **3**, 147 (1936).

which is quite similar to (3), with the same value $kT/f$ of $\overline{q^2}$ as that obtained before for $\overline{\xi^2}$.

If the central atom is assumed to remain fixed ($\xi_0 = 0$) the (absolute) displacement of the $s$th atom can be represented by the sum $q_1+q_2+...+q_s$. The average value of this sum is equal to zero (which corresponds to the absence of thermal dilatation in the chain, see Ch. IV). Taking the square of $\xi_s$ we get

$$\overline{\xi_s^2} = \sum_{i=1}^{s} \overline{q_i^2} = s\frac{kT}{f}.$$

A comparison of this expression with (4a) shows that in the present case the structure diffusion coefficient can be defined as

$$D = \frac{\overline{q^2}}{2a} = \frac{kT}{2af}.$$

This conclusion, arrived at by Prins, implies, however, a contradiction, for it identifies, from the structure point of view, a three-dimensional liquid with a one-dimensional crystal.

If this result could be applied to a three-dimensional crystal, the preceding theory of X-ray scattering would refer to crystals and not to liquids.

As has been, however, shown by Peierls† in the case of three-dimensional crystals, the average quadratic fluctuation $\overline{\xi_s^2}$ turns out to be independent of the distance and can be calculated in the same way as if the atoms were attached to absolute equilibrium positions (see below).

We thus see that the cause of the structure diffusion of liquids must not be *directly* connected with the heat motion, as assumed by Prins, and must be looked for in an entirely different direction.

Before turning our attention to this question we shall consider in more detail the above-mentioned work of Peierls, since its results have an essential bearing on the problem of the relationship between the crystalline and the amorphous state of matter.

Following the method introduced by Debye in the theory of specific heats of solid bodies, the heat motion in a system of particles (one, two, or three-dimensional) coupled by quasi-elastic forces can be represented as a superposition of elastic waves of various length from a double of the linear dimensions of the body to a double of the average spacing between the particles (approximately), the system of particles being treated as a continuous medium.

† R. Peierls, *Helv. Phys. Acta*, Suppl. ii, 81 (1936).

In the linear case the possible values of the wave-length are given by the formula

$$\lambda = \frac{2L}{N} n,$$

where $L$ is the length of the atomic chain and $n = 1, 2, \ldots, N$ ($N$ being the number of atoms and $2L/N = 2a$ the double of their distance apart). The number of normal vibration modes with a wave number $1/\lambda$ enclosed between the limits $k$ and $k+dk$ is equal to $dn = 2L\,dk$. In the two-dimensional case (plane lattice) the number of normal vibrations with a wave vector $\mathbf{k}$, the components of which are enclosed between $k_x$, $k_x+dk_x$, and $k_y$, $k_y+dk_y$, is equal to $dn = S\,dk_x\,dk_y$ where $S$ is the surface of the lattice, or

$$dn = 2\pi Sk\,dk$$

if all the waves with $k \leqslant 1/\lambda \leqslant k+dk$ are considered, irrespective of their direction of propagation. In the three-dimensional case, finally, the number of normal vibrations is given by the expression

$$dn = V\,dk_x\,dk_y\,dk_z,$$

or if the direction of propagation is not taken into account,

$$dn = 4\pi Vk^2\,dk,$$

where $V$ is the volume of the body.

The displacement of a particle of the body in a given direction as a result of the heat motion of the body can be represented as a sum of displacements corresponding to the different normal vibrations:

$$\xi_x = \sum_k \xi_{xk} = \sum_k A_k\, e^{i(\omega_k t - kx)}. \tag{6}$$

Here $x$ denotes the coordinate of the equilibrium position of the particle in the linear case, the set of two coordinates $x$, $y$ in the two-dimensional case, and the set $x$, $y$, $z$ in the three-dimensional one. Likewise $k$ denotes an ordinary number in the first case, a plane vector with the components $k_x$, $k_y$ in the second, and a space vector $k_x$, $k_y$, $k_z$ in the third. The product $kx$ indicates in the general case a scalar product of two vectors. The quantity $\omega_k$ is the frequency of the vibrations, connected with $k$ by the relation $\omega_k = v|k|$, where $v$ is the velocity of propagation of the corresponding waves.

In order to determine the Fourier coefficients, i.e. the amplitudes of the vibrations $A_k$, let us take the derivative of (6) with respect to the time and square it, or rather multiply by the conjugate complex quantity $\xi_x^*$ and by the mass of a particle and sum up over all the particles. We shall get in this way the double of the average value of the kinetic energy of the system, or since this average value coincides with that of the potential energy, the total energy of the heat motion

$$W = \sum_x \tfrac{1}{2} m \dot{\xi}_x \dot{\xi}_x^* = \sum_x \sum_k \sum_{k'} \tfrac{1}{2} m \omega_k \omega_{k'} A_k A_{k'}^* e^{i(k'-k)x}$$
$$= \tfrac{1}{2} m \sum_k \sum_{k'} \omega_k \omega_{k'} A_k A_{k'}^* \sum_x e^{i(k'-k)x}.$$

The sum $\sum_x e^{i(k'-k)x}$ vanishes if $k' \neq k$ and is reduced to the number of particles $N$ if $k' = k$. The preceding expression is thus reduced to

$$W = \tfrac{1}{2} m N \sum_k \omega_k^2 |A_k|^2 = \tfrac{1}{2} M v^2 \sum_k k^2 |A_k|^2 \tag{6 a}$$

($M$ = total mass of the body). The additivity of $W$ with respect to the different normal vibration modes corresponds, if no account is taken of quantum effects, to an equipartition of the thermal energy between them. Denoting the product of Boltzmann's constant and the absolute temperature by $\theta$ we have consequently

$$\tfrac{1}{2} M v^2 k^2 |A_k|^2 = \theta. \tag{6 b}$$

We thus see that the amplitudes $A_k$ are inversely proportional to the corresponding wave numbers.

We can now turn to a consideration of the main question we are interested in, namely, that of the fluctuations of the distance between two particles $x$ and $x'$, i.e. of the average value of the square of their displacement in any given direction

$$\xi_{xx'} = \xi_x - \xi_{x'}$$

as a function of the average distance $(x-x')$. Multiplying this expression by the conjugate complex we get

$$|\xi_{xx'}|^2 = |\xi_x|^2 + |\xi_{x'}|^2 - \xi_x \xi_{x'}^* - \xi_x^* \xi_{x'}.$$

We are interested in the average value of this expression not only with respect to the time but also in space, for a given relative position of the two particles, i.e. a given value of the (vector) difference $x-x' = r$ of this equilibrium position. Putting $x' = x-r$ we must accordingly sum up the preceding expression with respect to all the values of $x$ (for $r$ = const.) and divide the result by $N$. We get in this way, according to (6),

$$\overline{|\xi_{xx'}|^2} = 2\overline{|\xi_x|^2} - \frac{1}{N} \sum_x \sum_k \sum_{k'} [A_k A_{k'}^* e^{i(k'x'-kx)} + A_k^* A_{k'} e^{i(kx-k'x')}]$$
$$= 2\overline{|\xi_x|^2} - \frac{1}{N} \sum_k \sum_{k'} A_k^* A_{k'} e^{ik'r} \sum_x e^{i(k-k')x} -$$
$$-\frac{1}{N} \sum_k \sum_{k'} A_k A_{k'}^* e^{-ik'r} \sum_x e^{i(k'-k)x},$$

or since $\sum_x e^{i(k-k')x} = 0$ if $k \neq k'$ and $N$ if $k = k'$

$$\overline{|\xi_{xx'}|^2} = 2\overline{|\xi_x|^2} - 2\sum_k |A_k|^2 \cos kr,$$

that is finally, since $\overline{|\xi_x|^2} = \sum_k |A_k|^2$,

$$\overline{|\xi_{xx'}|^2} = 4\sum_k |A_k|^2 \sin^2\frac{kr}{2}. \tag{7}$$

Substituting here the expression (6 b) for $|A_k|^2$ and replacing the summation by an integration, we obtain the following results:

(1) in the linear case

$$\overline{|\xi_{xx'}|^2} = \frac{16\theta L}{Mv^2}\int \frac{\sin^2\frac{1}{2}kr}{k^2}\,dk;$$

(2) in the plane case

$$\overline{|\xi_{xx'}|^2} = \frac{16\pi S\theta}{Mv^2}\int \frac{\overline{\sin^2\frac{1}{2}kr}}{k}\,dk;$$

(3) in the three-dimensional case

$$\overline{|\xi_{xx'}|^2} = \frac{32\pi V\theta}{Mv^2}\int \overline{\sin^2\tfrac{1}{2}kr}\,dk.$$

The quantity $\overline{\sin^2\frac{1}{2}kr}$ appearing in the second and third cases denotes the average value of $\sin^2\frac{1}{2}\mathbf{kr}$ for different directions of the vector $\mathbf{k}$ with respect to $\mathbf{r}$, the magnitude of $\mathbf{k}$ being constant.

In all the three cases the integration can be carried out from $k = 0$ to $k_{\max} \approx 1/2a$.

In the first case we get, putting $\frac{1}{2}kr = u$,

$$\int_0^{k_{\max}} \frac{\sin^2\frac{1}{2}kr}{k^2}\,dk = \frac{r}{4}\int_0^{k_{\max}r} \frac{\sin^2 u}{u^2}\,du.$$

If $r \gg a$, i.e. $k_{\max}r \gg 1$, the upper limit can be replaced by infinity, which gives

$$\overline{|\xi_{xx'}|^2} = \text{const. } r,$$

i.e. Prins's result, obtained above in a simpler way.

In the second case we have, denoting the angle between $\mathbf{k}$ and $\mathbf{r}$ by $\phi$:

$$\overline{\sin^2\left(\frac{\mathbf{kr}}{2}\right)} = \frac{1}{2\pi}\int_0^{2\pi} \sin^2\left(\frac{kr}{2}\cos\phi\right)d\phi,$$

and consequently

$$\overline{|\xi_{xx'}|^2} = \frac{16\pi S\theta}{Mv^2}\frac{1}{2\pi}\int_0^{k_{\max}} \frac{dk}{k}\int_0^{2\pi} \sin^2\left(\frac{kr}{2}\cos\phi\right)d\phi.$$

The integral can easily be calculated approximately if $\overline{\sin^2(\frac{1}{2}kr\cos\phi)}$ is replaced by $(\frac{1}{2}kr)^2\overline{\cos^2\phi} = \frac{1}{8}k^2r^2$ for $\frac{1}{2}kr < \frac{1}{2}\pi$ and by $\frac{1}{2}$ for $\frac{1}{2}kr > \frac{1}{2}\pi$. We thus get

$$\overline{|\xi_{xx'}|^2} = \frac{\pi^3 S\theta}{Mv^2} + \frac{8\pi S\theta}{Mv^2}\log\frac{rk_{\max}}{\pi}.$$

This expression increases logarithmically with $r$ in agreement with the result obtained by Peierls (loc. cit.).

In the third case we have finally

$$\overline{\sin^2\tfrac{1}{2}\mathbf{kr}} = \tfrac{1}{2}[1-\overline{\cos(kr\cos\vartheta)}],$$

where $\vartheta$ is the angle between $\mathbf{k}$ and $\mathbf{r}$, or since

$$\overline{\cos(kr\cos\vartheta)} = \tfrac{1}{2}\int\limits_{-1}^{+1}\cos(krz)\,dz = \frac{\sin kr}{kr},$$

$$\overline{|\xi_{xx'}|^2} = \frac{16\pi V\theta}{Mv^2}\left[k_{\max} - \frac{1}{r}\int\limits_0^{k_{\max}r}\frac{\sin u}{u}\,du\right].$$

For large values of $r$ ($rk_{\max} \gg 1$) this expression is reduced to the first term, which is independent of $r$.

In a paper on the thermodynamical theory of melting L. Landau,† following Peierls's argument, attempts to prove that one-dimensional and two-dimensional crystals (i.e. atomic systems with long-range order) cannot exist. Simplifying this argument, Landau confines himself to a calculation of the square of the 'absolute' displacement of one of the atoms from its equilibrium position, i.e. of the quantity $\overline{|\xi_x|^2} = \sum A_k A_k^*$. Putting here $|A_k|^2 \sim 1/k^2$ according to (6 b) and replacing the summation by an integration from $k = 0$ to $k_{\max}$ we obtain a finite value in the case of a space lattice only, while in the two other cases the integral diverges (at the lower limit).‡ Hence the conclusion is drawn that one-dimensional and two-dimensional crystals cannot exist.

The fallacy of this conclusion is shown by the fact that one-dimensional and two-dimensional crystals of practically unlimited dimensions actually exist—the former in the form of chain-like molecules of rubber and other polymeric substances (see § 4, Ch. VIII), the latter in the form of very firm plane lattices connected with each other into three-dimensional bodies by van der Waals's forces (graphite, clays).

Peierls's result as to the increase of the quadratic fluctuations in the

† *Phys. Z. d. Sowjetunion*, **11**, 545 (1937).

‡ Which means simply that in the low-frequency range the summation must not be replaced by an integration.

relative positions of the atoms with increase of their average distance apart in the case of linear and plane lattices has no bearing whatsoever on the question of their mechanical or thermodynamical stability at temperatures different from the absolute zero. It can even be said that the argument of Peierls and Landau (as well as of Prins) is *based on the assumption* of the existence of a regular distribution of the equilibrium positions of the atoms in the one- and two-dimensional case as well as in the three-dimensional one. From Peierls's considerations it is only possible to draw the conclusion that one- and two-dimensional crystals must scatter X-rays in a way similar to that which characterizes ordinary three-dimensional liquids.†

## 5. Dependence of the Structure of Liquids on the Free Volume; Kirkwood's Theory

Coming back to the question of the 'structure-diffusion' in liquids we must, first of all, point out the fact that the fundamental factor which determines it is not the temperature but the *volume*. This result follows directly from the fact that at the fusion point the liquid differs from the crystal by its larger volume only, the temperature being the same for both phases. This extra volume of the liquid, usually denoted as its 'free volume', firstly ensures the individual mobility of the molecules to which liquid bodies owe their fluidity, and secondly is the necessary (though not sufficient) condition for relatively large deviations of the molecules from the regular arrangement characteristic of the crystal structure.

It is true that at very high pressures and correspondingly high temperatures the specific volume of a liquid can be smaller than that of a crystal at normal temperatures and pressures. The elevation of the temperature can thus compensate the ordering influence of high pressure (or small volume). This circumstance can be reconciled with our point of view if the particles are not treated as absolutely rigid (as is usually done), but their finite compressibility is allowed for. This compressibility enables them at elevated temperatures to be arranged in an irregular way in a volume smaller than that which they would occupy if treated, say, as hard spheres.

In their paper of 1927 Prins and Zernicke attempted to reduce the structure diffusion of liquids to their excess volume with respect to the

† It has been stated by F. Bloch and following him by a number of other authors, for reasons of a similar character, that ferromagnetism is possible in three-dimensional lattices only. I believe this statement to be just as erroneous as Landau's assertion of the non-existence of one- or two-dimensional crystals.

corresponding crystals;† later, however, Prins abandoned this view in favour of the erroneous theory which has been considered in the preceding section.

The influence of free volume on the degree of disorder in the arrangement of the particles can be illustrated by the example of a one-dimensional system, which in this respect is not essentially different from a three-dimensional one. Let us assume, for the sake of simplicity, that the particles do not attract each other but behave like hard spheres with a certain diameter $a_0$. Their regular distribution (in the 'crystalline' state) can be ensured by an external pressure in the line of their centres, so that they should be in contact with each other, the distance between nearest neighbours being equal to $a_0$, and the total length of the chain consisting of $N$ atoms to $L_0 = Na_0$.

Let us now imagine that the total length of the chain has been increased from this value to $L$, the length corresponding to each particle being now $L/N = a > a_0$. If the particles remained regularly distributed with a spacing $a$, there would exist between neighbouring particles a gap with a length $\Delta a = a - a_0$. This gap corresponds to the 'free volume' per particle and its product with $N$, i.e. the difference $L - L_0$, to the free volume of the whole system (in the present case we should speak, of course, of 'free length' and not of free volume).

Let us now imagine that, owing to the heat motion, the particles can assume all possible configurations along the straight line $L$ satisfying the condition

$$x_{s+1} - x_s \geqslant a_0 \quad (s = 1, 2,..., N-1)$$

for the coordinates of their centres, the centre of the particle $s = 0$ being fixed at the point $x = 0$, and of the $N$th particle at the point $x_N = L$.

With these simplifications the problem of the probable distribution of the particles with respect to one of them (say, the initial one $s = 0$), i.e. of the determination of the function $g(r)$, which has been introduced above and which in the one-dimensional case coincides with the function $\rho(r)$, can be solved in an elementary way by a method similar to that of Clausius or Smoluchowski for the distribution of the free paths of a molecule in a gas.

We shall consider this problem, to begin with, in a still more simplified form, corresponding to a vanishing size of the particles ($a_0 = 0$). Under such conditions the probability that a given particle will be

† *Z. f. Phys.* **41**, 184 (1927); see also Prins, ibid. **56**, 617 (1929); *Naturwiss.* **19**, 435 (1931).

found within a certain segment $x$ of the straight line $L$, irrespective of the position of this segment and of the distribution of all the other particles, is equal to the ratio $x/L$. The probability that this segment will contain no particles is equal consequently to

$$\left(1-\frac{x}{L}\right)^N = \left(1-\frac{x}{aN}\right)^N.$$

If $N \to \infty$ while $a$ is kept constant, this expression is reduced to Clausius's well-known formula $e^{-x/a}$. It can be defined as the probability that within a distance $x$ from some initial particle ($s = 0$) no other particle will be found if their average distance apart is equal to $a$.

The probability that the segment $x$ will contain $n$ particles out of the total number $N$ is given by the expression

$$\frac{N(N-1)...(N-n+1)}{1.2.\dots.n}\left(\frac{x}{aN}\right)^n\left(1-\frac{x}{aN}\right)^{N-n},$$

which in the limit $N \to \infty$ reduces to Smoluchowski's formula

$$P_n = e^{-x/a}\frac{1}{n!}\left(\frac{x}{a}\right)^n \tag{8}$$

and can be defined as the probability that the distance of the $(n+1)$th particle from the initial one will exceed $x$. The sum of the series $\sum_{n=0}^{\infty} P_n$ is equal to 1, in accordance with the physical meaning of $P_n$.

The maximum value of the expression (8) is obtained for $x = an$, i.e. $n = x/a$, which corresponds to the average number of particles in a segment with a length $x$, or, in other words, to the average length $x$ of a segment containing $n$ particles. Putting $x = na+\xi$ and treating $\xi$ as a quantity small compared with $\bar{x} = na$, we get if $n \gg 1$

$$\left(\frac{x}{a}\right)^n = \left(n+\frac{\xi}{a}\right)^n = n^n\left(1+\frac{\xi}{na}\right)^n = n^n e^{\xi/a-\xi^2/2a^2n}.$$

On the other hand, according to Stirling's formula, $n! = \sqrt{(2\pi n)}n^n e^{-n}$. Hence under the above conditions the expression (8) is reduced to Gauss's formula

$$P_n(\xi) = \frac{1}{\sqrt{(2\pi n)}}e^{-\xi^2/2na^2}, \tag{8 a}$$

the width of the maximum $\overline{\xi^2}$ being equal to $a\sqrt{n}$, i.e. proportional to the square root of the mean distance of the $n$th particle from the initial one. This result agrees with that which has been obtained by Prins from a consideration of the fluctuations in the distribution of quasi-elastically bound particles. It should be noted that in our case the average quadratic fluctuation $\overline{\xi^2}$ does not depend upon the temperature (for a given value of $a$).

The sum of the expressions (8) for all values of $n$ between 0 and $k$

$$Q_{k+1} = \sum_0^k P_n = e^{-x/a} \sum_{n=0}^{k} \frac{1}{n!}\left(\frac{x}{a}\right)^n \tag{8 b}$$

can be interpreted in our case as the probability that the $(k+1)$th particle is at a distance exceeding $x$ from the initial one. The probability that the $(k+1)$th particle will be found at a distance between $x$ and $x+dx$ is given by $R_{n+1}\,dx = -\frac{dQ_{k+1}}{dx}\,dx$, or according to (8 b) and (8) by

$$R_{k+1} = \frac{P_k(x)}{a}. \tag{8 c}$$

The probability $g(x)dx$ of finding in the range between $x$ and $x+dx$ *any* particle is equal to the product of $dx$ and the sum of these expressions for all values of $k$ from 0 to $\infty$, i.e. $dx/a$ whence $g = 1/a$, in agreement with the fact that $a$ is the mean value of a segment containing one particle.

We can now come back to the problem of the distribution along a line of particles with a finite diameter $a_0 > 0$. The formula referring to this case can be obtained from (8) by a simple substitution of $\Delta a = a - a_0$ for $a$ and of $x - a_0(n+1)$ for $x$, the latter expression representing the sum of the gaps between the first $n+1$ particles (including the initial one $s = 0$). We thus have

$$P_n(x) = \frac{1}{n!}\left[\frac{x - a_0(n+1)}{\Delta a}\right]^n e^{-\{x - a_0(n+1)\}/\Delta a} \tag{9}$$

with the condition $x \geqslant a_0 n$. The maximum of this expression is obtained for $x - a_0(n+1) = n\Delta a$, i.e. $x = an + a_0$, and corresponds to a uniform distribution of the particles along the segment $x$ at a constant distance $a$ from each other (the additional term $a_0$ is a correction for end effects). In the case $n \gg 1$ the preceding formula can be approximated by that of Gauss

$$P_n = \frac{1}{\sqrt{(2\pi n)}} e^{-\{(x-an)^2\}/2n(\Delta a)^2}. \tag{9 a}$$

In order to obtain the probability $Q_{k+1}(x)$ that the $(k+1)$th particle will be found at a distance $\geqslant x$ from the initial one, it is necessary to take into account the fact that if the segment $x$ contains $n < k$ particles, then the centre of the $(k+1)$th particle must be found at a distance exceeding $x$ by an amount equal at least to $(k-n)a_0$. We thus get instead of (8 b)

$$Q_{k+1}(x) = \sum_{n=0}^{k} P_n[x-a_0(k-n)],$$

or according to (9)

$$Q_{k+1}(x) = \sum_{n=0}^{k} \frac{1}{n!}\left(\frac{x-a_0(k+1)}{\Delta a}\right)^n e^{-\{x-a_0(k+1)\}/\Delta a}, \tag{9 b}$$

whence it follows that

$$R_{k+1}(x) = -\frac{dQ_{k+1}}{dx} = \frac{1}{\Delta a}P_k\{x-a_0(k+1)\}. \tag{9 c}$$

In order to determine $g(x)$ the preceding expressions must be summed up with respect to all those values of $k$ for which the condition $x > a_0(k+1)$ is satisfied. In particular we have $g = 1$ for $x < a_0$,

$$g(x) = \frac{e^{-(x-a_0)/\Delta a}}{\Delta a}$$

in the range $a_0 < x < 2a_0$,

$$g(x) = \frac{e^{-(x-a_0)/\Delta a}}{\Delta a} + \frac{x-2a_0}{\Delta a}e^{-(x-2a_0)/\Delta a}$$

in the range $2a_0 < x < 3a_0$, and so on.

The resulting distribution differs from that obtained by Prins by an application of Gauss's law, by the presence of a maximum at the point $x = a_0$.†

An extension of the preceding results to the three-dimensional case was given in 1939 by Kirkwood,‡ who set the problem of determining the density $\rho(r)$ as a function of the temperature and volume from general statistical principles, without recourse to any kind of models of liquid structure. The particles of the liquid are treated in his theory as hard spheres with a certain diameter $a_0$, just as in the one-dimensional case considered above, allowance being ultimately made for attractive forces between them.

Before reviewing Kirkwood's work we shall make the following remarks:

(1) The smallest volume $V_0$ which is necessary for the accommodation of the particles under consideration corresponds to a regular arrangement in a close-packed cubic or hexagonal lattice, each particle being in contact with twelve neighbours. The only possible type of structure

† This maximum is due to the replacement of repulsive forces between the molecules by their 'hardness', preventing them from approaching each other closer than at a distance $a_0$.

‡ J. Kirkwood, *J. Chem. Phys.* **7**, 919 (1939).

of a body under the condition of least volume is thus, irrespective of the temperature and of the cohesive forces, a regular crystal structure of the close-packed type.

(2) With increase of the difference $V-V_0$ a gradual increase of disorder in the arrangement of the particles becomes possible. It must be expected, however, that so long as $V-V_0$ remains very small compared with $V_0$, the free volume can be distributed in the body in the form of individual atomic holes only, the existence of which does not exclude the existence of a crystal lattice but, on the contrary, implies it. A breakdown of the crystal lattice, i.e. a complete disappearance of long distance order in the arrangement of the particles, can take place only when the number of atomic holes reaches a certain not very small fraction—a few per cent. say—of the number of particles. The free volume represented by them can then be distributed in the body in a continuous way, i.e. corresponding to its equipartition between all the atoms. The smallest volume compatible with the disappearance of distant order in the body, i.e. with the existence of the latter in an amorphous state, will be called the 'amorphization volume' and will be denoted by $V^*$ (it should be kept in mind that it has a definite meaning and value in so far only as the particle can be treated as absolutely rigid). The arrangement of the particles when $V = V^*$ must preserve a considerable degree of local order of the same type as the distant order existing when $V < V^*$. With a further increase of $V$ this local order must gradually decrease, tending to zero when $V$ becomes about twice as large as $V_0$.

(3) The above-described transformations of structure can be influenced by cohesive forces acting between the particles of the body in a three-fold way. In the first place, being to some extent equivalent to an external pressure, these forces must retard the process of amorphization and fusion caused by a rise of temperature (at a given external pressure). In the second place, they ensure the preservation by the resulting liquid of an elasticity of volume and also of *shape* (partially masked by fluidity). Finally, at low temperatures and relatively large volumes the attractive forces must enhance the local fluctuations of density transforming them into 'local ruptures' of the body.

Coming back to Kirkwood's theory, let us put

$$\rho(r) = \rho_0 e^{-W(r)/kT}, \tag{10}$$

where $\rho_0$ is the average value of the density, which in the sequel will be taken as equal to 1, and $W(r)$ the average work required to bring the centres of two particles from infinity to the distance $r$—not in a vacuum, of course, but within the body under consideration (for $r = \infty$, $W = 0$ and $\rho = 1$).

The centre of a second particle can be located in the point $O'$ at a distance $r$ from the centre $O$ of the first particle only if there is enough room to accommodate it, i.e. if a spherical cavity with a volume $\omega = \frac{4\pi}{3} a_0^3$ has been preliminarily created about the point $O'$. Let the work required for the creation of such cavity be denoted by $U(r)$, its value for $r = \infty$ by $U_0$, and finally the work done by attractive forces when the second particle is brought from infinity to a distance $r$ by $X(r)$. The work $W(r)$ can be expressed by

$$W(r) = U(r) - U_0 + X(r). \qquad (10\,a)$$

Let $p(r)$ denote the probability that the centre of one of the $N-2$ remaining particles lies in the cavity $\omega$ with the centre at the point $O'$.

The probability that this cavity will be left free for the accommodation of the 'second' particle is consequently equal to $1-p(r)$.

According to Boltzmann's law and the definition of $U(r)$ we have

$$1-p(r) = e^{-U(r)/kT}. \qquad (11)$$

Hence it follows in conjunction with (10) and (10 a) that

$$\rho(r) = \frac{1-p(r)}{1-p_0} e^{-X(r)/kT}, \qquad (11\,a)$$

where $p_0$ is the value of $p(r)$ for $r = \infty$, so that $1-p_0 = e^{-U_0/kT}$. On the other hand, according to the definition of $\rho$, the probability $p(r)$ must be proportional to the integral $\int\limits_\omega \rho(R)\,dV$ extended over the volume $\omega$ assigned to the cavity. Taking into account the fact that this cavity can accommodate the centres of several particles (up to, say, 12) Kirkwood puts†

$$p(r) = \text{const.}\,[1+\eta(r)] \int\limits_\omega \rho(R)\,dV, \qquad (12)$$

where $\eta(r)$ is a certain correction tending to 0 for $r \to \infty$. Since in the latter case the integral is reduced to $\omega$, the preceding formula can be rewritten as follows:

$$p(r) = p_0[1+\eta(r)]\frac{1}{\omega} \int \rho(R)\,dR. \qquad (12\,a)$$

† Erroneously identifying the constant in the following formula with the reciprocal of the total volume of the liquid.

Substituting this expression in (11a) we obtain the following integral equation for the function $\rho(r)$:

$$\rho(r) = \frac{e^{-X(r)/kT}}{1-p_0}\left\{1-p_0[1+\eta(r)]\frac{1}{\omega}\int\limits_{\omega}\rho(R)\,dV\right\}. \tag{13}$$

The integral over the volume $\omega$ can be simplified by using bipolar coordinates with the centres $O$ and $O'$. Denoting the distance of the

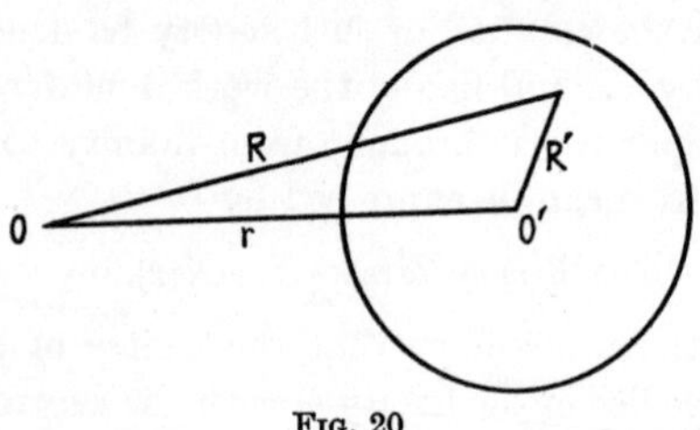


FIG. 20

volume element from $O$ and $O'$ by $R$ and $R'$ respectively, we have (see Fig. 20).

$$\int \rho(R)\,dV = \frac{2\pi}{r}\int\limits_{r-a}^{r+a}\int\limits_{|r-R|}^{a}\rho(R)RR'\,dR\,dR' = -\frac{\pi}{r}\int\limits_{r-a}^{r+a}[(r-R)^2-a^2]R\rho(R)\,dR$$

$$= \omega-\frac{\pi a^3}{x}\int\limits_{-\infty}^{+\infty}k(x-s)\phi(s)\,ds,$$

where $$x = \frac{r}{a}, \qquad s = \frac{R}{a}.$$

$$\frac{\phi(x)}{x} = \begin{cases}\rho(r)-1 & \text{if } x > 1\\ -1 & \text{if } 0 < x < 1,\end{cases}$$

and $$k(x-s) = \begin{cases}(x-s)^2-1 & \text{if } |x-s| < 1\\ 0 & \text{if } |x-s| > 1.\end{cases}$$

Putting further $$f(x) = x[e^{-X/kT}(1-\tfrac{1}{3}\eta\lambda)-1]$$

$$\lambda = \frac{3p_0}{1-p_0} = 3(e^{-U_0/kT}-1),$$

we can rewrite equation (13) as follows:

$$\phi(x) = f(x)+\tfrac{1}{4}\lambda(1+\eta)e^{-X/kT}\int\limits_{-\infty}^{+\infty}k(x-s)\phi(s)\,ds, \tag{13a}$$

or approximately

$$\phi(x) = f(x)+\tfrac{1}{4}\lambda \int_{-\infty}^{+\infty} k(x-s)\phi(s)\,ds, \tag{13 b}$$

since $\eta \to 0$ and $X \to 0$ when $r \to \infty$; in the same approximation we can put

$$f(x) = -x\left(\tfrac{1}{3}\lambda\eta+\frac{X}{kT}\right).$$

It should be noticed that this function has a physical meaning for $x > 1$ only, whereas $\phi(x)$ has physical meaning for $x > 0$.

In order to simplify the solution we shall extend these functions to negative values of $x$ by putting

$$\phi(-x) = \phi(x), \qquad f(-x) = f(x),$$

and shall represent them in the form of Fourier integrals

$$\phi(x) = \frac{1}{\sqrt{(2\pi)}}\int_{-\infty}^{+\infty} L(u)e^{-iux}\,du, \qquad f(x) = \frac{1}{\sqrt{(2\pi)}}\int_{-\infty}^{+\infty} l(u)e^{-iux}\,du$$

where

$$L(u) = \frac{1}{\sqrt{(2\pi)}}\int_{-\infty}^{+\infty} \phi(x)e^{iux}\,dx, \qquad l(u) = \frac{1}{\sqrt{(2\pi)}}\int_{-\infty}^{+\infty} f(x)e^{iux}\,dx.$$

Substituting these expressions in the approximate equation (13 b) we get

$$\frac{l(u)}{L(u)} = 1-\frac{\lambda}{4}\int_{-\infty}^{+\infty} k(t)e^{iut}\,dt,$$

or with $iu = z$ and $l(u)/L(u) = F(z)$

$$F(z) = 1+\left(\frac{\lambda}{z^3}\right)(z\cosh z-\sinh z). \tag{14}$$

If in the Fourier integral for $\phi(x)$, $L(u)$ is replaced by

$$\frac{l(u)}{F(z)} = \frac{l(-iz)}{F(z)},$$

then on the assumption that $l(-iuz)$ is analytical in the right half plane and that the expression $\dfrac{zl(-iz)}{F(z)}e^{-z}$ vanishes when $|z| \to \infty$, we obtain by the method of residues

$$\phi(x) = \sum_n A_n e^{-z_n x} \quad (x > 1), \tag{15}$$

where
$$A_n = \sqrt{2\pi}\frac{l(-iz_n)}{F'(z_n)},$$

$z_n$ being the roots of the function $F(z) = 0$ of the type $z_n = \alpha_n \pm i\beta_n$.

Confining ourselves to the first term of the series (15) corresponding to the smallest value of $|z_n|$, we get

$$\rho(x)-1 \cong \frac{A}{x} e^{-\alpha x} \cos(\beta x+\delta). \tag{16}$$

The amplitude $A$ and the phase $\delta$ can be determined without using the explicit expression for the function $f(x)$ from the conditions

$$\rho(a) = 0 \quad \text{and} \quad \int\limits_0^\infty [\rho(r)-1]r^2\, dr = \frac{a^3}{3},$$

which give

$$A = -\sqrt{(1+\tan^2\delta)}, \qquad \tan\delta = \frac{(\alpha^2+\beta^2)^2+3[\alpha(\alpha^2+\beta^2)+\alpha^2-\beta^2]}{3[\beta(\alpha^2+\beta^2)+2\alpha\beta]}.$$

The expression (16) corresponds to a density distribution of precisely the same type as follows from the X-ray diagrams of liquids. The 'damping' of the density oscillations with increase of $x$, which is determined by the real part of the first root of $F(z)$, is characteristic for the absence of long-range order and is similar to that which has been found above for the linear case (where it is determined by an exponential function of a Clausius and not of a Gaussian type). An essential distinction of the three-dimensional case consists in the fact that solutions of the type under consideration exist in the three-dimensional case if the parameter $\lambda$ is smaller than a critical value $\lambda^* = 34{\cdot}8$; in the contrary case the roots of the function $F(z)$ prove to be purely imaginary, which corresponds to a density distribution characteristic of long-range order, i.e. of crystalline structure. In the case of a close-packed arrangement the work $U_0$ which is necessary for the creation of a cavity $\omega$ (at a large distance from the 'central' particle) should, according to Kirkwood, be equal to $\infty$, so that we should have $p_0 = 1$ and consequently $\lambda = \infty$. For $\lambda = 35$, $1-p_0 = 3/38$. This number can apparently be regarded as the least value of the ratio of the free volume to the total volume compatible with the absence of distant order, i.e. with amorphous structure. The increase of volume on fusion must, from this point of view, be of the order of 8 per cent., which is in fair agreement with the experimental data.

According to the equation $1-p_0 = e^{-U_0/kT}$ the preceding value of $1-p_0$ corresponds to $U_0/kT = 2{\cdot}4$. The coincidence of this figure with the ratio of the latent heat of fusion to the fusion temperature (times $k$), given by Trouton's rule, must be regarded as accidental, for the work of formation of a cavity $\omega$ in a liquid has no direct connexion with the latent heat of fusion.

The preceding theory can hardly be regarded as a complete solution of the problem of the structure of simple liquids and of their fusion, for Kirkwood's argument implies a number of assumptions and simplifications which render questionable the physical meaning of the results obtained. It has been possible to give a more exact theory, based on Gibbs's distribution law, for the linear case only. Since this theory, which is a generalization of that given at the beginning of this section, has an illustrative character only and leaves aside the main question of the minimum increase of volume on fusion (or amorphization), we shall not reproduce it here.

It should be mentioned that according to Gibbs's equation the relative density function $\rho(r)$ can be defined in the general case by the following formula

$$\rho(r_{1,2}) = A \iint \dots \int e^{-U(r_1, r_2 \dots)/kT} \, dV_3 \, dV_4 \dots dV_N,$$

where the integration is extended over all the possible configurations of all the atoms with the exception of an arbitrarily chosen pair with a fixed distance between the corresponding atoms. The integral is obviously independent of the direction of the vector $\mathbf{r}_{1,2}$, or of the absolute values of the coordinates of one of the two partners, as well as of the total number of atoms $N$, so long as it is sufficiently large and the total value of the volume $V$ is kept proportional to it.

The coefficient $A$ is the reciprocal of the integral

$$\iint \dots \int e^{-U/kT} \, dV_1 \, dV_2 \dots dV_N$$

extended over the configuration space of all the atoms.

An alternative way of defining the function $\rho(\mathbf{r})$, which does not involve an integration over the configuration space of all the atoms, or of all of them but two, is based on Boltzmann's distribution law in the form

$$\rho(\mathbf{r}) = \rho_0 \, e^{-W(r)/kT},$$

where $W(r)$ is the average value of the potential energy in a point $P$ at a distance $r$ from the centre of a given atom with respect to a second atom supposed to be located in $P$. This average value can be defined as the sum of the potential energy $w(r)$ due to the first atom, and of the potential energy $w'(r)$ with respect to the second atom of all the remaining $N-2$ atoms. Now according to the definition of $\rho$ we have

$$w'(r) = \int \rho(r') w(|\mathbf{r}-\mathbf{r}'|) \, dV',$$

the integration being extended over all positions $P'$ of a third atom with a radius vector $\mathbf{r}' = \mathbf{OP}'$, $w(|\mathbf{r}'-\mathbf{r}|)$ being its potential energy with respect to the 'second' atom in $P$, and $\rho_0$ the average value of $\rho$ (i.e. its value for $r = \infty$). We thus obtain the following integral equation for the density function:

$$-kT\log\frac{\rho(r)}{\rho_0} = w(r) + \int w(|\mathbf{r}-\mathbf{r}'|)\rho(r')\,dV',$$

with the accessory condition $\lim \rho(r) = \rho_0$ for $r \to \infty$.

This method of reducing the problem of the relative distribution of a large number of atoms to an integral equation is similar to that used above by Kirkwood, the preceding equation being a stricter statement of the problem than Kirkwood's equation (13 b). Unfortunately the solution of the strict equation is made very difficult by the fact of its non-linearity.

An example of its solution for the case of an atomic chain with a very peculiar form of the potential energy function $w(r)$ has been recently discussed by Ufford and Wigner.†

## 6. Equation of State of Crystalline Bodies and Condition for Melting

In the preceding section the volume has been considered as a factor which determines the crystalline or amorphous structure of a body, with practically no reference to the cohesive forces acting between the particles. In Kirkwood's theory these forces are accounted for in an indirect way only and could be replaced by an external pressure. In this theory a liquid is treated, accordingly, as a strongly compressed gas, or as a substance above the critical temperature which can be reduced to a crystalline state by the application of a sufficiently high pressure (§ 1).

Such a treatment is hardly adequate for the description of the properties of solid and liquid bodies and of the phenomenon of fusion at moderate temperatures and pressures. In this case a fundamental role is played just by the cohesive forces, the action of which can be overcome by the heat motion, this overcoming being made easier by an increase of volume, depending in its turn on the heat motion.

It has been pointed out in § 1 that an increase of volume of 50 per cent. with respect to its value $V_0$ for $p = 0$ and $T = 0$ corresponds to the tensile strength limit of the body. For this limiting value of the volume $V^*$ the bulk modulus $K$ vanishes, i.e. the body becomes absolutely 'soft'. A marked softening of the body, characterized by a

† *Phys. Rev.* **61**, 524 (1942).

decrease of $K$, must obviously take place long before this limiting value is reached.

A regular crystal structure can clearly be preserved in this case under the condition only that the fusion temperature should be lowered. In the limit $V \to V^*$ the fusion or, more exactly, the 'amorphization' temperature must tend to the absolute zero.

If $T > 0$ the thermal vibrations of the atoms can lead to 'local ruptures' of the body at such volumes as lie far below the critical value $V^*$. These local ruptures, due to thermal fluctuations of the density, must have a transient character, since as long as the crystalline form of the body is maintained around them they must rapidly 'heal' again. As a result of such local and transient ruptures the regular arrangement of the atoms in the sites of a crystal lattice must be distorted to an extent increasing with an increase of the temperature and of the volume.

It should be remembered that the lattice sites must not be regarded as points determined by some *external* field of force and corresponding to certain 'absolute' equilibrium positions. This field of force is an *internal* one, due to the atoms of the body themselves. The regularity of their arrangement is at the same time the cause and the effect of this internal 'self-consistent' field, characterizing their mutual action. In other words, this regularity must be considered as a 'cooperative' effect, a decrease of which is a factor facilitating a further decrease in the presence of thermal motion.

A quantitative formulation of this conception is hampered by the absence of an adequate definition of the degree of order in the arrangement of the atoms. A rather natural and, at any rate, simple definition is based on a consideration of the thermal displacements of the atoms from their equilibrium positions in the corresponding lattice sites. As long as these displacements are small, the latter preserve their meaning of true equilibrium positions. As the atomic displacements are increased, however, this meaning must be gradually lost, the lattice points reducing to mere fictions. Let $\zeta'$ denote the displacement of an atom with respect to the 'corresponding' site (irrespective of whether it remains an actual equilibrium position or not) and $f'\zeta'$ the *average* value of the force tending to bring the atom back to this site (i.e. the mean value of the component of the actual force acting on the atom along the line connecting it with the site under consideration).

When all the actual equilibrium positions coincide with the lattice sites, the coefficient $f'$ assumes a definite value $f$, characteristic of the corresponding crystal lattice. In the general case $f'$ can be naturally defined as the product of $f$ and the degree of order $\eta$, which, in its turn, can be defined by the formula

$$\eta = 1-\frac{\overline{\zeta'^2}}{a^2},$$

where $a$ is the lattice constant.

Since, on the other hand, the force $-f'\zeta'$ has a quasi-elastic character, we can put

$$\tfrac{1}{2}f'\overline{\zeta'^2} = \tfrac{1}{2}kT,$$

i.e. $\overline{\zeta'^2} = kT/f' = kT/f\eta$. Expressing $\overline{\zeta'^2}$ as a function of $\eta$ we thus obtain the following equation for $\eta$:

$$\eta(1-\eta) = \frac{kT}{a^2 f},$$

which is identical in form with equation (16 a) of Ch. II. The temperature $T_0 = a^2 f/4k$ for which $\eta$ vanishes discontinuously can be regarded as the temperature of melting.

This result was obtained many years ago by F. A. Lindemann (now Lord Cherwell),† on the basis of the hypothesis that fusion takes place when the amplitude of thermal vibrations of the atoms in the crystal reaches a certain fraction,‡ say $\gamma$, of the lattice constant. This hypothesis is expressed by the equation

$$\overline{\zeta^2} = \frac{kT_0}{f} = (\gamma a)^2,$$

which is identical with that given above if $\gamma$ is set equal to $\frac{1}{2}$. In spite of its rather questionable foundation, Lindemann's formula yields a fair numerical agreement with the experimental data if the preceding value of $\gamma$ is replaced by a number between $\frac{1}{7}$ and $\frac{1}{10}$.

The coefficient $f$ is connected with the bulk modulus $K$ of the body by the approximate relation $K = f/a$. Lindemann's formula can thus be rewritten as follows:

$$T_0 = \frac{Ka^3\gamma^2}{k} = \frac{KV}{R}\gamma^2,$$

where $V = a^3 N$ is the atomic volume of the body and $R = kN$ the gas constant $8{\cdot}2\times 10^7$ ergs per degree. Putting $K = 10^{11}$ dynes/cm.$^2$, $V = 10$ cm.$^3$, and $\gamma = \frac{1}{2}$ we obtain for $T_0$ a figure of the order of a few thousand degrees, that is, only a few times larger than that found experimentally in the case of most metallic substances.

† See Lindemann, *Phys. Zs.* **11**, 609 (1910).

‡ This fraction is determined rather arbitrarily from the condition that the neighbouring atoms treated as rigid spheres should come in collision with each other if they vibrate in opposite phases. See Lindemann, loc. cit.

It should be noticed that the 'softening' of the crystal lattice with increase of the volume, as revealed by a decrease of $K$ and, consequently, of $f$, must entail according to the preceding formula a lowering of the fusion temperature in agreement with what has been said above on this point.

A more detailed investigation of the softening of the crystal lattice with increase of the volume shows that it must be considered as the

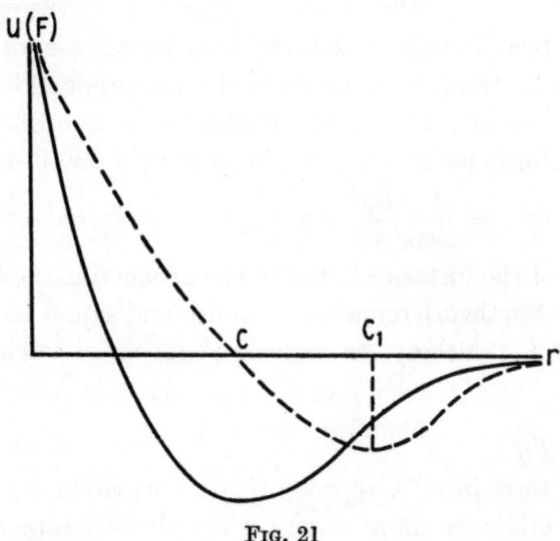


FIG. 21

immediate *cause* of the thermal expansion and that at sufficiently high temperatures it leads to a characteristic mechanical instability of the crystal lattice revealed by the appearance of a minimum of pressure on the isotherms $p(V)$. This important fact was indicated in 1934 by Herzfeld and Göppert Mayer,† who proposed to identify the corresponding point with the fusion point of the crystal (supporting this proposal by numerical calculations referring to argon). A more correct treatment was given by the present writer in 1935;‡ in 1939 Born§ developed a more general theory of the limit of stability of crystals, which suffered, however, from the same defect in the definition of the melting point as the theory of Herzfeld and Göppert Mayer.

Before we turn to a general solution of the problem in question we shall consider, just as in the preceding section, a linear model of a crystal, i.e. a chain of atoms, and, to begin with, the simplest case of two atoms.

The mutual potential energy of two atoms $U$, as a function of their distance apart, has a shape shown in Fig. 21. The minimum of $U$ at

† K. Herzfeld and M. Göppert Mayer, *Phys. Rev.*, **46**, 995 (1934).

‡ J. Frenkel, *Acta Physicochimica U.R.S.S.*, **3**, 913 (1935).

§ M. Born, *Journ. Chem. Phys.* **7**, 591 (1939).

the point $r = r_0$ determined by the equation $dU/dr = 0$ corresponds to the equilibrium position ($C$). In the case of small displacements from the latter $U$ can be approximated by the expression

$$U = U_0 + \tfrac{1}{2}f\xi^2 - \tfrac{1}{3}g\xi^3 + \dots, \tag{17}$$

where

$$\xi = r - r_0; \qquad f = \left(\frac{d^2U}{dr^2}\right)_{r=r_0} > 0; \qquad g = -\frac{1}{2}\left(\frac{d^3U}{dr^3}\right)_{r=r_0} > 0.$$

If the cubic term in this expression is neglected, the force $F$ between the atoms can be treated as quasi-elastic, i.e. proportional to the displacement: $F = -dU/d\xi = -f\xi$. Under the action of this force the atoms can perform harmonic vibrations with a small amplitude and with a frequency $\nu = \dfrac{1}{2\pi}\sqrt{\dfrac{2f}{m}}$ where $\frac{1}{2}m$ is their reduced mass. The average value of the distance between the atoms (i.e. the 'length of the chain' formed by them) remains constant and equal to $r_0$, since the mean value of $\xi$ vanishes. As regards $\xi^2$ its mean value is given by the formula

$$\tfrac{1}{2}f\overline{\xi^2} = \tfrac{1}{2}kT,$$

so that $\overline{\xi^2} = kT/f$.

If the cubic term in (17), representing a correction for the fact that the energy $U$ increases more slowly when the distance $r$ is increased than when it is decreased, is not dropped, the following quadratic expression for the force is obtained

$$F = -f\xi + g\xi^2. \tag{18}$$

Equating its mean value to zero we get

$$\bar{\xi} = \frac{g}{f}\overline{\xi^2}.$$

This equation shows that the free non-linear vibrations of one of the atoms with respect to the other must be accompanied by an increase of the average value of their distance apart. In the case of thermal vibrations this increase represents the thermal expansion of the system.

Replacing $\overline{\xi^2}$ by its approximate value $kT/f$, corresponding to $g = 0$, we get

$$\bar{\xi} = \frac{g}{f^2}kT.$$

Hence the thermal expansion coefficient $\alpha = (1/r_0)(d\bar{\xi}/dT)$ is found to be

$$\alpha = \frac{1}{r_0}\frac{gk}{f^2}. \tag{18a}$$

If the atoms are acted on by an extending force of constant magnitude $F_0$ (which may be imagined to be applied to the right-hand atom, the left-hand one being fixed at the point 0), then in the absence of thermal vibrations the distance between them will be increased by an amount $\xi_0$, determined by the equation

$$F \equiv -f\xi_0 + g\xi_0^2 = -F_0.$$

The equilibrium position is thus shifted from the point $C$ $(r = r_0)$ to the point $C_1$ $(r = r_0 + \xi_0)$, which corresponds to a minimum of the total energy $U - F_0 r$. The force experienced by the (movable) atom when it is displaced by an amount $\xi$ with respect to its original equilibrium position, that is, by an amount $\xi' = \xi - \xi_0$ with respect to the new one, is equal to the sum of $F_0$ and of the expression (18). Replacing $F_0$ by its expression as a function of $\xi_0$ and putting $\xi = \xi_0 + \xi'$, we get

$$F + F_0 = -f\xi' + 2g\xi_0\xi' + g\xi'^2. \tag{19}$$

If $\xi'$ is small compared with $\xi_0$ this expression is reduced to

$$F + F_0 = -f'\xi', \tag{19a}$$

where

$$f' = f - 2g\xi_0. \tag{19b}$$

We thus see that the atom can perform about the shifted equilibrium position small harmonic vibrations with a frequency

$$\nu' = \frac{1}{2\pi}\sqrt{\left(\frac{2f'}{m}\right)}, \tag{20}$$

which is smaller the larger $\xi_0$ is, and vanishes when $\xi_0 = f/2g$. It should be noted, however, that for large values of $\xi_0$, lying near $f/2g$, the above approximation becomes inapplicable. In the general case of an arbitrarily large force $F_0$ the shift of the equilibrium position is determined by the equation $-dU/dr + F_0 = 0$, i.e.

$$F_0 = +\frac{dU}{dr} = -F,$$

where $F$ is the 'inner' force due to the fixed atom and shown by the dotted line in Fig. 21. Expanding $U$ into a series of powers of

$$r - r_0' = \xi - \xi_0 = \xi'$$

we get

$$U = U_0' + \tfrac{1}{2}f'\xi'^2 - \tfrac{1}{3}g'\xi'^3$$

as before, with

$$U_0' = U_0 - F_0 r_0, \qquad f' = \left(\frac{d^2U}{dr^2}\right)_{r=r_0'}, \qquad g' = -\frac{1}{2}\left(\frac{d^3U}{dr^3}\right)_{r=r_0'}.$$

With approach to the inflexion point of the curve $U(r)$, corresponding to the maximum of the force $F$, the coefficient $f'$ of the quasi-elastic force gradually decreases, tending to zero at this point. Its distance from the point $C$ can easily be calculated if the form of the function $U(r)$ is known; the expression $\xi_0 = f/2g$ given above characterizes it with respect to the order of magnitude only.

It should be noted also that the increase of $F_0$, i.e. of $\xi_0$, is accompanied by an increase of the thermal expansion coefficient $\alpha' = g'k/r_0' f'^2$, since $g'$ remains positive, which vanishes in the limit $r \to \infty$ only.

The inner force $F$, given by (17), is usually regarded as the sum of the elastic force defined by the first term, and of a force of 'thermal pressure' expressed by the second term. This thermal pressure is an extending force, equal in the first approximation to

$$p = \frac{g}{f}kT, \tag{21}$$

i.e. proportional to the absolute temperature, just as in the case of a gas. From this point of view the average dimensions of the material body, represented by our diatomic model, are determined by the condition of equilibrium between the thermal pressure, tending to extend it, and the elastic force, tending to restore its normal size (length). The thermal expansion follows from the maintenance of this balance with elevation of the temperature.

We shall now turn from the diatomic model of a material body to a triatomic one, representing it much more accurately even if all the three atoms are supposed to remain on a straight line. The left and the right atoms $A_1$ and $A_2$ will be assumed to remain fixed, while the middle atom $A$ will be allowed to move freely between them. The force acting on it on the part of the left atom corresponds to the inner force of the preceding example, while the force exerted on it by the right atom corresponds to the external force. This correspondence is limited, however, to the case in which the distance $A_1 A_2$ is much larger than $2r_0$, so that the potential energy of $A$ with respect to $A_1$ and $A_2$ is represented by a curve of the type shown in Fig. 22, i.e. characterized by two minima at the points $C_1$ and $C_2$ ($C_1 A_1 = C_2 A_2 \cong r_0$) and a maximum at the middle point $O$. When the distance $A_1 A_2$ is decreased, this maximum is gradually lowered and finally vanishes (at the instant when the points $D_1$ and $D_2$, where the potential energy of $A$ with respect to $A_1$ and $A_2$ is reduced approximately to one-half, coalesce). With a further decrease of $A_1 A_2$ the curve of the total potential energy assumes a shape shown in Fig. 23, with one minimum at the centre ($O$). The depth of this minimum at the instant when it first appears is somewhat larger than $U_0$, the energy of $A$ with respect to one of its neighbours in the position of equilibrium; it increases to the value $2U_0$ when the points $C_1$ and $C_2$ coalesce ($A_1A_2 = 2r_0$). With further decrease of the distance $A_1A_2$ the depth of the minimum rapidly decreases (i.e.

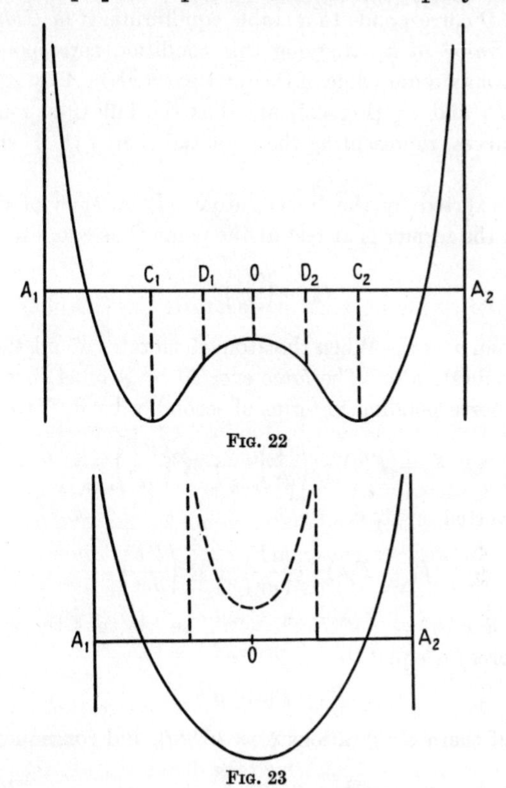


FIG. 22

FIG. 23

the lowest point of the curve $U(r)$ is raised), the minimum becoming sharper (Fig. 23, dotted line).

The potential energy of $A$ with respect to its two neighbours $W(r) = U(r_1)+U(r_2)$ remains, in all the three cases just considered, an even function of the distance $OA$. In the case where the point $O$ corresponds to a minimum of $W$, i.e. to an equilibrium position of $A$, we shall denote the displacement $OA$ (reckoned positive to the right) by $\xi$. Putting $r_1 = a+\xi$ and $r_2 = a-\xi$, where $a = OA_1 = OA_2$, and expanding $W$ into a series of powers of $\xi$, we get

$$W = W_0+f'\xi^2,$$

where $2f' = (d^2W/dr^2)_{\xi=0} = 2(d^2U/dr^2)_{r=a}$. The cubic term vanishes since $W$ is even, whereas the biquadratic term can be neglected so long as relatively small displacements are considered, for which the formula $\overline{\xi^2} = kT/2f'$ remains valid.

The point $O$ corresponds to a stable equilibrium if $(d^2U/dr^2)_{r=a} > 0$. The largest value of $a$ satisfying this condition corresponds, consequently, to a maximum value of the force exerted on $A$ by $A_1$ or by $A_2$. The points $D_1$ and $D_2$ (Fig. 22) are thus the inflexion points of the individual curves, representing the potential energy of $A$ with respect to $A_1$ or $A_2$.

The force exerted by the 'inner' atom ($A$) on each of the 'outer' atoms, when the former is at rest at the point $O$, is equal to

$$F_a = \left(\frac{dU}{dr}\right)_{r=a}$$

vanishing when $a = r_0$. When the atom $A$ vibrates about the point $O$, these forces vibrate also. The force exerted by $A$ on $A_2$ is equal, with an accuracy corresponding to terms of second order in $\xi$, to

$$F_2 = F(a) - \xi\left(\frac{dF}{dr}\right)_{r=a} + \tfrac{1}{2}\xi^2\left(\frac{d^2F}{dr^2}\right)_{r=a},$$

while that exerted on $A_1$ is

$$F_1 = F(a) + \xi\left(\frac{dF}{dr}\right)_a + \tfrac{1}{2}\xi^2\left(\frac{d^2F}{dr^2}\right)_a.$$

Noting that $d^2F/dr^2 = -d^3U/dr^3 = 2g'$, we see that the mean value of the two forces is equal to

$$\bar{F} = F(a) + g'\overline{\xi^2}.$$

In the case of thermal vibrations $\overline{\xi^2} = kT/2f'$, and consequently

$$\bar{F} = F(a) + \frac{g'}{2f'}kT. \tag{22}$$

The second term represents the thermal pressure, introduced above. The factor 2 in the denominator is due to the fact that the coefficient of the quasi-elastic force is equal in the present case not to $f'$ but to $2f'$ (because of the presence of two neighbours).

In order to ensure a constant value of the length $L = 2a$ of our triatomic model of a material body, an external force balancing the thermal pressure, and consequently increasing with rise of the temperature, must be applied to its ends.

If this external force remains constant, then, according to (22), the distance $a$ must change in a way corresponding to a constant value of the expression (22). Neglecting the variation of the coefficient $g'/2f'$ (which gives a second-order correction only) we get

$$\frac{d\bar{F}}{da}\frac{da}{dT}+\frac{g'}{2f'}k = 0,$$

that is, since $dF/da = -d^2U/da^2 = -f'$,

$$-f'\frac{da}{dT}+\frac{g'k}{2f'} = 0,$$

or, finally,

$$\frac{1}{a}\frac{da}{dT} = \alpha = \frac{g'k}{2af'^2}. \qquad (22\,\text{a})$$

This expression for the thermal expansion coefficient is practically identical with that previously found (with a correction for the doubled value of the coefficient $f'$).

For a given average value of the interatomic distance the vibration frequency of the middle atom (on the assumption that the end atoms remain fixed) is equal to

$$\nu' = \frac{1}{2\pi}\sqrt{\frac{2f'}{m}}.$$

An increase of $a$ by $da$ corresponds to a variation of $f' = d^2U/dr^2$ by the amount $df' = (d^3U/da^3)\,da = 2g'da$, i.e.

$$df' = -2g'da$$

in agreement with equation (19b) which refers to the special case $a = r_0$. We can thus put

$$\frac{d}{da}\log\nu' = -\frac{1}{2f'}\frac{df'}{da} = -\frac{g'}{f'}.$$

With the help of this relation the expression for the thermal pressure following from (22) and the expression (22a) for the thermal expansion coefficient can be rewritten as follows:

$$p = -\frac{kT}{2}\frac{d}{da}\log\nu' \qquad (23)$$

and

$$\alpha = -\frac{k}{2f'a}\frac{d}{da}\log\nu'. \qquad (23\,\text{a})$$

These results can easily be generalized for the case of a linear model of a solid crystalline body, consisting of any number of atoms ($N$). If it is assumed that each atom interacts with two nearest neighbours only (or with a single neighbour in the case of the end atoms), the preceding considerations remain unaltered, with the exception of this circumstance, that when all the atoms participate in the thermal vibrations, a single vibration frequency is replaced by a spectrum of frequencies corresponding to different normal vibration modes. So long as the spacing between the equilibrium positions does not reach the value corresponding to the maximum of the attractive force, these vibrations can be treated as small and harmonic.

Introducing the normal coordinates $\xi_1, \xi_2, \dots, \xi_N$ we can represent the total energy of the thermal motion as a sum of terms $W_n = \frac{1}{2}\omega_n^2 \xi_n^2 + \frac{1}{2}\dot{\xi}_n^2$ referring to the different normal vibration modes. The corresponding part of the free energy of the atomic chain $\Psi$ can be calculated with the help of the formula

$$\Psi = -kT \log z,$$

where

$$z = \int \dots \int e^{-W/kT}\, d\xi_1 d\dot{\xi}_1 \dots d\xi_N d\dot{\xi}_N$$

$$= \prod_{n=1}^{N} \int_{-\infty}^{+\infty} e^{-\omega_n^2 \xi_n^2/2kT}\, d\xi_n \int e^{-\dot{\xi}_n^2/2kT}\, d\dot{\xi}_n = \prod_{n=1}^{N} \frac{2\pi kT}{\omega_n},$$

that is,

$$\Psi = -NkT \log \frac{2\pi kT}{\bar{\omega}}. \tag{24}$$

Here $\bar{\omega}$ denotes the geometrical mean of all the vibration frequencies

$$\log \bar{\omega} = \frac{1}{N} \sum_{n=1}^{N} \log \omega_n.$$

Differentiating $\Psi$ with respect to the length of the chain $L = aN$ (or more exactly $a(N+1)$, if it consists of $N$ vibrating atoms and two fixed end atoms), at a constant temperature, we shall obtain the thermal pressure $P$ exerted by it on the end position. Thus

$$P = -NkT \frac{\partial}{\partial L} \log \bar{\omega}. \tag{24 a}$$

Since $\bar{\omega}$ is proportional to the vibration frequency of a single atom between two fixed neighbours (for a given value of $a$), i.e. to the quantity $\nu'$ (or $\sqrt{f'}$), which has already been considered, and since further $L/(N+1) = a$, this formula can be rewritten as follows:

$$P = -\frac{NkT}{N+1} \frac{\partial}{\partial a} \log \nu'.$$

It reduces to the expression (23) if $N = 1$, and to

$$P = -kT \frac{\partial}{\partial a} \log \nu \tag{24 b}$$

if $N \gg 1$ (with $\nu$ standing for $\nu'$).

The derivation given above is more general than the model to which it has been applied. It remains unaltered if the one-dimensional model of the solid crystalline body is replaced by a two- or a three-dimensional model, i.e. by an actual crystal lattice consisting of $N$ atoms, performing small vibrations about their equilibrium positions.

In view of the importance of this question we shall consider it in a somewhat more general form, taking account of quantum effects which, however, play only a secondary role in the region of high temperatures we are interested in.

Out of the total number of $3N$ degrees of freedom of the crystal, $3N-6$ are realized in the form of normal vibrations of different frequencies $\nu_1, \nu_2, \ldots, \nu_{3N-6}$, usually associated with the macroscopic picture of longitudinal or transverse waves satisfying certain boundary conditions on the surface. The crystal thus behaves as a system of harmonic oscillators with different frequencies. The energy of the vibrations with a frequency $\nu_n$ can assume quantized values only equal to $h\nu_n(r_n+\frac{1}{2})$, where $r_n = 0, 1, 2, \ldots$. Under such conditions the free energy of the corresponding oscillator is given by the formula

$$\Psi_n = -kT \log \sum_{r_n=0}^{\infty} e^{-(h\nu_n/kT)(r_n+\frac{1}{2})}.$$

The thermal part of the free energy of the whole body $\Psi$ is equal to the sum of these expressions for all the frequencies. If $kT \gg h\nu_{\max}$, then, neglecting a constant term, we get

$$\Psi = kT \sum_n \log \frac{h\nu_n}{kT},$$

or

$$\Psi = -3NkT \log \frac{kT}{h\bar{\nu}}, \tag{25}$$

where $\log \bar{\nu}$ is the average value of $\log \nu_n$.

The total free energy of the body $F$ is equal to the sum of $\Psi$ and the internal energy $E(V)$, to which $F$ is reduced for $T = 0$, if the volume $V$ is kept constant. This energy can obviously be identified with the mutual potential energy of all the atoms if they are fixed in the respective lattice points.

Putting

$$F(V,T) = E(V)+\Psi(V,T), \tag{25a}$$

we obtain the following expression for the pressure of the body

$$p = -\frac{\partial F}{\partial V} = f(V)+T\phi(V), \tag{26}$$

where $f(V) = -\partial E(V)/\partial V$ is the static or elastic part of the pressure and

$$T\phi(V) = -3RT\frac{\partial}{\partial V}\log\bar{\nu} \tag{26a}$$

is the thermal part. Differentiating $F$ with respect to $T$ we obtain the entropy of the body

$$S = -\frac{\partial\Psi}{\partial T} = 3R\left[1+\log\frac{kT}{h\bar{\nu}}\right], \tag{27}$$

where the constant term can be dropped as irrelevant.

The thermal part of the free energy corresponds to the thermal energy

$$W = \Psi - T\frac{\partial\Psi}{\partial T},$$

while the specific heat at constant volume is equal to

$$C_v = T\frac{\partial S}{\partial T} = \frac{\partial W}{\partial T} = 3R.$$

The specific heat at constant pressure can be calculated with the help of the equation

$$C_p = C_v + T\left(\frac{\partial S}{\partial V}\right)_T\left(\frac{\partial V}{\partial T}\right)_p = C_v - 3RT\left(\frac{\partial V}{\partial T}\right)_p\frac{\partial}{\partial V}\log\bar{\nu}. \tag{27a}$$

It increases monotonically with elevation of the temperature and increase of the volume.

If in calculating $E(V)$ only nearest neighbours could be taken into account we should have (with neglect of surface effects)

$$E = \tfrac{1}{2}NzU(a),$$

where $z$ is the coordination number of the lattice. The equilibrium value of $a$ at the temperature of absolute zero would be equal in this case to $r_0$, just as in the case of a diatomic model, considered above. If the interaction between more distant atoms is taken into account, the preceding expression must be replaced by

$$E = \tfrac{1}{2}N\sum_k n_k\,U(a\beta_k), \tag{28}$$

where $\beta_k$ is the ratio of the radius of the $k$th atomic layer to that of the first layer about a 'central' atom, and $n_k$ the number of atoms in the $k$th layer (see table on p. 113).

If the interaction of an atom with all the other ones, except the nearest and next nearest neighbours, is neglected, the condition of the equilibrium of the crystal lattice at $T = 0$ and $p = 0$ gives

$$n_1\,U'(a) + n_2\beta_2\,U'(a\beta_2) = 0.$$

Hence it follows that the signs of the derivative $dU/dr$ for $r = a$ and $r = a\beta_2$ must be different; this means that in the case under consideration $a < r_0$ and $a\beta_2 > r_0$. If the differences $r_0 - a = \delta$ and $(r_0 - \delta)\beta_2 - r_0 = a\beta_2 - r_0$ are assumed to be small compared with $r_0$, $\delta$ can be calculated from the approximate equation to which the preceding equation is reduced if we put

$$U'(a) = -U''(r_0)\delta \quad \text{and} \quad U'(a\beta_2) = U''(r_0)(a\beta_2 - r_0),$$

i.e.

$$n_1 \delta = n_2 \beta_2 [r_0(\beta_2 - 1) - \beta_2 \delta],$$

whence

$$\delta = r_0 \frac{n_2 \beta_2 (\beta_2 - 1)}{n_1 + n_2 \beta_2^2}.$$

In the case of a cubic close-packed lattice ($n_1 = 12$, $n_2 = 6$, $\beta_2 = \sqrt{2}$) we get, for example,

$$\frac{\delta}{r_0} = \tfrac{1}{4}\sqrt{2}(\sqrt{2} - 1) \approx 0{\cdot}146.$$

Before turning to the question of the stability of a crystal at $T > 0$ or in the presence of extending forces, we shall make one more remark, referring to the linear model. It can easily be seen that in the absence of external forces such a model cannot be stable simultaneously with respect to longitudinal and transverse displacements of the particles. Thus, for example, in the simple case of a triatomic chain the displacement of the middle atom from the point $O$ in a direction perpendicular to the line $A_1 A_2$ by an amount $\eta \ll a$ corresponds to an increase of the potential energy equal to

$$\Delta W = 2[U(r) - U(a)] = 2U'(a)(r - a) \simeq U'(a)\frac{\eta^2}{a},$$

since $r = \sqrt{(a^2 + \eta^2)} = a(1 + \eta^2/2a)$. If $a = r_0$, which corresponds to a stable equilibrium of the middle atom with respect to longitudinal displacements, this expression vanishes and the frequency of the transverse vibrations turns out to be equal to zero. In order to make it positive, i.e. to secure stability with respect to transversal displacements, $a$ must be larger than $r_0$, so that $U'(a) > 0$, which is incompatible with longitudinal stability in the absence of external forces.

In a three-dimensional crystal such situation does not arise, because in the case of transverse displacements (shear) each atom is pulled back not only by its neighbours in the same row, perpendicular to the direction of the displacement, but also by the next neighbours in the following and preceding rows, the larger distance being compensated by larger values of the longitudinal components of the (relative) displacements.

The determination of the average value of the vibration frequency $\bar{\nu}$ in a crystal lattice is a very complicated problem. We shall not follow a number of other authors, who have attempted to calculate it exactly, ignoring, for instance, the inaccuracy of the simplifying assumption as to the central character of the interatomic forces, and obtain numerical results for various special cases (solid argon or nitrogen, etc.). In order to obtain the general relationships characterizing the behaviour of crystals at high temperatures or large extending forces (negative pressures), we can confine ourselves to a qualitative estimate of the dependence of $\bar{\nu}$ upon the volume $V$, i.e. upon the average value of the interatomic distance $a$. For this purpose $\bar{\nu}$ can be replaced by the frequency $\nu$ of the vibrations performed in various directions by a *single* atom of the crystal lattice, all the other atoms remaining fixed in the corresponding lattice points. In the case of a cubic lattice the frequency $\nu$ must be the same for all directions, i.e. the central atom must behave as an isotropic oscillator.

In order to get an idea of the dependence of $\nu$ on $a$ we shall return for a moment to the one-dimensional three-atomic model, for which $\nu = 1/2\pi\sqrt{(2f/m)}$ where $f = (d^2U/dr^2)_{r=a}$. When $a$ is increased from zero up to the value corresponding to the tensile strength limit of our model, i.e. to the maximum of the force $F = -dU/dr$, $\nu$ falls off monotonically from infinity to zero, assuming imaginary values for $r > r_1$.†

We shall consider for the sake of illustration the special case of Morse's potential-energy function

$$U(a) = D[e^{-2\gamma(a-r_0)} - 2e^{-\gamma(a-r_0)}]; \tag{29}$$

this has the practically insignificant drawback of allowing negative values of $a$ which are devoid of physical meaning and which correspond to excessively high values of $U$.

The coefficient $D$ taken with a negative sign represents the value of $U$ for $a = r_0$ ($D$ is the 'dissociation energy' of a diatomic molecule).

Differentiating $U$ twice with respect to $a$ and putting $a - r_0 = \xi$ we get $f = 2D\gamma^2[2e^{-2\gamma\xi} - e^{-\gamma\xi}]$. Thus for $\xi = -r_0$ we get $f = 2D\gamma^2[2e^{2\gamma r_0} - e^{\gamma r_0}]$ instead of $\infty$, for $\xi = 0$, $f = 2D\gamma^2$, while for $\xi = \gamma^{-1}\log 2$, $f$ vanishes, becoming negative with further increase of $\xi$.

The derivative of $-\log\nu = \log 1/\nu$ with respect to $a$ is equal to

$$-\frac{1}{\nu}\frac{d\nu}{da} = -\frac{1}{2f}\frac{df}{da} = \frac{\gamma}{2}\,\frac{4e^{-2\gamma\xi} - e^{-\gamma\xi}}{2e^{-2\gamma\xi} - e^{-\gamma\xi}} = \gamma\,\frac{e^{-\gamma\xi} - \frac{1}{4}}{e^{-\gamma\xi} - \frac{1}{2}}.$$

† $r_1$ is the distance corresponding to the inflexion point of the curve for $U(r)$ of Fig. 21.

When $\xi$ is increased from $-\infty$ (or from $-r_0$) up to $\gamma^{-1}\log 2$ this expression increases monotonically from $\gamma$ to $\infty$, as shown by the dotted line in Fig. 24 (the full line representing the frequency $\nu$ and the line of dashes the force $F$ as a function of $a$). We thus see that at a constant temperature the thermal pressure, given by the expression (26a), must increase monotonically with increase of the volume (or of the length $L$)

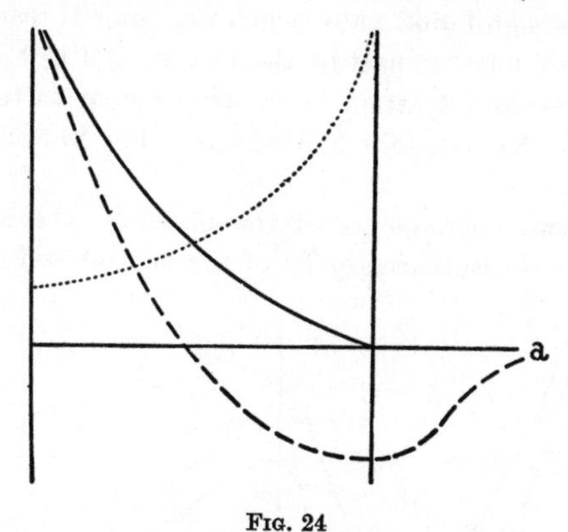


FIG. 24

tending to infinity at the breaking-point of the body (i.e. at the limit of its tensile strength). This result remains valid for any dependence of $U$ upon $r$ of the type shown in Fig. 21, inasmuch as $\nu$ vanishes at the inflexion point of the corresponding curve.

The preceding results are practically unaltered if the one-dimensional model is replaced by a three-dimensional crystal lattice. Thus, for example, in the case of a simple cubic lattice with a constant $a$, the forces exerted on an atom by all its six (fixed) neighbours, when it is displaced from its equilibrium position at a distance $\xi$ (in the direction connecting a pair of opposite neighbours, say), yield a resultant force

$$-\left[2U''(a)+\frac{4}{a}U'(a)\right]\xi = -f\xi, \tag{30}$$

where the first term in the brackets corresponds to the two 'longitudinal' neighbours, while the second one corresponds to four transverse neighbours.

Because of the cubic symmetry of the crystal the expression

$$f = 2U''+\frac{4}{a}U'$$

remains valid for any direction of $\xi$. Since $U'(a) \gg 0$ if $a > r_0$, $f$

vanishes for a value of $a$ somewhat larger than $r_1$, i.e. than the values corresponding to the tensile strength limit of the crystal (calculated from the interaction of nearest neighbours only; the value of $r_1$ is somewhat reduced if account is taken of the interaction between more distant atoms). Since the crystal cannot be extended beyond the limit of its tensile strength, the thermal pressure is seen to assume an extremely high (though finite) value when this limit is reached.

As to the static (elastic) part of the pressure $f(V)$, it is represented in the case under consideration by a curve similar to the dependence of the force $F$ on the distance $r$ (dotted line in Fig. 21 and line of dashes in Fig. 24).

Adding the two components of the pressure—the static and the thermal—we obtain isotherms $p(V)$ of the type shown in Fig. 25, the

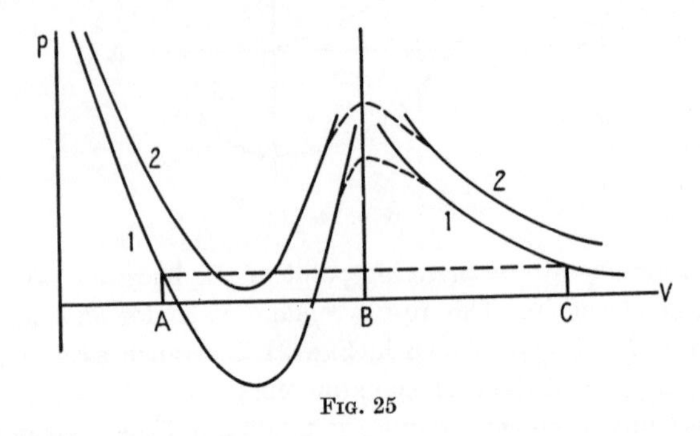


FIG. 25

lower isotherm corresponding to a lower temperature. The rising portion of the isotherm corresponds to thermodynamically unstable states. The lack of thermodynamical stability must, however, be revealed in the neighbourhood of this forbidden range.

It should be mentioned that the minimum of $p$ corresponds to an infinitely large compressibility of the body, which should be associated with infinitely large density fluctuations and would accordingly be incompatible with a regular distribution of the atoms, i.e. would imply the amorphization of the body.

In order to find the actual isotherm corresponding to such an amorphization, that is, to fusion, the theoretical isotherms must be extended beyond the volume $V_1$ for which $p$ reaches its maximum value ($\infty$), and this implies a knowledge of the equation of state of the resulting amorphous body (liquid). Fig. 25 shows two hypothetical curves representing the dependence of $p$ on $V$, characterizing this amorphous body and drawn as a continuation of the theoretical isotherms of the crystal for the temperatures $T_1$ and $T_2$. The actual transition from the crystalline phase to the amorphous one, satisfying the condition of thermodynamic equilibrium between the two phases, must take place along a horizontal isotherm, which is shown by a dotted line. The states of the amorphous (liquid) phase in the interval $BC$ are just as unstable (or metastable), from the thermodynamical point of view, as the states of the crystalline phase in the interval $AB$ (the point $B$ corresponding to the tensile strength limit).†

Similar results are obtained if, instead of the isotherms, the isobars,

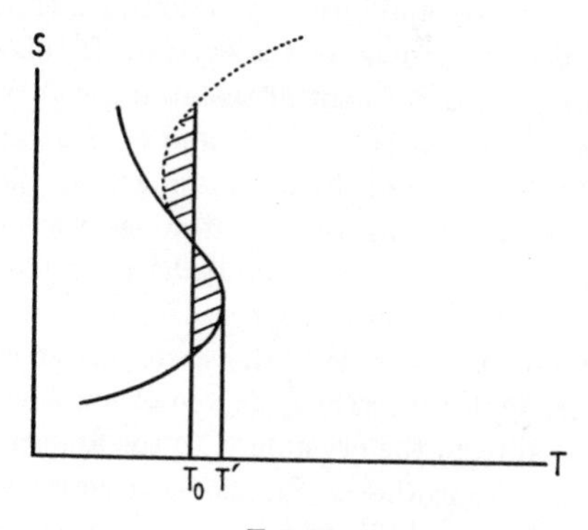


Fig. 26

representing the dependence of the entropy $S$ on the temperature $T$, are considered. It should be noticed that an increase of the volume, from $A$ to $B$ for example, at a constant pressure must be accompanied first by an increase of the temperature (the horizontal line intersects the isotherms obtained for a rising temperature) and thereafter by a decrease; at the point $B$ ($V = V_1$) a finite value of the pressure would be possible for $T = 0$ only. Since, according to (27), the dependence of the entropy on the temperature is reduced essentially to the temperature dependence of the quantity $\log 1/\nu$, which is a monotonically increasing function of the volume (becoming infinite for $V = V_1$), we see that the function $S(T)$ for a constant value of the pressure must be represented by the full curve of Fig. 26.

With increase of $T$ the specific heat $C_p = T\partial S/\partial T$ first increases in a normal way; gradually, however, this increase is accelerated, until

† It follows from the above argument that the volume of the liquid must exceed that which corresponds to the tensile strength limit of the body in the crystalline state.

finally, at a certain temperature $T'$, $C_p$ becomes infinite. This temperature corresponds to $dV/dT = \infty$, i.e. to $K$ (bulk modulus) $= 0$. With a further increase of $T$, $C_p$ jumps to $-\infty$.

The asymptotic increase of $S$ up to infinity for $T \to 0$ cannot actually take place, for this would contradict Nernst's heat theorem. This result is due to the erroneous assumption that the structure of the body remains regular (crystalline) for all values of the temperature and of the volume. In reality, as has been pointed out at the beginning of this section, the approach of the volume to the tensile strength limit $V_1$ must be accompanied by the increase of the fraction of the atoms vibrating about irregular equilibrium positions, which arise as a result of local and transient 'ruptures' of the crystal. If this decrease of the degree of order in the arrangement of the atoms is duly accounted for, the increase of $p$ on the isotherms $p(V)$ and of $S$ on the isobars $S(T)$ up to infinity must be replaced by a finite increase, the corresponding curves for the crystal passing in a continuous way into the curves specifying the resulting amorphous (liquid) phase, as shown by the dotted lines in Figs. 25 and 26. Intermediate states, for which $(\partial P/\partial V)_T > 0$ or $(\partial S/\partial T)_p < 0$, remain unstable in this case, just as when no account is taken of the gradually increasing degree of amorphization, so that the actual transition from the crystalline to the amorphous state takes place along a horizontal isotherm (Fig. 25) or a vertical isobar (Fig. 26) cutting the wave-like or $S$-like portion of the theoretical curve into two parts with equal areas.

The process of melting has been reduced by us in this section to the instability of the crystal lattice at volumes lying close to that which corresponds to the tensile strength limit of the body. Fusion can take place, however, at much smaller volumes if the body is subjected to a sufficiently high pressure and heated to a sufficiently high temperature. Not the slightest indication of the existence of a 'critical' temperature *above* which the body would remain liquid (amorphous) at any pressure, or above which fusion would lose its discontinuous character, has been found experimentally.†

This means, from the point of view of our theory, that unstable states with a negative compressibility and specific heat can be defined for arbitrarily high temperatures and pressures involving relatively small volumes. This is easily explained by the fact that with a rise of the temperature the thermal pressure $T\phi(V)$ increases for a given value of the volume, and consequently the curve of the total pressure

† See for example Bridgman, *The Physics of High Pressures*. (London 1931.)

$P = f(v)+T\phi(V)$ must not only preserve its wave-like form, but its minimum must be shifted towards smaller values of the volume.

As regards the maximum value of $p$, it would actually be reached for a constant value of the volume corresponding to the tensile strength of the body (as shown in Fig. 25) if the arrangement of the atoms remained regular, i.e. the body remained crystalline until this point is reached. In reality, however, this regularity must gradually be lost with approach to it, and this occurs the more rapidly the higher the temperature. As a result, the maximum of the pressure must not only be lowered, as explained above, but also shifted to the left, i.e. towards smaller values of the volume. This is illustrated by a comparison between the two 'theoretical' isotherms shown in Fig. 25, the second isotherm corresponding to a higher temperature. By drawing the horizontal isotherms, corresponding to the actual process of fusion, it will be seen that the volume of the liquid phase at the melting-point must decrease with a rise of the temperature and can in principle be smaller than the volume, corresponding to the tensile strength limit. As to the volume of the crystal at the melting-point, its dependence on the temperature cannot be ascertained in a general way.

Similar considerations refer to the usual process of melting due not to an isothermal increase of volume but to an isobaric rise of the temperature. We shall not engage, however, in a more detailed discussion of this case.

Since the thermal pressure $p_T = T\phi(V)$ decreases when the temperature is lowered, the maximum of the curve $p = f(V)+T\phi(V)$ due to it, which preserves a finite value if the gradual amorphization of the crystal is taken into account, must vanish for temperatures lying *below* a certain critical point $T_c$. Under such conditions the transition of the body from the crystalline to the amorphous state as a result of isothermal expansion would take place in a continuous manner—just as the transition from the 'liquid' to the 'gaseous' state above the usual critical temperature. The temperature $T_c$ defined above can be denoted, accordingly, as the 'critical temperature of fusion' (or rather amorphization, for the resulting amorphous body must remain practically solid if the temperature $T_c$ is sufficiently low). An experimental determination of this temperature requires the application of negative pressures (which are necessary for an isothermal expansion of the body) and is therefore very difficult to carry out.†

† Theoretical objections to the existence of the critical temperature in the above sense which have been advanced by F. Simon (*Trans. Faraday Soc.* **33,** 65 (1937)) do not

It should be mentioned that the usual identification of the process of amorphization of a crystal with its fusion, i.e. transition into the ordinary liquid state, is, in principle, incorrect, for the resulting amorphous body may prove to be not 'liquid' but 'solid'. Usually, however, at the 'amorphization temperature' the viscosity coefficient of the amorphous body is so small that the latter can be treated as liquid.

Taking into account the possibility of the preservation of the rigidity of a body on its fusion (in the general sense of this term) it would be possible to investigate by the methods of thermodynamics the influence of a shearing stress on the fusion temperature in connexion with the resulting change of strain, i.e. of the rigidity modulus. As has been already mentioned, the latter decreases by a factor of 2 to 8 when the crystal is heated from $T = 0$ to the melting-point.

Kornfeld's experiments on the propagation of transverse vibrations in certain supercooled liquids with a very high viscosity show that this decrease of rigidity with a lowering of the temperature is still more rapid in the case of amorphous bodies (see Ch. IV, § 7).

## 7. Temperature Dependence of the Rigidity of a Crystal Lattice

M. Born† has investigated theoretically the temperature dependence of the rigidity modulus of certain simple crystals (with a cubic lattice) and has shown that at a constant pressure it must decrease with a rise of the temperature at a gradually increasing rate. This result, which is in agreement with the experimental data, has induced him to define the melting point as corresponding to a vanishing value of the rigidity modulus. Such a definition of the fusion point is in principle just as fallacious as that proposed by Herzfeld and Göppert Mayer, for it does not take into account the liquid state. The fact that at a certain temperature (and pressure) the rigidity modulus $G$ of a crystal must vanish has the same meaning as the fact established by Herzfeld and Göppert Mayer that the bulk modulus $K$ must vanish (at a point $T$, $V$ corresponding to the minimum of the pressure); namely, that a crystal lattice becomes unstable with respect to variations of shape or density above a certain temperature depending on the pressure (or above a certain volume, depending on the temperature). The corresponding stability limits must in general be different and must lie

seem convincing. It has been surmised by many authors that a critical fusion temperature exists *above* which the crystalline state cannot exist. This hypothesis is, however, theoretically inadmissible and contradicted by the experiments both of Simon and especially of Bridgman.

† *J. Chem. Phys.* **7**, 591 (1939).

far above the actual fusion point—for the crystal structure must collapse before the stability limit is reached, as a consequence of thermal fluctuations. It should be noticed that, on the assumption that the arrangement of the atoms (i.e. of their equilibrium positions) remains regular above the stability limit defined by $K = 0$ or $G = 0$, negative values for both moduli are obtained for states lying beyond the corresponding limits. This has been shown above by extending the isotherms $p(V)$ beyond the minimum of $p$; a similar extension of Born's curves for $G$ as a function of the volume or the temperature is also possible.

We shall illustrate Born's theory with the help of a two-dimensional model, i.e. a square array of atoms which in a state of equilibrium form a simple quadratic lattice with a constant $a_0$. Such a state is realized at the temperature of absolute zero in the absence of external forces. With a rise of the temperature the lattice must expand unless prevented by external compressional forces. At a temperature $T > 0$ and under a given two-dimensional pressure $\pi$ the equilibrium positions of the atoms will form a quadratic lattice with a constant $a \neq a_0$. If under such conditions a two-dimensional shearing stress of a relatively small magnitude is introduced, it will give rise to a shearing strain $\theta = (1/G)\tau$, the modulus $G$ being a function of $a$, i.e. of $T$ and $\pi$.

Without changing the density of the lattice, i.e. the area $\sigma$ $(= a^2)$ per atom, the shear must convert the quadratic cells into rectangular ones—extending them, in the $x$ direction, say, and compressing them in the $y$ direction. Denoting the distance between nearest neighbours in the former direction by $a'$ and in the latter by $b'$, we must have $a'b' = a^2 = \sigma$. This additional deformation of the lattice can be described as an ordinary shearing strain $\theta$ with respect to the coordinate axes $x'$, $y'$ making an angle of 45° with the original ones, $\theta$ being the angle through which the diagonal of the cell is rotated (see Fig. 27.)† To a first approximation, used in the classical elasticity theory,

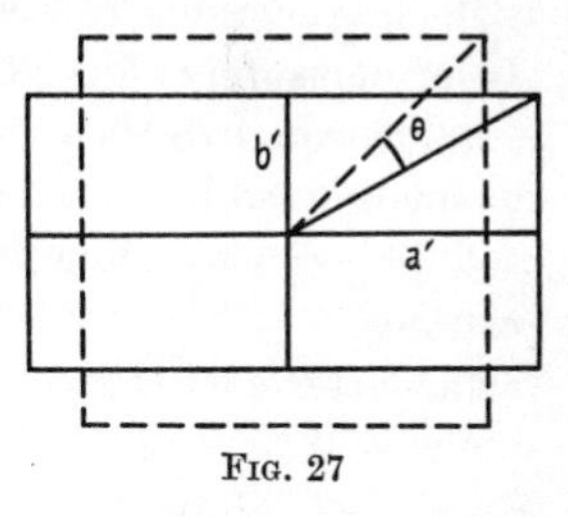

Fig. 27

$$a'-a = -(b'-a) = a\theta.$$

The exact relation between $a'$, $b'$, and $\theta$ can be obtained by noting that

$$\frac{b'}{a'} = \tan(45-\theta) = \frac{1-\theta}{1+\theta}.$$

† The displacements of the atoms in the $x'$, $y'$ direction are $u' = \theta y'$, $v' = \theta x'$; this is equivalent to the expressions $u = \theta x$, $v = -\theta y$ for the displacements along the $x$, $y$ axes.

This gives in conjunction with $a'b' = a^2$

$$a' = a\left(\frac{1+\theta}{1-\theta}\right)^{\frac{1}{2}}, \qquad b' = a\left(\frac{1-\theta}{1+\theta}\right)^{\frac{1}{2}},$$

whence to a second approximation

$$a'-a = a\left(\theta+\frac{\theta^2}{2}\right), \qquad b'-b = a\left(-\theta+\frac{\theta^2}{2}\right). \tag{31}$$

The pressure $\pi$ and shearing stress $\tau$, corresponding to given values of $a'$ and $b'$, or what amounts to the same thing, of $\sigma$ and $\theta$, can be calculated with the help of the equation

$$\pi = -\frac{\partial F}{\partial \sigma}, \qquad \tau = -\frac{\partial F}{\partial \theta}, \tag{32}$$

where $F(\sigma, \theta, T)$ is the free energy of the lattice referred to one atom. Differentiating it once more with respect to $\sigma$ and $\theta$ we obtain the bulk modulus $K$

$$K = \sigma\frac{\partial^2 F}{\partial \sigma^2} \tag{32 a}$$

and the rigidity modulus $$G = \frac{1}{\sigma}\frac{\partial^2 F}{\partial \theta^2} \tag{32 b}$$

($F/\sigma$ being the free energy per unit area).

The free energy $F$ can be represented as a sum of two parts: a statical one $F^0$ depending on the equilibrium arrangement of the atoms, i.e. on $\sigma$, $\theta$, and equal to their mutual potential energy if they are supposed to remain fixed in their displaced equilibrium positions; and a thermal part $F'$, corresponding to the vibrations of the atoms about these positions.

The latter part is given by the formula

$$F' = 2kT\log\frac{h\overline{\nu'}}{kT}, \tag{33}$$

where $\overline{\nu'}$ is the mean value of the vibration frequency.

Since $F$ must obviously be an even function of $\theta$, we can put, retaining terms of the second order in $\theta$,

$$\overline{\nu'} = \bar{\nu}(a)(1-\tfrac{1}{2}\gamma(a)\theta^2), \tag{33 a}$$

where $\gamma = -\partial^2\log\overline{\nu'}/\partial\theta^2$ just as $\bar{\nu}(a)$ is a certain function of $a$. Putting further

$$F^0(a, \theta) = E^0(a)+\frac{\sigma}{2}G^0(a)\theta^2,$$

where $G^0(a) = (1/\sigma)\partial^2E^0/\partial\theta^2$ is the statical value of the rigidity modulus for a given value of the lattice constant (which at $T = 0$ can be ensured by the application of an appropriate pressure $\pi$), we get

$$F = E(a, T)+\frac{\sigma}{2}G(a, T)\theta^2, \tag{34}$$

where
$$E(a, T) = E^0(a)+2kT\log\frac{h\bar{\nu}(a)}{kT} \tag{34 a}$$

is the free energy of the lattice in the absence of shear (which has already been considered in the preceding section), while

$$G(a, T) = G^0(a)-\frac{2kT}{\sigma}\gamma(a) \tag{34 b}$$

is the complete value of the rigidity modulus. The product of the second term with $\theta$ can be treated as the thermal part of the inner shearing stress tending to restore the undistorted structure of the lattice.

It can be shown that $G^0(a)$ decreases with increase of $a$, while $\gamma(a) = -(\partial^2\log\overline{\nu'}/\partial\theta^2)_{\theta=0}$ has a positive value, tending to infinity in the vicinity of the breaking-point, just as does $\partial^2\log\bar{\nu}(a)/\partial a^2$, which determines the thermal part of the bulk modulus. With a further increase of $a$ both $K$ and $G$ must become negative. The values of $a$ which correspond to $K = 0$ and $G = 0$ need not exactly coincide, but they must, in general, lie close to each other. Neither of them can of course be actually reached, for the crystal structure must collapse long before this, in a discontinuous way, unless the temperature $T$ is very low.

If $\theta$ is not assumed to be small, the rigidity modulus can be determined by the general equation

$$G(a,\theta, T) = G^0(a,\theta)+2\frac{kT}{\sigma}\frac{\partial^2}{\partial\theta^2}\log\overline{\nu'}(a,\theta),$$

where the first term decreases (slowly) and the second increases (rapidly) with increase both of $a$ *and* of $\theta$. Keeping $a$ constant, we thus obtain a certain limiting value of $\theta = \theta_a$, which corresponds to $G = 0$, i.e. to a maximum value of the shearing stress $|\tau(\theta)|$; the latter can probably be identified with the 'elasticity limit' of the crystal, i.e. that limiting value of the shearing stress for which plastic slipping must begin.

We shall not engage in numerical calculations, since they are very cumbersome and their result can have an illustrative value only. For the sake of illustration, however, we shall make these calculations for the simplest case, where the mutual action between nearest neighbours only is taken into account.†

† In reality it is necessary to take account of the mutual action with the next neighbours, at least, to obtain a finite value for Poisson's ratio.

Let us consider the variation of the potential energy of an atom with respect to its four neighbours $A_1 A_2 B_1 B_2$, when it is shifted from its equilibrium position $O$ to a point $Q$ on the $x$-axis, say, at a distance $\xi$ (Fig. 28), while the remaining atoms remain fixed.

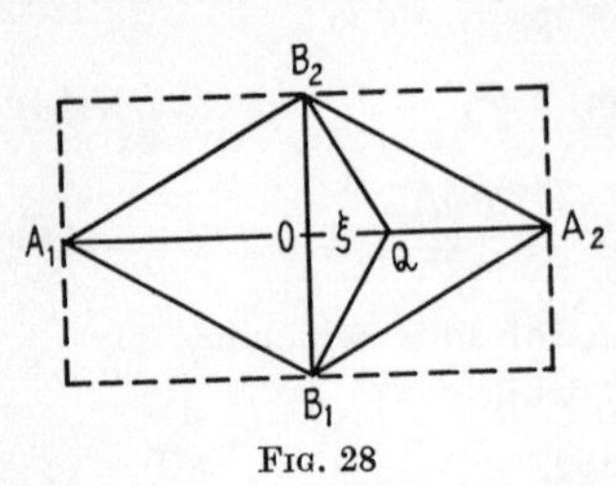


FIG. 28

This variation is easily seen to be $\frac{1}{2}f_1'\xi^2$, where

$$f_1' = U''(a')+\frac{1}{b'}U'(b'),$$

with $U'(r) = dU(r)/dr$ and $U''(r) = d^2U(r)/dr^2$. This coefficient determines the vibration frequency in the $x$ direction, according to the formula

$$\nu_1' = \frac{1}{2\pi}\sqrt{\frac{f_1'}{m}}.$$

The vibration frequency in the $y$ direction is determined by a similar formula

$$\nu_2' = \frac{1}{2\pi}\sqrt{\frac{f_2'}{m}},$$

where
$$f_2' = U''(b')+\frac{1}{a'}U'(a').$$

The mean frequency $\overline{\nu'}$ in the expression (33) can be defined (approximately, since all the atoms but one are supposed to remain fixed) by the formula

$$\log \nu' = \tfrac{1}{2}(\log \nu_1'+\log \nu_2') = \log \bar{\nu}+\frac{1}{2}\left(\log\frac{\nu_1'}{\bar{\nu}}+\log\frac{\nu_2'}{\bar{\nu}}\right),$$

that is,
$$\log \overline{\nu'} = \log \bar{\nu}+\frac{1}{4}\left(\log\frac{f_1'}{f}+\log\frac{f_2'}{f}\right),$$

where $f$ is the common value of $f_1'$ and $f_2'$ for $\theta = 0$, i.e. $U''(a)+(1/a)U'(a)$. Expanding $f_1'$ in powers of $(a'-a)$ and noting that $1/b' = a'/a^2$ we get

$$f_1'-f = \left[\frac{U'(a)}{a}-U''(a)+U'''(a)a\right]\theta+ \\ +\left[\frac{U'(a)}{2a}-\tfrac{1}{2}U''(a)+U'''(a)a+\tfrac{1}{2}U^{\text{iv}}(a)a^2\right]\theta^2.$$

The corresponding expression for $f_2'-f$ is obtained if $\theta$ is replaced by $-\theta$.

Writing, for the sake of brevity,

$$\frac{f_1'}{f} = 1+\alpha\theta+\beta\theta^2, \qquad \frac{f_2'}{f} = 1-\alpha\theta+\beta\theta^2,$$

we get, with an accuracy to terms of the second order in $\theta$,

$$\log\frac{f_1'}{f}+\log\frac{f_2'}{f} = (2\beta-\alpha^2)\theta^2.$$

The main terms in $\alpha$ and $\beta$ are those containing the second derivatives of the energy $U''(a)$ and these terms in $\beta$ are negative. Hence it is clear that the preceding expression must have a negative value, i.e. the vibration frequency must decrease when the lattice is subjected to shear. In the special case $a = a_0$, $T = 0$, $\pi = 0$ we have, taking into account the mutual action between nearest neighbours only and dropping the term in $\beta$ containing the fourth derivative of $U$,

$$\alpha = -1+\frac{2a_0 g}{f}; \qquad \beta = -\frac{1}{2}+\frac{2a_0 g}{f}$$

where

$$g = \tfrac{1}{2}U'''(a_0) > 0.$$

We thus get

$$-\gamma(a_0) = \frac{\partial^2 \log\overline{\nu'}}{\partial\theta^2} = \beta-\tfrac{1}{2}\alpha^2 = -\left(1-\frac{4a_0 g}{f}+\frac{2a_0^2 g^2}{f^2}\right).$$

If $a_0 g/f \ll 1$, this expression is reduced to $-1$ and the expression (34 b) for $G$ to $G^0(a_0)-2\dfrac{kT}{a_0^2}$.

If the thermal expansion of the lattice is allowed for, then, since $f = 0$ at the breaking-point, $\gamma(a_0)$ is easily seen to tend to infinity with approach to this point, which would mean that $G$ becomes negatively infinite, in exactly the same way as $K$.

As has been repeatedly stated above, the regular crystal structure must break down—i.e. be replaced by an amorphous structure—long before this point is reached. The fact that in calculating the rigidity modulus of a crystal lattice as a function of the temperature it is necessary to allow for the variation of the vibration frequencies produced by the corresponding shearing strain has been indicated by L. Brillouin,† who believed that it would be possible in this way to explain the decrease of $G$ with rise of the temperature, and that the melting point could be defined as corresponding to $G = 0$. Being conscious, however, of the fact that liquid bodies possess a latent rigidity (masked by their viscosity), Brillouin proposed to distinguish between the total (equilibrium) value of $G$ and the value $G^0$, which we have defined above as the statical part of $G$ and which remains positive when $G$ vanishes, treating the former as corresponding to slow deforma-

† L. Brillouin, *Phys. Rev.* **54**, 916 (1938).

tions, which do not disturb the state of statistical equilibrium, and the latter as corresponding to very rapid deformations, for which the re-adjustment of the equilibrium, connected with a change of the vibration frequencies due to these deformations, cannot take place. This would explain the fact that liquids preserve a latent rigidity above the point for which $G$ vanishes.

Brillouin's interpretation of the physical meaning of the two parts of $G$ ($G^0$ and $G' = G-G^0$) is wholly unfounded and actually wrong, as follows directly from a consideration of the situation in the case of solid amorphous bodies. The time necessary for the readjustment of the thermal equilibrium between the various vibration modes of a solid or liquid amorphous body can be and, in general, is much smaller than the relaxation time of this body, so that the value of the rigidity modulus obtained for rapid deformations must be identified with the total (equilibrium) value of $G$ and not with its statical part only (unless the deformations are excessively rapid). The value of $G$ must, of course, in this case be different from that corresponding to the crystalline state and must show a different dependence on the temperature and the volume.†

The fallacy of the identification of the melting point with the point of vanishing 'rigidity' has already been stressed at the beginning of this section and need not be discussed in greater detail. As we have just seen, nothing is changed if the 'equilibrium rigidity' in Brillouin's sense is distinguished from the statical one.

## 8. Thermodynamics of Relatively Stable States of Solid and Liquid Bodies

The determination of the melting point according to the usual thermodynamical or statistical methods consists in calculating the thermodynamic potentials $\phi_1$ and $\phi_2$ of the solid and liquid phase respectively as functions of $T$ and $p$ and equating them to each other. This procedure is based on the tacit assumption that the two phases are *wholly distinct*, i.e. that intermediate states connecting them in a continuous way cannot exist or, at least, need not be considered. It can easily be shown that from the point of view of the general principles of statistical mechanics such a procedure is essentially defective. In fact, the thermodynamic potentials $\phi_1 = F_1+pV_1$, $\phi_2 = F_2+pV_2$, where $F_1$ and $F_2$ are the corresponding free energies, are determined, in principle at least,

† It should not be forgotten that the decrease of $G$ with increase of the temperature is partially explained by the decrease of the statical part, due to the thermal expansion of the lattice (at constant pressure).

with the help of the statistical expressions for the free energy of a system of $N$ particles (atoms)

$$F_i = -kT\log Z_i, \qquad Z_i = \frac{1}{N!\,h^{3N}}\int e^{-W_i/kT}\,d\Gamma_i \quad (i = 1, 2)$$

(we are neglecting here quantum effects), the integration being supposed to be carried out, in the case $i = 1$, over all those configurations (and velocities) of the atoms which correspond to the solid (crystalline) state with a given specific volume $v_1$; and in the case $i = 2$, over all those configurations (and velocities) which correspond to the liquid (amorphous) state with a specific volume $v_2$ (satisfying the condition $\partial F_1/\partial V_1 = \partial F_2/\partial V_2 = -p$).

The two states thus appear to be sharply separated from each other beforehand. Now, as a matter of fact, such a separation not only cannot be performed exactly but, strictly speaking, *must not* and *need not* be performed. In order to obtain a complete description of the equilibrium states of a given atomic system we must define its free energy by a single generalized partition function

$$Z = \frac{1}{N!\,h^{3N}}\int e^{-W/kT}\,d\Gamma,$$

where the integration is extended over *all* conceivable configurations and velocities of the atoms, including not only those which are believed to correspond to a certain stable aggregate state (solid or liquid) and not only to other possible aggregate states (the gaseous, say) which under the conditions contemplated cannot be realized, but also to a practically innumerable set of intermediate states of various kinds, which are usually ignored in carrying out the integrations in the approximate expressions for the free energies of supposedly definite aggregate states. The latter must emerge automatically from the partition function $Z$, defined for the whole phase space of the system under consideration in the form of a certain expression for $F$ as a function of $T$ and $V$, or $\phi = F+pV$ as a function of $T$ and $p$, a function of one type $\phi_1(T, p)$ being approximately valid within a certain region of the $T, p$ plane and corresponding to the solid (crystalline) state, while a function of a second type $\phi_2(T, p)$ corresponding to the liquid state is approximately valid in a contiguous region of this plane, the boundary line between the regions, defined by the equation $\phi_1 = \phi_2$, corresponding to an equilibrium between the two respective phases.

Such a generalized and unified statistical treatment of molecular systems has never yet been actually carried out, with the exception of Mayer's theory of condensation† which has been further developed by Uhlenbeck,‡ Born,§ and a few other authors, who, however, have apparently failed to reach a clear understanding of its relation to the usual treatment. Mayer's theory is based on an approximate method of calculating the partition function of a system of atoms allowing for the formation of clusters, corresponding to the initial stages of condensation. The equation of state obtained in this way describes the course of condensation as observed under ideal conditions of unperturbed thermodynamical equilibrium, the isotherms $p$, $V$ consisting of a gas or vapour branch for $V \geqslant V_2$ and a horizontal line $p = \text{const.}$ for $V < V_2$, which refers to the gradual condensation of the saturated vapour into a liquid; the method applied does not enable one to trace theoretically the change of $p$ with a further compression of the system, corresponding to the behaviour of the liquid phase and subsequently to its crystallization.

The generalization of Mayer's theory thus remains a programme for future work in this line.

Now, the point to be stressed is that such a theory will be very interesting from the point of view of the general principles of thermodynamic equilibrium, but will fail to describe a large variety of so-called 'metastable' states, which are observed in reality and, which without being stable in the absolute sense of this word, can have a relatively long and often a practically infinite duration ('life-time'). The simplest examples of such metastable or, as we shall call them in the sequel 'relatively stable' states are afforded by a supersaturated (supercooled) vapour or solution, a supercooled liquid (including substances classed as amorphous solids), a superheated liquid or crystal (the latter state can be observed if the body is heated internally, its surface remaining relatively cool), a mixture of two gases, such as $H_2$ and $O_2$, at low temperatures, when they cannot react with each other because of the high value of the activation energy, and so forth.

Such relatively stable states can be described theoretically by a *conscious* return to the approximate statistical treatment, forming the basis of the usual thermodynamic theory, and consisting in defining the partition function $Z$ for a *limited* region of the phase space $\Gamma_i$, corresponding more or less approximately to a definite physical or chemical state of the system under consideration ($i$). The approximate

† J. E. Mayer, *J. Chem. Phys.* **5**, 67 (1937); S. F. Harrison and J. E. Mayer, ibid. **6**, 101 (1938).
‡ B. Kahn and G. E. Uhlenbeck, *Physica*, **5**, 399 (1938).
§ M. Born, *Physica*, **4**, 1034 (1937); Born and Fuchs, *Proc. Roy. Soc.* A, **166**, 391 (1938).

partition functions $Z_i$ referring to a definite aggregation state or chemical composition of a given atomic system can be regarded as defining, with the help of the equation $F_i = -kT \log Z_i$, the *minimum* value of the free energy, corresponding to given values of the temperature and of the specific volume; this minimum property of the free energy acquires a definite physical and mathematical meaning only by comparing it with other values $F'_i = -kT \log Z'_i$ corresponding to a different range $\Gamma'_i$ of integration over the phase space serving to define the partition function

$$Z'_i = \frac{1}{h^3N!}\int e^{-W'_i/kT}\,d\Gamma'_i.$$

If the two ranges $\Gamma_i$ and $\Gamma'_i$ are not very different, the states defined by $\Gamma'_i$ are treated as *fluctuations* with respect to the average state, defined by $\Gamma_i$.

These fluctuations are usually considered as a complement to the description of the equilibrium state of the system with the help of $\Gamma_i$.† By extending the range of $\Gamma'_i$ or by taking it farther away from $\Gamma_i$ we obtain states more or less removed from that corresponding to the absolute minimum of the free energy, and either tending to return to it by way of relaxation processes with a more or less exponential course, or representing relative minima, i.e. relatively stable states. These relatively stable states can actually be extremely stable and possess a practically unlimited life-time, as seen in glasses at a low temperature, so that fluctuations and relaxing deviations about them must be taken into account only; or they may have a relatively short duration, measured by a certain 'relaxation' time, as seen in a liquid subjected to a negative pressure or to a shearing stress. They can represent an extrapolation of a type of structure, absolutely stable within a certain range of conditions, to another range where they are 'durably unstable', or they can represent a kind of interpolation between two distinct structures, such as a solid crystalline and liquid amorphous, of a type envisaged in § 6. In introducing such 'extrapolated' or 'interpolated' states we are actually transgressing the borders of classical thermodynamics, which has to do with absolutely stable states only and entering the realm of *statistical kinetics*, or more exactly the borderland only, dealing with relatively slow processes, but nevertheless involving

† If states with the same or nearly the same energy are considered, we get $F'_i - F_i = -kT\log\frac{Z'_i}{Z_i} = -kT\log\frac{\Gamma'_i}{\Gamma_i}$, that is $\frac{\Gamma'_i}{\Gamma_i} = e^{-(F'_i-F_i)/kT}$. Identifying the ratio $\frac{\Gamma'_i}{\Gamma_i}$ with the probability of the corresponding fluctuation, we obtain the usual formula for this probability as a function of the variation of the free energy.

the notion of life-time or relaxation time. A well-known example of this extended thermodynamical theory is afforded by the Polanyi-Wigner-Eyring thermodynamic theory of the rate of chemical reactions. This theory deals with a system in a state of 'partial equilibrium', an equilibrium with respect to distribution of the molecules of various kinds between different states according to the Maxwell-Boltzmann law being assumed to hold (approximately at least) in the absence of chemical equilibrium with respect to the concentrations of the molecules of various kinds, in the sense of the law of mass action.

We do not intend to present here a further development of this generalized thermodynamic theory and of its application to other branches of physics and chemistry. Our main object is to provide a theoretical basis for that extended treatment of the solid and liquid states, involving 'extrapolated' and 'interpolated' configurations of the particles, which has been foreshadowed in the preceding sections.

We have seen, in particular, that the extrapolation of the crystalline state characterized by a perfectly regular arrangement of the equilibrium positions of the atoms leads to states not only relatively stable or durably unstable, but also, if pushed to an extreme, to absolutely unstable states, corresponding to vanishing and even negative values of the compressibility and rigidity modulus (and also of the specific heat at constant pressure).

From the point of view of the traditional theory this means that the crystalline structure, being maintained in a wholly unaltered form up to a certain melting point $T$, $V$ (or $T, p$), must suddenly collapse and be replaced in a discontinuous way by an amorphous structure, characteristic of the liquid state, the melting point being derived by equating the thermodynamical potential of the 'perfect' crystal $\phi_1$ to that of the 'perfect' liquid.

In reality we are not only allowed, but even compelled to consider a number of intermediate states, obtained by a gradual change of the degree of order in the structure both of the crystal and of the liquid. The scheme of isotherms $p$, $V$ and isobars $S$, $T$ which has been introduced in § 6 to describe the melting process as a virtually continuous transformation from the crystalline to the amorphous state involves the use of these 'interpolated' states, in conjunction with states extrapolated with respect to the classical 'perfect' structure of a crystal in the direction of increasing values of the temperature or the specific volume, and with respect to the classical 'perfect' liquid in the opposite directions. These extrapolated states, smoothed by the introduction of a variable degree of order, can obviously be joined together by a continuous curve.

The above scheme is, of course, very incomplete. In attempting to make it more complete we must bear in mind, however, the fact that absolutely unstable states (corresponding to $\partial p/\partial V > 0$ or $\partial S/\partial T < 0$) which it introduces as intermediate states, along with others which are relatively stable, must be considered as a theoretical artifice only, and not as an observable reality, since they have an infinitely short duration. It would be possible to trace the corresponding unstable portions of the isotherms or isobars in a number of different ways, corresponding to various choices in the character of the variation of the degree of order, under the condition that all these curves should be bisected into two equal halves by the corresponding horizontal line $p =$ const. or vertical line $T =$ const.

Such an ambiguity vanishes when, instead of the absolutely unstable interpolated states, the relatively stable extrapolated states of a crystal or of an amorphous body are considered. This refers in particular to the states of a supercooled (or overcompressed) liquid, which under certain conditions, depending on the chemical structure of the molecules, can be gradually transformed into a practically absolutely stable amorphous glass.

Since in the classical statistics the velocities give an additive contribution to the free energy which is independent of the configuration and accordingly irrelevant for the definition of the type of aggregation or chemical composition, we can limit ourselves to a consideration of the configurational part of the free energy only. The restriction of the range of integration to states corresponding to a perfect crystalline structure does not present any difficulties, as soon as the type and size of the lattice, formed by the equilibrium positions of the atoms, has been chosen (as a matter of fact, various choices must be allowed for, and the corresponding free energies determined as functions not only of the volume, but also of the shape of the body, as defined by the components of the strain tensor in such a way that the stress components should vanish or assume given values).

## 9. Liquids in the Solid-like State

We meet a more difficult situation when we wish to define the integration range of the configurational space, corresponding to a homogeneous amorphous structure of the body, formed by the same atoms. And this is the only general way of obtaining an equation of state applicable not only to ordinary liquids, but also to supercooled liquids and, in particular, to glasses.

The structure of a liquid (amorphous) body can be specified by a relative density function $\rho(r)$ which has been introduced in § 4, the product $\rho(r)4\pi r^2\,dr$ representing the (probable) number of atomic centres at a distance between $r$ and $r+dr$ from one of them. Such a function can also be used for the description of a crystalline structure. In this case, however, it must have a very special character, becoming discontinuous for $T = 0$. We can thus restrict ourselves to the description of the amorphous state by requiring that this function should remain continuous for all values of $T$ (as well as of the specific volume $v$).

With the help of the function $\rho$ it is an easy matter to calculate the (potential) energy of the body, which, if surface effects are neglected, and if the atoms are supposed to remain fixed, is equal to

$$W^0 = \tfrac{1}{2}N\int\limits_0^\infty U(r)\rho(r)4\pi r^2\,dr. \tag{35}$$

Since the function $\rho$ gives the average distribution of the atoms, account must be taken of the density fluctuations due to the heat motion. Inasmuch as the latter can be represented by vibrations about equilibrium positions (whose average distribution is defined by the function $\rho(r)$) or, more exactly, by a superposition of normal vibrations in the form of longitudinal and transverse waves, as in the case of a solid (crystalline) body, the additional potential energy due to the density fluctuations is reduced, for not too low temperatures, to the classical expression $\frac{3}{2}NkT$.

The total energy of the body $W$ including the kinetic energy of the heat motion is thus reduced to $W^0+3NkT$.

We thus see that so far as the calculation of the energy of a liquid body is concerned, we need not consider the distribution of the atoms $\Gamma$ in the $6N$-dimensional phase space or $R$ in the $3N$-dimensional configuration space, and can limit ourselves to the determination of the relative density function $\rho$ in ordinary space.

This can be done approximately by Kirkwood's method, described in § 5 and based on the somewhat objectionable application of Boltzmann's principle. A more satisfactory and general method would consist in defining the entropy of the body $S$ as a *functional* of $\rho$ and determining the latter from the minimum condition for the free energy $F = W-TS$, which must yield an integral equation for $\rho$.

It is easier to state this programme than to carry it out, for there seems to be no simple method for finding the entropy as a functional of $\rho$. The configurational part of the entropy can be directly defined by the corresponding extension $R$ in the configuration space, according to the formula $S = k \log R$. The problem is thus reduced to the determination of the relation between $R$ and $\rho$.

No approach to its solution is known at present. We shall limit ourselves therefore to a few remarks concerning the approximate calculation of the energy and entropy of amorphous bodies as functions of the temperature, volume, and shearing strain, and the resulting equation of state.

The energy can be calculated with the help of equation (35) if the density function is determined experimentally (from an analysis of X-ray diagrams) or if the approximate expressions for it given by the theory of Prins or of Kirkwood are used.

An estimate of the entropy of a liquid can be obtained with the help of the concept of free volume over which the centres of the atoms can be distributed in the same way as the point-like particles of an ideal gas. If the volume of the latter is equal to $V$, then, according to the general definition of entropy,

$$S = -\frac{\partial F}{\partial T}, \qquad F = -kT \log Z,$$

$$Z = \frac{1}{N!\,h^{3N}} \int e^{-W/kT}\, d\Gamma = \frac{1}{N!\,h^{3N}} V^N (2\pi mkT)^{\frac{3}{2}N},$$

or simply

$$S = k \log \frac{\Gamma}{N!\,h^{3N}},$$

where $\Gamma = V^N(\frac{4}{3}\pi g_{\max}^3)^N$, $g_{\max}$ denoting the maximum value of the momentum when the total kinetic energy of the gas $\frac{3}{2}NkT$ is supposed to be concentrated in a single molecule, we get, using Stirling's formula $N! \approx (N/e)^N$:

$$S = Nk \log \frac{Ve(2\pi mkT)^{\frac{3}{2}}}{Nh^3}.$$

Replacing here $V/N$ by the free volume of the liquid $\omega$, referred to one atom, we get

$$S_{\text{liq}} = Nk \log \frac{\omega e(2\pi mkT)^{\frac{3}{2}}}{h^3}. \tag{36}$$

The free volume of the liquid $V_f = N\omega$ can be defined approximately as the difference between the actual volume of the liquid and that of the corresponding solid (in the absence of external pressure).

Comparing the preceding expression with the entropy of a solid (crystalline body)

$$S_{\text{sol}} = 3Nk\log\frac{kT}{h\bar{\nu}} = Nk\log\left(\frac{kT}{h\bar{\nu}}\right)^3,$$

we obtain the following approximate expression for the entropy of melting:

$$\Delta S = S_{\text{liq}} - S_{\text{sol}} = kN\log \omega e\bar{\nu}^3\left(\frac{2\pi m}{kT}\right)^{\frac{3}{2}},$$

or, if $\bar{\nu}$ is replaced by $(1/2\pi)\sqrt{(f_s/m)}$,

$$\Delta S = R\log \omega e(f_s/2\pi kT)^{\frac{3}{2}} \quad (R = kN). \tag{36 a}$$

The ratio $kT/f_s$ is equal to the mean square of the amplitude of the thermal vibrations of an atom in the solid body. The quantity $(2\pi kT/f_s)^{\frac{3}{2}}$ can thus be defined as the average volume swept by the centre of an atom in the solid state, owing to the thermal vibrations about its equilibrium position.

If the liquid is treated as a solid body with irregularly distributed equilibrium positions, then its entropy can be defined by the same formula

$$S_{\text{liq}} = R\log(kT/h\nu_l)^3 \tag{37}$$

as that of the solid, with a different (smaller) value of the average vibration frequency $\bar{\nu}_e$. Replacing the latter by $(1/2\pi)\sqrt{(f_l/m)}$, we get in this case

$$\Delta_1 S = R\log(f_s/f_l)^{\frac{3}{2}} = 3R\log(\bar{\nu}_s/\bar{\nu}_l). \tag{37 a}$$

This expression could be identified with (36 a) if the free volume of the liquid was defined as $(2\pi kT/f_l)^{\frac{3}{2}}$. In reality, however, the expression (37 a) represents but that part of the entropy of melting, which is connected with a variation of the frequency of the atomic vibrations about their equilibrium positions. In order to obtain the total value of the entropy of fusion $\Delta S = S_{\text{liq}} - S_{\text{sol}}$, we must add to $\Delta_1 S$ a term $\Delta_2 S$, corresponding to the increase of the average distance between the equilibrium positions (i.e. to the actual increase of the free volume) and—what is especially important—to the loss of long-range order in the distribution of these positions. From the point of view of the Lennard-Jones and Devonshire theory of melting the latter effect is determined by the formula

$$\Delta S_2 = R\log\frac{N!}{[\frac{1}{2}N!]^2}.$$

Equating this expression to the ratio between the latent heat and the temperature of fusion we obtain a result practically identical with Trouton's rule.

Eyring† has attempted to define the entropy of fusion as the increase of entropy due to the fact that in the solid state the motion of the individual atoms is restricted to the corresponding individual cells with a volume $v = V/N$, whereas in the liquid each atom can be found in any one of the $N$ cells. Treating the atoms as free to move within the space assigned to them, we get in this case for the configurational part of the entropy of the solid the expression $kN \log V/N$, while for the liquid it is equal to $k \log V^N/N! \approx kN \log Ve/N$, which corresponds to $\Delta S = R$. Eyring's argument is based on the wholly unwarranted assumption that the atoms of a solid body are separated from each other by absolutely rigid compartments. This assumption ignores the fact that a mixing up of all the atoms, by the mechanism of self-diffusion, takes place in the solid (crystalline) state as well as in the liquid one (although at a much slower rate, which is of no importance from the thermodynamic point of view). If Eyring's theory were correct, then a transition from the liquid to the solid amorphous state, by way of supercooling, would be accompanied by the same decrease of entropy as crystallization, which is obviously wrong.

The melting, or rather amorphization, entropy $\Delta S$ considered above is not a constant quantity, but varies with the temperature and pressure.

Bridgman's experiments show that the bulk modulus of liquids sharply increases (by a factor up to 10 and even 15) when the pressure is increased to a few thousand atmospheres, preserving thereafter a constant magnitude of the same order as in solid bodies. This means that at such pressures the free space in the liquids which is due to the irregular arrangement of their particles and which constitutes one of their characteristic distinctions from the crystalline bodies, disappears or, at least, is reduced to a small value.

The compressibility of the liquids $\kappa = -(1/V)(\partial V/\partial p)$ can be represented apparently as the sum of two parts: of a 'geometrical' part, due to a simultaneous contraction of all the intermolecular distances of the body under the influence of an external pressure, and of a 'structural' compressibility $\kappa'$, which depends upon a variation in the relative arrangement of the molecules in the sense of an increase of the degree of regularity and consequently of compactness. Introducing the thermodynamic potential of the liquid $\phi = F+pV$ and treating it, and consequently that part of it $-T\Delta_2 S$ which is connected with the structural entropy, as a function of the pressure (instead of the volume), we can

† Eyring, *J. Chem. Phys.* **4**, 283 (1936).

represent the structural part of the compressibility coefficient of the liquid by the formula

$$\kappa' = \frac{T}{V}\frac{\partial^2 \Delta_2 S}{\partial p^2}.$$

Under ordinary conditions it must be a few times larger than the geometrical or purely elastic part, which depends on the variation of the potential energy of the body under the assumption of a constant structure (i.e. a degree of order). The separation of the total compressibility of a liquid body into these two components can be carried out experimentally with the help of high-frequency ultrasonic vibrations (see Ch. IV, § 5).

A similar remark refers to the specific heat of liquid bodies. At low pressures it must be larger than at high ones by an amount

$$\Delta C_p = T\frac{\partial \Delta S}{\partial T},$$

which depends on the increase of the amorphization entropy with a rise of the temperature.

Apart from these complications, the equation of state of a liquid body can be derived from the same expression for the free energy

$$F = E(V) - TS_{\text{liq}}$$

with $S_{\text{liq}} = 3R\log kT/h\bar{\nu}_l$ as in the case of a solid amorphous or crystalline body. It should be mentioned that the mean vibration frequency $\bar{\nu}$ is usually determined, starting from Debye's simplified conception of a solid body, as an isotropic (i.e. amorphous) continuous medium, whose thermal motion can be represented as a superposition of longitudinal and transverse elastic waves, propagated with a velocity independent of the wave-length and of the direction. Hence it is seen that Debye's approximate form of the theory refers rather to liquids—especially in the supercooled state—than to crystals.

It is thus clear that the equation of state derived from the preceding expression for the free energy can be applied with sufficient approximation both to amorphous solids and to liquid bodies, near the crystallization point.

In doing this the following corrections to the theory of the preceding sections must be introduced.

(1) In the case of an irregular (amorphous) structure of the body the frequency cannot be such a simple decreasing function of the volume as in the case of a crystalline structure. The increase of the *average* value of the interatomic distances can take place without an increase

of the distances between the equilibrium positions within the individual atomic groupings which arise in a liquid as a result of local and transient ruptures. Hence the frequency $\bar{\nu}_l$ must not tend to zero with increase of the volume, as in the case of crystalline bodies; accordingly, the thermal pressure need not increase with $V$, but for large $V$'s must decrease, approximately as $1/(V-b)$.

(2) With increase of $V$ and $T$ the self-diffusion in a liquid body becomes more and more important, the fraction of the atoms which at any given instant are in a transition state between the neighbouring equilibrium positions steadily increasing. These atoms form, as it were, the 'gas fraction' of the liquid, for in the vicinity of a position corresponding to a local maximum of the potential energy they must move in a way similar to that corresponding to the gaseous state. So long as this 'gas-fraction' of the liquid remains insignificant, the liquid behaves as a 'solid-like' body; in the contrary case it becomes 'gas-like'.

(3) The usual thermodynamical theory of simple liquid bodies specifies their state by one geometrical variable only—the (specific) volume; whereas in the case of a solid body besides the volume the *shape* is also taken into account and specified, along with the volume, by six components of the symmetrical strain tensor (or its three principal components, representing the relative extensions in three mutually perpendicular directions). Now between a solid amorphous body, i.e. a supercooled liquid, and a liquid in a state of absolute thermodynamical equilibrium, no distinction of a qualitative character can be made. Hence it is clear that dealing with such a liquid we are entitled and, even more than that, compelled to take into account not only the volume deformations but also shearing strains, associating the latter not with viscous forces, as is usually done, but with the corresponding elastic stresses. It will be shown in the next chapter that ordinary liquids are distinguished from solid amorphous bodies only by the relative smallness of their 'relaxation time', i.e. the time required for the disappearance of shearing stresses of an elastic nature. This circumstance does not, however, exclude the possibility of visualizing such stresses, and of connecting these with the corresponding elastic strains by the usual equations of thermodynamical theory, e.g. $\tau = -\partial F/\partial \theta$, provided that the length of time involved in the phenomena under consideration (the period of vibration, for instance, in the case of transverse waves) is small compared with the relaxation time, during which the body behaves practically as a solid, and simultaneously large compared with the time required for the establishment of an equilibrium distribution

of the velocities and positions of the atoms in the body supposed to be deprived of fluidity.

Likewise, although a liquid under a negative pressure cannot be considered as thermodynamically stable in the absolute sense of this term, since its free energy is diminished if it is allowed to break up by a process of cavitation (with the formation of a vapour bubble), yet this state can be relatively very stable, so that we are fully entitled to extend the usual thermodynamic treatment of liquids to the region of negative pressures (see Ch. VII).

## 10. Hole Theory of the Liquid State

The main difference in the behaviour of liquids at temperatures lying near the crystallization point from that of the corresponding crystalline bodies is due, under ordinary small pressures, to their relatively large specific volume. The latter increases on melting by about 10 per cent., i.e. by an amount which at ordinary temperatures corresponds to the theoretical value of the tensile strength of solid bodies (in practice they break down at much smaller extensions, which lie within the range of the validity of Hooke's law).

This circumstance points to the fact that the homogeneity of a liquid body is to a certain extent but an apparent one, the liquid body being in reality permeated by a large number of surfaces of rupture, which in the absence of external forces do not have an opportunity to develop into a macroscopic size, but are spontaneously closed up in certain places while arising in neighbouring ones, and constituting at any given instant a system of microscopic cavities in the form of holes, cracks, etc., in the whole volume of the liquid.

If this conception corresponds to reality, then the free volume of a liquid body (equal, roughly speaking, to the excess of its volume over that of the corresponding crystal at the temperature of absolute zero and in the absence of external pressure) is not distributed uniformly between all its molecules as in the case of crystals, but is concentrated in the form of separate micro-cavities, which play, as it were, the role of vacuum atoms or 'quanta'. The appearance and disappearance of such micro-cavities, which in the sequel will be called simply 'holes', is realized as a result of fluctuations connected with the heat motion of the liquid.

In the usual theory of the density fluctuations in solid and liquid bodies such variations of the density are only considered as are connected with a general increase or decrease of the intermolecular distances, distorting the homogeneity of the body in small volumes, without, however, destroying it in a more radical way. We shall see below (Ch. VII) that in every macroscopically homogeneous body there exist along with such 'homophase' fluctuations, 'heterophase' fluctuations leading to the appearance of a new phase (for example, of the solid or gaseous phase within the liquid one).

The appearance in a liquid of 'holes' can be regarded as a particular case of such heterophase fluctuations. These holes can be treated as gas bubbles in the case when they are large enough to accommodate a sufficiently large number of vapour molecules. Such a condition can actually exist in a liquid near the boiling-point only; in other cases the cavities arising in them as a result of thermal fluctuations are too small to justify their identification with vapour bubbles. They must, accordingly, be treated as empty; the fluctuations giving rise to them can therefore be termed 'cavitation fluctuations'.

From the point of view of the usual thermodynamic theory which has to do with average values of different quantities for sufficiently long time intervals, the distinction between these cavitation fluctuations and ordinary density fluctuations is irrelevant. More than that, the very existence of density fluctuations is here ignored and the free volume of the liquid is supposed to be distributed uniformly between all the molecules, i.e. to be connected with a general increase of the average distance between neighbouring molecules. This conception is certainly correct so long as the average values of the distances for very long intervals of time are concerned. If, however, the instantaneous, and not the average, distribution of the molecules of the liquid is considered, the notion of a uniform distribution is substantially incorrect. According to the cavitation theory, the distances between the neighbouring molecules of the liquid outside the regions of rupture remain the same as in a solid body, being, however, sharply increased within these regions.

This point of view cannot, of course, be perfectly correct. In reality the free volume of a liquid body must be distributed *partly* in a discontinuous way in the form of separate holes, and partly in a continuous way in the form of a general increase of the average distances between the particles in those regions which preserve their homogeneity. This state of affairs is quite similar to that found in the case of crystals where the increase of the volume on heating (or on extension if $T > 0$) is realized partly by an increase of the lattice constant, i.e. of the size of the interstices, and partly by an increase of the number of vacant sites, i.e. of the atomic holes. Whereas, however, in the case of crystals the increase of volume is due mainly to the first of these two causes, in the case of liquids, according to the above theory, the main role is played by the second one.

One more distinctive feature of liquids must be noted here. In the case of crystals we have to do with 'holes' of two perfectly definite kinds, namely with interstices and with vacant sites, the term 'hole' being applied by us to the latter only. In the case of liquids the notions of regular sites and interstices become meaningless. Accordingly, the notion of 'holes' as vacant sites loses its physical meaning, as well as the distinction between this type of hole and that corresponding to interstitial positions.

The two notions must be replaced in this case by a single notion of holes as more or less widened gaps between the molecules. These gaps have neither a definite size nor a definite shape; they can spontaneously arise, increase, dwindle down, and disappear; they can also move from one place to another by closing at some places and opening at neighbouring ones (just as in the case of movable holes in crystals).

The preceding conception about holes in liquids has been advanced independently by a number of authors.† In the most radical form it was developed in 1935 by Altar, who treated the liquid as a system of freely moving holes, with respect to which the molecules play the role of a framework.‡

Similar ideas have been set forth by Fürth,§ who treated the holes in a liquid as small vapour bubbles (ignoring the fact that they are on the average too small to contain even a single molecule of the gas phase) and attempted, with a very poor degree of success, to apply this conception to the quantitative interpretation of a number of fundamental properties of liquids: their compressibility, thermal expansion, viscosity, and thermal conductivity. Before considering these applications we shall investigate in more detail the processes connected with the opening and closing of holes in a liquid.

In the first place it must be remembered that both in a liquid and in a solid body all the interstices ('gaps') between the atoms or molecules, even in the absence of marked density fluctuations, must, strictly speaking, be treated as holes of embryonal size ($\delta$). The number of

† The first mention seems to have been made by the present writer in 1926. See also the papers by Eyring and co-workers, *J. Chem. Phys.* 1935–6. In these papers Eyring erroneously treats the holes in a liquid as analogous to vacant sites in a crystal lattice.

‡ Altar, *J. Chem. Phys.* **5**, 577 (1937).

§ R. Fürth, *Proc. Camb. Phil. Soc.* **37**, 252 (1941).

such embryonic holes is obviously equal to the number of particles. Since holes of a larger size (micro-cavities) can arise only by way of growth of embryonic holes, the total number of holes of various sizes in a liquid can always be identified with the number $N$ of molecules.

In the second place, the cavitation fluctuations in a liquid can be regarded as due to a small stability—or even instability—of a regular arrangement of the molecules in view of the large value of the average distance between them. This circumstance has been discussed by us in detail on the basis of a three-atomic model of a solid or liquid body. Inasmuch as the melting of a crystal is due to the instability of a regular distribution of its particles, it seems quite natural that in the resulting liquid body these particles tend to be distributed in a non-uniform way, forming more or less compact 'bunches', separated from each other by fluctuating cracks, or to be more exact—a relatively compact mass with a density but slightly below that of the corresponding crystal, permeated by a system of fluctuating fissures.

The preceding 'hole' conception of the liquid state is obviously applicable in the region of not too elevated temperatures and pressures only. In the vicinity of the critical point the average density of the liquid becomes so low (about 2·5 times lower than that of the solid body) that the notion of holes becomes meaningless, just as in the case of the gaseous state (in the latter case the holes coalesce into a vacuum, which plays the role of the dispersing medium instead of the disperse phase). Besides, the molecular forces become immaterial near the critical point and can ensure neither a regular nor even a compact arrangement of the molecules.

If, on the other hand, the liquid is subjected to a very strong compression at a relatively low temperature, it must either crystallize or lose its 'porosity', acquiring thus new properties, which are characteristic of such a compact structure and are essentially different from those connected with the ordinary 'porous' state.

These considerations are in agreement with Bridgman's experiments on the dependence of the compressibility of liquids on the external pressure. At low pressures the bulk modulus is a few times (up to 10 and even 15) smaller than in the case of the corresponding solid bodies. This excessive compressibility vanishes, however, when the pressure is increased to 1,500–2,000 atmospheres, the compressibility modulus of liquids reaching, under such conditions, a value of the same magnitude as in solid bodies.

The excessive compressibility of liquids at low pressures is ascribed by Bridgman to their 'slack'. From our point of view this slack means nothing but 'porosity'—the presence of a large number of fluctuating fissures or holes.

Let us now investigate the quantitative conclusions for the thermodynamic (equilibrium) properties of liquids under normal temperatures and pressures, which are implied in the hypothesis of their 'porous' structure.

For the sake of simplicity we shall neglect the circumstance that the free volume of a liquid is partially realized by its general expansion (in the more compact portions) with respect to the solid state. In this case the free volume $V-V_0$, where $V_0$ is the smallest volume, equal to the constant $b$ in van der Waals's equation, can be represented in the form $V-V_0 = N(\bar{v}-v_0)$, where $v_0$ is the smallest volume of the holes and $\bar{v}$ their average volume at a given temperature $T$ and pressure $p$.

The average size of the holes and their statistical distribution over the scale of sizes can be determined by treating these holes as cavities in a *continuous* medium with a constant density. The formation of such a cavity ('local rupture') is connected with the expenditure of a certain energy $W$, depending on the size and shape of the cavity. For the sake of simplicity all the cavities will be treated as spheres with a variable radius $r$. Under such conditions the number of holes with a radius lying in the range between $r$ and $r+dr$ can be represented by the formula

$$dN_r = Ne^{-W(r)/kT}\phi(r)\,dr,$$

where $\phi(r)$ is a certain function of $r$, which cannot be determined unambiguously (see below).

If the energy $W(r)$ is identified with the surface energy (or free energy) of the spherical cavity $4\pi\sigma r^2$, where $\sigma$ is the surface tension of the liquid, the following expression for its average value is obtained:

$$\overline{W} = \int_0^\infty e^{-W/kT}W\phi\,dr \Big/ \int_0^\infty e^{-W/kT}\phi\,dr = -\frac{\partial}{\partial\alpha}\log I,$$

where $\alpha = 1/kT$ and $I = \int_0^\infty e^{-\alpha W}\phi(r)\,dr$.

Putting $\phi = \text{const.}$ we get $\overline{W} = \frac{1}{2}kT$ which corresponds to the expression

$$\bar{r} = \frac{1}{8\pi}\sqrt{(kT/\sigma)}$$

for the average value of the radius. If the function $\phi$ is assumed to be proportional to the $s$th power of the radius, $\overline{W}$ and $\overline{r^2}$ are found to increase $s$-fold with respect to their value for $\phi = \text{const.}$

Fürth (just as does Altar) treats the holes in a liquid as the particles of an ideal gas, possessing three degrees of freedom of translation motion and one inner degree of freedom, corresponding to a variation of their radius. This conception leads to $s = 9$. We shall not discuss it in more detail, for it is devoid of physical meaning, as follows *inter alia* from the impossibility of applying it to crystals. The actual motion of the holes in liquids, which is realized by a displacement of the particles surrounding them, must take place in the same jerk-like way as in crystals, the hole being closed in one place while a new hole arises in its vicinity. Each hole must remain stationary during a certain time, which increases with the lowering of the temperature according to the same formula $\tau = \tau_0 e^{U/kT}$ as in the case of atomic holes in crystals. The difference between crystals and liquids consists in the fact that in the former case the holes have a definite size and perform elementary displacements of a constant magnitude comparable with their size, whereas in the latter case the size of the holes (as well as their shape) is variable while their elementary displacements can be quite different from their linear dimensions.

Let us imagine, for example, a chain of identical balls with a diameter $a$, pressed against each other, and let us assume that a gap with a length $\Delta a$ arises in this chain between two neighbouring atoms. If one of them is moved towards the other over a distance $\Delta a$, this gap or 'hole' is moved in the opposite direction over the distance $a$. Similar relationships must hold in the case of three-dimensional aggregates. The average size of the holes, specified by their mean radius $r$, is, in principle, quite independent of the average size $a$ of the molecules enframing them, coinciding with $a$ with respect to the order of magnitude in the case of very small (monatomic) molecules only, but remaining small compared with $a$ in the case of large molecules.

From this point of view the preceding calculation gives a fairly accurate idea about the size of the holes, stressing, in particular, the fact that this size is practically independent of the size of the molecules; at room temperature the mean value of the radius of the holes as determined by the formula $\bar{r} = \sqrt{(kT/\sigma)}$ turns out to be of the order $2.10^{-8}$ cm. (for $\sigma = 100$ dynes/cm.). It should be noted, however, that this value hardly differs from the normal value of the distance between neighbouring molecules, or, more exactly, between the adjacent regions of their surfaces. Under such conditions it would be meaningless to talk about holes, cracks, fissures, etc. The preceding result is explained by the fact that the surface energy of an embryonic crack or hole must in general be much smaller than its normal value $\sigma_0$, corresponding to a free surface. If the potential energy of molecular forces is assumed to be inversely proportional to the sixth power of the distance (as is actually the case for ordinary van der Waals forces), then the surface energy of a crack with a width $h$ is equal per unit area to $\sigma = \sigma_0(1-\delta^2/h^2)$, where $\delta$ is the minimum value of $h$ ($10^{-8}$ cm.; see Ch. VI, § 5). Applying this formula to the case of a spherical hole we get

$$W = 4\pi r^2\sigma_0\left(1-\frac{\delta^2}{r^2}\right) = 4\pi\sigma_0(r^2-\delta^2).$$

This correction does not alter essentially the estimates of the average size of the holes obtained above; putting $\phi$ = const. $r$, for example, we find $\overline{r^2} = \delta^2+kT/4\pi\sigma_0$ and accordingly $W = kT$, as before.

The latter result, as will be seen below, is in disagreement with the experimental data on the temperature dependence of the viscosity of liquids. These data can be explained on the basis of the hole theory of liquids only in the case where it is assumed that the formation of a hole requires a certain *minimum* amount of work $U$, practically independent of the temperature, as in the case of crystals. If the holes are treated as cavitation fluctuations, then this result can be obtained on the assumption that their radius must exceed a certain minimum value $r_0$, corresponding to an activation energy $U = 4\pi r_0^2\sigma$. The reason for the non-existence (or instability) of holes of smaller size remains, however, unclear.

Since under such conditions the size of the holes must lie more or less close to the smallest one, and the number of holes must be equal to a small fraction, of the order of $e^{-U/kT}$ of the total number of molecules, the additional 'free' volume of the liquid must be given by the expression

$$V-V_0 = Ne^{-U/kT}\Delta v \tag{38}$$

of the same form as in the case of solid bodies; here $\Delta v$ denotes the smallest volume of a hole equal to $\frac{4}{3}\pi(r_0^3-\delta^3)$.

If the liquid is subjected to a pressure $p$, then the activation energy $U$ can be represented in the form

$$U = U_0+p\,\Delta v,$$

where $U_0$ is the value of $U$ at $p = 0$.

In the region of not excessively high temperatures and pressures the behaviour of a liquid can thus be described by the following 'equation of state':

$$V = V_0[1+n\,\Delta v\, e^{-(U_0+p\Delta v)/kT}],$$

where $n = N/V$ is the number of molecules per unit volume at $T = 0$ and $p = 0$. This equation refers to liquids in the ordinary 'porous' state, and explains their abnormally large compressibility

$$\kappa = -\frac{1}{V_0}\left(\frac{\partial V}{\partial p}\right)_T$$

(with respect to solid bodies) and also their large expansion coefficient $\alpha = \frac{1}{V_0}\left(\frac{\partial V}{\partial T}\right)_p$.

The former is found to be given by the expression

$$\kappa = n\,\Delta v\, e^{-(U_0+p\Delta v)/kT}\frac{\Delta v}{kT},$$

i.e.
$$\kappa = \frac{V-V_0}{V_0}\frac{\Delta v}{kT}, \tag{38 a}$$

and the latter by the expression $\alpha = n\,\Delta v\, e^{-U/kT}U/kT^2$, that is,

$$\alpha = \frac{V-V_0}{V_0}\frac{U}{kT^2}. \tag{38 b}$$

The increase of the number of holes $Ne^{-U/kT}$ with rise of temperature at constant pressure must entail an additional value of the specific heat of the liquid (with respect to the corresponding solid), namely $\Delta C_p = U\frac{d}{dT}Ne^{-U/kT}$, which amounts per unit volume to

$$\Delta C_p = \frac{V-V_0}{V_0\,\Delta v}\frac{U^2}{kT^2}. \tag{38 c}$$

Comparing this expression with the preceding ones we obtain the following relation:

$$\Delta C_p = \alpha\frac{U}{\Delta v} = \frac{\kappa}{T}\left(\frac{U}{\Delta v}\right)^2.$$

These relations are in qualitative agreement with the experimental data.†

It must be noted, however, that similar relations are obtained in that case if the free volume of the liquid is assumed to be distributed uniformly between all the molecules. The important advantage of the hole theory of liquids becomes apparent when such phenomena are considered, as are connected with *non-equilibrium* states, and especially

† Thus, for example, the preceding expression for $\alpha$ yields values of the correct order of magnitude if the ratio $U_0/kT$ is assumed to lie between 1 and 10 (for $T = 300$–1,000) while the free volume $V-b$ is equal to a fraction lying between 1/100 and 1/1,000 of the total volume.

the phenomena of diffusion (self-diffusion) and internal friction. The corresponding questions will be discussed in the next chapter (§ 4).

## 11. The Gas-like State of Liquids

The state of a liquid at high temperatures lying near the critical point is essentially different from its state at low temperatures, near the crystallization point, in this respect, that the role of cohesive forces is diminished, the liquid becoming accordingly more and more 'gas-like'. A more or less satisfactory theory of the thermal and mechanical properties of a liquid in this region can be obtained with the help of an approximative method which has already been applied by us in § 5 in the investigation of crystals, and which consists in replacing the problem of the motion of $N$ particles under their mutual influence by the problem of the motion of each separate particle in the field of the remaining $N-1$ particles, under the assumption that they remain fixed in their mean positions. This method, which has received an extensive development in modern atomic physics (where it has been generalized to allow for the motion of the other particles and is usually referred to as the method of self-consistent field), has recently been applied to the theory of compressed gases and critical phenomena by Lennard-Jones and Devonshire.† Since in compressed gases—or liquids at an elevated temperature—there remains practically no trace of crystalline structure, the field of force exerted on each atom‡ by the surrounding atoms can be treated as spherically symmetrical, and can be identified with the average field, corresponding to an equal probability of all the positions of these atoms on a sphere of a given radius, the centre of which coincides with the average position of the 'movable' atom.

Such an averaging is justified, not only by the resulting simplification of the calculations, but also by the fact that the field in which each atom is moving and which is created by the surrounding atoms must on the average be isotropic, i.e. spherically symmetrical.

Each atom is thus situated in a spherical cell with a certain radius $a$ which the above authors identify with interatomic distance in a 'close-packed' cubical arrangement having the same specific volume (the number of nearest neighbours being in this case twelve). Since the edge of an elementary cubic cell, containing four atoms, is equal to $a\sqrt{2}$,

† *Proc. Roy. Soc.* A, **163**, 53 (1937).

‡ We shall be concerned in this section with monatomic liquids only and shall treat the atoms as mass points.

we get for the volume per atom $v = \frac{V}{N} = \frac{(a\sqrt{2})^3}{4} = \frac{a^3}{\sqrt{2}}$. This figure is practically equal to, though slightly smaller than, the volume of a sector of a spherical shell with a radius $a$, $\frac{1}{6}\pi a^3$.

The potential energy of an atom moving in such a spherical shell depends on its distance $r$ from the centre of the latter, and on its radius $a$ in approximately the same way as in the case of the triatomic model with fixed end-atoms, which has been investigated in § 7. This potential energy will be denoted in the sequel by $U_a(r)$. It is equal to the product of the number of nearest neighbours, $z = 12$, and the average value of the potential energy $U(\mathbf{r}-\mathbf{a})$ of the given atom, situated at a distance $r$ from the centre of the cell, with respect to one of the neighbouring atoms on the assumption that all the positions of the latter on the surface of the cell are equally probable.

Since the energy $U(\mathbf{r}-\mathbf{a})$ depends on the distance

$$|\mathbf{a}-\mathbf{r}| = \sqrt{(a^2+r^2-2ar\cos\theta)}$$

only, where $\theta$ is the angle between $\mathbf{r}$ and $\mathbf{a}$ we have

$$U_a(r) = \tfrac{1}{2}z \int_0^{\pi} U\{\sqrt{(a^2+r^2-2ar\cos\theta)}\}\sin\theta\, d\theta,$$

or

$$U_a(r) = \tfrac{1}{2}z \int_{-1}^{+1} U\{\sqrt{(a^2+r^2-2ar\xi)}\}\, d\xi. \tag{39}$$

Putting for example

$$U = -\frac{A}{r^m}+\frac{B}{r^n} \quad (m < n)$$

we get

$$U_a(r) = \frac{z}{2}\left\{\frac{B}{(n-2)a^n}\frac{a}{r}\left[\left(1-\frac{r}{a}\right)^{-n+2}-\left(1+\frac{r}{a}\right)^{-n+2}\right]-\right.$$

$$\left.-\frac{A}{(m-2)a^m}\frac{a}{r}\left[\left(1-\frac{r}{a}\right)^{-m+2}-\left(1+\frac{r}{a}\right)^{-m+2}\right]\right\}. \tag{39 a}$$

In so far as the mutual action between the atoms is replaced by the action on each of them of an (approximately) equivalent external field of force, the free energy of the whole system can be calculated in the same way as in the case of an ideal gas placed in the corresponding field.

It is thus equal to $N\psi$, where $\psi$ is defined by the equation

$$e^{-\psi/kT} = \frac{(2\pi mkT)^{\frac{3}{2}}}{h^3} \int_0^a e^{-U_a(r)/kT}\, 4\pi r^2\, dr.$$

Putting further $$\int_0^a e^{-U_a(r)/kT} 4\pi r^2\, dr = ve^{-\chi(v)/kT}, \tag{40}$$

where $v = \frac{4}{3}\pi a^3$ is the volume of the liquid per atom and $\chi$ a certain function of $v$, and which can be considered as the average value of the energy $U_n(r)$ for the whole cell, we get

$$\psi = -kT \log \frac{(2\pi mkT)^{\frac{3}{2}}}{h^3} + \chi(v). \tag{40 a}$$

The first term in this expression corresponds to an ideal gas in the absence of external forces and leads to the usual formula for the pressure of such a gas $p = kT/v = nkT$ $(n = N/V)$. The second term determines, consequently, the deviations in the behaviour of the liquid from the ideal gas laws.

With increase of $a$ the energy $U_a(r)$ tends to the constant limiting value 0, which corresponds to a free motion of all the atoms. It is clear, however, that the above approximation is not valid in the case of large $a$'s, for the conception of an atom locked in a spherical cell with impermeable walls formed by its neighbours can be applied when the latter are situated on the average sufficiently close to each other to prevent the central atom from escaping from the cell. Hence it follows that the equation (39 a) can be applied to such values of the volume only as do not exceed the volume of the body at $T = 0$ and $p = 0$ by more than a factor 2–3.

Since the evaluation of the function $\chi(v)$ with the help of (39) and (39 a) is a difficult task, and since the expression $U = -A/r^m + B/r^n$ for the potential energy of two atoms is nothing but a rough approximation, Lennard-Jones and Devonshire define this function by a similar formula:

$$\chi(v) = -\frac{\alpha}{v^\mu} + \frac{\beta}{v^\nu}, \tag{41}$$

where $\mu = \frac{1}{3}m$ and $\nu = \frac{1}{3}n$, choosing the coefficients $\alpha$ and $\beta$ in such a way that the minimum of this expression should correspond to $v = \frac{4}{3}\pi a^3$.

The resulting equation of state for the 'gas-like' liquid runs as follows:

$$p = \frac{kT}{v} - \frac{\partial \chi}{\partial v}, \tag{41 a}$$

that is, $$p = \frac{kT}{v} + \frac{\alpha\mu}{v^{\mu+1}} - \frac{\beta\nu}{v^{\nu+1}}. \tag{41 b}$$

The sum of the last two terms can be represented graphically by a curve of the same type as that illustrating the mutual potential energy of two atoms as a function of their distance apart. Adding to them the first (hyperbolic) term we obtain for different values of $T$ a set of curves similar to the isotherms of van der Waals with a characteristic oscillation of the pressure at temperatures lying below the critical value, determined by the condition $\partial p/\partial V = \partial^2 p/\partial V^2 = 0$,

$$T_c = \frac{\mu(\mu+1)}{kv_c^\mu}\alpha\left(1-\frac{\mu}{\nu}\right), \tag{42}$$

where
$$v_c = \left[\frac{\nu^2(\nu+1)}{\mu^2(\mu+1)}\frac{\beta}{\alpha}\right]^{1/(\nu-\mu)} \tag{42 a}$$

is the critical volume.

We get further
$$\frac{kT_c}{p_c v_c} = \left(1+\frac{1}{\mu}\right)\left(1+\frac{1}{\nu}\right) \equiv c, \tag{42 b}$$

where $p_c$ is the critical pressure.

Putting $\mu = 2$, i.e. $m = 6$ (which corresponds to dispersion forces of attraction between neon or argon atoms) and $\nu = 4$ ($n = 12$), we get $c = 1{\cdot}87$, whereas the actual value of this constant lies between 3 and 4.

Introducing further the normal value of the volume $v = v_m$, corresponding to the minimum of $\chi$ (i.e. $a = r_0$), we find $v_c/v_m = 1{\cdot}82$, whereas the critical volume exceeds that of the crystal at $T = 0$ by a factor of the order 2·2.

If the atoms of the substance under consideration are treated not as material points but as rigid spheres with a diameter $d$, the equation (40) for the function $\chi(v)$ must be replaced by

$$\int_0^a e^{-U_a(r)/kT} 4\pi r^2\, dr = \frac{4\pi}{3}(a-d)^3 e^{-\chi(v)/kT},$$

which corresponds to the following expression for the pressure:

$$p = \frac{kT}{v[1-(v_0/v)^{1/3}]} - \frac{\partial\chi}{\partial v}$$

instead of (41 a). This expression is very similar to that following from van der Waals's theory, especially if one puts $\chi = -a/v$.

It is clear that under such conditions the above approximation will be valid for such values of $a$ only as lie between $d$ and $2d$ (so that the regions corresponding to neighbouring atoms do not overlap).

It should be added that the formula $\chi = -\alpha/v$, following from van der Waals's theory, does not imply that the atoms are mutually attracted by a force inversely proportional to the cube of the distance. In reality it is independent of the actual law of force, inasmuch as the latter falls off with increase of the distance more rapidly than $1/r^3$, and follows from the assumption that all the relative positions of any two atoms, satisfying the condition $r > d$, are equally probable. This assumption can be justified in the case of rarefied gases only.

A closer examination of the isotherms, following from the equations (40) and (40 a), requires an allowance for the temperature dependence of the function $\chi(v)$, i.e. of the coefficients $\alpha$ and $\beta$. This leads to a considerable complication of the preceding theory and to a slight improvement of the agreement between theory and experiment. Thus, for example, Lennard-Jones and Devonshire obtain for the critical temperature of neon and argon the values 48 and 161° K., which are very close to the experimental values 44 and 150° K. respectively.

If the dependence of $\chi(v)$ on the temperature is neglected, there follows from (40 a) that the specific heat of a liquid at constant volume must have the same value $\frac{3}{2}k$ (i.e. 3 cal./mole) as that of an ideal gas. Hence it is clear that the temperature dependence of $\chi(v)$ must not be neglected if we wish to obtain a more or less accurate description of the thermodynamic properties of liquids.

If $a$ is not very different from $r_0$ and if the temperature is sufficiently low, each atom of a liquid body must remain in the neighbourhood of the centre of the corresponding cell. Since this centre corresponds to a minimum of the energy $U_a(r)$ we can put in this case

$$U_a(r) = U_a(0)+\tfrac{1}{2}fr^2,$$

just as in the case of a solid body, and consequently

$$\int\limits_0^a e^{-U_a(r)/kT}4\pi r^2\,dr \approx e^{-U_a(0)/kT}\int\limits_0^\infty e^{-\alpha r^2}4\pi r^2\,dr = e^{-U_a(0)/kT}\left(\frac{\pi}{\alpha}\right)^{\frac{3}{2}},$$

where $\alpha = f/2kT$, which gives

$$\psi = -kT\log\left[\frac{(2\pi mkT)^{\frac{3}{2}}}{h^3}\left(\frac{2\pi kT}{f}\right)^{\frac{3}{2}}\right]+U_a(0),$$

or, since $\sqrt{(f/m)} = 2\pi\nu$,

$$\psi = -3kT\log\frac{kT}{h\nu}+U_a(0).$$

We thus come back to the expression for the free energy which has already been obtained for the case of liquids in the solid-like state.

Of special interest (and practical importance for the understanding of the action of high explosives) is the question of the equation of state of strongly compressed gases at temperatures and pressures above the critical point. In this case the cohesive forces can practically be neglected, and the compressibility of the body is determined essentially by the repulsive forces which arise between the atoms when they are pressed close together. These forces can be described approximately as elastic forces due to the compressibility of the atoms (or molecules) themselves. In the usual simplest form of van der Waals's theory the molecules are dealt with as absolutely rigid spheres. This point of view leads to absurd results when applied to the supercritical region. As P. Weiss† has shown by the example of liquid helium, the relationship between volume and pressure at supercritical temperatures (up to 700° K.) can be described with the help of the van der Waals equation

$$\left(p+\frac{a}{v^2}\right)(v-b) = RT$$

only if the coefficients $a$ and $b$ are treated as decreasing functions of the temperature, the coefficient $a$ becoming *negative* at sufficiently high temperatures.

We give below a table of values of $a$ and $b$ obtained by Weiss. It can be seen from this table that the coefficient $b$, which characterizes the 'volume' of the particles, is likewise somewhat decreased with a rise of the temperature.

The above results are explained by the fact that the atoms on colliding with each other are mutually compressed to an extent which is larger the larger the kinetic energy of their thermal agitation. Their mutual action can be described under such conditions as a repulsion, characterized partly by $b$ and by a positive internal pressure, corresponding to negative values of the coefficient $a$.

TABLE IV

| *Temperature range* | $a.10^6$ | $b.10^6$ |
|---|---|---|
| 400°, 300° C. | −240 | 355 |
| 300°, 200° C. | −267 | 344 |
| 100°, 50° C. | −145 | 407 |
| 0°, −50° C. | −40 | 491 |
| −50°, −100° C. | −6 | 520 |
| −150°, −183° C. | +35 | 592 |
| −252°, −258° C. | +57 | 663 |

† P. Weiss, *Jubilé de M. Brillouin*, Paris, 1936.

# IV

# HEAT MOTION IN LIQUIDS AND THEIR MECHANICAL PROPERTIES

## 1. Heat Motion in Simple Liquids

In the preceding chapter we have established the fact that in the neighbourhood of the crystallization point the heat motion in liquid bodies must have the same character as in solids, i.e. consist, in its main features, in the vibration of particles (atoms) about certain equilibrium positions.

This conclusion leads at first sight to a contradiction. There exists between crystals and liquids a sharp difference, the former being rigid (i.e. capable of elastic resistance to shearing stress), while the latter are fluid. The rigidity of crystals is in full agreement with the conception that the heat motion of the atoms reduces to vibrations of small amplitude about invariable equilibrium positions. This conception seems, however, to be wholly inappropriate in the case of liquids with their characteristic fluidity.

A way out of this contradiction lies in the assumption that the equilibrium positions of the atoms in a liquid body are not absolutely permanent, but, for every given atom, have a temporary character. After performing a more or less large number of oscillations about the same equilibrium position during a certain time $\tau$, each atom of the liquid can jump to a new equilibrium position, at a distance $\delta$ of the same order of magnitude as the mean distance between the adjacent atoms, where it is surrounded, partially at least, by new neighbours.

If the time $\tau$ is large compared with the vibration period, this sporadic change of the equilibrium position cannot affect the magnitude of the specific heat of the liquid (which in this respect must remain 'solid-like'). If, however, at the same time, $\tau$ is small compared with the unit of the ordinary time scale or more exactly with the time $t$, during which the body is acted upon by a force of constant magnitude and direction, it will yield to this force in the sense described by the ordinary process of liquid flow.

In the contrary case, when $\tau$ is large compared with $t$, the same force will produce only an elastic deformation of the body, consisting of a small shift of the equilibrium positions of all the atoms, just as in an ordinary solid body. In other words, the characteristic 'fluidity' of liquids can be displayed only under the action of forces which vary sufficiently slowly with respect to magnitude, and especially to direction, that is in such a way that the time of their action in a given direction is large compared with the average value of $\tau$—the mean life of an atom in a definite equilibrium position. Under such conditions the 'rigidity' of liquids, i.e. their capability of elastic (and not viscous) resistance to shearing stress, connected with the existence of temporary equilibrium positions of the atoms, is, as it were, 'masked' by their fluidity.

This conception, which was put forward by the present author in 1925, enables one to unify such seemingly opposite and mutually exclusive properties as rigidity and fluidity.

An early attempt at such a unification was made for the first time by Maxwell,† who, however, based it on a purely formal argument consisting in representing the total strain due to a given shearing stress as the sum of an elastic part characteristic of a rigid body and a viscous part characteristic of a 'purely' liquid body.

The conception that the molecules of a liquid are vibrating about equilibrium positions which are shifted now and then to adjacent sites forms the molecular-kinetic basis for Maxwell's phenomenological theory (which will be discussed in detail in § 3).

This conception must not be considered as introduced *ad hoc*, i.e. for the special purpose of explaining the fluidity of liquids, in connexion with the similarity between liquid and solid bodies with respect to the value of their specific heat. In our treatment of the heat motion in crystals (Ch. I) we have arrived, on the basis of general statistical considerations, at the conclusion that even in this case the equilibrium positions of the atoms are not permanent, each atom wandering throughout the whole volume of the crystal from one position to the next, by exchanging its place with an adjacent atom or with an adjacent hole, or by getting dislocated and moving from one 'interstitial' site to the next.

This step by step wandering or self-diffusion motion, leading to a gradual mixing up of all the atoms, must proceed much faster in liquids than in solid bodies and must have a simpler character because of the absence of definite lattice sites. Each elementary shift of the equilibrium position of an atom in a liquid body can be described as a sequence of two processes: the 'evaporation' of the atom from its initial equilibrium

† J. C. Maxwell, *Phil. Trans.* **157**, 49 (1867).

position into an intermediate one, connected with the increase by a certain amount $\Delta U = W$ (activation energy) of its potential energy—or, more exactly, of the free energy of the whole complex constituted by it and by the surrounding atoms—and the 'condensation' from this intermediate position, corresponding to a maximum value of the potential (or free) energy, into a new equilibrium position, the resulting extra value of the kinetic energy, into which the activation energy is transformed, being instantaneously shaken off, as it were, i.e. distributed between the given atom and its new surroundings so that it cannot get back at once into its initial equilibrium position.

Under such conditions the dependence of the 'mean life' of an atom in the same equilibrium position on the temperature is expressed by the equation

$$\tau = \tau_0 e^{W/kT}, \tag{1}$$

the average velocity of translation of the atoms through the whole volume of the liquid being given by

$$w = \frac{\delta}{\tau} = \frac{\delta}{\tau_0} e^{-W/kT}, \tag{1a}$$

and the self-diffusion coefficient, which determines the rate of their mixing together, by

$$D = \frac{\delta^2}{\sigma\tau} = \frac{\delta^2}{\sigma\tau_0} e^{-W/kT}. \tag{1b}$$

This last formula can be and has been verified experimentally by the method of radioactive tracer atoms first applied by Hevesy in the case of fused lead.† The energy $W$ turns out to be much smaller than in the case of the corresponding solid (crystalline) bodies, which is easily explained by the larger volume of the liquid, in connexion with the fact that $W$ decreases with increase of the interatomic distances.

If, on lowering the temperature, the simple monatomic liquid we are considering did not crystallize, it would gradually lose its fluidity, and, at such temperatures as those for which $\tau$ is of the order of hours and days, would become practically rigid.

The possibility of such a continuous transition from the liquid state into the solid amorphous one, which is actually realized in the case of a number of complex substances on rapid cooling, must be considered as a direct proof of the fact that the properties of fluidity and rigidity can coexist in the same body, the classification of condensed bodies into solids and liquids having thus but a relative meaning convenient for practical purposes but devoid of scientific value.

† Hevesy and Seith, *Z. Elektrochem.* **37**, 528 (1931).

## 2. The Viscosity of Simple Liquids

The conception set forth in the preceding section serves as a basis for a kinetic theory of the viscosity of liquids which was developed by the author in 1926.†

It should be mentioned that earlier attempts to explain the viscosity of liquids were based on the generally accepted analogy between the liquid and the gaseous state and attributed the viscosity in both cases to the same mechanism, namely the transfer of momentum in the mixing up of the molecules. In the case of gases this mechanism is justified by the fact that the molecules move most of the time uniformly in a constant direction, their momentum being altered by their interaction with each other during the relatively very short periods when they get into direct 'contact', i.e. suffer a 'collision'. Under such conditions the levelling out of the average (macroscopic) velocities of contiguous layers (or elements of volume) can be treated as a result of a mixing together of the molecules with different additional (macroscopic) velocities. It is natural that in this case the coefficient of viscosity $\mu$, which is a measure of the rate of this 'levelling-out' process, turns out to be proportional to the diffusion (or self-diffusion) coefficient $D$, which is a measure of the rate of the mixing up of the molecules. The relation between these two coefficients can be found directly from a comparison between the equation of motion of a viscous fluid:

$$\rho\frac{d\mathbf{v}}{dt} = \mu\nabla^2\mathbf{v} - \nabla p, \tag{2}$$

where $\rho$ is the density, $\mathbf{v}$ the macroscopic velocity, and $p$ the pressure, with the equation of self-diffusion:

$$\frac{\partial n^*}{\partial t} = D\nabla^2 n^*, \tag{2a}$$

where $n^*$ is the concentration of 'tracer' atoms (distinguished by the value of their additional velocity, for example).

If in equation (2) the last term, representing the influence of pressure, is dropped and $d\mathbf{v}/dt$ is replaced by $\partial\mathbf{v}/\partial t$ (which is allowed in the case of small velocities), it assumes the form

$$\frac{\partial\rho\mathbf{v}}{\partial t} = \frac{\mu}{\rho}\nabla^2(\rho\mathbf{v}), \tag{2b}$$

which differs from (2a) by the substitution of the macroscopic density of momentum $\rho\mathbf{v}$ for the concentration $n^*$. The fact that in the case

† J. Frenkel, *Z. f. Phys.* **35**, 652 (1926).

of gases the levelling out of the macroscopic momentum takes place through the mixing together of 'slow' and 'fast' molecules can thus be expressed by the equality of the corresponding coefficients, i.e.

$$\frac{\mu}{\rho} = D. \tag{3}$$

The same result is obtained, as is well known, by a direct calculation of the rate of momentum transfer in a gas, the diffusion coefficient being given by the formula

$$D = \tfrac{1}{3}lw, \tag{3a}$$

where $l$ is the mean free path of the molecules and $w$ the average velocity of their thermal agitation.

A similar approach to the question of the viscosity of liquids has a certain sense in the case of very high temperatures, lying near the critical one, when the heat motion of the molecules in the liquid state becomes similar to that in a gas ($e^{W/kT} \approx 1$, $\tau \approx \tau_0$). In this case it is sufficient to introduce a minor correction for the finite size of the molecules (in calculating the time of collision).

Leaving this question aside and coming back to a consideration of liquids at low temperatures (near the crystallization point), we must proceed along an entirely different path for the explanation of their viscosity, a path starting from the analogy between the heat motion in liquid and in solid bodies.

From this point of view it is devoid of any meaning to treat the viscosity of a liquid as the result of a transfer of momentum by the individual particles (atoms), since the momentum of each atom cannot be considered—even in the roughest approximation—as a constant of the motion, as in the case of gases, but oscillates rapidly along with the vibrations of the atom about its equilibrium position. The fact to be explained in the case of liquids is *not their viscosity*, that is the resistance to shearing stress, but rather *their fluidity*, i.e. the capability of yielding to such a stress. Under such conditions it is natural to start directly from the *mobility* of the individual particles, i.e. the average velocity which is acquired by them with respect to the surrounding particles under the action of an external force of unit magnitude. The *fluidity* of a liquid, which can be measured by the reciprocal value of the viscosity coefficient ($1/\mu$), must obviously be proportional to the mobility ($\alpha$) of the individual particles constituting it. Now since the latter, according to Einstein's relation, is proportional to the diffusion coefficient, it follows that the viscosity of liquids in the solid-like state (i.e. near the crystallization point) is not directly proportional to the diffusion coefficient, as in the case of gases, but *inversely* proportional to it. This explains at once the fact that the viscosity of liquids decreases when the temperature is raised, instead of increasing, as in the case of gases. Since the self-diffusion coefficient of a liquid body is proportional to the expression $e^{-W/kT}$, this expression must also determine the temperature variation of its fluidity. We thus see that the viscosity of a liquid, as a function of the temperature, must be represented by an equation of the form

$$\mu = Ae^{W/kT} \tag{4}$$

with an approximately constant coefficient $A$.

The same result is obtained with the help of a more detailed argument which enables one, in addition, to determine the numerical value of the coefficient $A$.

Let us treat one of the particles of the liquid as a small sphere with a radius $a$, and let us determine the resistance $F$ suffered by it when moving with an *average* velocity $\bar{v}$ with respect to the surrounding particles (the liquid being supposed to remain at rest at large distances) by Stokes's law

$$F = 6\pi a\mu\bar{v}. \tag{5}$$

Writing this expression in the form $\bar{v} = \alpha F$ we see that the mobility of the particle under consideration can be expressed through the viscosity coefficient of the liquid $\mu$ by the formula

$$\alpha = \frac{1}{6\pi a\mu}. \tag{5a}$$

On the other hand, according to Einstein's relation, we have

$$\alpha = \frac{D}{kT}.$$

Hence

$$\mu = \frac{kT}{6\pi aD}. \tag{6}$$

Now, the 'self-diffusion' coefficient of the liquid $D$ is given, according to our theory, by the expression

$$D = \frac{\delta^2}{6\tau_0}e^{-W/kT}.$$

Substituting it in the preceding formula we get

$$\mu = \frac{kT\tau_0}{\pi a\delta^2}e^{W/kT}, \tag{6a}$$

which agrees with (4) if

$$A = \frac{kT\tau_0}{\pi a\delta^2}. \tag{7}$$

Equation (4) describes very accurately the temperature dependence of the viscosity of all the liquids, not only simple, for which it has been derived, but also complex (with the exception of 'associating' ones), at a *constant pressure*. The experimental values of $A$ are, however, usually 100 to 1,000 times *smaller* than the theoretical ones.† This discrepancy can be explained in the same way as the apparent discrepancy of the factor outside the exponential in the empirical expression (1 b) for the diffusion coefficient with the theoretical value $\delta^2/\sigma\tau_0$, namely by a practically linear decrease of the activation energy $W$ with increase of the temperature, owing to the thermal expansion of the liquid at constant pressure. Putting, as in equation (40) of Ch. I,

$$W = W_0 - \gamma kT,$$

we get
$$D = \frac{\delta^2}{\sigma\tau_0} e^{\gamma} e^{-W_0/kT},$$

which brings us back to the previous expression (4) for $\mu$ with a value of the coefficient $A$ smaller by $e^{\gamma}$:

$$A = \frac{kT\tau_0}{\pi a\delta^2} e^{-\gamma}. \tag{7 a}$$

In order to remove the discrepancy between the theoretical and the experimental values of $A$ we must put $e^{\gamma} \approx 100$, that is $\gamma \approx 5$ which corresponds to a decrease of the activation energy by 10 cal./mole per degree. This means that the values of $\tau$ previously obtained must be increased by a factor of 100.

If we take into account the dependence of $W$ not only on the temperature but also on the pressure, according to the equations

$$W = W_0 - \beta(v - v_0) \quad \text{and} \quad v - v_0 = -(v_0/K)p,$$

the coefficient $A$ turns out to be an exponential function of the pressure

$$A = A_0 e^{p/p_0}, \tag{8}$$

where $A_0$ is the value of $A$ for $p = 0$ and, if $\alpha$ is the coefficient of thermal expansion,

$$p_0 = \frac{\alpha KT}{\gamma} \tag{8 a}$$

is a pressure which corresponds to an $e(= 2{\cdot}71)$-fold increase of the viscosity. The exponential increase of the viscosity with the pressure is in agreement with the experimental results.

† In calculating $A$ according to (7) one can put $a \approx \delta \approx 10^{-8}$ cm. and $\tau_0 \approx 10^{-13}$ sec., which for $T = 300°$ gives $A = 10^{-4}$ c.g.s.

Putting $\alpha \approx 10^{-5}$ and $K = 10^{12}$ dynes/cm.$^2$ we get for $\gamma = 5$ and $T = 300°$ K.

$$p_0 \approx 10^9 \text{ dynes/cm.}^2 = 1{,}000 \text{ atmospheres.}$$

Hence it follows that when the pressure is increased up to $10^4$ atmospheres the viscosity must increase by a factor of $e^{10} \approx 10^4$.

This result is somewhat exaggerated; nevertheless, it gives a correct idea of the magnitude of the influence produced by the pressure on the viscosity of certain liquids.†

It should be borne in mind that the application of equation (8) to the case of very high pressures can hardly give exact results, since the dependence of the volume on the pressure, and of the energy $W$ on the volume, deviates from a linear law in this region.

The above derivation of equations (4) and (7) may raise certain doubts, for it is based on the application of the macroscopic expression (5 a) for the mobility of a hard sphere moving in a viscous liquid to the particles of the liquid itself. It should be noted in this connexion that the application of this macroscopic method to the theoretical determination of the mobilities of *ions* in solutions of electrolytes leads to values which are in fair agreement with the theoretical ones both with respect to the order of magnitude and to the dependence on the temperature (which reduces to the temperature dependence of the 'fluidity' $1/\mu$). The theoretical justification of such a procedure lies in the fact that it accounts—though but in a roughly approximate way—for the partial participation of all the molecules of the liquid in the translational motion of one of them.

In order to make clearer the molecular mechanism of the flow of a viscous liquid I shall give an alternative derivation of the preceding results, which, moreover, is free from the above objection.

Like the preceding one, it is based on the notion of the *mobility* of the individual molecules of the liquid. It does not make use, however, of the phenomenological connexion between the mobility and the macroscopic viscosity of the liquid, but derives this viscosity from a consideration of the mechanism of its flow.‡

† According to Ewell and Eyring (*J. Chem. Phys.* **5**, 734, 1937) the quantity $p_0$ for ethyl bromide, ethyl ether, and $CS_2$ lies close to 2,000 (at room temperature). The ratio $\mu/\mu_0$ for $p = 2{,}000$ is equal for these three liquids to 3·74, 2·20, and 2·03 respectively. It should be remarked that within the range between 5,000 and 12,000 atmospheres the viscosity of many liquids has been found to rise as the cube of the pressure.

‡ In my first publication (1926) on the viscosity of liquids I confined myself to the derivation of the expression for the viscosity coefficient given above. This probably explains the fact that Andrade (*Phil. Mag.* **17**, 497, 698, 1934), who a few years later proposed an essentially similar though more qualitative theory, did not notice its connexion with mine. I pointed out this connexion in a discussion in *Nature* (**136**, 167, 1935),

### 3. Connexion between the Viscosity and the Rigidity of Liquid Bodies

Let the flow of a liquid take place in the direction of the $x$-axis (from left to right), its average (macroscopic) velocity increasing in the direction of the $y$-axis (upwards). Let us consider a layer of the liquid with a thickness $dy = \delta$ (where $\delta$ is the average distance between adjacent molecules), enclosed between the planes $y = y_0$ and $y = y_0+\delta$. If the layer lying below it moves as a whole with an average velocity $v_0$, then the layer under consideration moves with respect to it with an average velocity $\Delta v_x = (\partial v_x/\partial y)\delta$. This motion must be ascribed to the action of the force by which this layer is pulled (to the right) by the layer lying above it. If this force referred to unit area is denoted by $P_{xy}$ (shearing stress), then the force acting on each molecule is given by $F = P_{xy}\delta^2$ ($\delta^2$ being the average area per molecule of the layer).

While the equilibrium positions of all these particles move with an average velocity $v_0$ (the same as that of the preceding layer), each of them vibrates about its equilibrium position, jumping over now and then to a new equilibrium position, which in the presence of the force $F$ lies as a rule in the direction of the latter with respect to the initial position at a distance $\delta$ from it. This jerk-like diffusion motion of the individual molecules, taking place at different instants in the direction by preference of the pulling force, constitutes the average motion of the whole layer with respect to the preceding one.

The (relative) velocity of this motion is given by the expression

$$\Delta v_x = \alpha F = \alpha P_{xy}\delta^2.$$

Putting here $\Delta v_x = (\partial v_x/\partial y)\delta$ we obtain the usual relation between the velocity gradient and the shearing stress

$$\frac{\partial v_x}{\partial y} = \alpha\delta P_{xy},$$

the product $\alpha\delta$ standing for the reciprocal of the viscosity coefficient $\mu$. We thus get

$$\mu = \frac{1}{\alpha\delta}. \tag{9}$$

This expression differs from (5 a) only by the absence of the factor $6\pi$ in the denominator and by the substitution of the average distance between neighbouring particles $\delta$ for the radius of one of them $a$.

where a more detailed derivation, reproduced in the next section, was given. It is rather surprising that both Andrade and Eyring, who in 1937 developed a theory of exactly the same kind, persisted in ignoring my earlier publications on the subject.

Replacing $\alpha$ by $D/kT$ we obtain the following expression for the coefficient of viscosity:

$$\mu = \frac{6kT\tau_0}{\delta^3} e^{W/kT}, \tag{9a}$$

which is practically identical with (6 a).

The above analysis of the mechanism of viscous flow opens the way to an alternative determination of the viscosity coefficient along a line first introduced by Maxwell and based on a combination of a viscous flow with an elastic shearing strain due to the same shearing stress $P_{xy}$.

If the direction of the latter alternated with a period small compared with the mean life of the particles in the same equilibrium position, then in jumping from one position to the next they would exhibit no preference for any particular direction, so that the diffusion motion would not give rise to a viscous flow. The influence of the shearing stress would reduce in this case to a purely *elastic* strain, consisting in a small simultaneous shift of the equilibrium positions of all the particles within each layer of the liquid with respect to the adjacent layers in the same way as in an ordinary solid elastic body, i.e. according to the equation

$$\frac{\partial u_x}{\partial y} = \frac{1}{G} P_{xy},$$

where $u_x$ is the elastic displacement (from left to right, say) of a layer at a height $y$ from the base, and $G$ the rigidity modulus. Differentiating this equation with respect to the time and noting that $du_x/dt = v'_x$ where $v'_x$ is the velocity of the elastic displacement, we can rewrite it in the form

$$\frac{\partial v'_x}{\partial y} = \frac{1}{G}\frac{dP_{xy}}{dt}.$$

If the direction of the stress $P_{xy}$ remains constant or is changed relatively slowly, the liquid must suffer, in addition to this elastic strain, a viscous flow with a velocity $v''_x$ determined by the equation

$$\frac{\partial v''_x}{\partial y} = \frac{1}{\mu} P_{xy}.$$

The total velocity of the layer $v_x$ is obviously equal to the sum of $v'_x$, and $v''_x$. We thus obtain the following equation of the resulting motion of a 'condensed' body, combining the properties of an idealized elastic solid and of an idealized viscous liquid:

$$\frac{\partial v_x}{\partial y} = \frac{1}{G}\frac{dP_{xy}}{dt} + \frac{1}{\mu} P_{xy}. \tag{10}$$

This equation forms the basis of Maxwell's 'relaxation theory of elasticity'. This denomination follows from the fact that when the motion comes suddenly to a standstill, the stress does not preserve the value $G(\partial u_x/\partial y)$ corresponding to the instantaneous magnitude of the strain, as in the case of an ordinary elastic body, nor does it vanish at once, as required by the ordinary (macroscopic) theory of viscosity, but gradually 'relaxes' from the initial value $P_0$ at the instant $t = 0$ down to zero, according to the equation

$$\frac{1}{G}\frac{dP}{dt}+\frac{1}{\mu}P = 0,$$

to which (10) is reduced if we put $v_x = 0$. We thus get

$$P = P_0 e^{-t/\tau_M}, \tag{10a}$$

where

$$\tau_M = \frac{\mu}{G} \tag{10b}$$

is Maxwell's 'relaxation time'.

In Maxwell's phenomenological theory this time remained wholly arbitrary. From the point of view of our molecular-kinetic theory it seems natural that it should be identified, approximately at least, with the mean duration of the 'sedentary' life of a particle, i.e. the average time $\tau$ it remains attached to the same equilibrium position. This identification is substantiated by a consideration of the influence of a harmonically varying force $P = Ae^{i\omega t}$. The right-hand side of equation (10) is reduced in this case to $\left(\frac{1}{\mu}+\frac{i\omega}{G}\right)Ae^{i\omega t} = \frac{1}{\mu}(1+i\omega\tau_M)P$. If the product $\omega\tau$ is small compared with 1, i.e. if the vibration period of the force $\theta = 2\pi/\omega$ is large compared with the relaxation time $\tau_M$, the second term in the brackets can be neglected. This means that under such conditions the vibrational motion of the body is reduced practically to a viscous flow. In the opposite case $\omega\tau \gg 1$, i.e. $\theta \ll \tau$, the first term in the brackets can be neglected, so that the right-hand side of equation (10) is reduced to the term $(1/G)(dP/dt)$ corresponding to purely elastic vibrations of the body.

Hence it follows that Maxwell's relaxation time cannot be much different from our 'mean life of a sedentary state' $\tau = \tau_0 e^{W/kT}$. Substituting it in the expression (10 b) we get

$$\mu = G\tau = G\tau_0 e^{W/kT}. \tag{11}$$

This equation is identical with (4) if we put $A = G\tau_0$, or with a view to the temperature dependence of $W$ $(= W_0-\gamma kT)$:

$$A = G\tau_0 e^{-\gamma}.$$

It differs slightly from the equations (6 a) and (9 a), previously derived by us, by the substitution of the rigidity modulus $G$ for the expression $kT/\pi a\delta^2$ or $6kT/\delta^3$. Since $1/a\delta^2 \approx 1/\delta^3 \approx n$, where $n$ is the number of particles in unit volume, the original expressions for $\mu$ turn out to be equivalent to the new one, following from Maxwell's relaxation theory, if the rigidity modulus $G$ is identified with the pressure $p = nkT$ which would be produced by the particles of the liquid if for a given concentration $n$ they behaved as particles of an ideal gas.

Such a definition of the rigidity modulus is of course devoid of physical meaning. Its actual magnitude for a liquid body can be determined theoretically from a consideration of the intermolecular forces, in exactly the same way as in the case of solid bodies, if allowance is made for the somewhat larger value of the interatomic distances and for the absence of distant order in the arrangement of the atoms. This circumstance must lead to a certain decrease of the rigidity modulus of liquids compared with that of the corresponding solids, without, however, affecting the order of magnitude. The rigidity modulus of a liquid must thus have a magnitude of the order of $10^{11}$ dynes/cm.$^2$, slowly decreasing with increase of the temperature, just as in the case of solid bodies. An increase of it, which would be required by an identification of $G$ with $kT/\delta^3$ is, of course, out of the question.

A reconciliation of our theory with that of Maxwell can be reached only by refraining from the identification of Maxwell's relaxation time $\tau_M$ with the mean life-time of an equilibrium position and by introducing the relation

$$\tau_M = \tau \frac{kT}{G\delta^3}.$$

Since at $T = 300$ the pressure $kT/\delta^3$ is of the order of $10^{10}$–$10^{11}$ dynes/cm.$^3$, i.e. of the same order of magnitude as $G$, $\tau_M$ turns out to be under ordinary conditions only slightly different from $\tau$.

The equations (6 a) or (9 a) have the advantage over (11) of being applicable to the limiting case of very high temperatures, at which the liquid ceases to be 'solid-like' and becomes rather gas-like. In this case the exponential factor $e^{W/kT}$, accounting for the decrease of the viscosity with rising temperature, becomes practically unity (the mean life-time $\tau$ reducing to the vibration period $\tau_0$), and the dependence of the non-exponential factor $A = kT/\delta^3$ (or $kT/\delta^3 e^{\gamma}$) on the temperature, which was masked by it for lower values of $T$, corresponds to an increase of the viscosity with the temperature, characteristic of the gaseous state.

It is true that in the latter case the viscosity should be proportional to $\sqrt{T}$ rather than to $T$. It is interesting to note, however, that the magnitude of the viscosity coefficient which follows from our theory in the case of high temperatures lies very close to that which is obtained in the usual way from the kinetic theory of gases. Putting in the corresponding equations (3) and (3 a) $\rho = nm$, where $m$ is the mass of a molecule, and $l = 1/\delta^2 n \approx \delta$ (since in the case of a liquid $n \approx 1/\delta^3$), we get

$$\mu = \tfrac{1}{3} nm\delta v.$$

On the other hand, equation (6 a) reduces in the case $e^{W/kT} \approx 1$ to

$$\mu = nkT\tau_0 \pi \approx nmv^2 \tau_0 \pi.$$

This expression becomes identical with the preceding one if $\tau_0$ is identified with the time required for moving over the distance $\delta$ with the thermal velocity $v$ (as has been done in § 1 of Ch. I in the derivation of equation (10 a)). At elevated temperatures such an identification becomes quite natural.

If $\tau_0$ is treated as a constant of the order of $10^{-13}$ sec., the ratio $\delta/\tau_0$ becomes a constant of the order of $10^5$ cm./sec., which lies close to the actual value of $v$ within the practically accessible range of temperatures.

## 4. The 'Hole' Theory of Diffusion and Viscosity of Liquids

In deriving the expression (6 a) for the viscosity of a liquid body we have assumed that the average resistance of the liquid to the motion of one of its particles can be calculated with the help of Stokes's law.

If now a molecule of the liquid under consideration is replaced by a molecule of some foreign substance dissolved in it, the application of Stokes's formula yields for the mobility of this foreign molecule a value of the same order of magnitude as that corresponding to its proper molecules (unless their radii are very different). This result is directly verified in the case of electrolytic ions whose mobility can be calculated from the specific conductivity. In the case of ordinary solvents the latter turns out to be inversely proportional to the coefficient of viscosity of the solvent ($\sigma\mu =$ const.), in agreement with the results of the application of Stokes's theory.

This result appears at first sight to be quite natural and even somewhat trivial.

From the approximate equality between the mobilities of different (dissolved) molecules in the same liquid solvent there follows, however, the somewhat unexpected conclusion that their diffusion coefficients must also be approximately equal to each other and to the self-diffusion coefficient of the solvent. This conclusion is in full agreement with the experimental facts, which show that the diffusion coefficients of widely different substances dissolved in the same liquid vary with the temperature as the reciprocal of the viscosity of the solvent. Hence it follows that the activation energy $W$, which determines the temperature dependence of the diffusion coefficient in the equation $D = \text{const.}\, e^{-W/kT}$ must be approximately the same for various solutes, being thus characteristic of the mutual action between the molecules of the solvent and not of that between these molecules and those of the dissolved substance.

This result seems certainly far less trivial than that from which it is derived.

It should be remembered that in the case of solid bodies the diffusion coefficients of various 'impurities' are widely different from each other both with respect to the order of magnitude and to their dependence on the temperature.

Instead of this remarkable variety, we find in the case of liquid solvents a perhaps still more remarkable uniformity, the diffusion coefficients of widely different dissolved substances lying at room temperature near the same value 1 cm.$^2$/day, i.e. $10^{-5}$ cm.$^2$/sec. and differing from each other by a factor of 10 at most. Thus, for example, the diffusion coefficients of radon, oxygen, HCl, and sugar in water at 18° C. are equal to 2·33, 1·6, 1·39, and 0·34 cm.$^2$/day respectively; the difference between these figures is quite insignificant when compared with the difference between the chemical constitution and geometrical dimensions of the molecules of the corresponding substances.

It is interesting to note that the diffusion coefficients in the case of liquid solvents vary to only a relatively slight extent from one solvent to another. Thus, for example, the diffusion coefficients of lead, cadmium, gold, and copper in mercury in the range between room temperature and 500° C. lie in the range 0·72 to 3·18 cm.$^2$/day. It should be mentioned for the sake of comparison that the diffusion coefficients of gold in molten lead and tin at 500° C. are equal respectively to 3·19 and 4·65 cm.$^2$/day, while the diffusion coefficients of various organic substances in organic liquids at 20° C. vary between 0·4 cm.$^2$/day (glycerine in ethyl alcohol) and 2·6 cm.$^2$/day.

The comparison of these facts with the theoretical expression

$$D = \frac{\delta^2}{6\tau_0} e^{-W/kT}$$

for the diffusion coefficient leads, at first sight, to a serious difficulty.

In fact, the activation energy $W$ should apparently be determined by the mutual action between the molecules of the solvent on the one hand, and the molecules of the dissolved substance on the other; it should, accordingly, vary more or less sharply with the variation of the nature of either of them.

Before discussing the difficulty the following circumstance must be pointed out.

Since in the case of liquids the activation energy $W$ is much smaller than in that of crystals, being of the order of the heat of fusion, the factor $e^{-W/kT}$ must in the former case lie much closer to 1 and display a much smaller variation with the temperature than in the latter. This explains at once the fact that the diffusion coefficients of various substances in liquid solvents are much larger (by a few orders of magnitude) than in solids, and are at the same time much less sensitive to a variation of the temperature or of the nature of the solute and solvent. In the limiting case $W/kT \to 0$, i.e. $e^{-W/kT} \to 1$, the above expression for $D$ must reduce to a practically constant value

$$\frac{\delta^2}{6\tau_0} \approx \frac{10^{-16}}{10^{-13}} \approx 10^{-3}\ \text{cm.}^2/\text{sec.} \cong 100\ \text{cm.}^2/\text{day.}$$

The actual values of $D$ are, as has been shown above, about 100 times smaller than this figure, so that $e^{W/kT} \approx 100$ or $W \approx 2{,}400$–$10{,}000$ cal./mole (for $T \approx 300$–$800°$ K.). It should be remembered, for the sake of comparison, that in the case of solid bodies the energy $W$ lies between 20,000 and 60,000 cal./mole, which corresponds to a decrease of $D$ by a factor of $10^6$ and even $10^9$ at room temperatures and to a much sharper dependence on the temperature.

The approximate equality of the energy $W$ for various substances dissolved in the same liquid, and the (approximate) coincidence of this energy with the activation energy which determines the temperature dependence of the viscosity of the solvent, can now be explained as follows:

1. If the molecules of the dissolved substance are very large (compared with those of the solvent) their heat motion cannot be described as an alternation of vibrations about an equilibrium position and displacements of the latter, but must be similar to the Brownian motion of colloidal particles. Accordingly, the expression $D = (\delta^2/6\tau_0)e^{-W/kT}$ cannot be applied to this case. On the other hand, the Einstein–Stokes equations $D = \alpha kT = kT/6\pi\mu a$ becomes more exact the larger the radius $a$ of the 'macromolecules'. Putting $\mu = (kT\tau_0/\pi\delta_0^2 a_0)e^{W_0/kT}$, where

the quantities with the suffix 0 refer to the molecules of the solvent, we obtain the following expression for the diffusion coefficient:

$$D = \frac{\delta_0^2 a_0}{6a\tau_0} e^{-W_0/kT} = \frac{a_0}{a} D_0,$$

which both with respect to the dependence on the temperature and to the order of magnitude of the factors outside the exponential is in full agreement with the experimental data.

2. If the molecules of the dissolved substance are comparable in respect of their size with the molecules of the solvent, the usual conception of the thermal motion in a liquid body is applicable to them, and the activation energy $W$ in the equation $D = (\delta^2/6\tau_0)e^{-W/kT}$ should be determined by the mutual action of the molecules of solute and the solvent, and not of the latter alone, as found experimentally.

This circumstance can be explained in two different ways:

(*a*) In the first place it can be assumed that when a molecule of the solute moves about in a liquid solvent, the surrounding molecules of the latter are carried along by it in the same way as in the case of macromolecules, i.e. in accordance with the macroscopic hydrodynamical theory. This does not necessarily mean a 'solvation' of the dissolved molecules and a motion of the solvated complex as a rigid whole. Such a solvation would practically bring us back to the case of macromolecules, considered above. If it does not take place, then the 'dragging' of the solvent molecules by a molecule of the dissolved substance must be quite similar to the 'mutual dragging' of the solvent molecules in the case of self-diffusion. Under such conditions the activation energy $W$ must be referred to the whole complex of particles participating in the elementary transition of the particle under consideration from one equilibrium position to the next and in the case of a dilute solution cannot markedly differ from $W_0$.

(*b*) This collective motion of a complex of particles can be pictured in such a way that the central particle (of the solute or of the solvent) should not play the role of the 'leader', but, on the contrary, should be 'led' by the surrounding ones, thus participating in the transition in a passive rather than in an active way. Let us imagine that the transition of the ('central') particle under consideration to a new equilibrium position takes place owing to a recession of the surrounding particles, which clear the way for it to this new position by making a 'hole' near the initial one. The transition to the new equilibrium position thus consists essentially in the filling up of this hole, whereby a similar hole must be left at the initial position, this hole being thereafter closed by a process opposite to that which gave rise to it. From this point of view the activation energy $W$ for the diffusion or self-diffusion in a liquid can be treated as the energy which is necessary for the formation of a 'hole', i.e. a small cavity of such size that it could accommodate a whole particle or at least a certain portion of it (in the case of large particles).

Identifying this energy with the surface energy of such a cavity and treating it as a sphere with a radius $r$ we have $W = 4\pi\sigma r^2$, where $\sigma$ is the surface energy of the liquid. Putting $\sigma \approx 400$ (mercury) and $r = 10^{-8}$ cm. we get $W = 5.10^{-13}$ erg, i.e. about 10,000 calories per mole. This figure is somewhat exaggerated, yet of the correct order of magnitude. It is clear that in the case of a dilute solution the activation energy defined in this way must be practically identical with that which corresponds to the pure solvent $W_0$.

We are thus led to the 'hole' theory of liquid bodies, which has been developed in § 10 of Ch. III in connexion with their equilibrium properties. This theory enables one also to understand the relationship between the viscosity of a given liquid and its specific volume, which was long ago discovered by Batschinski† and which is represented by the equation

$$\mu = \frac{B}{V-b}, \tag{12}$$

where the parameters $B$ and $b$ are approximately independent both of the temperature and of the pressure. The constant $b$ is practically the same as that appearing in van der Waals's equation, so that the difference $V-b$ represents the 'free volume' of the liquid, Batschinski's equation thus reducing to a proportionality of the fluidity to the free volume, irrespective of the temperature and the pressure which affect the viscosity in so far only as they influence the specific volume of the liquid.

This result, which forms the essence of Batschinski's relation, has been shown to be but approximately correct (in the region of high pressures, in particular). Nevertheless, its approximate validity within even a limited range of temperatures and pressures requires an explanation.

Equating Batschinski's expression for the viscosity of a liquid with the equation (4) of § 2 we get

$$V-b = Ce^{-W/kT}, \tag{12a}$$

where $C = B/A =$ constant.

† Batschinski, *Z. phys. Chem.* **84**, 643 (1913).

This equation coincides with the 'equation of state' of a liquid body which has been shown in § 10 of the preceding chapter.

The exponential dependence of the free volume on the pressure, which follows from this equation, is certainly a roughly approximate one and can hold in a very limited range only.

According to an empirical equation which was proposed long ago by Tait, the dependence of $V$ on $p$ can be represented with sufficient accuracy up to pressures of the order of 10,000 atmospheres by the logarithmic expression

$$V = V_0 - \alpha \log(1+p/\beta). \tag{13}$$

The fact that the viscosity of a liquid is inversely proportional to its free volume, as required by Batschinski's formula, is explained by the hole theory of liquids in a quite natural way.

As has been shown in § 5 of Ch. I, the hole mechanism of the diffusion (or self-diffusion) in a crystalline body leads to the following relation between the diffusion coefficients of the holes $D'$ and that of the particles $D$:

$$D = \frac{n'}{n} D'$$

(cf. eq. (36 a)). Hence it follows that $D$ is proportional to the concentration of the holes $n'$. Using Einstein's relation $q = D/kT$ between the mobility of the particles and their self-diffusion coefficient, it is possible to calculate the viscosity coefficient of the liquid $\mu$ in the same way as has been done in § 1 and § 2 with exactly similar results. We thus get

$$\frac{1}{\mu} = \text{const.} \frac{n'}{n} D',$$

or, since $n'/n \cong e^{-U'/kT}$ and $D' \sim e^{-\Delta U'/kT}$ (where $\Delta U'$ is the activation energy for the diffusion of holes)

$$\mu = \text{const.}\ e^{(U'+\Delta U')/kT}.$$

In order to bring this result in agreement with the relations (12) and (12 a), where $W$ is obviously identical with the energy of hole formation $U'$, we must neglect $\Delta U'$ in comparison with $U'$. This is, on our view, the actual nature of the approximation involved in Batschinski's formula, and the reason why it fails to give an exact representation of the dependence of the viscosity on the temperature and on the pressure.

It follows from the preceding considerations that a viscous flow can exist not only in the case of liquids (and amorphous solids) but also in the case of crystals. The fact that it has not been observed experimentally in the latter case is probably explained by the prevalence of plastic slipping, which, in contradistinction to viscous flow, can take place at the lowest temperatures.

The conception of atomic (or molecular) holes in liquids has been developed in recent years in connexion with a number of questions referring to the equation of state of liquid bodies and to their viscosity by a number of authors, especially by Eyring and his co-workers.†

Since the energy of hole formation in a crystal is approximately equal to the latent heat of evaporation (per molecule) if the elastic strain around a hole is neglected, it should follow from the 'hole' theory of viscosity that the activation energy in the equation $\mu = Ae^{W/kT}$ for the viscosity coefficient must be approximately equal to the latent heat of evaporation $U_0$. In reality $W$ is usually much smaller than $U_v$, lying rather closer to the latent heat of fusion $U_f$, as can be seen from the following table:

| *Substance* | *W cal./mole* | $U_v$ *cal./mole* | $U_f$ *cal./mole* |
|---|---|---|---|
| Na | 0·96 | 25 | 0·61 |
| Ag | 4·87 | 59·5 | 2·63 |
| Hg | 0·6 | 14 | 0·57 |
| A | 0·52 | 1·5 | 0·27 |
| $N_2$ | 0·47 | 1·34 | 0·17 |
| $H_2O$ | 3·05 | 9·65 | 1·43 |
| $CH_3OH$ | 1·84 | 8·4 | 0·53 |

The discrepancy between $W$ and $U_v$ is especially striking in the case of metals. Since in this case the diffusion motion is due to the displacement of *ions* rather than of neutral atoms, the smallness of $W$ compared with $U_v$ could be explained here, according to Eyring, by the smallness of the ionic holes compared with the atomic volume.

It should be mentioned in conclusion that our conception of the viscosity refers to ordinary liquids, which with respect to the character of their heat motion are similar to solid bodies and are endowed with a (latent) rigidity. In a first approximation they are wholly deprived of fluidity, which can be obtained in the second approximation by taking into account the elementary displacements of the equilibrium positions of each particle in the crowd formed by the surrounding particles.

There exist a number of attempts to approach the problem of the viscosity of liquid from the other end, assuming the liquid in the first approximation to be wholly devoid of viscosity, and introducing various

† Eyring and Hirschfelder, *J. Phys. Chem.* **41**, 249 (1937).

processes of dissipation of energy and momentum to explain the origin of viscosity.†

In application to ordinary 'solid-like' liquids this second line of approach cannot give satisfactory results, being probably applicable only to the unique case of liquid helium II.‡

In our theory the viscosity of liquids is intimately connected with their 'rigidity'; according to Maxwell's relation the coefficient of viscosity must vanish along with the shear modulus.§

The fact that gases which are wholly deprived of rigidity ($G = 0$) possess, nevertheless, a finite viscosity shows that Maxwell's theory can be applied to 'solid-like' bodies only. In those cases where the cohesive forces between the molecules do not play an essential role, because of their smallness (liquid helium) or of the small density of the substance (gases) or, finally, because of a very high temperature (lying above the critical point), the conception of thermal motion as a series of small vibrations about a certain equilibrium position interrupted by a jerk-like shift of the latter is no longer valid and must be replaced by the familiar picture of molecules colliding with each other as rigid or elastic spheres, which forms the basis of the treatment of viscosity in the kinetic theory of gases.

The question of the behaviour of liquids in the gas-like state under extremely high temperatures and pressures will not be considered here.

The experiments of Bridgman and others have shown that while in the case of chemically complex substances the dependence of the viscosity on the pressure is extremely sharp, in the case of metallic bodies in the molten state the viscosity coefficient preserves a constant order of magnitude up to pressures of the order of 50,000 atmospheres.

This difference between the behaviour of the two kinds of substances with respect to pressure can be reduced to the fact that the increase of volume $\Delta V$, corresponding to the formation of a hole, which determines the dependence of $\mu$ on $p$ according to the formula

$$\mu = \text{const.}\, e^{p\Delta V/kT},$$

is in the case of metallic bodies much smaller than in that of substances with complex molecules. It should be mentioned that a similar difference is found in these two cases with regard to the dependence of the

† See, for instance, L. Brillouin, *Journ. de Phys.* (vii) **7**, 153 (1936); *Trans. Faraday Soc.* **33**, 54 (1937).

‡ P. Kapitza, *Journ. of Phys.* **5**, 59 (1941) and L. Landau, ibid. **5**, 71 (1941).

§ Landau's theory of the superfluidity of liquid helium II is based on the assumption that the potential energy of a liquid is a function of its *density* only, being independent of the magnitude of the shearing strain, which means that $G = 0$ even at $T = 0$.

viscosity on the temperature at a constant pressure. This correlation is easily explained by the relationship, indicated above (see p. 204), between $\Delta V$ and the activation energy $W$, required for the formation of a hole, which is proportional to the surface tension $\sigma$ multiplied by the surface of the hole, i.e. by $(\Delta V)^{\frac{2}{3}}$.

The preceding considerations have an important bearing on the problem of the structure and physical condition of the Earth. The crust, consisting mainly of silicates and extending to a depth of about 3,500 km., is characterized by an extremely strong increase of the viscosity with pressure. Accordingly, in spite of the fact that it is molten (owing to a temperature of the order of 3,000 degrees), it must be treated as an amorphous solid rather than a liquid body, as is clearly shown by the fact that transversal seismic waves of relatively low frequency can travel through it with but a very small damping. On the other hand, the metallic core of the Earth, which is a sphere with a radius of the order of 3,000 km., is known to be impermeable to such waves. This result is in full agreement with the fact that the viscosity of molten metals is but slightly affected both by the pressure and the temperature, being of the same order of magnitude as that of water under normal conditions (0·01–0·1 poise).†

## 5. Visco-elastic Effects due to Structural Changes

The relation between the volume $V$ and the pressure $p$ of a liquid is usually characterized by the linear equation

$$p = -K_1 s, \tag{14}$$

where $s = \Delta V/V_0$ denotes the relative expansion or compression (supposed to be small) and $K_1$ the bulk modulus at constant temperature or constant entropy.

Leaving this distinction aside we shall consider here certain complications due to the accompanying variation of the *structure* of the liquid.‡

In the simplest case of a monatomic liquid this variation of the structure must reduce to a change of the degree of local order in the arrangement of the particles—in the sense of a more compact arrangement when the liquid is compressed or a more open distribution when it is expanded.

In the case of binary alloys similar changes in the degree of alterna-

† Cf. Inglis, *Phys. Rev.* **59**, 178 (1941).

‡ This question has been investigated by L. Mandelstam and M. Leontovich by a method somewhat different from that developed below; see *Journ. Exp. Theor. Phys.* (Russ.), **7**, 438 (1937).

tion order must take place, and so on. This change of the degree of local order must in general *lag* with respect to the variation of the volume (or the pressure), since it is connected with a rearrangement of the particles or a redistribution of their mutual orientations, i.e. with processes requiring a certain activation energy, and proceeding accordingly with a finite velocity only.

In the case of monatomic liquids this time-lag of the arrangement with respect to the volume must obviously coincide with the mean life-time of vibrations about the same equilibrium positions which determines the ordinary viscosity of the liquid. The time-lag due to a change of the orientation of the molecules must, in general, be different from the preceding one.

Without attempting to estimate the numerical value of these time-lags, which determine the rate of the corresponding relaxation processes (i.e. of the approach to the equilibrium condition), we shall limit ourselves to the consideration of the dependence between a certain structure factor (specified by the degree of local order $\eta$, say) and the relative change $s$ of the volume.

If the latter is changed very slowly, the value of $\eta$ remains at any instant equal to that of $\bar{\eta}(s)$, which corresponds to thermodynamic equilibrium. So long as $s$ remains small this equilibrium value can be represented as a function of $s$ by the linear expression:

$$\bar{\eta} = \overline{\eta_0} - as, \tag{15}$$

where $a$ is a constant coefficient.

If at a certain instant $t = 0$, $\eta$ differs from its equilibrium value $\bar{\eta}$, then for a constant value of $s$ the difference $\eta - \bar{\eta} = \xi$ must tend to zero at a rate $-d\xi/dt$, which in the first approximation must be proportional to $\xi$, that is, according to the relaxation equation,

$$-\frac{d\xi}{dt} = \frac{1}{\tau_2}\xi, \tag{16}$$

or $\xi = \text{const.}\, e^{-t/\tau_2}$. In the general case when $s$ does not remain constant, it is necessary to introduce in the right side of this equation an additional term, proportional to $ds/dt$. This term can be determined from the obvious condition that in the limiting case of an infinite relaxation time ($\tau_2 = \infty$) the parameter $\eta$ must retain a constant value irrespective of $s$. Under such conditions $d\xi/dt$ reduces to $-d\bar{\eta}/dt$, i.e. to $a(ds/dt)$, according to (15). The general equation for $\xi$ must thus run as follows:

$$\frac{d\xi}{dt} = -\frac{1}{\tau_2}\xi + a\frac{ds}{dt}. \tag{16 a}$$

We must now determine how the pressure must depend upon $\eta$ for a constant value of the volume. To this effect let us consider the free energy of the liquid $F$ as a function of $v$ (or $s$), $\eta$, and the temperature (which will be assumed to remain constant and will therefore be left out of account in the sequel). The equilibrium value $\bar{\eta}(V)$ of $\eta$ will then be determined from the condition $F =$ minimum, i.e. $(\partial F/\partial \eta)_V = 0$.

The pressure of the liquid in the equilibrium state is given by the equation

$$\bar{p} = -\frac{d}{dV}[F, \bar{\eta}(V)] = -\left(\frac{\partial F}{\partial V}\right)_{\eta=\bar{\eta}} - \left(\frac{\partial F}{\partial \eta}\right)_{\eta=\bar{\eta}} \frac{d\bar{\eta}}{dV},$$

which in virtue of the preceding condition reduces to

$$p = -\left(\frac{\partial F}{\partial V}\right)_{\eta=\bar{\eta}}.$$

If $\eta \neq \bar{\eta}$ the equation $\quad p = -\left(\frac{\partial F}{\partial V}\right)_{\eta}$

can be used for the determination of the non-equilibrium value of the pressure, corresponding to a fixed value of $\eta$.

Putting $\eta = \bar{\eta}+\xi$ we have

$$\left(\frac{\partial F}{\partial V}\right)_{\eta} = \left[\frac{\partial}{\partial V} F(V, \bar{\eta}+\xi)\right]_{\bar{\eta},\xi} = \left[\frac{\partial}{\partial V} F(V, \bar{\eta})\right]_{\bar{\eta}} + \xi\left[\frac{\partial^2}{\partial \eta \partial V} F(V, \eta)\right]_{\eta=\bar{\eta}},$$

that is,

$$p = \bar{p} - \xi\left[\frac{\partial^2 F(V, \eta)}{\partial V \partial \eta}\right]_{\eta=\bar{\eta}}.$$

On the other hand, from the identity

$$\frac{d}{dV}\left(\frac{\partial F}{\partial \eta}\right)_{\eta=\bar{\eta}} = \left(\frac{\partial^2 F}{\partial V \partial \eta}\right)_{\eta=\bar{\eta}} + \left(\frac{\partial^2 F}{\partial \eta^2}\right)_{\eta=\bar{\eta}} \frac{d\bar{\eta}}{dV} = 0$$

there follows

$$\left(\frac{\partial^2 F}{\partial V \partial \eta}\right)_{\eta=\bar{\eta}} = -\frac{d\bar{\eta}}{dV}\left(\frac{\partial^2 F}{\partial \eta^2}\right)_{\eta=\bar{\eta}}.$$

Substituting this expression in the preceding equation we get

$$p = \bar{p} + \left(\frac{\partial^2 F}{\partial \eta^2}\right)_{\eta=\bar{\eta}} \frac{d\bar{\eta}}{dV} \xi.$$

Since $\eta = \bar{\eta}$ corresponds to a minimum of $F$, the second derivative of $F$ with respect to $\eta$ must have a positive value, which will be denoted by $V_0 b$. Noting further that $d\bar{\eta}/dV = -a/V$, according to (15) we get, writing $V_0+V_0 s$ for $V$ and $\Delta p$ for $p$,

$$\Delta p = \Delta\bar{p} - ab\xi, \tag{17}$$

or finally, according to (14),

$$\Delta p = -K_1 s - ab\xi. \tag{17 a}$$

In order to obtain a relationship between $\Delta p$ and $s$ we must eliminate $\xi$ from this equation and the equation (16 a).

Let us put
$$\Delta p = \Delta p_1 + \Delta p_2, \tag{18}$$
where $\Delta p_1 = -K_1 s$ (equilibrium part of $\Delta p$) and $\Delta p = ab\xi$ (non-equilibrium part). Substituting the expression $\xi = \Delta p_2/ab$ in (16 a) we get
$$\frac{1}{ab}\left(\frac{d\Delta p_2}{dt} + \frac{1}{\tau_2}\Delta p_2\right) = a\frac{ds}{dt}, \tag{18 a}$$
that is,
$$-\frac{ds}{dt} = \frac{1}{K_2}\frac{d\Delta p_2}{dt} + \frac{1}{\mu_2}\Delta p_2, \tag{18 b}$$
where
$$K_2 = a^2 b \quad \text{and} \quad \mu_2 = K_2 \tau_2. \tag{18 c}$$
The equation (18 b) is of exactly the same form as Maxwell's equation (10), the parameter $K_2$ playing the role of the modulus of compressibility, and $\mu_2$ of the viscosity coefficient. Since they characterize the corrections in the expression of $p$ as a function of $s$ which are due to a deviation from the equilibrium state, they will be denoted as the 'deviation' modulus of compressibility and the 'deviation' volume-viscosity coefficient.

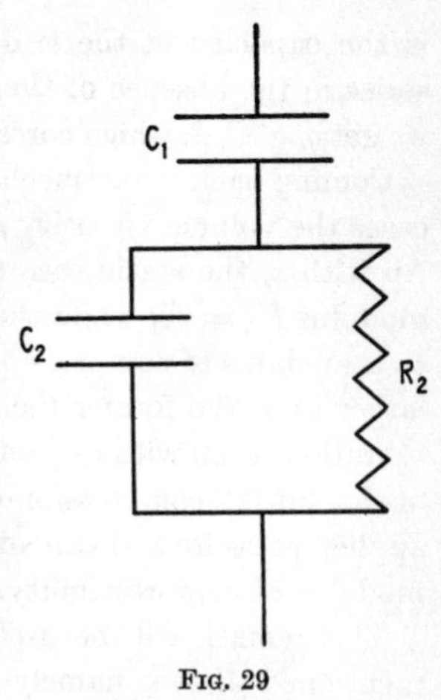

Fig. 29

The relation between $\Delta p$ and $s$, described by the preceding equations, is quite similar to the relation between the voltage $\phi$ and the quantity of electricity $q$ in the case of an electric circuit consisting of a capacity $C_1$ connected in series with a circuit formed by a parallel connexion of a capacity $C_2$ and a resistance $R_2$ (Fig. 29).† In fact, the total value of the voltage is equal to the sum of a part $\phi_1 = (1/C_1)q$ corresponding to the charging of the first condenser and of a part $\phi_2 = (1/C_2)q' = R_2(dq''/dt)$ where $q'$ is the fraction of $q$ passing through the second condenser, while $dq''/dt = I$ is the current flowing through the resistance $R_2$; the sum $q'+q''$ is equal to $q$. It should be noted that the capacities $C_1$ and $C_2$ play the role of the coefficients of compressibility $\kappa_1 = 1/K_1$, $\kappa_2 = 1/K_2$, while $R_2$ corresponds to the volume viscosity $\mu_2$. The expression (18 c) for $\tau_2$ corresponds to

† This analogy has been developed by Burgers, *First Report on Viscosity and Plasticity*, Amsterdam (1935), and by Guemant, *Trans. Faraday Soc.* **21**, 1583 (1935).

the well-known formula $\tau_2 = R_2 C_2$ for the electric relaxation time of the circuit $(R_2, C_2)$.

We shall make use of this analogy to illustrate two very simple cases, namely the case of steady harmonic vibrations and that of a suddenly applied voltage of constant magnitude.

In the former case we have, assuming $q$ and $\phi$ to be proportional to $e^{i\omega t}$,

$$\phi_2 = \frac{1}{C_2} q' = i\omega R_2 q'',$$

and consequently $q'+q'' = q = C_2 \phi_2 + \frac{\phi_2}{R_2 i\omega} = C_2\left(1+\frac{1}{i\omega\tau_2}\right)\phi_2$, whence

$$\phi = \phi_1+\phi_2 = q\left[\frac{1}{C_1}+\frac{1}{C_2(1+1/i\omega\tau_2)}\right].$$

In the case $\omega = \infty$ this expression reduces to $q = C\phi$, where

$$C = \frac{C_1 C_2}{C_1+C_2}$$

is the capacity of the two condensers connected with each other in series in the absence of the resistance $R_2$. In the opposite case $\omega = 0$ we get $q = C_1 \phi$, which corresponds to the absence both of $R_2$ and of $C_2$.

Coming back to our mechanical problem, we see that in both extreme cases the volume viscosity $\mu_2$ disappears from the equation connecting $\Delta p$ with $s$, the static case $(\omega = 0)$ corresponding to a compressibility modulus $K_0 = K_1$ while the case of very rapid vibrations corresponds to a modulus of compressibility $K_\infty = K_1+K_2$. The latter is naturally larger than the former (i.e. the body is 'harder' with respect to rapid vibrations than with respect to slow ones). It is obviously characteristic of the 'initial' compressibility of the body when subjected to a suddenly applied pressure and can accordingly be denoted as the 'instantaneous' modulus of compressibility.

This remark will be useful for the solution of the second problem, mentioned above, namely the variation of the volume of the body under the influence of a suddenly applied pressure.

Availing ourselves of the electric analogy, we have in this case $\frac{dq}{dt} = C_2\frac{d\phi_2}{dt}+\frac{\phi_2}{R_2}$ and $q = C_1\phi_1$ under the condition $\phi_1+\phi_2 = \phi = \text{const.}$ for $t > 0$ and $q = 0$ for $t < 0$. Replacing $\phi_2$ by $\phi-\phi_1 = \phi-q/C_1$ we get

$$\frac{dq}{dt} = -\frac{C_2}{C_1}\frac{dq}{dt}-\frac{q}{C_1 R_2}+\frac{\phi}{R_2},$$

that is,

$$\left(1+\frac{C_2}{C_1}\right)\frac{dq}{dt}+\frac{q}{C_1 R_2} = \frac{\phi}{R_2}.$$

The solution of this equation has the following form:

$$q = C_1\phi + Ae^{-t/\tau_2'} \quad (t \geqslant 0)$$

where $\tau_2' = R_2(C_1+C_2) = \tau_2(1+C_1/C_2)$, while $A$ is a certain constant. It can be determined from the condition that at the instant $t = 0$, when the voltage $\phi$ is applied, the charge $q$ must be determined by the 'instantaneous' capacity $C = C_1 C_2/(C_1+C_2)$.

We thus have
$$C_1\phi + A = q_0 = \frac{C_1 C_2}{C_1+C_2}\phi,$$

whence $A = -C_1^2\phi/(C_1+C_2)$ and finally

$$q = C_1\phi\left[1 - \frac{C_1}{C_1+C_2}e^{-t/\tau_2'}\right],$$

or
$$q = q_0 + q',$$

where $q_0 = C_1 C_2\phi/(C_1+C_2)$ is the initial charge at the instant when the voltage $\phi$ is applied, while

$$q' = \frac{C_1^2}{C_1+C_2}\phi(1-e^{-t/\tau_2'})$$

is the additional 'relaxation' charge, acquired gradually after this application. At $t = \infty$ the total charge $q$ reduces to the static value $C_1\phi$. It should be noted that the corresponding relaxation time $\tau_2'$ differs (by a factor $1+C_1/C_2$) from the 'proper' relaxation time $\tau_2 = R_2 C_2$.

In a similar way the total compression of a body due to a sudden application of a constant pressure $\Delta p$ consists of an instantaneous part $s_0 = -\Delta p/(K_1+K_2)$ and of a relaxation part

$$s' = -\frac{\Delta p}{K_1(1+K_1/K_2)}(1-e^{-t/\tau_2'})$$

with a 'relaxation' modulus of compressibility

$$K' = K_1\left(1+\frac{K_1}{K_2}\right)$$

and an effective relaxation time

$$\tau_2' = \tau_2\left(1+\frac{K_2}{K_1}\right) = \mu_2\left(\frac{1}{K_1}+\frac{1}{K_2}\right).$$

The dependence of the compression on the time is represented in Fig. 30 for the case in which the constant pressure applied at the instant $t = 0$ is suddenly removed at an instant $t_1$. This brings out an instantaneous decrease of $s$ by the value $s_0$, the remaining compression taking place gradually according to the equation $s' = s_0'(1-e^{-t/\tau_2'})$.

These results can be checked experimentally only when the relaxation time $\tau_2$ or $\tau_2'$ is large enough—of the order of a second or more. This condition is realized for amorphous bodies (i.e. supercooled liquids) in the vicinity of the so-called 'solidification temperature', below which they acquire an enormous viscosity (of the order of $10^{13}$).

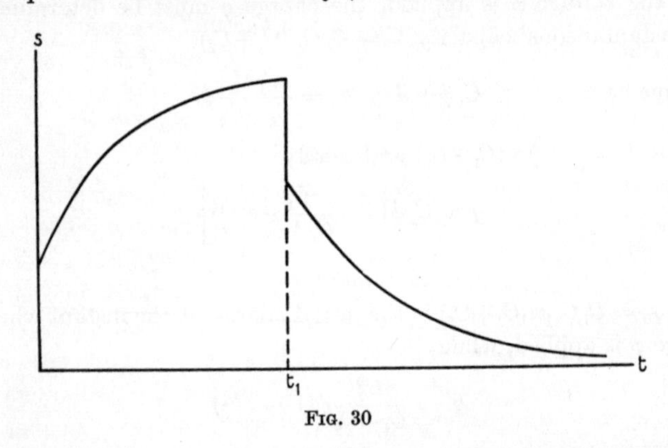


FIG. 30

It has usually been supposed, following a view originally expressed by Tammann, that this increase of viscosity taking place near a certain temperature $T_g$ is accompanied by a sharp change of all the other properties of the body, namely by a decrease of its compressibility, its thermal expansion coefficient, electric conductivity, etc. Systematic investigations carried out in recent years, essentially by P. Kobeko and his co-workers, on the properties of amorphous bodies† have shown, however, that no such abrupt change actually takes place if the time of observation is sufficiently increased on cooling the body below $T_g$, and that the results obtained are due to an enormously rapid increase of the relaxation time with decrease of temperature in the neighbourhood of $T_g$ from values of the order of a small fraction of a second for, say, $T = T_g+5°$, up to extremely high values of the order of minutes, hours, and even days for $T = T_g-5°$. The solidification temperature has thus no objective meaning and can be defined as a temperature for which the relaxation time, determining the approach of the structure of the body towards equilibrium, is of the order of 1 second. Using the ordinary method of measuring the compressibility of the body (by means of low-frequency acoustical vibrations, for example) we obtain

† Kobeko, Kuwshinsky, and Gurewitch, *Bull. Acad. Sci. U.R.S.S.*, série physique, **3**, 329 (1937); Kobeko, Kuwshinsky, and Shishkin, *Acta Phys. Chim. U.R.S.S.* **6**, 225 (1937); *Journ. of Phys.* **3**, 287 (1940).

for the compressibility modulus $K$ the static value $K$ just above the 'solidification' temperature and the instantaneous value $K_1+K_2$ just below it. More accurate measurements show that in both cases the total deformation of the body can be represented as the sum of the instantaneous and of the relaxation parts.

Similar results are obtained for the thermal expansion coefficient (the 'static' value of which at $T > T_g$ is larger than the 'instantaneous' one at $T < T_g$, since this coefficient is inversely proportional to the compressibility modulus) and also for the electrical conductivity of glasses with an admixture of alkali metals (see Ch. VIII, § 3).

It should be mentioned that the notion of equilibrium structure and equilibrium properties has a somewhat relative meaning when applied to an amorphous solid, which can be treated as a liquid in a metastable 'supercooled' state. The structure of such a body is, by definition, quite different from that crystalline structure which corresponds to thermodynamic equilibrium. So long, however, as the crystallization velocity remains negligibly small, we can speak of an amorphous structure with local order only, which corresponds to a smaller value of the free energy of the body than all the other slightly different structures of the same type as that of an 'equilibrium' structure. The minimum of the energy characterizing such a 'relative equilibrium' must be considered, accordingly, as a relative minimum, which is separated from the absolute minimum by a very high potential (or rather free energy) barrier.

That part of the compressibility of amorphous bodies which is due to a small variation of their structure accompanying a variation of the specific volume is intimately connected with their volume viscosity. These two properties can therefore be conveniently amalgamated under the title of 'structural visco-elasticity'.

A quite similar 'visco-elasticity' of structural origin has been recently discovered by P. Kobeko and his co-workers in the case of such deformations of amorphous solid bodies as affect mainly their shape, leaving the volume practically constant, and as can, accordingly, be reduced to a shearing strain of the same type as is found in the flow of practically incompressible liquids. They differ, however, essentially from this case with respect to the character of the dynamical resistance, i.e. with respect to the relationship between this strain and the corresponding shearing stress. In the simplest case (of which rubber is a most ostensible example) the flow or shear under consideration turns out to be wholly *reversible*, as in ordinary elastic bodies, and yet, at the same time, it is associated not only with an elastic but also with a viscous stress. The investigations of P. Kobeko have shown that the total shear (flow) due to the sudden application of a shearing stress $P_{xy}$ of a constant magnitude consists of two parts: an instantaneous one $s_0 = 1/G_\infty$ and a 'visco-elastic' part, increasing with the time according to the relaxation law of exactly the same type

$$s' = \frac{1}{G'}P(1-e^{-t/\tau_2'})$$

as the structural part of the change of volume under a suddenly applied pressure, considered above. On the removal of the stress $P_{xy}$ the first part of $s$ vanishes instantly, while the second is gradually diminished according to the equation

$$s' = \text{const.}\ e^{-t/\tau_2'}.$$

This *reversible* character of the flow which we are here considering sharply differentiates it from the usual irreversible flow, observed in most liquids both in the normal and in the supercooled state. Since the relaxation time $\tau_2'$ rapidly increases as the temperature is decreased below a certain point $T_g$, the viscosity associated with the reversible flow often escapes attention, the body being described as purely elastic with a shear modulus $G_0 = G_1$ above $T_g$ and a larger shear modulus $G_\infty = G_1+G_2$ below it.

The existence of the reversible flow of amorphous solids above $T_g$ can be established with the help of high-frequency vibrations, and below $T_g$ by a sufficiently long, sometimes a year long, exposure to the action of a constant force.

Making use of the vibration method M. Kornfeld† has shown that the relaxation time $\tau_2'$ of rubber at room temperature is of the order of $10^{-7}$ sec., while at $-60°$ C. it becomes very large, of the order of a few minutes at least. This explains the fact that rubber loses its characteristic high elasticity at low temperatures (and even becomes brittle at the temperature of liquid air). The special feature of rubber which distinguishes it from ordinary amorphous bodies consists in the smallness of its relaxation shearing modulus $G' = G_1(1+G_1/G_2)$ compared with the instantaneous one $G_1+G_2$, or what amounts to the same thing, in the smallness of the static modulus $G_1$ compared with the deviation modulus $G_2$; whereas the instantaneous modulus has the same order of magnitude as in the case of ordinary solid bodies ($10^6$ kg./cm.$^2$), the static (or relaxation) shearing modulus is of the order of only 10–20

† M. Kornfeld, *C.R. Acad. Sci. U.R.S.S.* **38**, 312 (1943).

kg./cm.², i.e. 100,000 times smaller. This explains—though in a purely formal way—the huge visco-elastic deformations of a reversible character that are caused in rubber by relatively weak forces (at sufficiently high temperatures for which the relaxation time $\tau_2'$ is small enough).

The question of the cause of the smallness of the relaxation rigidity modulus of rubber and certain other rubber-like substances will be considered in detail in § 6 of Ch. VIII. It should be noted here that apart from this peculiarity rubber does not differ from ordinary 'glassy' amorphous bodies.

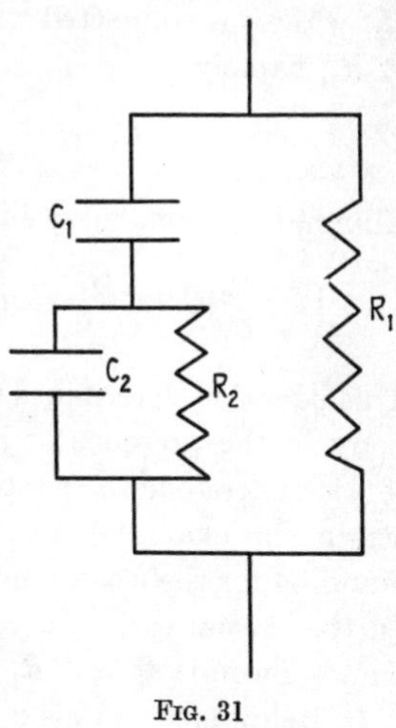

FIG. 31

The preceding results referring to the visco-elasticity of shape can be derived in a general way with the help of equations of exactly the same type as in the case of the visco-elasticity of volume. To this effect the free energy of the body $F$ must be treated as a function of a parameter $s$ specifying the change of shape (at constant volume) and of a certain structure parameter $\eta$, defining for example the degree of orientation of the molecules (or their extension in a given direction), the equilibrium value of this parameter being determined by th condition $F =$ minimum. In this way equations of the same type (18) and (18 a) are obtained as in the case of deformations that reduce to a change of volume, without change of shape, the deviation modulus of rigidity $G_2$ having an essentially positive value $ba^2$ (where $b > 0$).

The above theory does not take into account the fact that, along with the reversible fluidity due to a modification of the structure with change of shape, all amorphous bodies, however rigid they may appear, possess a certain amount of ordinary irreversible fluidity which may escape notice because of its smallness, i.e. because of an excessively high value of the ordinary viscosity coefficient $\mu_1$.

Coming back to the electric analogy we can account for this ordinary fluidity by connecting with the circuit $(C_1, C_2, R_2)$ considered above (Fig. 29) a resistance $R_1$ in parallel with it. This is equivalent to the introduction, into a simple circuit $(C_1, R_1)$ illustrating the connexion of the shearing elasticity with the irreversible fluidity, of an exactly similar circuit $(C_2, R_2)$ switched in series with the capacity $C_1$. The resulting complex circuit is represented in Fig. 31.

The relationship between the quantity of electricity $Q$ that has been passed through such a circuit and the applied voltage $\phi$ is given by the following equations

$$Q = q_0 + q, \qquad \phi = R_1 \dot{q}_0, \tag{19}$$

where $\dot{q}_0$ is the strength of the current flowing through the resistance $R_1$, while $q$ is connected with $\phi$ by the same equation as in the absence of $R_1$, namely

$$q = C_1 \phi_1, \qquad \dot{q} = C_2 \dot{\phi}_2 + \frac{\phi_2}{R_2}, \qquad \phi_1 + \phi_2 = \phi. \tag{19 a}$$

Eliminating from these equations $q$, $q_0$, $\phi_1$ and $\phi_2$, we get

$$\left(1+\frac{C_2}{C_1}\right)\ddot{Q} + \frac{\dot{Q}}{C_1 R_2} = C_2 \ddot{\phi} + \left[\frac{1}{R_1}\left(1+\frac{C_2}{C_1}\right) + \frac{1}{R_2}\right]\dot{\phi} + \frac{\phi}{C_1 R_1 R_2}. \tag{19 b}$$

This equation determines the motion of a visco-elastic (incompressible) body in the presence of both the reversible and irreversible fluidity, if $Q$ is understood to denote the change of shape (defined by the shearing strain for example) and $\phi$ the corresponding force, $1/C_1$ and $1/C_2$ standing for the elastic moduli and $R_1$, $R_2$ for the viscosity coefficients. In the special case of a constant force equation (19 b) reduces to the simple formula $\dot{Q} = \phi/R_1$ defining the usual irreversible flow.

P. Rehbinder and his co-workers have recently obtained and investigated (very incompletely) a number of 'structurated' non-Newtonian liquids (gels), which combine a high fluidity of the usual irreversible type with a peculiar elasticity similar to that of rubber, though of a much smaller magnitude.† These highly elastic liquids can be specified, just as rubber, by a small static modulus $G_1$, in connexion with a relatively small viscosity coefficient $\mu_1$. This relationship between $G_1$ and $\mu_1$ fully agrees with Maxwell's equation $\mu_1/G_1 = \tau$ on the assumption that the relaxation time defined by it preserves the same meaning as in the absence of complicating structural effects.‡ As a matter of fact, however, in the presence of such complications the relaxation time becomes dependent upon the character of the corresponding process. This is illustrated by the fact, considered above, that in the special case $\mu_1 = \infty$ the relaxation time for harmonic vibrations is equal to $\tau_2 = \mu_2/G_2$, while for a reversible deformation due to the sudden application of a constant force it is equal to $\tau_2' = \mu(1/G_1 + 1/G_2)$. In the

† The oscillation period of a pendulum was *decreased* by dipping it into such a liquid.

‡ It should be noted that in the case of rubber $\mu_1$ is extremely large in spite of the smallness of $G_1$.

general case the notion of relaxation time becomes devoid of a definite meaning.†

This question has not yet been subjected to a systematic experimental study. The experiments of Kobeko and his co-workers always referred to amorphous bodies practically incapable of irreversible flow ($\mu_1 = \infty$) and displaying accordingly a definite relaxation time. The

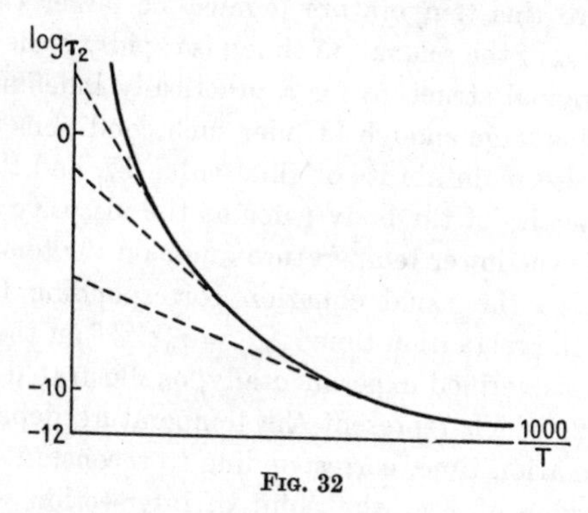


FIG. 32

dependence of the latter on the temperature can be represented with sufficient accuracy by the usual equation $\tau_2 = \text{const.}\, e^{U/kT}$ in the region of high temperatures only—much higher than Tammann's solidification temperature $T_g$ and, indeed, lying close to the crystallization point. On further cooling, the increase of $\tau_2$ becomes much more rapid and can be represented by the preceding formula if the activation energy $U$ is treated as a function of the temperature of the form $U_0 e^{W/kT}$, where $U_0$ and $W$ are constants (Waterton). Fig. 32 illustrates the dependence of $\log \tau_2$ upon the temperature or rather on $1/T$, which Shishkin‡ has obtained by measuring the electric conductivity of glycerine. The limiting value of $\tau$ obtained by extrapolation for $T \to \infty$ is equal to $3.10^{-12}$ sec., that is, has the same order of magnitude as the period of the vibrations, according to the simple formula $\tau = \tau_0 e^{U_0/kT}$ (with $U_0 = \text{const.}$).

The increase of $U$ on lowering the temperature is obviously due to the accompanying change of the structure. If the latter is specified by a parameter $\eta$ (having the meaning of the degree of local order) the activation energy $U$ must obviously be treated as a certain function of $\eta$, and consequently of the temperature $T$, if we are dealing with

† The difference between $\tau_2$ and $\tau_2'$ has not been checked experimentally hitherto.
‡ N. Shishkin, *Diss. Kazan*, 1942.

thermodynamically stable states (in the relative sense, defined above), for which $\eta$ is a definite function of $\eta = \bar{\eta}(T)$.

The relaxation time $\tau_2$ can be used in the consideration of very small deviations of $\eta$ from its (relative) equilibrium value. If, however, the amorphous body, after being kept at a given temperature $T_0$ for a sufficient length of time $t$ in order to reach the equilibrium structure corresponding to this temperature ($t$ must be larger than the corresponding value $\tau_2$ of the relaxation time), is rapidly cooled down, it can maintain its original structure for a practically indefinite time if the new value of $\tau_2^0$ is large enough. Under such conditions the activation energy $U$ will also maintain its original value $U_0$, and the dependence of various properties of the body (such as the viscosity or the electric conductivity) in the lower temperature range on the temperature must again conform to the usual equation corresponding to the normal dependence of the relaxation time $\tau_{\eta=\eta_0} = \tau_0 e^{U_0/kT}$ on the temperature. This conclusion is verified experimentally, as illustrated by the dotted lines of Fig. 32, which represent the temperature dependence of the 'apparent' relaxation time, corresponding to a constant structure (defined by the value of $\eta$ at the point of intersection with the curve representing the temperature dependence of the 'equilibrium' relaxation time).

## 6. The Thermal Theory of the Visco-elasticity of Gases and Liquids (Kneser)

The theory of the volume viscosity of liquids developed in the preceding section is formally similar to Einstein's theory of the anomalous viscosity of a diatomic gas, as revealed by the abnormally large absorption of sound waves propagated at a high temperature, when a large fraction of the molecules is dissociated into separate atoms.† So long as the vibrations of the gas can be treated as adiabatic, the degree of dissociation, which in a state of thermodynamical equilibrium is a definite function of the temperature, must deviate from this equilibrium value, lagging to a smaller or larger extent with respect to the temperature. This circumstance, due account being taken of the dependence of the pressure on the temperature and on the number of atoms and molecules in unit volume, leads to an equation of the form (17a), the parameter $\xi$ denoting the deviation of the degree of dissociation from the equilibrium value.

If the temperature of the gas has a moderate value, the dissociation

† A. Einstein, *Berl. Ber.* **19**, 380 (1920).

and the volume viscosity associated with it in the case of acoustical vibrations can be neglected. It has been shown, however, by Kneser† that in this case the same role can be played by a deviation from equilibrium of the distribution of the energy of heat motion between the 'external' and 'internal' degrees of freedom. The former are understood to represent the translation and rotation motion of the molecules (since they remain in equilibrium with each other so far as the energy distribution between them is concerned), while the latter refer to the vibrations of the atoms constituting the molecule under consideration.

In the case of statistical equilibrium a change of the energy $E$ of the gas by $dE$, corresponding to the increase of the temperature by $dT$, can be represented as the sum of two parts $dE_e = C_e\,dT$ and $dE_i = C_i\,dT$, where $C_e$ is the fraction of the total specific heat of the gas $C$ which corresponds to the external degrees of freedom, while $C_i$ corresponds to the internal degrees of freedom ($C_e + C_i = C$).

Since the energy exchange between the external and internal degrees of freedom requires a certain finite length of time, the equilibrium partition of $dE$ between $dE_e$ and $dE_i$ is departed from in the case of sufficiently rapid vibrations. This condition can be described as a departure of the 'external' temperature of the gas $T_e$, as determined by the average kinetic energy of the translation or rotation motion, from the 'internal' temperature $T_i$, specifying in the usual way (with due allowance for quantum effects) the energy of the intermolecular vibrations. In Kneser's theory the difference $T_e - T_i$ plays the role of the parameter $\xi$.

This theory can be applied, in principle, not only to gases but also to liquids and solid bodies, and can be stated in the following general form.

In the case of statistical equilibrium the dependence of the pressure $p$ on the volume $V$, with due allowance for the accompanying variation of the temperature, is expressed by the equation

$$\Delta p = \left(\frac{\partial p}{\partial V}\right)_T \Delta V + \left(\frac{\partial p}{\partial T}\right)_V \Delta T,$$

the relationship between $\Delta V$ and $\Delta T$ being determined by the condition

$$\Delta S = \left(\frac{\partial S}{\partial V}\right)_T \Delta V + \left(\frac{\partial S}{\partial T}\right)_V \Delta T = 0,$$

where $S = -\partial F/\partial T$ is the entropy of the body (or of a given part of it). With the help of the well-known relations $(\partial S/\partial V)_T = (\partial p/\partial T)_V$ and

† H. Kneser, *Zeits. techn. Phys.* **16**, 213 (1937); *Ann. d. Phys.* **32**, 277 (1938).

$(\partial S/\partial T)_V = C/T$ where $C$ is the specific heat at constant volume, the preceding equation may be rewritten in the form

$$\left(\frac{\partial p}{\partial T}\right)_V \Delta V + \frac{C}{T}\Delta T = 0,$$

whence
$$\left(\frac{\partial T}{\partial V}\right)_S = -\frac{T}{C}\left(\frac{\partial p}{\partial T}\right)_V$$

and consequently
$$\Delta p = \left[\left(\frac{\partial p}{\partial V}\right)_T - \frac{T}{C}\left(\frac{\partial p}{\partial T}\right)_V^2\right]\Delta V.$$

If, on the other hand, $V$ is considered as a function of $p$ and $T$, we get from the condition $dV = 0$

$$\left(\frac{\partial V}{\partial p}\right)_T dp + \left(\frac{\partial V}{\partial T}\right)_p dT = 0,$$

that is,
$$-\frac{1}{K_0}dp + \alpha\, dT = 0$$

or
$$\left(\frac{\partial p}{\partial T}\right)_V = K_0\alpha, \tag{20}$$

where $\alpha$ is the thermal expansion coefficient and $K_0$ the isothermal modulus of compressibility. We thus get

$$\Delta p = -K_1 s, \tag{20 a}$$

where
$$K_1 = K_0\left(1 + \frac{V_0 K_0 \alpha^2 T}{C}\right) \tag{20 b}$$

is the adiabatic compressibility modulus. In the case of an ideal gas $\alpha = \frac{1}{V_0}\left(\frac{dV}{dT}\right)_p = \frac{R}{pV_0} = \frac{1}{T}$ and $K_0 = p$, so that $\frac{V_0 K_0 \alpha^2 T}{C} = \frac{R}{C}$ and $K_1 = K_0\frac{C+R}{C}$, where $C+R$ is the specific heat at constant pressure. This relation is easily generalized to the case of condensed bodies. In fact, the specific heat at constant pressure is equal to

$$C_p = T\left(\frac{\partial S}{\partial T}\right)_p = T\left(\frac{\partial S}{\partial T}\right)_V + T\left(\frac{\partial S}{\partial V}\right)_T\left(\frac{\partial V}{\partial T}\right)_p = T\left(\frac{\partial S}{\partial T}\right)_V + T\left(\frac{\partial p}{\partial T}\right)_V\left(\frac{\partial V}{\partial T}\right)_p,$$

so that

$$C_p - C_v = T\left(\frac{\partial p}{\partial T}\right)_V\left(\frac{\partial V}{\partial T}\right)_p = -T\left(\frac{\partial V}{\partial T}\right)_p^2\left(\frac{\partial p}{\partial V}\right)_T = V_0 K_0 \alpha^2 T,$$

and consequently
$$K_1 = K_0\frac{C_p}{C_v} \quad (C_v = C). \tag{20 c}$$

Turning now to the case of states deviating from that of equilibrium, we must introduce, instead of a single temperature $T$, two different temperatures $T_e$ and $T_i$. Since the pressure $p$ (at constant volume) must depend on $T_e$ only, in exactly the same way as it depends on $T$ in the case of thermodynamical equilibrium, the original expression for $\Delta p$ must be replaced by the following one:

$$\Delta p = \left(\frac{\partial p}{\partial V}\right)_{T_e} \Delta V + \left(\frac{\partial p}{\partial T_e}\right) \Delta T_e,$$

or according to (20)

$$\Delta p = -K_0 s + K_0 \alpha \Delta T_e, \tag{21}$$

where $\Delta T_e = T_e - T_0$ denotes the deviation of the 'external' temperature from the normal (average) value $T_0$. Denoting the corresponding deviation of the internal temperature by $\Delta T_i$ we can write the condition for the adiabatic character of the vibrations in the form

$$C_e \Delta T_e + C_i \Delta T_i + V_0 K_0 \alpha T_0 s = 0,$$

or introducing the parameter $\xi = \Delta T_i - \Delta T_e = T_i - T_e$,

$$C \Delta T_e + C_i \xi + V_0 K_0 \alpha T_0 s = 0. \tag{21 a}$$

The dependence of this parameter upon the time is determined by an equation of the usual relaxation type

$$\frac{d\xi}{dt} = -\frac{1}{\tau_2} \xi + f,$$

where $\tau_2$ is the relaxation time for the establishment of equilibrium between the external and internal degrees of freedom, while the additional term $f$ can be identified with the limiting value of $d\xi/dt$ for $\tau_2 = \infty$. Since in this case $\Delta T_i = 0$, i.e. $-\xi = \Delta T_e$, we must have

$$\frac{d\xi}{dt} = -\frac{d}{dt} \Delta T_e = \frac{V_0 K_0 \alpha T_0}{C_e} \frac{ds}{dt}.$$

Hence, finally,

$$\frac{d\xi}{dt} = -\frac{1}{\tau_2} \xi + \frac{V_0 K_0 \alpha T_0}{C_e} \frac{ds}{dt}. \tag{22}$$

Substituting in (21) the value of $\Delta T_e$ from (21 a) we have, on the other hand,

$$\Delta p = -K_0 \left(1 + \frac{V_0 K_0 \alpha^2 T_0}{C}\right) s - \frac{K_0 \alpha C_i}{C} \xi,$$

or

$$\Delta p = -K_1 s - \frac{K_0 \alpha C_i}{C} \xi, \tag{22 a}$$

where, according to (20 a), $K_1$ is the adiabatic modulus of compressibility. The equations (22) and (22 a) are identical with the equations (16 a) and (17 a) if we put

$$a = \frac{V_0 K_0 \alpha T_0}{C_e} \quad \text{and} \quad ab = \frac{K_0 \alpha C_i}{C}.$$

The mechanism we are now considering thus leads to the following values of the 'deviation compressibility modulus':

$$K_2 = V_0 K_0^2 \alpha^2 T_0 \frac{C_i}{CC_e} = K_0 \frac{C_p - C_v}{C_v} \frac{C_i}{C_e},$$

the corresponding viscosity coefficient being equal to the product $K_2 \tau_2$.

Kneser believes that this mechanism is capable of giving a satisfactory explanation of the abnormally large absorption of the acoustic (and ultrasonic) vibrations in liquid bodies without any reference to structure effects. This point of view is, however, contradicted by the fact that Kneser's theory is obviously inapplicable to the case of transverse vibrations in amorphous bodies, which, as we have seen above, are characterized by visco-elastic effects of exactly the same kind as ordinary (longitudinal) sound vibrations. We shall consider this question at a greater length in the next section.

## 7. Generalization of the Equations of the Elasticity Theory of Amorphous Bodies

The classical hydrodynamical theory, as expressed by the Navier–Stokes equations, left out of account Maxwell's relaxation theory of shearing elasticity as well as the visco-elastic structure effects discussed in § 5 (although Stokes has recognized, in principle, the necessity of considering a second 'volume' viscosity besides the ordinary shearing viscosity). On the other hand, the classical theory of elasticity of amorphous bodies wholly ignored their fluidity and the associated viscous effects.

After establishing the fact that liquids and amorphous solids can be distinguished from each other in a purely quantitative way only, we must consider the problem of finding such a generalization of the equations of classical hydrodynamics and elasticity theory as would be capable of describing the laws of motion of actual condensed bodies, combining the properties of ordinary liquids and solids.

The necessity of such a revision of classical hydrodynamics and theory of elasticity directly follows from the continuous character of the transition from the liquid state into the solid one when this transition is not accompanied by crystallization.

It can be concluded from this continuity, among other things, that transverse vibrations can be propagated not only in solid bodies, as usually admitted, but also in liquids. The fact that this conclusion is not verified experimentally in the case of ordinary liquids is explained by the smallness of their relaxation time compared with the period of the vibrations which can be obtained even with the help of modern electro-acoustical methods. Under such conditions the transverse vibrations must undergo a very strong damping.

Limiting ourselves to the case of small vibrations, we shall take as our starting-point the equations of the classical elasticity theory and shall try to generalize them by introducing the various visco-elastic effects discussed in the preceding sections (including the ordinary fluidity).

The equations of motion of a continuous isotropic medium can be written in the following general form:

$$\rho \frac{\partial^2 u_i}{\partial t^2} = \sum_{n=1}^{3} \frac{\partial f_{ik}}{\partial x_k}, \tag{23}$$

where $\rho$ is the density of the medium, $u_i(x_1, x_2, x_3, t)$ the components of the (small) displacement of a particle originally situated at the point $x_1$, $x_2$, $x_3$, and $f_{ik}$ the components of the stress tensor.

In the case of idealized solids (deprived of fluidity and other properties of a relaxation character) the quantities $f_{ik}$ are connected with the components of the strain tensor

$$s_{ik} = \frac{1}{2}\left(\frac{\partial u_i}{\partial x_k} + \frac{\partial u_k}{\partial x_i}\right)$$

by linear relations of the form

$$f_{ik} = \delta_{ik} Ls + 2Ms_{ik}, \tag{24}$$

where $s = s_{11}+s_{22}+s_{33} = \operatorname{div} \mathbf{u}$ is the relative change of specific volume $\Delta V/V_0$, $\delta_{ik} = 1$ for $i = k$ and $0$ for $i \neq k$, while $L$ and $M$ denote two coefficients, usually denoted as $\lambda$ and $\mu$; $M$ is nothing but the modulus of rigidity $G_1$.

If the expressions (24) are substituted in the equations (23), the latter acquire the following form:

$$\rho \frac{\partial^2 u_i}{\partial t^2} = L \frac{\partial s}{\partial x_i} + M \sum_{k=1}^{3} \left(\frac{\partial^2 u_i}{\partial x_k^2} + \frac{\partial^2 u_k}{\partial x_i \partial x_k}\right) = (L+M) \frac{\partial s}{\partial x_i} + M \nabla^2 u_i,$$

or in vector notation:

$$\rho \frac{\partial^2 \mathbf{u}}{\partial t^2} = (L+M) \nabla s + M \nabla^2 \mathbf{u}. \tag{25}$$

Taking the divergence of both sides and remembering that $\operatorname{div} \mathbf{u} = s$, we obtain an equation

$$\rho \frac{\partial^2 s}{\partial t^2} = K \nabla^2 s, \tag{25 a}$$

which describes the propagation of compression (longitudinal) waves with a velocity $v = \sqrt{(K/\rho)}$, where $K = L+2M$ is the appropriate elastic modulus.

In the case of transverse vibrations, for which the density remains constant ($s = 0$), equation (25) reduces to

$$\frac{\partial^2 \mathbf{u}}{\partial t^2} = M\nabla^2 \mathbf{u} \tag{25 b}$$

and describes the propagation of waves with a velocity $v_t = \sqrt{(M/\rho)}$.

We shall now consider the way these equations must be generalized in order to include the effects of fluidity and other relaxation effects discussed in § 5.†

The strain tensor $s_{ik}$ can be resolved in a way invariant with respect to rotations of the coordinate system, into two parts, one part

$$\sigma_{ik} = \tfrac{1}{3}\delta_{ik}\, s \tag{26}$$

specifying the volume change, while the other part

$$\tau_{ik} = s_{ik} - \tfrac{1}{3}\delta_{ik}\, s \tag{26 a}$$

specifies the change of shape at constant volume ($\sum \tau_{ii} = 0$).

In a similar way it is possible to resolve the stress tensor $f_{ik}$ into a volume part

$$\phi_{ik} = \tfrac{1}{3}\delta_{ik} f = -\delta_{ik}\, p, \tag{27}$$

where $p = -\frac{1}{3}(f_{11}+f_{22}+f_{33})$ is a certain pressure, representing both elastic and viscous effects, connected with a change of volume, specified by $\sigma_{ik}$ (i.e. by $s$), and a second part

$$\psi_{ik} = f_{ik} - \tfrac{1}{3}\delta_{ik} f, \tag{27 a}$$

which can be reduced to a system of shearing stresses‡ and which is connected with the change of shape, specified by $\tau_{ik}$.

The equations (24) of the classical elasticity theory can be rewritten in the form of two independent covariant equations

$$-p = Ls, \qquad \psi_{ik} = 2M\tau_{ik}$$

for the volume and the shape part of the deformation, considered separately.

The first of these equations must be replaced by the equations (18), (18 a), and (18 b) of § 5, which can be written in the following more convenient form.

† Cf. J. Frenkel and J. Obrastzov, *Journ. of Phys.* **2**, 131 (1940).

‡ It should be mentioned that a complete separation of normal stresses from tangential (shearing) ones is impossible, since in a suitable coordinate system any symmetrical tensor can be reduced to its normal components.

Let us introduce the linear differential operator

$$A_2 = \left(1+\tau_2 \frac{d}{dt}\right),$$

and let $A_2^{-1}$ denote the reciprocal operator defined by the condition $A_2 A_2^{-1} = A_2^{-1} A_2 = 1$.

With the help of these operators equation (18 b) can be rewritten as follows:

$$-\frac{ds}{dt} = \frac{1}{\mu_2} A_2 \Delta p_2, \qquad -\Delta p_2 = \mu_2 A_2^{-1} \frac{ds}{dt}.$$

Inserting this in (18) we get

$$-\Delta p = K_1 s + \mu_2 A_2^{-1} \frac{ds}{dt} = \left(K_1 + K_2 A_2^{-1} \tau_2 \frac{d}{dt}\right) s,$$

or since $\tau_2 d/dt = A_2 - 1$

$$-\Delta p = [K_1 + K_2(1 - A_2^{-1})] s. \tag{28}$$

This equation has the same form as the original equation $-\Delta p = Ls$ of the classical elasticity theory if the coefficient $L$ is replaced by the operator

$$L = K_1 + K_2(1 - A_2^{-1}). \tag{28 a}$$

Turning now to the generalization of the equations $\psi_{ik} = 2M\tau_{ik}$ we shall take into account, to begin with, the irreversible fluidity only, which is specified by the ordinary viscosity coefficient $\mu$ and the rigidity modulus $G$. The tensor $\tau_{ik}$ must be resolved accordingly into two parts, an elastic one $\tau'_{ik}$ and a viscous $\tau''_{ik}$, which are connected with the corresponding stress tensor by the equations

$$\psi_{ik} = 2G\tau'_{ik} = 2\mu \frac{d\tau''_{ik}}{dt}.$$

We thus get

$$\frac{d\tau_{ik}}{dt} = \frac{d\tau'_{ik}}{dt} + \frac{d\tau''_{ik}}{dt} = \frac{1}{2G} \frac{d}{dt} \psi_{ik} + \frac{1}{2\mu} \psi_{ik} = \frac{1}{2\mu}\left(1 + \tau \frac{d}{dt}\right) \psi_{ik},$$

where $\tau = \mu/G$ is Maxwell's relaxation time, that is,

$$\tau_{ik} = \frac{1}{2\mu} A \psi_{ik},$$

$A$ being an operator which is obtained from $A_2$ by substituting $\tau$ for $\tau_2$, or

$$\psi_{ik} = 2\mu A^{-1} \frac{d}{dt} \tau_{ik} = 2GA^{-1} \tau \frac{d}{dt} \tau_{ik},$$

i.e.

$$\psi_{ik} = 2G(1 - A^{-1}) \tau_{ik}. \tag{29}$$

This equation can be derived from the original one $\psi_{ik} = 2M\tau_{ik}$ by replacing the coefficient $M$ ($= G$) by the operator

$$M = G(1-A^{-1}). \tag{29a}$$

In order to account for the 'reversible' fluidity, along with the usual one, we must make use of the more general equations (19), (19a), and (19b) of § 5, where $Q$ and $\phi$ must be understood to stand for the tensors $\tau_{ik}$ and $\psi_{ik}$ respectively.

The equations (19a) have exactly the same form as in the case just considered of a change of volume, and can be written down accordingly as follows:

$$\phi = \left[\frac{1}{C_1}+\frac{1}{C_2}(1-A_2^{-1})\right]q$$

with $\tau_2 = C_2 R_2$. In conjunction with (19) this gives

$$Q = \frac{1}{R_1}\int \phi\,dt+\left[\frac{1}{C_1}+\frac{1}{C_2}(1-A_2^{-1})\right]^{-1}\phi.$$

The integration with respect to the time can be represented as a result of the application of an operator reciprocal to $A$ or $A_2$. In fact since

$$\frac{d}{dt}\int \phi\,dt = \phi \quad \text{and} \quad \frac{d}{dt} = \frac{1}{\tau}(A-1)$$

we have
$$\int \phi\,dt = \tau(A-1)^{-1}\phi = \tau_2(A_2-1)^{-1}\phi.$$

Replacing $1/C_1$, $1/C_2$ by $2G_1$, $2G_2$; $R_1$, $R_2$ by $2\mu_1$, $2\mu_2$; and $Q$, $\phi$ by $\tau_{ik}$, $\psi_{ik}$ we obtain an equation of the original form

$$\psi_{ik} = 2M\tau_{ik}.$$

If $M$ is defined as an operator reciprocal to

$$M^{-1} = \frac{\tau_2}{\mu_1}(A_2-1)^{-1}+[G_1+G_2(1-A_2^{-1})]^{-1}, \tag{30}$$

or

$$M^{-1} = \frac{1}{G_1}(A_1-1)^{-1}+[G_1+G_2(1-A_2^{-1})]^{-1}, \tag{30a}$$

where $\tau_1 = \mu_1/G_1$ and $A_1 = 1+\tau_1 d/dt$. In the limiting case $\tau_2 = 0$ which corresponds to the absence of a reversible fluidity $A_2 = A_2^{-1} = 1$ and

$$M^{-1} = \frac{1}{G_1}(A_1-1)^{-1}+\frac{1}{G_1} = \frac{1}{G_1}[(A_1-1)^{-1}+1].$$

Multiplying this operator by $A_1-1$ we get

$$[(A_1-1)^{-1}+1](A_1-1) = 1+A_1-1 = A_1,$$

whence
$$(A_1-1)^{-1}+1 = A_1(A_1-1)^{-1} = (1-A_1^{-1})^{-1},$$

so that in this particular case $M$ is reduced to $G(1-A_1^{-1})$, in agreement with (29 a).

In the opposite case of the absence of the usual (irreversible) fluidity we must put $\tau_1\ (=\tau) = \infty$, the operator $A_1-1$ reducing to infinity, so that the first term in (30 a) can be dropped and $M$ assumes a form similar to the expression (28 a) for $L$.

The relaxation time $\tau_2$ in these two equations, equal to $\mu_2/G_2$ in one of them and $\mu_2/K_2$ in the other, can and, as a rule, must have entirely different values. When, however, both the volume and the shear viscosity are due to a common cause—the orientation of the molecules, for example—the two values of $\tau_2$ can be identical.

## 8. Application of the Preceding Theory to the Propagation of Small Vibrations in Amorphous Bodies

In the particular case of harmonic vibrations, corresponding to the propagation of sound waves, for example, the dependence of the strain and stress tensors upon the time is given by a factor $e^{i\omega t}$, so that differentiation with respect to the time is reduced to multiplication by $i\omega$, and integration with a division by $i\omega$. The operators $A$, $L$, $M$ reduce in this case to complex factors, namely

$$A = 1+i\omega\tau, \tag{31}$$

$$L = K_1+\frac{K_2}{1+1/i\omega\tau} \tag{31a}$$

and

$$M = \frac{G}{1+1/i\omega\tau} \tag{32}$$

in the absence of reversible fluidity, or

$$M^{-1} = \frac{1}{G_1\, i\omega\tau_1}+\frac{1}{G_1+G_2(1+1/i\omega\tau_2)^{-1}} \tag{32a}$$

if the latter exists.

In the case of sine-waves propagated in the direction of the $x$-axis the dependence of the quantities $s_{ik}$ and $f_{ik}$ on $t$ and $x$ is given by the factor

$$e^{i\omega(t-x/v)},$$

where $v$ is the complex velocity of propagation, defined by the formula

$$v = \sqrt{\frac{N}{\rho}},$$

$N$ standing for $M$ in the case of transverse vibrations and for $L+2M$ in that of longitudinal ones. Putting $N = Re^{i\phi}$ we have

$$\frac{1}{v} = \sqrt{\frac{\rho}{R}}e^{-\frac{1}{2}i\phi} = \sqrt{\frac{\rho}{R}}\left(\cos\frac{\phi}{2}-i\sin\frac{\phi}{2}\right), \tag{33}$$

where

$$\cos\frac{\phi}{2} = \sqrt{\left(\frac{1+\cos\phi}{2}\right)};\quad \sin\frac{\phi}{2} = \sqrt{\left(\frac{1-\cos\phi}{2}\right)};\quad \cos\phi = \frac{1}{\sqrt{(1+\tan^2\phi)}}.$$

The wave-length $\lambda$ and the absorption coefficient $\beta$ (referring to the amplitude of the vibrations) are determined by the equations

$$\frac{2\pi}{\lambda} = \omega\sqrt{\frac{\rho}{R}}\cos\frac{\phi}{2};\qquad \beta = \omega\sqrt{\frac{\rho}{R}}\sin\frac{\phi}{2}. \tag{34}$$

An especially simple expression is obtained for the coefficient $\alpha$, specifying the absorption of the waves over a length $x$ equal to the wave-length. We have, namely,

$$\alpha = \beta\lambda = 2\pi\tan\tfrac{1}{2}\phi. \tag{34 a}$$

If $\phi$ is small, this formula can be replaced by the approximation

$$\alpha = \pi\phi \approx \pi\tan\phi. \tag{34 b}$$

We shall apply these formulae first of all to the simplest case of the propagation of transverse vibrations in an amorphous body characterized, in the sense of Maxwell's theory, by a rigidity $G$ ($= G_1$) and an irreversible fluidity $1/\mu$ ($= 1/\mu_1$). In this case

$$N = M = \frac{G}{1+1/i\omega\tau},$$

and consequently

$$R = \frac{G}{\sqrt{\{1+1/(\omega\tau)^2\}}}\quad\text{and}\quad \tan\phi = \frac{1}{\omega\tau}.$$

If $\omega\tau \ll 1$ (ordinary liquids with a small viscosity, vibrations of moderate frequency) the damping of the waves is so large ($\alpha \approx 2\pi$) that it is hardly possible to talk about their propagation. In the opposite case $\omega\tau \gg 1$ (amorphous bodies in a partially solid state, i.e. with an extremely large viscosity and vibrations of a sufficiently high frequency) we have in a first approximation with respect to $1/\omega\tau$

$$|v_t| = \frac{\omega\lambda}{2\pi} = \sqrt{\left(\frac{G}{\rho}\right)},$$

just as in the complete absence of viscosity, and

$$\alpha = \frac{\pi}{\omega\tau} = \frac{1}{2}\frac{\theta}{\tau} = \frac{1}{2}\frac{G\theta}{\mu}, \tag{35}$$

where $\theta = 2\pi/\omega$ is the period of the vibrations. We thus see that in the case under consideration the absorption coefficient of the transverse waves varies *inversely* as the viscosity of the medium (whereas in the case of longitudinal vibrations it usually increases in direct proportion with the viscosity; see below).

In order to account for the reversible fluidity the preceding expression for $M$ must be replaced by (32a). Let us first consider, for the sake of simplicity, the case of a practically solid body ($\tau_1 = \infty$). The expression (33b) reduces in this case to

$$M = G_1 + \frac{G_2}{1+1/i\omega\tau_2}.$$

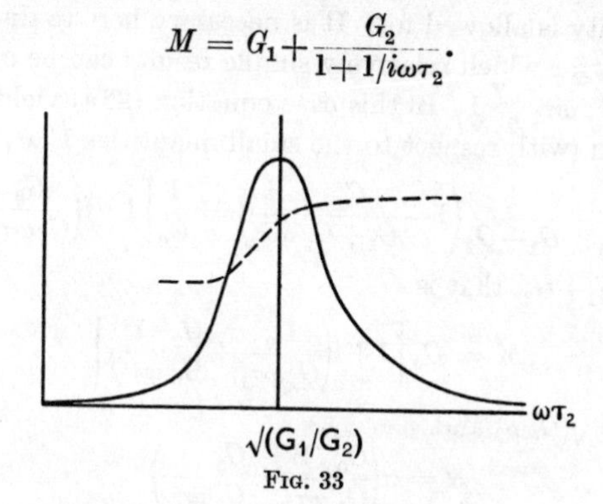


Fig. 33

If $\omega\tau_2 \gg 1$, we have in the first approximation

$$M = G_1 + G_2\left(1+\frac{i}{\omega\tau_2}\right) = G_1 + G_2 + \frac{iG_2}{\omega\tau_2},$$

and consequently
$$\alpha = \frac{\pi}{(1+G_1/G_2)\omega\tau_2}. \qquad (35\,a)$$

The velocity of propagation of the waves in the same approximation is

$$|v_t| = \sqrt{\left(\frac{G_1+G_2}{\rho}\right)} = \sqrt{\left(\frac{G_0}{\rho}\right)},$$

$G_0 = G_1 + G_2$ being the instantaneous rigidity modulus.

If $\omega\tau_2 \ll 1$, then $M \approx G_1 + G_2\, i\omega\tau_2$, so that in this case

$$\alpha = \pi \frac{G_2}{G_1}\omega\tau_2, \qquad (36)$$

$$|v_t| = \sqrt{\left(\frac{G_1}{\rho}\right)}.$$

The transition from low frequencies ($\omega\tau_2 \ll 1$) to high frequencies ($\omega\tau_2 \gg 1$) is thus characterized by an increase of the propagation velocity from the value $\sqrt{(G_1/\rho)}$ to $\sqrt{\{(G_1+G_2)/\rho\}}$, while the absorption coefficient $\alpha$ first increases as $\omega\tau_2$ and after reaching a maximum value (for $\omega\tau_2 = \sqrt{(G_1/G_0)}$) drops as the reciprocal of $\omega\tau_2$. These relationships are illustrated in Fig. 33, where $|v_t|$ is plotted with a dotted line, while the full curve represents the absorption coefficient $\alpha$. It should be mentioned that the coefficient $\beta$ in the region $\omega\tau_2 \ll 1$ is proportional to $\omega^2$ and not to $\omega$, as $\alpha$.

The preceding results are greatly complicated if the ordinary (irreversible) fluidity is allowed for. It is necessary here to distinguish two limiting cases, for which relatively simple results can be obtained.

(1) $\omega\tau_1 \gg 1$; $\omega\tau_2 \gg 1$. In this case equation (32a) yields to the first approximation (with respect to the small quantities $1/\omega\tau_1$ and $1/\omega\tau_2$):

$$M^{-1} = \frac{-i}{G_1\omega\tau_1}+\frac{1}{G_1+G_2}\left(1-\frac{G_2}{G_1+G_2}\frac{i}{\omega\tau_2}\right) = \frac{1}{G_0}\left[1-i\left(\frac{G_0}{G_1\omega\tau_1}-\frac{G_2}{G_0}\frac{1}{\omega\tau_2}\right)\right],$$

where $G_0 = G_1+G_2$, that is

$$M = G_0\left[1+i\left(\frac{G_0}{G_1\omega\tau_1}+\frac{G_2}{G_0}\frac{1}{\omega\tau_2}\right)\right],$$

whence $|v_t| = \sqrt{(G_0/\rho)}$ and

$$\alpha = \pi\left(\frac{G_0}{G_1}\frac{1}{\omega\tau_1}+\frac{G_2}{G_0}\frac{1}{\omega\tau_2}\right). \tag{37}$$

(2) $\omega\tau_1 \gg 1$ and $\omega\tau_2 \ll 1$. In this case

$$M^{-1} \approx -\frac{i}{G_1\omega\tau_1}+\frac{1}{G_1+G_2\,i\omega\tau_2} \approx \frac{1}{G_1}\left[1-i\left(\frac{1}{\omega\tau_1}+\frac{G_2}{G_1}i\omega\tau_2\right)\right],$$

i.e.

$$M = G_1\left[1+i\left(\frac{1}{\omega\tau_1}+\frac{G_2}{G_1}\omega\tau_2\right)\right],$$

so that $|v_t| = \sqrt{(G_1/\rho)}$ and

$$\alpha = \pi\left(\frac{1}{\omega\tau_1}+\frac{G_2}{G_1}\omega\tau_2\right). \tag{37a}$$

If $\omega\tau_1 \ll 1$, the waves are very strongly damped ($\alpha$ is of the order $2\pi$), irrespective of the value of $\omega\tau_2$. This case presents no interest. M. O. Kornfeld† has recently investigated the propagation of transverse vibrations in rosin for different temperatures between 20° C. and 70° C. At the latter temperature rosin acquires a marked fluidity, although it behaves more like a solid than like a liquid. Kornfeld tested the validity of the relations following from Maxwell's theory (in the absence of reversible fluidity) by checking the constancy of the quantities $\mu_1$ and $G_1$ with a variation of the frequency within a wide range (from $3\times10^3$ to $1{\cdot}3\times10^5$ sec.$^{-1}$). They actually proved to be independent of the frequency; however, both of them showed a decrease with increasing temperature, the decrease of $G$ being much less rapid than that of $\mu$. At 20° C. Kornfeld obtained for $G$ a value of the order of $10^{10}$ dynes/cm.$^2$,

† M. Kornfeld, *C.R. Ac. Sci. U.R.S.S.* **36**, 58 (1942).

which decreased by a factor of 10 as the temperature was raised to 70° C. The value of $\mu$ for 70° C. was found to be $10^5$, which corresponds to a value of $10^{-4}$ sec. for $\tau$.

It should be noted, for the sake of comparison, that in the case of crystalline substances the rigidity modulus $G$ decreases by a factor of 2–3 only when the temperature is raised from the absolute zero to a few degrees below the melting-point. In the case of tin, however, $G$ decreases from $22\times10^{10}$ to $2{\cdot}5\times10^{10}$, i.e. by a factor of 8 when the temperature is raised from 100° K. to 500° K. In the case of stearine the approach to the melting-point is accompanied by a catastrophic drop in $G$, as may be seen from the following table:

| $T$° K. | 88 | 273 | 300 | 314 | 319 | 321·5 | 322·8 |
|---|---|---|---|---|---|---|---|
| $G\times10^{-10}$ | 0·78 | 0·54 | 0·34 | 0·14 | 0·048 | 0·014 | 0·005 |

The cause of this abnormally large rate of decrease of $G$ near the melting-point of stearine is not yet clear.

Turning to the question of the propagation of longitudinal vibrations we must make use, for the determination of the complex propagation velocity, of the formula $v_l = \sqrt{[(L+2M)/\rho]}$. The dispersion and damping of these vibrations thus depends not only on volume properties, which are specified by the complex coefficient $L$, but also on 'shape' properties, which determine the complex rigidity modulus $M$.

For the sake of simplicity we shall limit ourselves to the case of a body devoid of reversible fluidity, i.e. shall use the expression (32) for $M$. As to the quantity $L$, it is expressed in exactly the same way as $M$ in the absence of irreversible fluidity (with $G_1$, $G_2$ replaced by $K_1$, $K_2$). We thus have

$$L+2M = K_1+\frac{K_2}{1+1/i\omega\tau_2}+\frac{2G}{1+1/i\omega\tau_1}.$$

We must distinguish four practically interesting cases.

(1) $\omega\tau_1 \ll 1$; $\omega\tau_2 \ll 1$ (ordinary liquids with a small viscosity both of the usual and of the volume type, at low frequencies). The preceding expression reduces in this case to

$$K_1+K_2\,i\omega\tau_2+2Gi\omega\tau_1 = K_1+i\omega(\mu_2+2\mu_1),$$

which corresponds to a propagation velocity $|v_l| = \sqrt{(K_1/\rho)}$ and to an absorption coefficient

$$\alpha = \pi\omega(2\mu_1+\mu_2)/K_1. \tag{38}$$

(2) $\omega\tau_1 \gg 1$; $\omega\tau_2 \gg 1$ (practically solid amorphous body at high frequencies). In this case

$$L+2M = K_1+K_2+2G+i\left(K_2\frac{1}{\omega\tau_2}+2G\frac{1}{\omega\tau_1}\right)$$
$$= K\left[1+i\left(\frac{K_2}{K}\frac{1}{\omega\tau_2}+\frac{2G}{K}\frac{1}{\omega\tau_1}\right)\right],$$

where $K = K_1+K_2+2G$ is the static elastic modulus for deformations constrained to one dimension. We thus get $|v_l| \approx \sqrt{(K/\rho)}$ and

$$\alpha = \pi\left(\frac{K_2^2}{K}\frac{1}{\omega\mu_2}+2\frac{G^2}{K}\frac{1}{\omega\mu_1}\right). \tag{38 a}$$

(3) $\omega\tau_1 \gg 1$; $\omega\tau_2 \ll 1$. In this case

$$|v_l| = \sqrt{\left(\frac{K_1+2G_1}{\rho}\right)}; \qquad \alpha = \frac{\pi}{K_1+2G_1}\left(\omega\mu_2+\frac{2G_1^2}{\omega\mu_1}\right). \tag{38 b}$$

(4) $\omega\tau_1 \ll 1$; $\omega\tau_2 \gg 1$.

$$|v_l| = \sqrt{\left(\frac{K_1+K_2}{\rho}\right)}; \quad \alpha = \frac{\pi}{K_1+K_2}\left(\frac{K_2^2}{\omega\mu_2}+2\omega\mu_1\right). \tag{38 c}$$

The available experimental data refer mainly to the first case. With the exception of simple (monatomic) liquids, such as fused metals, the absorption coefficient of liquids, both for low- and high-frequency vibrations, has been found to be much larger (by a factor of a few hundreds and sometimes even of a few thousands) than the theoretical value which follows from classical hydrodynamics and which corresponds to the first term in the brackets of the expression (38). It should be noticed that the classical expression for $\alpha$ is

$$\alpha = \frac{4\pi}{3}\frac{\omega\mu_1}{K_1},$$

differing from the first term of (38) by the factor $\frac{4}{3}$ (which we have neglected since it is of no importance compared with the effect due to the volume viscosity $\mu_2$). We are thus led to the conclusion that the volume viscosity of liquids is, as a rule, much larger (by one, two, and even three orders of magnitude) than the ordinary viscosity $\mu_1$, at least for room temperatures (the dependence of $\mu_2$ on the temperature has not been investigated hitherto).

The fact that the coefficient $\alpha$ remains strictly proportional to $\omega$ ($\beta$ to $\omega^2$) up to frequencies of the order $10^8$ sec.$^{-1}$ shows that the inequality $\omega\tau_2 \ll 1$ remains valid even for such high frequencies, which means that the relaxation time $\tau_2$ is smaller than $10^{-8}$ sec. (at room temperatures), just as is $\tau_1$.

The smallness of $\tau_2$ involves a certain difficulty, since the abnormally large absorption of sound in liquids can be explained by large values of the volume friction coefficient $\mu_2$ which, as we know, is proportional to $\tau_2$. Comparing the equations $\mu_2 = K_2\tau_2$ and $\mu_1 = G_1\tau_1$ we see that the inequality $\mu_2 \gg \mu_1$ required by the experimental data can be satisfied on the condition either that $K_2 \gg G_1$ if $\tau_2$ is of the same order of magnitude as $\tau_1$, or that $\tau_2 \gg \tau_1$ if $K_2$ is of the same order of magnitude as $G_1$. As a matter of fact $G_1$ must be smaller than $K_2$ by a factor of 10–100. Hence $\tau_2$ need not be much larger than $\tau_1$ in order to explain the fact that $\mu_2$ can be a thousandfold as large as $\mu_1$.

It has been mentioned in § 6 that Kneser attempted to explain the abnormally large absorption of sound in liquids by the thermal relaxation mechanism which has been considered in § 6. Noting that $K_2 = K_0 \frac{C_p - C_v}{C_v} \frac{C_i}{C_e}$ we see that according to this mechanism $K_2$ must be *smaller* than the static compressibility modulus (by a factor of 10, say), so that an explanation of the large value of $\mu_2 = K_2\tau_2$ requires from this point of view a large value of $\tau_2$ of the order of $1000\tau_1$, i.e. $10^{-8}$ sec. at room temperature, which is contradicted by the absence of any trace of dispersion (increase of velocity of sound) in the neighbourhood of the frequency $10^8$ sec.$^{-1}$†

## 9. Hypersonic Waves in the Heat Motion of Liquid Bodies

Elastic vibrations with a frequency of the order $10^4$–$10^8$ sec.$^{-1}$, which can be generated artificially by radio methods, are called 'supersonic'. Vibrations of a still higher frequency—called here 'hypersonic'—cannot be produced by artificial methods. Such hypersonic vibrations with a frequency reaching $10^{12}$–$10^{13}$ sec.$^{-1}$ are known, however, to exist under natural conditions in solid bodies, constituting, according to Debye's theory, the main part of the heat motion in such bodies. In the case of simple (monatomic) bodies this motion may be described as a superposition of longitudinal and transverse vibrations (waves) such that the number of vibrations within the frequency range between $\nu$ and $\nu + d\nu$ is proportional to $\nu^2 d\nu$.

It is natural to expect that this picture can be applied, with some

† In the case of diatomic gases at normal temperature and pressure $\tau_2$ is of the order of $10^{-5}$–$10^{-6}$ sec. Taking into account that the average number of collisions of a molecule under such conditions is equal to $10^{10}$ sec.$^{-1}$, we see that the probability of an energy exchange between the translation and vibration motion during the time of a single collision ($10^{-13}$ sec.) is of the order of $10^{-4}$–$10^{-5}$. It is difficult, however, to make from these figures even an approximate estimate of the probability of such an exchange in the liquid state.

minor limitations, to the case of *liquid* bodies, the more so because the simple form of Debye's theory refers not to crystals, but to amorphous solids, which can be treated as supercooled liquids. The only important limitation refers to the spectrum of transverse vibrations, which must start with a frequency $\nu_{\min}$ of the order of the reciprocal of Maxwell's relaxation time (or the mean life of an equilibrium position according to our scheme), since vibrations of a lower frequency are too strongly damped (see eq. (35)). The low-frequency part of the spectrum of transverse vibrations, constituting a (relatively negligible) part of the heat motion in a solid body, must thus be replaced in a liquid by some motion of a different kind, the exact nature of which is still obscure. This motion must reduce itself, to some extent, to the self-diffusion of the particles of the liquid. Noting that the number of normal vibration modes with a frequency $\leqslant \nu_1$, in a solid body with a volume $V$, is equal to $\frac{8\pi V}{v_t^3}\nu_1^3$ and putting $\nu_1 = \frac{1}{\tau_1} = \frac{1}{\tau_0}e^{-W/kT}$, we get

$$Z_1 = \frac{8\pi V}{v_t^3\,\tau_0^3}e^{-3W/kT}.$$

On the other hand, the relative number of particles which at any given instant of time can be found in a 'transitional state', moving from an equilibrium position to the next, i.e. possessing an activation energy $W$ must obviously be equal to $Ne^{-W/kT}$. This expression does not agree with the preceding one, yielding much larger values of $Z$, so long as $kT \ll W$. We thus see that the actual number of vibrational degrees of freedom which must be removed from the low-frequency part of the spectrum of transverse vibrations of a liquid and must be represented by a 'gas-like' diffusion motion is much larger than that following from the preceding argument.

In particular, it seems improbable that in ordinary liquids at room temperature transverse vibrations with a frequency of the order of $10^{10}$ sec.$^{-1}$ should exist. The above limitations do not refer, however, to longitudinal vibrations.

It is interesting that such longitudinal hypersonic vibrations with a frequency in the range of a few octaves near $10^{10}$ can be studied experimentally, with respect to their dispersion, i.e. the dependence of their propagation velocity on the wave-length, by the help of an optical method based on a principle which was introduced in 1923 by L. Brillouin in his theory of light scattering in solid bodies.

Let us imagine a system of standing sine waves with a wave-length $\lambda$

and a frequency $\nu$ representing one of the normal vibrational modes of an amorphous solid body. These standing waves can be replaced by two systems of progressive waves propagated in opposite directions along the $x$-axis for instance. The density of the vibrating body at different points will be represented by a function of the form

$$\rho = \rho_0 + A \cos\frac{2\pi}{\lambda}x \sin 2\pi\nu t.$$

Since the refractive index of a transparent body with respect to light rays varies with its density, we see that the propagation of such rays in a transparent medium, agitated by an acoustical wave system, must take place in a way similar to the propagation of X-rays in a crystal, the role of the crystalline planes being played by the planes of the sound waves, corresponding to a definite (arbitrarily) chosen phase or amplitude.

The scattering of light due to this optically inhomogeneous character of the body must take place according to the same law as the scattering of X-rays in a crystal lattice with a constant $d = \lambda$. Their scattering reduces itself, as is well known, to a reflection of the rays for the values of the glancing angle $\theta$ given by Bragg's equation

$$2d \sin\theta = n\lambda',$$

where $\lambda'$ is the wave-length of the X-rays and $n$ an integer (order of reflection). For any other values of $\theta$ the scattered rays are mutually extinguished.

This result can be applied to the case under consideration, i.e. to the passage of the rays of ordinary light through a body with a sinusoidal distribution of the index of refraction. In this case, however, which was investigated by Rayleigh long before the discovery of the diffraction of X-rays, a reflection of the first order only ($n = 1$) takes place, while the diffraction spectra of higher orders vanish.

This result is not exactly true, for it is based on the assumption that the wave-length of the light $\lambda'$ remains constant, whereas for a given frequency $\nu'$ of the light vibration $\lambda'$ must vary inversely as the index of refraction. This gives rise to the appearance of higher order diffraction spectra, which, however, can be neglected because of their relatively low intensity.

A marked reflection of the light takes place accordingly for a single value of the glancing angle, given by the equation

$$2\lambda \sin\theta = \lambda' \tag{39}$$

to which Bragg's formula is reduced if we put $d = \lambda$ and $n = 1$.

If the sinusoidal distribution of the index of refraction remained constant with respect to the time, the frequency of the scattered (reflected) light would be the same as that of the incident one. In reality, however, the refractive index vibrates at any given point of the body with a frequency $\nu$. The resulting modulation of the amplitude of the reflected light waves is, as is well known, equivalent to a splitting up of their frequency according to the formula

$$\nu' \pm \Delta\nu' = \nu' \pm \nu.$$

Hence it follows that for an adequate value of the glancing angle, given by (39), two reflected light rays must emerge from the body with a frequency differing from that of the incident rays by the frequency of the sound vibrations.

This result can be obtained in a still simpler way if the standing wave is resolved into two progressive ones with opposite directions of propagation. Each of them must then reflect light as a mirror moving in the corresponding direction with the velocity of sound $v$; this entails, according to Doppler's principle, a change of frequency by the amount $\Delta\nu'$ given by the equation

$$\nu' \pm \Delta\nu' = \nu'\left(1 + \frac{2v}{c} \sin\theta\right),$$

where $c$ is the velocity of light. Noting that $c = \nu'\lambda'$ and $v = \nu\lambda$ we see that $\Delta\nu'$ is equal to $\nu$.

Let us now consider the actual case of a transparent solid or liquid body vibrating simultaneously in a number of different normal modes corresponding to longitudinal waves of all possible lengths and directions of propagation. Light rays incident upon it in a definite direction are scattered in all directions. The scattering of monochromatic rays of a given frequency $\nu'$ in a given direction, specified by a glancing angle $\theta$ is, however, due to those hypersonic vibrations only for which the condition (39) is satisfied, and accompanied by a shift of the frequency $\nu'$ by an amount $\pm\Delta\nu'$ equal to the frequency of the corresponding hypersonic waves $\nu$. This frequency shift can be detected experimentally. On the other hand, the wave-length of the hypersonic vibrations that are responsible for the scattering can be calculated with the help of equation (39). It is thus possible to calculate the velocity of propagation of these hypersonic vibrations

$$v = \nu\lambda = \frac{\Delta\nu'\lambda'}{2\sin\theta} \qquad (39\,\text{a})$$

as a function of their frequency $\nu = \Delta\nu'$ by varying the angle of scattering $2\theta$.

Unfortunately, such an optical determination of the dispersion of mechanical vibrations in the hypersonic region can be carried out only for waves with a length greater than $\frac{1}{2}\lambda'$, i.e. for hypersonic waves with a length of the order of $10^{-5}$ cm., which is a few hundred times as large as the shortest waves constituting the heat motion in a solid or liquid body. Accordingly, the maximum frequency of these experimentally detectable hypersonic waves is of the order of $10^{10}$ sec.$^{-1}$, a few hundred times smaller than the limiting frequency of the Debye spectrum.

This method of investigation of the dispersion of sound in the hypersonic region has been recently applied by Rao† to liquid $CCl_4$ and acetone, and somewhat later by Raman and Venkateswaran‡ to glycerine. It has been found that in the case of $CCl_4$ and of glycerine the velocity of sound slightly increases as we pass from the ultrasonic ($\nu < 10^8$) to the hypersonic region, as would be expected according to the theory of the preceding section (if the relaxation times $\tau_1$ or $\tau_2$ or both are much smaller than $10^{-10}$ sec.). In the case of acetone, however, the velocity of sound, instead of increasing, was found to *decrease* from the value $v = 1205$ m./sec. for $\nu = 7{\cdot}3\times 10^6$ to a value $v = 978$ m./sec. for $\nu = 5\times 10^9$.

This result must not be considered as disproving the preceding theory, for the latter did not take into account a number of complicating factors, which may also be responsible for the dispersion of sound both in the positive and in the negative sense (i.e. in the sense of a decrease of $v$ with increase of $\nu$).

The most prominent of these factors is the *thermal conductivity* of the body, which levels out the temperature differences between the compressed and extended volume elements and thus tends to reduce the compressibility modulus from the adiabatic to the lower isothermal value. It is usually supposed that this influence of thermal conductivity is largest for the slowest vibrations and that high-frequency vibrations must be purely adiabatic. A simple argument shows, however, the opposite to be true. In fact, the influence of thermal conductivity can be specified by a coefficient $D$ equal to the ratio of the heat conductivity $\kappa$ to the specific heat of unit volume $C_v$; $D$ plays the same role as the diffusion coefficient in the theory of diffusion phenomena. With respect to its physical dimensions it is equal, accordingly, to the ratio

† Rao, *Nature*, **139**, 885 (1937); Rao and Ramaiya, *Phys. Rev.* **60**, 615 (1941).
‡ Raman and Venkateswaran, *Nature*, **143**. 798 (1939).

of the square of the wave-length $\lambda$ to the vibration period $\tau = 1/\nu$. Hence it follows that the influence of heat conductivity on the dispersion and absorption of sound waves must be determined by a dimensionless coefficient equal to the ratio between $D$ and $\lambda^2/\tau = v^2/\nu$, where $v = \nu\lambda$ is the velocity of sound. If this ratio is small compared with 1, the role of the heat conductivity must be relatively small, the vibrations being practically adiabatic (they can be wholly adiabatic in the limiting case $D\nu = 0$, i.e. $\nu = 0$ only and not $\nu = \infty$, as usually assumed). In the opposite case the vibrations must acquire an isothermal character. The limiting frequency $\nu_0$ corresponding to a transition from the low-frequency adiabatic vibrations to the high-frequency isothermal ones is thus given by the formula

$$\nu_0 \approx \frac{v^2}{D}.$$

In the case of solid and liquid (non-metallic) bodies at room temperatures $D$ is of the order of 1 cm.$^2$/sec. Putting $v \approx 10^5$ cm./sec., we get $\nu_0 \approx 10^{12}$ sec.$^{-1}$ We thus see that the hypersonic vibrations in acetone and in other organic liquids should remain adiabatic up to a frequency of the order of $10^{12}$ sec.$^{-1}$ The marked decrease of the propagation velocity found by Rao in the region of $\nu = 10^{10}$ cannot therefore be explained by the above mechanism.†

Leaving open the question of the actual cause of the negative (or positive) dispersion of hypersonic waves in liquids, we shall give, following Rayleigh,‡ a more complete treatment of the effect just discussed.

The equation

$$\left(\frac{\partial p}{\partial T}\right)_V \frac{\partial V}{\partial t}+\frac{C_v}{T}\frac{\partial T}{\partial t} = 0,$$

expressing the condition that the sound vibrations should be adiabatic must be replaced in the case of a non-vanishing heat conductivity by

$$T\left(\frac{\partial p}{\partial T}\right)_V \frac{\partial V}{\partial t}+C_v\frac{\partial T}{\partial t} = \kappa\nabla^2 T.$$

This equation expresses the fact that the quantity of heat flowing to a given volume element by way of thermal conductivity is used partly to heat it and partly for external work.

Noting that $(\partial p/\partial T)_V = \alpha K_0$ (see § 6) and putting $V = V_0(1+s)$ and $T = T_0+\theta$ we can rewrite the preceding equation in the following form:

$$K_0\,\alpha V_0\,T_0\frac{\partial s}{\partial t}+C_v\frac{\partial \theta}{\partial t} = \kappa\nabla^2\theta. \tag{40}$$

† Cf. V. Ginsburg, *C.R. Ac. Sci. U.R.S.S.* **36**, 9 (1942).
‡ *Theory of Sound*, ii, § 247.

In the case of longitudinal sine-waves propagated in the direction of the $x$-axis all the small quantities including $\theta$ can be assumed to vary as $e^{i(\omega t-qx)}$, the ratio $\omega/q$ representing the complex propagation velocity $v$. Equation (40) reduces in this case to the relation

$$\theta = \frac{-f_0}{1+Dq^2/i\omega}s, \tag{40a}$$

where $D = \kappa/C_v$ and $$f_0 = \frac{K_0\alpha V_0 T_0}{C_v}.$$

It should be noticed that in the case where $D = 0$ this relation becomes identical with the relation (21 a) of § 6, for $\xi = 0$ and $T_e = T_i = T$.

Substituting (40 a) in the equation (21): $\Delta p = -K_0 s+K_0\alpha\theta$, which is the approximate form of the equation $dp = \left(\frac{\partial p}{\partial T}\right)_V dT+\left(\frac{\partial p}{\partial V}\right)_T dV$ for small values of $s$ and $\theta$, we get the usual relation

$$\Delta p = -Ls,$$

with a complex compressibility modulus

$$L = K_0\left[1+\frac{f_0\alpha}{1+Dq^2/i\omega}\right],$$

which for $Dq^2/\omega \to \infty$ ($\omega \to 0$) reduces to the isothermal value $K_0$, and for $Dq^2/\omega \to 0$ ($\omega \to \infty$) to the adiabatic value $K_1 = K_0(1+K_0\alpha^2 V_0 T_0/C_v)$. The limiting frequency, corresponding to a transition from the adiabatic to the isothermal case, is obviously equal to $\omega_0 = v^2/D$, in agreement with the result obtained above with the help of an analysis of dimensions.

Near this limiting frequency, along with a negative dispersion of sound, an abnormally large absorption must take place, which can be determined by the general equations of the preceding section if $K_1$ is identified with $K_0$, $K_2$ with $K_0 f\alpha$, and the relaxation time $\tau_2$ with $1/Dq^2$. This 'relaxation time' has, however, no intrinsic meaning characteristic of the substance, since it depends upon the wave-length $\lambda = 2\pi/q$.

The fact that at very high frequencies the hypersonic vibrations must acquire an isothermal character follows, irrespective of the preceding formal theory, from the impossibility of applying the macroscopic notion of temperature, as a function of the time and position, to very small time intervals and distances.

It should be noted that in Debye's theory of the heat motion in a solid body the elastic vibrations describing this motion are treated without any *a priori* reference to the temperature, the latter being introduced merely as a measure of the average intensity of these vibrations. Such a treatment implies a strict validity of the principle of superposition of different normal vibration modes, i.e. a neglect of their deviations from a linear law of force (or harmonicity).

Owing to these deviations the energy of a vibration mode representing a sound wave, for example if it exceeds the average value corresponding to statistical equilibrium, is transferred to a number of other modes. This mechanism underlies the thermal effects connected with the adiabatic propagation of acoustic vibrations in a solid or liquid body. In fact such vibrations must give rise to a periodic variation of the intensity of high-frequency hypersonic waves, constituting the major part of the heat motion of the body, a compression of the latter being associated with an increase and an expansion with a decrease of their intensity. These non-linear effects become irrelevant near the short-wave length limit of the spectrum, the corresponding hypersonic vibrations being propagated in a practically 'isothermal' way, i.e. without energy exchange with vibrations of still higher frequency.

The preceding considerations show that Debye's 'acoustic' theory of the heat motion in a solid body, inasmuch as it does not take into account the non-linear effects leading to an energy exchange between the different vibration modes, gives an incomplete picture of reality.

The heat motion in a macroscopically homogeneous material body gives rise to a number of fluctuations, i.e. local and transient variations of its properties. In the case of a solid body these fluctuations are reduced, according to Debye's theory, to longitudinal vibrations, i.e. variations of the density connected with variations of the pressure, and to transverse vibrations, i.e. variable torsions connected with shearing stresses by the equations of the ordinary (linear) elasticity theory. The actual heat motion of the solid is represented by a superposition of these fluctuations. The latter are thus treated not as the effects of the heat motion but as its mechanical constituents.

Now, we have seen that this picture is incomplete, for it fails to account for the variations of the temperature which are associated with the variations of the density (or pressure), especially in the region of relatively long hypersonic waves. As a matter of fact these temperature variations cannot be fitted into the frame of Debye's theory so long as it aims at a purely mechanical description of the heat motion. An accurate description of this kind requires, as has been stated above, the introduction of anharmonicity effects, due to the non-linearity of the equations of motion. This results in an enormous complication of the mechanical picture—a complication which is necessary for an adequate interpretation of a number of *kinetic* effects (such as the conduction of heat), but can be dispensed with so long as we are interested only in reversible processes, i.e. in equilibrium properties, even if they are ultimately due to anharmonicity effects, as is the thermal expansion, for example. In order to account for such effects without an explicit introduction of the complications connected with the purely mechanical description of the motion, we must complete the simple mechanical description, which leaves them out of account, by an *a priori* introduction of thermal elements into the picture of the heat motion.

This has already been partially done in Ch. III, where in deriving an expression for the free energy of a homogeneous solid body we have treated the vibration frequencies as functions of its volume and shape; if instead of the volume and of other parameters specifying the shape of the body, we took the pressure as the independent variable, along with the temperature or with the specific entropy, these vibration frequencies would turn out to be functions of the latter quantities. In order to give a complete picture of the heat motion in a solid body in a state of thermodynamic equilibrium we must, accordingly, treat this motion as a superposition of mechanical (elastic) fluctuations in the form of acoustic waves, and of thermal fluctuations, associated with local variations of the temperature $T$ or of the specific entropy $s$, which cannot, of course, be propagated in the form of waves.

This does not exclude the possibility of representing $\Delta T$ or $\Delta S$ (for a given value of the average temperature $\overline{T}$ of the whole body) as functions of the coordinates in the form of a Fourier series with coefficients depending upon the time, i.e. in a way similar to that used for the representation of the mechanical fluctuations in the form of standing waves.

We thus obtain for $\Delta T$ or $\Delta S$ a 'wave-like' description, which differs, however, essentially from that corresponding to actual waves in that the amplitudes of the latter are harmonic functions of the time (with eventually a certain amount of damping), while the amplitudes of the former, as functions of the time, have a wholly aperiodic character, partly reducing to an ordinary relaxation.

In other words, the waves resulting from a Fourier expansion of the fluctuations of a mechanical quantity, the pressure $p$ for instance, are propagated with a definite velocity, constituting standing vibrations by way of interference of progressive waves with opposite directions of propagation, while the 'waves' of temperature or entropy variation cannot be propagated, being alternately excited and damped and remaining stationary in space.

If the density of the body $\rho$ is considered as a function of the (local) pressure $p = \bar{p}+\Delta p$ and of the local temperature $T = \bar{T}+\Delta T$ or of the specific entropy $S = \bar{S}+\Delta S$, then a Fourier expansion of $\Delta p$ and $\Delta T$ (or $\Delta S$) leads to a similar expansion of $\Delta\rho = \left(\frac{\partial\rho}{\partial p}\right)_T \Delta p+\left(\frac{\partial\rho}{\partial T}\right)_p \Delta T$ or $\Delta\rho = \left(\frac{\partial\rho}{\partial p}\right)_S \Delta p+\left(\frac{\partial\rho}{\partial S}\right)_p \Delta S$, the first (mechanical) part being propagated in the form of progressive waves, or vibrating harmonically with a frequency corresponding to the length of the waves if they are treated as standing, while the second (thermal) is non-vibrating, displaying a relatively slow and irregular variation with the time.

Coming back to the question of the scattering of light by a solid or liquid (transparent) body, we see that the theory given at the beginning of this section and based on a consideration of mechanical (pressure) waves alone, must be completed by a consideration of the thermal 'waves'.

Inasmuch as the scattering of light is directly due to density fluctuations (the index of refraction being a function of the density alone) and the variation of density is due both to a variation of the pressure and of the temperature or entropy, the light scattered in a given direction owing to the density waves (whose length and direction is given by Brillouin's equation (39)) must consist of two parts: a 'mechanical' one with an altered frequency which has already been considered, and an additional thermal part, which must have the same frequency as the incident light (the corresponding unshifted Rayleigh line being somewhat broadened as a result of the irregular variation of the amplitude of the thermal 'waves' with the time).

This important correction to the simple Brillouin theory of light scattering in solid bodies was introduced in 1934 by Landau and Placzek,† who showed it to be especially important in the case of liquid bodies, where the entropy fluctuations are much larger than in solids, and where, accordingly, the intensity of the unshifted component of the Rayleigh line has been found to be much more intense than in the case of solid bodies.

The ratio of the intensity of this unshifted line $I_0$ to that of the two shifted components $I_1$ must obviously be equal to the ratio between

† *Phys. Z. d. Sowjetunion*, **5**, 172 (1934).

the square of the thermal part of the density fluctuation $\Delta\rho = \left(\frac{\partial\rho}{\partial T}\right)_p \Delta T$ or $\Delta\rho = \left(\frac{\partial\rho}{\partial T}\right)_p \Delta S$ and the square of its mechanical part $\Delta\rho = \left(\frac{\partial\rho}{\partial p}\right)_T \Delta p$ or $\Delta\rho = \left(\frac{\partial\rho}{\partial p}\right)_S \Delta p$. If, following Landau and Placzek, the pressure and the specific entropy are chosen as independent variables (which is a reasonable choice for relatively long waves capable of effectively scattering light) and the volume $V$ of a given small mass of the body as the dependent variable (instead of the density) we have

$$(\Delta V)_{S=\text{const.}} = \left(\frac{\partial V}{\partial p}\right)_S \Delta p = -\frac{V_0}{K_S}\Delta p,$$

where $K_S$ is the adiabatic bulk modulus and

$$(\Delta V)_{p=\text{const.}} = \left(\frac{\partial V}{\partial S}\right)_p \Delta S = \left(\frac{\partial T}{\partial p}\right)_S \Delta S,$$

the latter relation following from the differential expression for the total heat

$$dJ = T\,dS + V\,dp.$$

Denoting the minimum value of the latter for the whole system (made up of the element considered and of the rest of the body) by $J_0$ we have further

$$-(\Delta J)_S \approx \frac{1}{2}\frac{\partial^2 J}{\partial p^2}(\Delta p)^2 = -\frac{1}{2}\left(\frac{\partial V}{\partial p}\right)_S(\Delta p)^2 = \tfrac{1}{2}VK_S(\Delta p)^2$$

and $$-(\Delta J)_p \approx \frac{1}{2}\frac{\partial^2 J}{\partial S^2}(\Delta S)^2 = \frac{1}{2}\left(\frac{\partial T}{\partial S}\right)_p(\Delta S)^2 = \frac{T}{2C_p}(\Delta S)^2,$$

whence it follows that

$$\overline{(\Delta p)^2} = \frac{\int\limits_{-\infty}^{+\infty}(\Delta p)^2 e^{-(\Delta J)_S/kT}\,d(\Delta p)}{\int\limits_{-\infty}^{+\infty} e^{-(\Delta J)_S/kT}\,d(\Delta p)} = -\frac{kT}{\left(\frac{\partial V}{\partial p}\right)_S} = \frac{kT}{V}K_S$$

and $$\overline{(\Delta S)^2} = \frac{\int\limits_{-\infty}^{+\infty}(\Delta S)^2 e^{-(\Delta J)_p/kT}\,d(\Delta S)}{\int\limits_{-\infty}^{+\infty} e^{-(\Delta J)_p/kT}\,d(\Delta S)} = \frac{kT}{\left(\frac{\partial T}{\partial S}\right)_p} = C_p k.$$

We thus get
$$\frac{I_0}{I_1} = \frac{\left(\frac{\partial V}{\partial S}\right)_p^2 \overline{(\Delta S)^2}}{\left(\frac{\partial V}{\partial p}\right)_S^2 \overline{(\Delta p)^2}}.$$

Now, in virtue of the identities
$$\frac{\left(\frac{\partial V}{\partial S}\right)_p}{\left(\frac{\partial V}{\partial p}\right)_S} = -\left(\frac{\partial p}{\partial S}\right)_V, \quad \frac{\left(\frac{\partial T}{\partial p}\right)_S}{\left(\frac{\partial T}{\partial S}\right)_p} = -\left(\frac{\partial S}{\partial p}\right)_T,$$

and the thermodynamical relation
$$\left(\frac{\partial V}{\partial S}\right)_p = \left(\frac{\partial T}{\partial p}\right)_S,$$

this ratio can be rewritten in the form
$$\frac{I_0}{I_1} = \left(\frac{\partial p}{\partial S}\right)_V \left(\frac{\partial S}{\partial p}\right)_T.$$

We have, further,
$$\left(\frac{\partial p}{\partial V}\right)_T = \left(\frac{\partial p}{\partial V}\right)_S + \left(\frac{\partial p}{\partial S}\right)_V \left(\frac{\partial S}{\partial V}\right)_T,$$

that is,
$$\frac{I_0}{I_1} = \left[\left(\frac{\partial p}{\partial V}\right)_T - \left(\frac{\partial p}{\partial V}\right)_S\right] \frac{\left(\frac{\partial S}{\partial p}\right)_T}{\left(\frac{\partial S}{\partial V}\right)_T} = \frac{\left(\frac{\partial p}{\partial V}\right)_T - \left(\frac{\partial p}{\partial V}\right)_S}{\left(\frac{\partial p}{\partial V}\right)_T},$$

or finally,
$$\frac{I_0}{I_1} = \frac{K_S - K_T}{K_T} = \frac{C_p - C_v}{C_v} \tag{41}$$

according to (20c), where $K_T = -V(\partial p/\partial V)_T$ is the isothermal bulk modulus.

In the case of solid bodies the ratio $(C_p - C_v)/C_v$ is very small, while in the case of liquids it is of the order of 1, which explains the relatively large intensity of the unshifted line observed in the latter case. From the point of view of the physical considerations regarding the origin of the unshifted Rayleigh line, as due to the anharmonicity of the mechanical vibrations, this line would be expected to be wholly absent in the region of very short wave-lengths; the thermodynamical relations which have been used above lose their validity when the rate of change of the quantities involved, both with respect to the time and to the space coordinates, becomes too large.

## 10. Generalization of the Equations of Hydrodynamics

In generalizing the equations of the elasticity theory we have confined ourselves to the case of small displacements of the particles, excluding in this way those types of motion which are characteristic of liquid bodies. We must now approach the problem of the generalization of the equations of motion of amorphous bodies from the opposite—and thus from the liquid—end.

We shall replace, accordingly, the displacements $u_i$ by the velocities $v_i = du_i/dt$ and treat the latter, following Euler, as functions of the time $t$ and of the coordinates $x_1$, $x_2$, $x_3$ of the displaced position. The equation (23) of § 7 must now be rewritten in the form

$$\rho \frac{dv_i}{dt} = \rho \frac{\partial v_i}{\partial t} + \rho \sum_k \frac{\partial v_i}{\partial x_k} = \sum_k \frac{\partial f_{ik}}{\partial x_k} \tag{42}$$

and must be completed by the continuity equation

$$\frac{\partial \rho}{\partial t} + \sum_k \frac{\partial (\rho v_k)}{\partial x_k} = 0. \tag{42a}$$

Inasmuch as liquids are similar to solids in respect of their small compressibility we can use Hooke's law for the determination of the hydrostatic pressure $p$ as a function of the volume expansion $s = \Delta V/V_0$, which is equal to the relative variation of density with the opposite sign $-\Delta\rho/\rho_0$. Such a procedure would, however, be of practical interest only in the case of small vibrations, which has already been examined in § 8 by the methods of the generalized elasticity theory. If we wish to study such types of motion of liquids, and, in general, of amorphous bodies, as essentially depend upon their *fluidity*, both irreversible or reversible, we can wholly neglect the complications arising from the finite value of the compressibility, i.e. treat the liquid as incompressible. In this case the pressure must be derived from the dynamical equation expressing the general law of motion, which in classical hydrodynamics has the form

$$\rho \frac{d\mathbf{v}}{dt} = -\nabla p + \mu \nabla^2 \mathbf{v} - \nabla U, \tag{43}$$

where $\mu$ is the (ordinary) viscosity and $U$ the potential energy of the external forces per unit volume.

Equation (43) leaves out of account the shearing elasticity of a liquid body, i.e. its rigidity, which is masked by small values of $\mu$, but becomes a feature of primary importance when the viscosity is large enough (the body being actually transformed from liquid into solid). The influence of this rigidity, along with that of viscosity, on the tangential part $\phi_{ik}$ of the stress tensor $f_{ik}$ (the 'normal' part of it reducing to $-\delta_{ik}p$) has already been found in § 7 (eq. (27)) and can be written in the following form, corresponding to the substitution of the velocities $v_i$ for the displacements $u_i$:

$$\frac{d}{dt}\tau_{ik} = \frac{1}{2\mu}A\phi_{ik}. \tag{44}$$

Here $$\frac{d}{dt}\tau_{ik} = \frac{1}{2}\left(\frac{\partial}{\partial x_i}\frac{du_k}{dt}+\frac{\partial}{\partial x_k}\frac{du_i}{dt}\right) = \frac{1}{2}\left(\frac{\partial v_k}{\partial x_i}+\frac{\partial v_i}{\partial x_k}\right)$$

is the velocity tensor and $A$ the operator $1+\tau(d/dt)$, $\tau$ being Maxwell's relaxation time $\mu/G$.

We thus see that the simplest generalization of the equation (43), taking into account Maxwell's relaxation elasticity, associated with the irreversible fluidity, consists in replacing the factor $1/\mu$ by the operator $\frac{1}{\mu}A = \frac{1}{\mu}+\frac{1}{G}\frac{d}{dt}$. Rewriting (43) in the form

$$\nabla^2\mathbf{v} = \frac{1}{\mu}\left[\rho\frac{d\mathbf{v}}{dt}+\nabla(p+U)\right],$$

we obtain the following generalized equation of motion

$$\mu\nabla^2\mathbf{v} = A\left[\rho\frac{d\mathbf{v}}{dt}+\nabla(p+U)\right], \tag{45}$$

or, in view of the relation $dF/dt = \partial F/\partial t+(\mathbf{v}\nabla)F$ (valid for any function $F$ of the coordinates and the time)

$$\mu\nabla^2\mathbf{v} = \left[1+\tau\frac{\partial}{\partial t}+\tau(\mathbf{v}\nabla)\right]\left\{\rho\left[\frac{\partial\mathbf{v}}{\partial t}+(\mathbf{v}\nabla)\mathbf{v}\right]+\nabla(p+U)\right\}. \tag{45 a}$$

In order to account for the reversible fluidity of an amorphous body we must start from the relations $\phi_{ik} = 2M\tau_{ik}$ containing the generalized operator $M$, according to (30 a). Differentiating this relation with respect to the time, we get

$$\frac{d\tau_{ik}}{dt} = \frac{1}{2}\frac{d}{dt}M^{-1}\phi_{ik} = \frac{1}{2\tau_1}(A_1-1)M^{-1}\phi_{ik},$$

or according to (30 a) and remembering that $G_1\tau_1 = \mu_1$

$$\frac{d\tau_{ik}}{dt} = \frac{1}{2}\left\{\frac{1}{\mu_1}+\frac{1}{\tau_1}(A_1-1)[G_1+G_2(1-A_2^{-1})]^{-1}\right\}\phi_{ik}.$$

Hence it is seen that the desired generalization of the equation of motion of an incompressible amorphous body, taking account of the fluidity (both irreversible and reversible) and of the rigidity can be obtained from (45) if the operator $A$ $(=A_1)$ is replaced by

$$B = 1+G_1(A_1-1)[G_1+G_2(1-A_2^{-1})]^{-1},$$

and can accordingly be written as follows:

$$\mu_1 \nabla^2 \mathbf{v} = B\left[\rho \frac{d\mathbf{v}}{dt} + \nabla(p+U)\right], \tag{46}$$

or

$$\mu_1[G_1+G_2(1-A_2^{-1})]\nabla^2\mathbf{v}$$
$$= [G_1+G_2(1-A_2^{-1})+G_1(A_1-1)]\left[\rho\frac{d\mathbf{v}}{dt}+\nabla(p+U)\right]. \tag{46 a}$$

Besides these dynamical equations the incompressibility condition

$$\operatorname{div} \mathbf{v} = 0 \tag{47}$$

must be used along with the usual boundary conditions referring to an ordinary viscous fluid.

If the kinematics of the motion were fully determined by these conditions, the motion of a rigid fluid such as we are considering would be exactly the same—under identical external conditions—as that of an ordinary viscous fluid.

As a matter of fact, however, the dynamical equations (43), (45), or (46) do not only serve the purpose of determining the pressure $p$ for a given motion, but at the same time determine this motion, in conjunction with (47). To make this point clearer it may suffice to note that by taking the curl of (43) we can eliminate $p$ and obtain an equation for the rotational part of the motion.

It would be out of place to investigate this question at greater length here.

# V

# ORIENTATION AND ROTATIONAL MOTION OF MOLECULES IN LIQUID BODIES

## 1. Rotational Heat Motion in Liquids

As already mentioned in the preceding chapter (§ 1) the rotational motion of molecules even in relatively simple liquids at not too elevated temperatures consists essentially in rotational oscillations about equilibrium orientations, which are determined by the action of the surrounding molecules and changed jerkily from time to time. The duration $\tau$ of a certain equilibrium orientation must, as a rule, be large compared with the period $\tau_0$ of rotational oscillations and connected with the latter by relations of the same type $\tau = \tau_0 e^{U/kT}$, as in the case of the translation motion of the molecules of the liquid. Only in the limit of very high temperatures, when $kT$ becomes comparable with the activation energy $U$ which is required for a sharp change of the equilibrium orientation, the rotational motion of the molecules is reduced to a free rotation of the same kind as in the gaseous state.† The difference between the rotational and the translational motion of molecules in liquids consists, from this point of view, in the fact that in the case of translational motion the equilibrium positions of the molecules, irrespective of their size, are shifted by very small amounts of the order of $10^{-8}$ cm., whereas the equilibrium orientations—in the case of small molecules, at least—are rotated through large angles.

If the elementary displacements of the centres of gravity of the molecules were large, compared with their distance apart, the translational component of the heat motion of the molecules in a liquid could not be described as a kind of Brownian motion, i.e. as a self-diffusion, defined by a differential equation; it would be described by an integral equation‡ and could not be associated with the conception

† Just as in the case of translation motion, $U$ must be defined as the smallest energy, or rather free energy, required for such a rearrangement of a group of molecules as results in a sharp change of the orientation of the central molecule. The details of the mechanism of such reorientation processes and, in particular, the effective number of molecules involved in them, are not yet clear. In particular it is not clear whether and to what extent the changes of orientation are connected with changes of position.

‡ Of the same type as that introduced by Einstein in his theory of Brownian motion. This equation is reduced to a differential equation of diffusion on the assumption that the average displacements of the particles are small. If this assumption is not justified—as in the case of the scattering of photons or neutrons—the notion of differential diffusion must be rejected.

of 'mobility', i.e. of a frictional force proportional to the average velocity of a molecule with respect to rest.

Just this situation is apparently found in the case of the rotational motion of molecules. This motion can have a differential character, similar to the rotational Brownian motion of colloidal particles, only in the case of liquids with relatively *large* molecules, for which the notion of oscillations about an equilibrium position or orientation becomes devoid of physical meaning—or at least of practical value. In the case of liquids with simple molecules of a small size the rotational 'diffusion' or rather 'self-diffusion' motion must be characterized by sharp changes of the equilibrium orientations and cannot be associated with the conception of rotational friction (such as is used, for example, in Debye's theory of the polarization of dipole liquids in alternating electrical fields; see below, § 6).

It should be mentioned that in the simplest case of colloidal particles symmetrical about a certain axis—a dipole axis, for instance—the rotational motion can be reduced to an ordinary translational diffusion of a swarm of points on the surface of a sphere (with an arbitrary radius) if each point is imagined to represent a particle whose axis, supposed to be drawn from the centre of the sphere, intersects the latter in this point.

If a small portion of the surface of the sphere is considered, the angular distribution of the colloidal particles—or rather of their axes—can be described with the help of an ordinary equation of diffusion in two dimensions:

$$\frac{\partial f}{\partial t} = D\left(\frac{\partial^2 f}{\partial x^2}+\frac{\partial^2 f}{\partial y^2}\right), \tag{1}$$

where $x$, $y$ are two rectangular axes in a plane tangential to the corresponding portion of the spherical surface, $f(x,y)\,dxdy$ the number of particles whose axes are contained in a solid angle corresponding to the area $dxdy$, and $D$ the coefficient of rotational diffusion. In the presence of external forces with a moment $M$, the axis of each particle must rotate in a plane perpendicular to $\mathbf{M}$ with an average angular velocity $\omega$ proportional to $M$, i.e. $\omega = \alpha M$, where $\alpha$ is the coefficient of 'rotational mobility'. It can easily be shown, in the same way as in the case of translational Brownian motion, that it must be connected with the coefficient of rotational diffusion by Einstein's relation

$$\alpha = \frac{D}{kT}. \tag{1 a}$$

These conceptions and relations can be applied to the rotational motion or angular distribution of ordinary molecules in a liquid only if these molecules are sufficiently large. In the contrary case the notion of differential angular diffusion described by the equation (1) must be replaced by that of an integral angular diffusion, characterized by large rotations of the equilibrium orientations, about which the molecular axes perform small oscillations.

It should be remembered that this picture refers to the case of relatively low temperatures only, when $kT \ll U$. With approach of $kT$ to $U$ the rotational motion of the molecules must become more and more 'free', the liquid thus becoming 'gas-like' in this respect. It need not necessarily become simultaneously gas-like with respect to the *translation* motion of the molecules; more than that, a free rotation of the molecules can take place in certain cases even in the solid (crystalline) state.†

In the case of substances with complicated rod-shaped molecules the rotational motion must preserve the character of small oscillations far above the ordinary melting-point; in the case of 'liquid crystals' the corresponding equilibrium orientations preserve, moreover, a regular distribution, remaining more or less parallel to each other.

The gradual transition from rotational oscillations to free rotation with a rise of temperature must be revealed by a decrease of the specific heat of liquids—by an amount of 2 cal./mole in the case of diatomic molecules and 3 cal./mole in the case of more complicated ones, according to the number of rotational degrees of freedom; this decrease must, in general, take place in a temperature range different from that which corresponds to a similar effect due to the translational motion. Both effects refer to the value of the specific heat at constant volume $C_v$. Owing to the rapid increase of the volume when the liquid is heated at constant pressure to elevated temperatures the specific heat at constant pressure $C_p$ is found, on the contrary, to increase very sharply with a rise of the temperature. This increase is preserved even if the pressure is simultaneously increased, being maintained above that of the saturated vapour (in order to prevent the liquid from partial evaporation) up to the critical point.

In the case of substances whose molecules are rod-shaped or plate-shaped the transition to free rotation (which can be denoted as 'orienta-

† This is probably the case with hydrogen, both liquid and solid, as has been pointed out by Pauling, who believes that ortho-hydrogen molecules must persist in a state of free one-quantum rotation even at $T = 0$.

tional evaporation' of the corresponding bodies) must, in general, take place at different temperatures with respect to different axes. Thus, for example, in the case of liquid paraffins free rotation of the molecules about their longitudinal axes can start at relatively low temperatures, while free rotation about transverse axes requires much higher temperatures (and larger values of the specific volume).

In the sequel we shall limit ourselves to a consideration of substances composed of simple molecules possessing a symmetry axis, a rotation about which is either wholly absent (as in the case of diatomic molecules) or does not play an essential role. To begin with, we shall consider polar substances, the molecules of which possess an electric moment of constant magnitude in the direction of their axis of symmetry.

The possibility of influencing the behaviour of such molecules by the application of a homogeneous electric field of a constant or variable magnitude and direction enables one to study a number of questions connected with the mutual orientation and rotational motion of molecules in liquids much more extensively than can be done by a consideration of the purely thermal properties only. Of special interest are the phenomena of the dielectric polarization and losses of dipole liquids in high-frequency alternating fields, since in these phenomena not only the equilibrium properties of the corresponding liquids but also their kinetic properties, depending on the electric relaxation time (i.e. the average duration of a constant equilibrium orientation of the molecules), are revealed. Electrical vibrations with a period smaller than the relaxation time must influence the liquid in the same way as if in the absence of external forces the equilibrium orientations of the molecules never changed; the influence of the electrical forces must reduce in this case to a purely elastic effect, consisting of small, practically undamped, forced vibrations of the molecules about their equilibrium orientations. If, on the other hand, the vibration period is large compared with the relaxation time, then, *in the case of large molecules*, the action of the electric field must reduce to a viscous effect, consisting of a gradual increase of the degree of orientation of the molecules in its own direction. This effect can be denoted as an orientational (or angular) 'flow' of the liquid; it is quite similar to the usual viscous flow of a liquid body under the influence of a shearing stress of a constant or slowly variable direction. The main difference between them consists in the fact that the ordinary (translational) flow is, in principle, unlimited, whereas the orientational flow is limited by a rotation of the molecular axes by an angle of 180°.

The distinction between the 'orientational elastic' and the 'orientational viscous' behaviour of dipole liquids in rapidly or slowly alternating electrical fields refers, however, to liquids with *large*, slowly rotating molecules only. The behaviour of small, sharply reorientated molecules must preserve the same 'orientational elastic' character both in variable and in constant fields.

## 2. Polarization of Dipolar Liquids in a Constant Electrical Field (Old and New Theory of Debye)

According to Debye's old theory, which is merely a replica of Langevin's theory of paramagnetism, the electrical moment of a liquid due to a permanent electric field is equal per unit volume to

$$P = P_0 L\left(\frac{pE_e}{kT}\right), \tag{2}$$

where $P_0 = pn$ is the maximum saturation-value of $P$ ($p$ is the dipole moment of a molecule, $n$ the number of molecules in unit volume), while $E_e$ denotes the 'effective' field acting on each molecule, supposed to be connected with the average (macroscopic) field in the liquid $E$ by Lorentz's formula

$$\mathbf{E}_e = \mathbf{E} + \frac{4\pi}{3}\mathbf{P}. \tag{2 a}$$

$L(x) = \coth x - 1/x$ is Langevin's function, which for $x \ll 1$ reduces to $\frac{1}{3}x$. We thus get in this case

$$P = \frac{p^2 n}{3kT} E_e, \tag{3}$$

or according to (2 a)

$$P = \frac{p^2 n/3kT}{1 - \frac{4}{3}\pi(p^2 n/3kT)} E,$$

whence the following well-known equation for the dielectric constant $\epsilon = E + 4\pi P/E$ is obtained:

$$\frac{\epsilon - 1}{\epsilon + 2} = \frac{4\pi}{9} \frac{p^2 n}{kT}. \tag{3 a}$$

The last two equations can be applied to the case of relatively weak fields (not exceeding a few thousand volts/cm.). With a further increase of $E$ the polarization $P$ increases more slowly, tending to the constant limiting value $P_0 = pn$. This saturation effect is characterized by a decrease of the dielectric constant $\epsilon$, which in the limit $E \to \infty$ tends to 1. If the function $L(x)$ is expanded into a series of powers of $x$, then the second term, proportional to $E_e^3$, yields a correction $\Delta\epsilon < 0$ to the value of $\epsilon$ corresponding to the first term (i.e. to $E \to 0$), given by the following formula:

$$\Delta\epsilon = -\frac{4\pi}{15} n \frac{p^4}{k^3T^3}\left(\frac{\epsilon+2}{3}\right)^4 E^2. \tag{3 b}$$

The equations (3 a) and (3 b) are in excellent agreement with the experimental data in the case of dipolar *gases* (for which they are greatly simplified, since in this case $E_e$ can be identified with $E$, i.e. $\epsilon+2$ replaced by 3). With respect to dipole liquids the agreement between theory and experiment is of a qualitative character only. At the same time sharp discrepancies are found between the values of $p$ obtained for the same substance in the vapour and in the liquid state with the help of equation (3 a), and between the values of $p$ obtained for the same *liquid* with the help of (3 a) for the case of weak fields and of (3 b) for that of strong ones.

Thus for example, in the case of water vapour, the dipole moment of the molecules, calculated according to (3 a) or according to the simplified equation $\epsilon-1 = \frac{4\pi}{3}\frac{np^2}{kT}$, is equal to $1{\cdot}84\times10^{-18}$, whereas in the case of liquid water it proves to be equal to $0{\cdot}9\times10^{-18}$, i.e. nearly half the quantity. If, further, the latter value is substituted in equation (3 b), then for $E = 10^5$ c.g.s. one gets $\Delta\epsilon/\epsilon = -3{\cdot}87$, whereas the corresponding experimental value is found to be $1{\cdot}1\times10^{-3}$, i.e. 3,500 times smaller.

The discrepancy between the values of $p$ obtained according to equation (3 a) from the experimental values of $\epsilon$ in the vapour and liquid phase of the same dipole substance could be explained, in principle at least, by assuming that a fraction of the molecules in the liquid are associated into astatic pairs, with oppositely directed moments. Such an assumption cannot, however, explain the discrepancy between the values of $p$ obtained *for the same liquid* with the help of (3 a) on the one hand and of (3 b) on the other. This discrepancy must be considered as an intrinsic contradiction, pointing to the fallacy of some basic conceptions or assumptions of Debye's old theory leading to equation (2).

This circumstance was noted in 1935 by Debye himself,† who attempted to improve his old theory by accounting in a more correct and complete way for the mutual action between the molecules of the liquid. In the old theory this mutual action was assumed to be reduced to a mutual orientation of the molecules in the direction of the average electric field **E** and was allowed for by replacing the latter by the effec-

† P. Debye, *Phys. Z.* **36**, 100, 193 (1935).

tive field $\mathbf{E}_e$, according to Lorentz's formula (2 a). A mutual orientation of the molecules in the absence of an external electric field was thus supposed to be lacking. In reality, as has been shown in the preceding section, a strong mutual orientation of the molecules must exist in the absence of external forces, the equilibrium orientations of the molecules being distributed irregularly with a certain degree of local order and being specified by a local field $F$. Inasmuch as the latter is due to the dipole moments of the surrounding molecules, it must have a magnitude of the order $p/r^3$, where $r$ is the average distance between nearest neighbours ($2.10^{-8}$ cm.), i.e. $10^{-18}/10^{-23} = 10^5$ c.g.s., or $3.10^7$ volt/cm. The product $pF \approx 10^{-13}$ is thus about 10 times as large as the value of $kT$ at room temperatures. We thus see that even in the absence of any other mutually orientating influences not reducible to the mutual action between the dipole moments, the molecules of a dipole liquid cannot rotate freely as in the gas phase, but must oscillate about certain equilibrium orientations. So long as we are interested in the action of external fields of constant magnitude and direction, the fact that these orientations have a limited duration need not concern us, provided $\tau$ is much larger than the oscillation period $\tau_0$.

Since the strongest fields $E$ which are applied for the polarization of liquids are very weak compared with the inner or local field $F$, their influence can be reduced, according to Debye's new theory, to a very small rotation of the equilibrium orientation as determined by the local field alone, in the direction of the applied field $\mathbf{E}$ or rather $\mathbf{E}_e$, so that the new equilibrium orientation should coincide with the direction of the resulting field $\mathbf{F}' = \mathbf{F}+\mathbf{E}_e$.

It is thus clear in Debye's new theory that a dipole liquid is treated as an orientationally elastic or orientationally rigid body, without any allowance for the eventually possible effects of orientational fluidity or viscosity. It is interesting to note that in his earlier theory of the polarization of dipole liquids in alternating electrical fields (1912) Debye treated all such liquids as orientationally fluid bodies, without making any allowance for orientationally elastic effects. A recent theory aiming at combining the effects of the two kinds, which was developed by Debye jointly with Ramm in 1937,† again for all dipole liquids irrespective of the size of their molecules, is, as will be shown below, self-contradictory and leads to wrong results.

As has been pointed out in the preceding section, Debye's newest theory, involving the orientationally elastic effects alone, is applicable

† Debye and Ramm, *Ann. d. Phys.* (v) **28**, 28 (1937).

to liquids with small molecules, whereas his earlier theory, based on a consideration of orientationally viscous effects alone, can be applied to liquids with large molecules. In the latter case, as will be seen below, Debye's old theory of the polarization in constant fields remains valid (with certain important corrections which, however, are not connected with orientationally elastic effects).

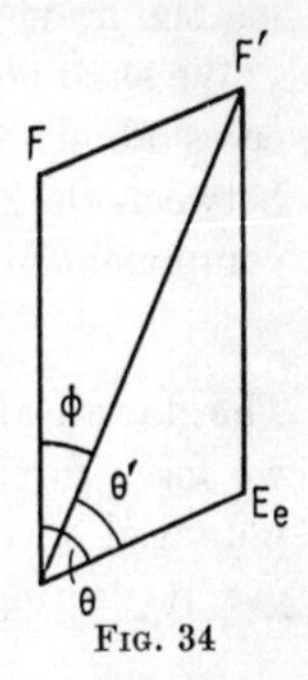

FIG. 34

For the sake of clarity we shall first give a simplified presentation of Debye's new theory,† holding good for the case, usually encountered, where $pE \ll kT \ll pF$. In this case it is possible, as a first approximation, to neglect the rotational oscillations of the dipoles and assume that they are directed along the resulting electric field $\mathbf{F}' = \mathbf{F}+\mathbf{E}_e$. Following Debye, we shall use for $\mathbf{E}_e$ Lorentz's expression (1 a), which is supposed to account for the mutual orientation of the molecules in the preferred direction.

Let us denote by $\theta$, $\theta'$, and $\phi$ the angles between the vectors $(\mathbf{F}, \mathbf{E}_e)$, $(\mathbf{F}', \mathbf{E}_e)$, and $(\mathbf{F}, \mathbf{F}')$ (Fig. 34). The equality of the torques acting on the dipole on the part of $\mathbf{F}$ and $\mathbf{E}_e$ is expressed by the equation

$$E_e \sin\theta' = F\sin\phi, \tag{4}$$

where

$$\sin\theta' = \sin\theta\cos\phi - \cos\theta\sin\phi, \qquad \cos\theta' = \cos\theta\cos\phi + \sin\theta\sin\phi.$$

In the first approximation with respect to the ratio $E_e/F$ we can replace $\theta'$ in (4) by $\theta$, which gives

$$\sin\phi = \frac{E_e}{F}\sin\theta, \tag{4 a}$$

and further

$$\cos\theta' = \cos\theta + \frac{E_e}{F}\sin^2\theta. \tag{4 b}$$

The polarization of the liquid $P$ can be obtained by multiplying the number of molecules $n$ in unit volume by the mean value of the component of the electric moment of one of them along the direction of the field $\mathbf{E}$ (or $\mathbf{E}_e$), i.e. of $p\cos\theta'$. If in calculating this mean value all the directions of the vector $\mathbf{F}$ with respect to $\mathbf{E}_e$ are regarded as equally probable,‡ we get $\overline{\cos\theta} = 0$, $\overline{\cos^2\theta} = \frac{1}{3}$, $\overline{\sin^2\theta} = \frac{2}{3}$, and consequently

$$\overline{p\cos\theta'} = \frac{2}{3}\frac{pE_e}{F},$$

that is,

$$P = \frac{2}{3}\frac{np}{F}E_e. \tag{5}$$

† Frenkel, *Acta Physicochimica, U.R.S.S.* **4**, 341 (1936).

‡ According to A. Anselm, *Acta Physicochimica U.R.S.S.*, **19**, 400 (1944), this assumption is not justifiable and can lead to erroneous results.

This formula is a substitute for the formula (3) of Debye's old theory. It is obtained from the latter if $kT$ is replaced by $\frac{1}{2}pF$, i.e. by multiplying the previous expression by the factor $R = 2kT/pF$.

We shall now take into account the thermal oscillations of the molecules about their equilibrium orientation. Let $\delta$ denote the angle between the oscillating dipole and the direction of the vector $\mathbf{F}'$. The component of $\mathbf{p}$ along $\mathbf{E}_e$ is equal to

$$p\cos(\theta'-\delta) = p(\cos\theta'\cos\delta+\sin\theta'\sin\delta).$$

The statistical average of $\sin\delta$ vanishes. In the case of small oscillations we have further $\overline{\cos\delta} = 1-\frac{1}{2}\overline{\delta^2}$. Since $pF'(1-\cos\delta) \simeq \frac{1}{2}\delta^2 pF'$ is the potential energy of the dipole, whose mean value is equal to $\frac{1}{2}kT$, we get, neglecting the difference between $F'$ and $F$,

$$\overline{\delta^2} = \frac{kT}{pF},$$

and consequently

$$\overline{p_E} = p\,\overline{\cos\theta'}\,\overline{\cos\delta} = p\,\overline{\cos\theta'}(1-\tfrac{1}{2}\overline{\delta^2}) = \frac{2}{3}\frac{pE_e}{F}\left(1-\frac{kT}{2pF}\right),$$

that is,

$$P = \frac{2}{3}\frac{np}{F}\left(1-\frac{kT}{2pF}\right)E_e. \qquad (5\,\text{a})$$

According to this formula, just as according to the formula (2 a) in Debye's old theory, the polarization of a dipole liquid decreases with a rise of the temperature, the two formulae being approximately equivalent in this respect within the relatively narrow range of temperatures for which measurements of $\epsilon$ are possible. Formula (5 a) corresponds to the following equation for $\epsilon$:

$$\frac{\epsilon-1}{\epsilon+2} = \frac{8\pi}{9}\frac{np}{F}\left(1-\frac{kT}{2pF}\right). \qquad (5\,\text{b})$$

If we substitute the value $p = 1{\cdot}84\times10^{-18}$ for the molecules of water in the vapour state, and the experimental value 81 for $\epsilon$, we can determine the magnitude of the local field $F$. The result agrees with the estimate previously made, the value of $pF$ proving to be nine times as large as that of $kT$ at room temperatures.

Turning to an exact formulation of Debye's new theory we shall note, first of all (see Fig. 34), that

$$F' = (F^2+E_e^2+2E_e F\cos\theta)^{\frac{1}{2}},$$

that is, to an accuracy of the first order with respect to $E_e/F$:

$$F' = F\left(1+\frac{E_e}{F}\cos\theta\right).$$

Let us introduce the notations

$$a = \frac{pF}{kT}, \qquad a' = \frac{pF'}{kT}$$

and expand the function $L(a')$ in powers of $E_e/F$. Limiting ourselves to first order terms we get

$$L(a') = L(a) + \frac{dL}{da}\frac{aE_e}{F}\cos\theta.$$

The product $pL(a')$ is the mean value of the component of the moment $\mathbf{p}$ in the direction of $F'$. In order to obtain its component $\overline{p_E}$ along $\mathbf{E}_e$ we must multiply $L(a')$ by $\cos\theta'$ and average over all values of $\theta$. On the assumption that they are equally probable we get with the help of (4 b):

$$\overline{L(a')\cos\theta'} = L(a)\frac{E_e}{F}\overline{\sin^2\theta} + \frac{dL}{da}a\frac{E_e}{F}\overline{\cos^2\theta}$$

$$= \frac{E_e}{3F}\left[2L(a) + a\frac{dL}{da}\right] = \frac{E_e}{3F}a(1-L^2),$$

since according to the definition of $L$

$$\frac{dL}{da} = 1 - \frac{2L}{a} - L^2.$$

Thus

$$P = n\overline{p_E} = \frac{np^2}{3kT}E_e(1-L^2). \tag{6}$$

This formula, derived by Debye in 1937, can be obtained from his old formula (2 a) by multiplying it by the factor $R = 1-L^2(a)$. From the point of view of Debye's old theory this would correspond to a decrease of the dipole moment in the liquid phase compared with that in the vapour phase by the factor $\sqrt{R}$. If $a = pF/kT \gg 1$, $L(a)$ is reduced to $1-kT/pF$ and $1-L^2$ to $2kT/pF$, which is the approximate value of $R$ previously found. If the quadratic term in the expression $1-L^2 \cong 2kT/pF-(kT/pF)^2$ is retained, formula (6) is reduced to (5 a).

In order to account for the saturation effect, the preceding calculations must be performed with an accuracy to terms of the next (third) order in $E_e/F$. According to (4) we have, putting $E_e/F = x$,

$$\sin\phi = x\sin\theta - x^2\sin\theta\cos\theta + x^3\sin\theta(\cos^2\theta - \tfrac{1}{2}\sin^2\theta),$$

$$\cos\phi = 1 - \frac{x^2}{2}\sin^2\theta + x^3\sin^2\theta\cos\theta,$$

$$\cos\theta' = \cos\theta + x\sin^2\theta - \tfrac{3}{2}x^2\sin^2\theta\cos\theta + x^3\sin^2\theta(2\cos^2\theta - \tfrac{1}{2}\sin^2\theta),$$

and further

$$F' = F(1+x\cos\theta+\tfrac{1}{2}x^2\sin^2\theta-x^3\cos\theta\sin^2\theta),$$

whence

$$L(a') = L(a)+\frac{dL}{da}ax\cos\theta+x^2\left[\frac{1}{2}\frac{d^2L}{da^2}a^2\cos^2\theta+\frac{1}{2}\frac{dL}{da}a\sin^2\theta\right]+$$

$$+x^3\left[-\frac{1}{2}\frac{dL}{da}a\cos\theta\sin^2\theta+\frac{1}{2}\frac{d^2L}{da^2}a^2\cos\theta\sin^2\theta+\frac{1}{6}\frac{d^3L}{da^3}a^3\cos^3\theta\right].$$

With the help of these expressions we obtain after elementary but cumbersome calculations

$$P = \frac{1}{3}np\left(\frac{pE_a}{kT}\right)R(a)-\frac{np}{45}\left(\frac{pE_e}{kT}\right)^3R^*(a), \tag{6 a}$$

where $R(a) = 1-L^2$, while

$$R^*(a) = 3\left[1-4L^2+3L^4+\frac{4L}{a}(2L^2-1)+6\frac{L^2}{a^2}\right]$$

is a correction factor to the second term of the expression for $P$ following from Debye's old theory and accounting for the saturation effect.

Using the same value of $pF/kT$ which is needed to remove the discrepancy between the values of $p$ for water molecules in the vapour and in the liquid state, Debye has succeeded in removing simultaneously the discrepancy between the values of $p$ which followed from the first (linear) and second (cubical) terms of his former theory corresponding to $R = R^* = 1$.

## 3. Polarization of Dipolar Liquids in a Constant Electric Field (Onsager's Theory)

Inasmuch as Debye's new theory, just as the old one, is based on Lorentz's formula (2 a) for the effective field, they both lead to an equation of the Lorentz type for the dielectric constant as a function of the polarizability $\alpha = \overline{p_E}/E$:

$$\frac{\epsilon-1}{\epsilon+2} = \frac{4\pi}{3}n\alpha, \tag{7}$$

where $\alpha = p^2/3kT$.

This equation involves the following difficulty. Its left-hand side cannot evidently exceed 1 (for $\epsilon = \infty$), whereas the right-hand side is, in principle at least, unlimited. This difficulty is in part due to the trivial fact that equation (7) is an approximation, based on the assumption of the smallness of $E_e$ (for in this case only is $\overline{p_E}$ proportional to $E_e$), whereas in the case $\epsilon \to \infty$ the effective field $E_e$ tends to infinity.

We thus see that, strictly speaking, equation (7) cannot be applied to very large values of $\epsilon$. It shows, however, that both liquid and solid bodies can possess extremely large electrical susceptibilities in very weak electrical fields.

This behaviour has not hitherto been observed in the case of dipolar liquids.† Likewise, no liquid is known which would display the phenomenon of spontaneous electric polarization (analogous to the spontaneous magnetization of ferromagnetic bodies), whereas according to Debye's old theory this phenomenon would be expected to be of frequent occurrence. Substituting in equation (2a) the expression $E_e = \frac{4}{3}\pi P$ for the effective field in the absence of an external one, we get

$$\xi = L(\gamma\xi), \tag{7 a}$$

where $\xi = P/P_0$ and $\gamma = \frac{4}{3}\pi np^2/kT$. This equation is identical with the equation (25) of Ch. II for the degree of orientation in a dipolar crystal as a function of the temperature. The Curie temperature below which such a spontaneous polarization is possible is equal to $T_c = \frac{4}{9}\pi np^2/k$. Putting here $n = 10^{22}$, $p = 10^{-18}$, $k = 10^{-16}$, we get $T_c \cong 100°$ K. We thus see that at a temperature of the order of a few hundred degrees above absolute zero, at which a large number of dipole substances can exist in the liquid state, these liquids would behave as electrical analogues of permanent magnets.

The first of the above-mentioned difficulties subsists in Debye's new theory. Putting, for example, $R \doteq 2kT/pF$, i.e. $\alpha = \frac{2}{3}p/F$, and noting that $F \approx p/r^3 \approx pn$ (since $r^3$ is approximately equal to the volume of the liquid per molecule), we see that $\frac{4\pi}{3}\alpha n = \frac{8\pi}{9}r^3 n \approx 1$, which in virtue of (7) is just the condition for $\epsilon \to \infty$.

Thus, according to this theory, practically all dipole liquids should possess an exceedingly high susceptibility in weak electric fields.

It is therefore clear that Debye's old theory must be further modified in a direction quite different from that considered by Debye himself and connected with a critical revision of the Lorentz expression for the effective field.

This point was recognized in 1936 by L. Onsager,‡ who, leaving aside the complications due to Debye's local field, has derived a new expression for the effective field, essentially different, in the case of dipolar liquids, from that of Lorentz.

† The maximum value of $\epsilon$ found in HCN is equal to 120. The abnormal behaviour of Rochelle salt crystals is due to specific factors and cannot be generalized to ordinary dipole substances.

‡ *Journ. Am. Chem. Soc.* **58**, 1886 (1936).

According to Onsager the effective field $\mathbf{E}_e$ must consist of the following two parts:

The first part $\mathbf{G}$ is that field which would be obtained in a spherical cavity containing the molecule under consideration, if the latter were removed from this cavity, under the condition that the field $\mathbf{E}$ and the polarization $\mathbf{P}$ should remain constant at large distances from the latter (in the vicinity of the cavity the field must be essentially modified and in particular must lose its homogeneous character).

The second part of the effective field $\mathbf{R}$ is that field which is due to the additional polarization of the liquid produced by the introduction of the molecule in question into the cavity with a given direction of its permanent dipole moment. This field is called by Onsager the 'reaction field', for it specifies the action of the molecule on itself through the polarization of the surrounding medium.†

We thus have
$$\mathbf{E}_e = \mathbf{G}+\mathbf{R}. \tag{8}$$
Let us denote the potential of the reaction field by $\psi$ ($\mathbf{R} = -\nabla\psi$) and determine it as follows: (1) it must satisfy Laplace's equation $\nabla^2\psi = 0$ both outside the cavity ($r > a$) and inside it ($r < a$) ($a$ is the radius of the cavity); (2) for $r \to 0$, i.e. near the centre of the cavity, it reduces to the expression $\psi = p\cos\theta/r^2$, corresponding to an elementary dipole placed at this centre; (3) on the surface of the cavity the boundary conditions
$$\psi_{r=a+0} = \psi_{r=a-0}, \qquad \left(\frac{\partial\psi}{\partial r}\right)_{r=a-0} = \epsilon\left(\frac{\partial\psi}{\partial r}\right)_{r=a+0}$$
must be satisfied.

A molecule is thus treated as an elementary (point-like) dipole, surrounded by a sphere with a dielectric constant equal to 1, while the surrounding liquid is treated as a continuous medium with a constant (macroscopic) value of $\epsilon$.

The solution of the preceding problem is given by the formulae
$$\psi = \frac{p\cos\theta}{r^2} - Rr\cos\theta \quad (r < a)$$
$$\psi = \frac{p^*\cos\theta}{\epsilon r^2} \quad (r > a), \tag{9}$$
where the vector
$$\mathbf{p}^* = \frac{3\epsilon}{2\epsilon+1}\mathbf{p} \tag{9a}$$
can be defined as the 'external' moment of the dipole located at the

† Onsager's reaction field is essentially similar to the field of the image forces, attracting an elastic charge or dipole to the surface of a conducting body.

centre of the cavity, taking into account the polarization of the surrounding medium, while

$$\mathbf{R} = \frac{2(\epsilon-1)}{2\epsilon+1}\frac{\mathbf{p}}{a^3}. \tag{9 b}$$

Let us now determine the modification of the average field $\mathbf{E}$, due to the presence of the spherical cavity, obtained by removing a molecule of the liquid from its place. This problem is practically equivalent to the preceding one, the conditions $\psi = p\cos\theta/r^2$ for $r \to 0$ being replaced by the condition

$$\psi(r,\theta) \to -Er\cos\theta \quad \text{for } r \to \infty,$$

where $\mathbf{G} = -\nabla\psi$. We thus get

$$\begin{aligned} \psi &= -Er\cos\theta - \frac{p'}{r^2}\cos\theta \quad (r > a) \\ \psi &= -Gr\cos\theta \qquad\qquad\quad (r < a), \end{aligned} \tag{10}$$

where the vector

$$\mathbf{p}' = \frac{\epsilon-1}{2\epsilon+1}a^3\mathbf{E} \tag{10 a}$$

is the electric moment of the cavity (due to the bound charges which cover its surface), while

$$\mathbf{G} = \frac{3\epsilon}{2\epsilon+1}\mathbf{E} \tag{10 b}$$

is the resulting homogeneous field, which must exist in it for a fixed value of $E$ at large distances.

The total 'effective' field acting on a spherical molecule in a polarized dielectric is thus equal to

$$\mathbf{E}_e = \frac{3\epsilon}{2\epsilon+1}\mathbf{E} + \frac{2(\epsilon-1)}{2\epsilon+1}\frac{\mathbf{p}}{a^3}. \tag{11}$$

The 'cavity field' $\mathbf{G}$ has the same direction as the average (macroscopic) field $\mathbf{E}$, which is also the average direction of the reaction field $\mathbf{R}$ (for different molecules or different instants). In Debye's theory, both old and new, it is tacitly assumed that the resulting orientating influence experienced by each molecule is determined by the average value (and direction) of the total field

$$\overline{\mathbf{E}_e} = \mathbf{G} + \overline{\mathbf{R}}. \tag{11 a}$$

Now, this is obviously incorrect, for the reaction field has always the same direction as the electric moment of the molecule producing it, and can therefore exert no orientating influence on this molecule. It is thus clear that so long as the electric moment of the molecules is supposed to have a fixed value, the effective field which determines its orientation must be identified with the cavity field **G**.

The moment of the torque acting on a molecule is equal to

$$\mathbf{M} = \mathbf{p}\times\mathbf{E}_e = \mathbf{p}\times\mathbf{G} = \mathbf{p}^*\times\mathbf{E}$$

(cf. eq. (9)). This corresponds to a potential energy

$$U = -Ep^* \cos\theta = -Gp\cos\theta.$$

The polarization of the liquid in a macroscopic field **E** can thus be calculated according to equation (2) if $\mathbf{E}_e$ is replaced by **G**. This gives

$$P = P_0 L\left(\frac{Gp}{kT}\right), \tag{12}$$

or in the case of weak fields

$$P = \frac{\epsilon}{2\epsilon+1}\frac{p^2 n}{kT}E. \tag{12 a}$$

This formula leads to the following equation for the dielectric constant:

$$\frac{(\epsilon-\ )(2\epsilon+1)}{\epsilon} = 4\pi\frac{np^2}{kT}, \tag{13}$$

replacing the equation (3 a) or (7) of Clausius–Mosotti (or Lorentz–Lorenz). According to (13) the dielectric constant increases monotonically with increase of the parameter $\alpha = 4\pi(np^2/kT)$, remaining finite for finite values of this parameter. In the limit $\alpha \gg 1$, i.e. $\epsilon \gg 1$, we can put approximately

$$\epsilon \approx \frac{2\pi np^2}{kT}. \tag{13 a}$$

We have supposed thus far that the polarization of the liquid is entirely due to the orientation of the molecules with permanent dipole moments of a constant magnitude. In reality this orientation polarization is always associated with an elastic polarization, due to a change of the magnitude of the electric moment under the action of the electrical forces, and depending essentially on a deformation of the electron distribution about the nuclei of the corresponding atoms (to a very small extent also on a change of the internuclear distances).

Since Debye's theory makes no distinction between the orientational and elastic polarization with respect to the definition of the effective field, it leads, in the case of weak fields, with allowance for the two components of the polarization, to the same equation (7) as in the case when one of them only is taken into account, the polarizability $\alpha$ being equal to the sum of the orientational part $p^2/3kT$ (or $\frac{2}{3}p/F$) and of the elastic part $\alpha_0$ which is independent of the temperature.

An entirely different situation arises in the case of Onsager's theory. In the special case of the absence of an orientation effect the moment **p** in equation (11) can be identified with the elastic or induced moment $\alpha.\mathbf{E}$. Since this moment is always parallel to **E**, equation (11) is in this case equivalent to (11 a). Replacing $\mathbf{p} = \bar{\mathbf{p}}$ by $\bar{\mathbf{P}}/n$ and putting

$$\frac{4\pi}{3}a^3n = 1, \tag{14}$$

i.e. identifying the volume of the spherical cavity containing a molecule with the volume of the liquid per molecule, we can rewrite (11) as follows:

$$\mathbf{E}_e = \frac{3\epsilon}{2\epsilon+1}\mathbf{E}+\frac{2(\epsilon-1)}{2\epsilon+1}\frac{4\pi}{3}\mathbf{P}. \tag{14a}$$

Now this equation is easily seen to be identical with that of Lorentz $\mathbf{E}_e = \mathbf{E}+\frac{4}{3}\pi\mathbf{P}$. In fact, putting $4\pi\mathbf{P} = (\epsilon-1)\mathbf{E}$, we get

$$\mathbf{E}_e = \frac{1}{2\epsilon+1}[3\epsilon+\tfrac{2}{3}(\epsilon-1)^2]\mathbf{E} = \frac{2\epsilon^2+5\epsilon+2}{3(2\epsilon+1)}\mathbf{E},$$

that is,

$$E_e = \frac{\epsilon+2}{3}E, \tag{15}$$

since $2\epsilon^2+5\epsilon+2 = (2\epsilon+1)(\epsilon+2)$. The same result is obtained on substituting the expression $(\epsilon-1)E$ for $4\pi P$ in Lorentz's equation.

It should be mentioned that from equation (15) in connexion with the relation

$$n\alpha_0 E_e = P = \frac{\epsilon-1}{4\pi}E$$

the following expression for the polarizability $\alpha_0$ is obtained:

$$\alpha_0 = \frac{3}{4\pi n}\frac{\epsilon-1}{\epsilon+2}, \tag{15a}$$

or, according to (14),

$$\alpha_0 = \frac{\epsilon-1}{\epsilon+2}a^3. \tag{15b}$$

This equation was derived by Clausius and Mosotti on the assumption that the molecules can be treated as small conducting spheres.

In the general case, that is, in the presence of both an elastic and an orientation effect, the permanent moment **p** in equation (11) must be increased by an additional moment $\Delta\mathbf{p} = \alpha_0\mathbf{E}_e$ induced by the field, the effective value of the latter ($\mathbf{E}_e$) being different both from that of the Lorentz theory $(\epsilon+2)E/3$ and from that $G = 3\epsilon E/(2\epsilon+1)$ of the special case of Onsager's theory corresponding to $\alpha_0 = 0$.

Using the relation (15b) in which $\epsilon$ must be replaced by $\epsilon_0$ (i.e. by the square of the refractive index) we get instead of (11)

$$\mathbf{E}_e\left[1-\frac{2(\epsilon-1)(\epsilon_0-1)}{(2\epsilon+1)(\epsilon_0+2)}\right] = \frac{3\epsilon}{2\epsilon+1}\mathbf{E}+\frac{2(\epsilon-1)}{2\epsilon+1}\frac{\mathbf{p}}{a^3},$$

whence it follows that

$$\mathbf{E}_e = \left[1+\frac{\epsilon_0(\epsilon-1)}{2\epsilon+\epsilon_0}\right]\mathbf{E}+\frac{2(\epsilon-1)(\epsilon_0+2)}{3(2\epsilon+\epsilon_0)}\frac{\mathbf{p}}{a^3}. \tag{16}$$

In the special case $p = 0$ and $\epsilon = \epsilon_0$ this equation is reduced to (14b).

The total value of the moment of a molecule is thus found to be

$$\mathbf{p}+\Delta\mathbf{p} = \frac{(\epsilon_0+2)(2\epsilon+1)}{3(2\epsilon+\epsilon_0)}\mathbf{p}+\frac{\epsilon(\epsilon_0-1)}{2\epsilon+\epsilon_0}a^3\mathbf{E}. \tag{16a}$$

The moment of the torque acting on a molecule is given by

$$\mathbf{M} = (\mathbf{p}+\Delta\mathbf{p})\times\mathbf{E}_e = (\mathbf{p}+\Delta\mathbf{p})\times\mathbf{G} = \frac{3\epsilon}{2\epsilon+1}(\mathbf{p}+\Delta\mathbf{p})\times\mathbf{E},$$

or, according to (16a),

$$\mathbf{M} = \mu\mathbf{p}\times\mathbf{G} = \mu^*\mathbf{p}\times\mathbf{E}, \tag{17}$$

where

$$\mu = \frac{(\epsilon_0+2)(2\epsilon+1)}{3(2\epsilon+\epsilon_0)} \tag{17a}$$

and

$$\mu^* = \frac{3\epsilon}{2\epsilon+1}\mu. \tag{17b}$$

The product $\mu\mathbf{p}$ is the sum of the molecule's own permanent electric moment $\mathbf{p}$ and of the moment induced by the elastic polarization in the reactive field. The vector $\mu^*\mathbf{p}$ is the effective dipole moment of the molecule, specifying the field produced by it outside the cavity which it is supposed to fill. It should be noted that the total moment of a molecule $\mathbf{p}+\Delta\mathbf{p}$ includes not only that part of the elastic polarization which is due to the reaction field $\mathbf{R}$ but also the contribution due to the cavity field $\mathbf{G}$ (whose direction is, in general, different from that of $\mathbf{p}$).

The potential energy corresponding to expression (17) for the torque is equal to $U = -\mu^*pE\cos\theta$. The orientation part of the polarization can thus be calculated with the help of formula (2) if $p$ is replaced by $\mu p$ and $E_e$ by $\mu^*E/\mu = 3\epsilon E/(2\epsilon+1)$. In the case of weak fields the orientational part of the polarization is thus found to be equal to

$$\mu\mu^*\frac{np^2}{3kT}\mathbf{E} = \frac{\epsilon}{2\epsilon+1}\mu^2\frac{np^2}{kT}\mathbf{E}.$$

Strictly speaking, the separation of the total polarization into an orientation part and an elastic part is impossible, the two effects being intimately interlocked with each other. The total polarization is equal to

$$\mathbf{P} = n\left[\mu\mu^*\frac{p^2}{3kT}+\frac{\epsilon(\epsilon_0+2)}{2\epsilon+\epsilon_0}\alpha_0\right]\mathbf{E}. \tag{18}$$

This corresponds to the following equation for $\epsilon$:

$$\frac{(\epsilon-\epsilon_0)(2\epsilon+1)}{2\epsilon+\epsilon_0} = 4\pi n\frac{\mu\mu^* p^2}{3kT},$$

or, according to (17 a) and (17 b),

$$\frac{(\epsilon-\epsilon_0)(2\epsilon+\epsilon_0)}{\epsilon(\epsilon_0+2)^2} = \frac{4\pi np^2}{9kT}. \tag{18 a}$$

This equation is a generalization of equation (13). In the case of very large values of $\epsilon$ it is reduced to

$$\epsilon = \frac{2\pi np^2}{9kT}(\epsilon_0+2)^2.$$

In the opposite case $\epsilon-\epsilon_0 \ll \epsilon_0$ equation (18 a) can be written in the form

$$\epsilon = \epsilon_0+\frac{4\pi}{27}\frac{np^2(\epsilon_0+2)^2}{kT},$$

which differs but slightly from that of the old Lorentz–Debye theory.

In his paper Onsager does not attempt to account for saturation effects. Limiting ourselves in the expansion of $L$ to the first two terms (of the first and third order with respect to $E$) we get

$$P = n\left[\frac{\mu\mu^* p^2}{3kT}-\frac{\mu\mu^{*3}}{45}\frac{p^4E^2}{(kT)^3}+\frac{\epsilon(\epsilon_0+2)}{2\epsilon+\epsilon_0}\right]\mathbf{E}, \tag{19}$$

which leads to the following equation:

$$\frac{(\epsilon-\epsilon_0)(2\epsilon+\epsilon_0)}{(\epsilon_0+2)^2\epsilon} = \frac{4\pi np^2}{9kT}\left\{1-\frac{1}{15}\left[\frac{\epsilon(\epsilon_0+2)}{2\epsilon+\epsilon_0}\frac{pE}{kT}\right]^2\right\}. \tag{19 a}$$

Onsager's theory is in good agreement with the experimental data in the case of liquids with a weak polarity. In the case of strongly polar liquids it leads to too small values of the dielectric constant. Thus, for example, for the dielectric constant of water a value 31 is obtained from Onsager's theory, while the experimental value is 81.

In Debye's theory, both old and new, the effective field acting on a molecule is identified with that of Lorentz, Onsager's argument being thus wholly ignored.† On the other hand, Onsager's theory wholly ignores Debye's local field. It seems natural to unify the two theories by replacing the Lorentz effective field by Onsager's field **G** and the dipole moment of a molecule **p** by the product $\mu\mathbf{p}$, allowing for the influence of the reaction field (in the presence of elastic polarizability).

† In spite of the fact that Debye's latest publications on this subject appeared after the publication of Onsager's work.

We thus get in the first approximation

$$\mathbf{P} = \frac{n\mu^2 p^2 \mathbf{G}}{3kT}\left[1-L^2\left(\frac{\mu pF}{kT}\right)\right]. \tag{20}$$

This formula is a generalization of Debye's formula (6) on the one hand and of Onsager's formula (18) on the other (without the last term representing the direct contribution of the elastic polarization).

Onsager's formula (18 a), taking into account Debye's correction for the local field, assumes the following form:

$$\frac{(\epsilon-\epsilon_0)(2\epsilon+\epsilon_0)}{\epsilon(\epsilon_0+2)^2} = \frac{4\pi np^2}{9kT}\left[1-L^2\left(\frac{\mu pF}{kT}\right)\right]. \tag{20 a}$$

The combination of Onsager's theory with Debye's theory of the local field, instead of improving the agreement between theory and experiment, leads, on the contrary, to a still sharper disagreement between them so far as the numerical value of $\epsilon$ is concerned. As has just been mentioned, Onsager's theory, as applied to water, gives $\epsilon = 31$; the introduction of Debye's factor $1-L^2$ lowers this value still further.

## 4. Kirkwood's Improvement of Debye's and Onsager's Theories

Onsager's theory is open to a number of objections, which can be summarized as follows:

(1) Onsager uses an artificial and roughly simplified model of a molecule. Although such procedure often leads to correct results, which prove to be independent of the model used, it is nevertheless desirable that the theory should not be based on wrong assumptions about the molecular structure.

(2) The liquid surrounding an arbitrarily chosen molecule is treated as a continuum with a constant value of $\epsilon$.

(3) The interaction of a molecule with its neighbours is accounted for (in the absence of an external field) by the reactive field only, which, being parallel to the electric moment of the molecule, produces no orientation effect whatsoever.

Kirkwood has developed Onsager's ideas in a stricter form and on a broader basis, allowing, in principle, for a mutual action of any kind between the molecules (and not simply for the mutual orientation of elementary dipoles, as in Debye's theory).† Since, however, this mutual action is thus far not known exactly even in the case of the simplest

† J. Kirkwood, *J. Chem. Phys.* **7**, 911 (1939).

substances, it has not yet been possible to obtain reliable numerical results for any actual liquid from Kirkwood's theory.

Instead of a single molecule let us consider, following Kirkwood, a dielectric sphere $B$ with a radius $r_0$ large enough (compared with the distance between the nearest molecules) to justify a treatment of the surrounding liquid as a continuous medium with the macroscopic dielectric constant $\epsilon$.

In the presence of a weak electric field $\mathbf{E}$, the average value of the total electric moment of a molecule (in the direction of $\mathbf{E}$) $\overline{p'}$ can be represented as the sum of a part $\overline{p_E}$, due to the orientation of the permanent dipole moment $p$ and of the induced moment $\Delta p = \alpha F$, where $F$ is the effective field (previously denoted by $E_e$).

In order to calculate $\overline{p_E}$ let us consider a large dielectric sphere $A$ with a radius $R \gg r_0$, consisting of $N$ molecules and introduced into an external field $\mathbf{E}_0$ (the latter should not be confused with the average field $\mathbf{E}$). The sphere $B$ will be imagined to form a small inner portion of $A$.

One of the molecules with a moment $\mathbf{p}_i$ induces in the sphere $A$ a certain electric moment $\mathbf{m}_i$. The total moment of $A$ is obviously equal to the sum of the dipole moments of its molecules

$$\mathbf{m} = \sum_1^N \mathbf{p}_i, \tag{21}$$

which can also be written in the form

$$\mathbf{m} = \sum_1^N \mathbf{m}_i \tag{21 a}$$

in view of the linearity of the mutual polarization effects, so far as they are supposed to be small (along with $E$).

Owing to its moment the sphere $A$ has in the external field $\mathbf{E}_0$ a potential energy $-\mathbf{m}.\mathbf{E}_0$. The total value of its potential energy is obtained by adding to this expression the mutual potential energy $V_N$ of the intermolecular forces (including the mutual action between the dipole moments). We then have, according to Gibbs's equation,

$$\overline{p_{iE}} = \frac{\int \dots \int p_{iE}\, e^{-(V_N - \mathbf{m}.\mathbf{E}_0)/kT}\, d\tau_1\, d\tau_2 \dots d\tau_N}{\int \dots \int e^{-(V_N - \mathbf{m}.\mathbf{E}_0)/kT}\, d\tau_1\, d\tau_2 \dots d\tau_N}, \tag{22}$$

where $d\tau_k$ is an element of configurational space of the $k$th molecule and $\overline{p_{iE}}$ is the component of $\overline{p_i}$ along $E$.

Expanding the integrand in (22) into a series of powers of $E_0$ we get in the first approximation

$$\overline{p_{iE}} = \frac{1}{kT} \overline{p_{iE}\, m_E}\, E_0, \tag{22 a}$$

where the average value of $p_{iE} m_E$ refers to the case $E_0 \to 0$. While the average value of $p_{iE}$ vanishes, the average of its product with $m_E$—the corresponding component of $A$'s total moment—is different from zero. In fact, according to (21 a), the total moment $\mathbf{m}$ contains a part $\mathbf{m}_i$, induced by the $i$th molecule. In an isotropic body $\mathbf{m}_i$ must always have the same direction as $\mathbf{p}_i$, i.e. make the same angle $\theta_i$ with the (arbitrary) direction of $\mathbf{E}_0$. Since in the case $\mathbf{E}_0 \to 0$ all the directions of $\mathbf{p}_i$ are equally probable, we get

$$\overline{p_{iE} m_{iE}} = p_i \overline{m_i \cos^2\theta_i} = \tfrac{1}{3} p_i \overline{m_i},$$

where $\overline{m_i}$ denotes the average value of $m_i$ calculated so as to take into account the mutual action between the molecules, i.e. according to Gibbs's formula

$$\overline{m_i} = \frac{\int \dots \int m_i \, e^{-V_N/kT} \, d\tau_1 \dots d\tau_N}{\int \dots \int e^{-V_N/kT} \, d\tau_1 \dots d\tau_N}.$$

It should be mentioned that for $k \neq i$, $\overline{p_{iE} m_{kE}} = 0$. Dropping the index $i$ (since $\overline{m_i}$ is independent of the position and orientation of the corresponding molecule) we can write

$$\overline{p_E} = \frac{p\overline{m}}{3kT} E_0. \tag{23}$$

The average field $E$ in a spherical dielectric placed in a homogeneous external field $E_0$ is given by the formula

$$E = \frac{3}{\epsilon + 2} E_0$$

similar to that of Lorentz. The preceding expression can thus be rewritten in the form

$$\overline{p_E} = \frac{\epsilon+2}{3} \frac{p\overline{m}}{3kT} E. \tag{23 a}$$

Substituting this expression in the formula $P = n(\overline{p_E} + \alpha F)$ we get

$$\frac{\epsilon - 1}{\epsilon + 2} = \frac{4\pi}{3} n \left( \frac{p\overline{m}}{3kT} + \frac{3}{\epsilon + 2} \alpha \frac{F}{E} \right). \tag{24}$$

The total (orientational) moment $\overline{\mathbf{m}}$, induced in the sphere $A$ by one of the central molecules, is practically due to surface charges appearing as a result of its polarization. The depolarizing field of these charges is similar to the demagnetizing field in the case of ferromagnetic bodies. If the surface of the sphere $A$ is removed to infinity ($R \to \infty$), the depolarizing field in the central spherical region $B$ with a fixed radius $r_0$

tends to zero. Under such conditions the moment $\mathbf{m}$ of $A$ is reduced to the sum of the moment $\mathbf{M}(R, r_0)$ of the sphere $B$, immersed in a continuous homogeneous medium with a dielectric constant $\epsilon$, and of the moment due to the polarization of this medium:

$$\mathbf{m} = \mathbf{M}(R, r_0) + \int\limits_{(A-B)} \mathbf{P}\, dV. \tag{25}$$

Now the polarization of the dielectric is equal to

$$\mathbf{P} = -\frac{\epsilon-1}{4\pi}\nabla\psi_i,$$

where $\psi_i$ is the electric potential *inside* the sphere $A$. Substituting the expression in (25) and replacing the integration over the volume enclosed between $A$ and $B$ by an integration over the surfaces of the two spheres (with the help of Green's theorem) we get

$$\mathbf{m} = \mathbf{M}(R, r_0) - \frac{\epsilon-1}{4\pi}\int\limits_R \psi_i\, \mathbf{n}\, dS + \frac{\epsilon-1}{4\pi}\int\limits_{r_0} \psi_i\, \mathbf{n}\, dS. \tag{25 a}$$

The potential $\psi_i$ is given by the formula (where $\mathbf{r}'$ is the vector joining the centres of $A$ and $B$)

$$\psi_i = -\frac{p^*}{\epsilon}\nabla\frac{1}{|\mathbf{r}-\mathbf{r}'|} + \chi \quad (r > r_0), \tag{26}$$

where $\mathbf{p}^*$ denotes the 'external' moment of the region $B$, due to the presence at its centre of the $i$th molecule with a fixed direction of its permanent moment $p$ (in this respect Kirkwood's sphere $B$ replaces Onsager's spherical molecule); $\chi$ is a solution of Laplace's equation without singular points:

$$\chi = Cr\cos\theta. \tag{26 a}$$

Noting that, for $r \gg r'$,

$$-\frac{p^*}{\epsilon}\nabla\frac{1}{|\mathbf{r}'-\mathbf{r}|} \approx \frac{p^*}{\epsilon r^2}\cos\theta,$$

we can represent the potential outside $A$ by the formula

$$\psi_e = (\bar{m}/r^2)\cos\theta,$$

where $\theta$ is the angle between $\mathbf{r}$ and the direction of polarization. The boundary condition for $\psi$ and $\partial\psi/\partial r$ on the surface of $A$

$$\psi_i = \psi_e, \qquad \epsilon\left(\frac{\partial\psi_i}{\partial r}\right)_{r=R} = \left(\frac{\partial\psi_e}{\partial r}\right)_{r=R}$$

gives $\qquad \dfrac{p^*}{\epsilon} + CR^3 = \bar{m}, \qquad -\dfrac{2p^*}{\epsilon} + CR^3 = -\dfrac{2\bar{m}}{\epsilon},$

whence $\qquad \mathbf{m} = \dfrac{3}{\epsilon+2}\mathbf{p}^*, \qquad CR^3 = \dfrac{2}{\epsilon}\dfrac{\epsilon-1}{\epsilon+2}p^*. \qquad (27)$

On the other hand, substituting (26) and (26 a) in (25 a) we have

$$\overline{\mathbf{m}} = \mathbf{M}(R, r_0) - \frac{\epsilon-1}{3} C(R^3 - r_0^3)\mathbf{p}^*.$$

Eliminating $\mathbf{p}^*$ and $C$ between these two equations we get in the limit $R \to \infty$ i.e. $r_0/R \to 0$,

$$\overline{\mathbf{m}} = \mathbf{m}_\infty = \frac{3}{\epsilon+2} \frac{3\epsilon}{2\epsilon+1} \mathbf{M}, \tag{28}$$

where $\mathbf{M}$ is the total moment of the sphere $B$, due to one of its molecules, when $B$ is immersed in an unlimited medium with the same macroscopic value of the dielectric constant $\epsilon$.

If the elastic polarization $\alpha F$ is relatively small, the effective field $F$ can, according to Kirkwood, be identified with Onsager's cavity field $G$, i.e. $3\epsilon E/(2\epsilon+1)$. This gives, according to (23) and (28),

$$\frac{\epsilon-1}{3} = \frac{3\epsilon}{2\epsilon+1} P_0, \qquad P_0 = \frac{4\pi}{3} n\left(\alpha + \frac{pM}{3kT}\right), \tag{29}$$

or, in the case $\epsilon \gg 1$,

$$\epsilon \approx \frac{9}{2} P_0. \tag{29 a}$$

The effective permanent dipole moment of a molecule in the liquid $p$ is in general somewhat larger than the corresponding true value (in the gas state) $p_0$, owing to the additional elastic polarization due to the reactive field.

We must now turn to the determination of the moment $M$.

If in equation (23 a) $m$ is identified with $p$, i.e. if the mutual action between the molecules is wholly neglected, Kirkwood's theory reduces to the old theory of Debye. If, on the other hand, $M$ is identified with $\mu^* p$, then Kirkwood's formula (29) reduces to that of Onsager's theory.

In the general case the product $pM$ can be defined by the formula

$$pM = p^2\left[1 + \frac{n}{v} \int\int_{v_0} \cos\gamma\, e^{-W/kT}\, d\omega dv\right] \tag{30}$$

with the accessory condition that $\int\int e^{-W/kT}\, d\omega dv = 1$ and that outside the sphere $B$ with a volume $v = \frac{4}{3}\pi r_0^3$ the dielectric constant is equal to $\epsilon$. Here $\gamma$ denotes the angle between the dipole moment of the given molecule and that of some other molecule (enclosed in the solid angle $d\omega$); $W$ is the potential energy depending on their mutual orientation.

If it is assumed that the volume $v$ contains the given molecule and its $z$ nearest neighbours only, we get

$$pM \approx p^2(1+z\overline{\cos\gamma})$$
$$\overline{\cos\gamma} = \iint \cos\gamma\, e^{-W_0/kT}\, d\omega dv, \tag{31}$$

where $W_0$ is the value of $W$ for nearest neighbours.

Equation (29) is now reduced to the form

$$\epsilon-1 = 6\pi n\left[\alpha+\frac{p^2}{3kT}(1+z\overline{\cos\gamma})\right]. \tag{32}$$

It should be mentioned that $\overline{\cos\gamma}$ specifies the correlation between the orientations of nearest neighbours, accounting, in principle, not only for dipole-dipole interaction, but also for interactions of a more complicated character.

Kirkwood expresses the opinion that if the latter interactions are left out of account, his theory must reduce to that of Onsager. This opinion is contradicted, however, by Kirkwood's own later work,† where $\overline{\cos\gamma}$ is actually calculated for the case of a purely dipolar interaction with the result $\overline{\cos\gamma} = -s^2$, $s$ being the solution of the equation $s = L(zUs/2kT)$, where $U$ is the height of the potential barrier preventing the free rotation of a molecule with respect to its neighbour.

Substituting this value of $\overline{\cos\gamma}$ in (32) we get

$$\epsilon-1 = 6\pi n\left\{\alpha+\frac{p^2}{3kT}\left[1-L^2\left(\frac{zUs}{2kT}\right)\right]\right\}, \tag{32 a}$$

which is similar to our formula (20 a), combining the results of the theories of Onsager and of Debye. A minor difference refers to the term representing the elastic polarization; this difference is due to the fact that in Kirkwood's theory the effective field **F** is identified with Onsager's cavity field **G**.

Kirkwood illustrates his theory by calculating the dielectric constant of water. In doing this he does not, however, use the exact expression for $\overline{\cos\gamma}$ given by (31), but assumes, for the sake of simplicity, that the neighbouring molecules $H_2O$ form a quasi-rigid structure with a fixed value of the angle between their dipole moments and a free rotation about O—H bonds. This gives $\overline{\cos\gamma} = \cos^2 50^\circ = 0{\cdot}41$, and consequently, according to (31), since the number of nearest neighbours in water $z$ is equal to 4, $pM = 2{\cdot}64p^2$.

The mean value of the electric field due to the four nearest neighbours, taking into account their free rotation about the respective OH bonds,

† J. Kirkwood, *J. Chem. Phys.* **8**, 205 (1940).

is equal to $E' = 8\cos^2 50° p/a^3$ and is parallel to the permanent dipole moment $\mathbf{p}_0$ of the central molecule. Its total moment is thus equal to $\mathbf{p} = \mathbf{p}_0 + \alpha \mathbf{E}'$, i.e. $p = p_0/(1-3{\cdot}28\alpha/a^3)$. Putting $\alpha = 1{\cdot}5\times10^{-24}$ and $a = 3{\cdot}27\times10^{-8}$, we get $p = 1{\cdot}16p_0$ and $pM = 3{\cdot}55p^2$. With $p_0 = 1{\cdot}98\times10^{-18}$ (a value derived from the measurement of the dielectric constant of water vapour) the following numerical expression for the polarization of liquid water is obtained:

$$\frac{P_0}{E} = 3{\cdot}8 + \frac{7{\cdot}74\times10^4}{T},$$

which for $T = 25°$ C. yields $\epsilon = 67$. This value is much closer to the experimental one than that of Onsager.

If the angle between the O—H bonds in the water molecule is assumed to be equal to 90°, instead of 100°, $\overline{\cos\gamma} = 0{\cdot}5$ and $\epsilon = 82$, in full agreement with experiment.

This agreement is probably fortuitous, for the preceding calculation is based on a very rough and inconsistent picture of the behaviour of the molecules in liquid water. It is difficult to imagine that they can freely rotate about each of the O—H bonds, remaining rigidly bound with their neighbours, for a rotation of a molecule as a whole about one O—H bond implies a temporary breaking of the second O—H bond, which connects it with a second nearest neighbour.

## 5. Polarization of a Liquid with Anisotropic Non-polar Molecules

We have hitherto supposed that outside their permanent electric moment the molecules are isotropic, their elastic polarizability being specified by the scalar $\alpha$.

In the absence of a permanent moment Onsager's theory, applied to this case, gives exactly the same results as that of Lorentz.

An essentially different situation arises in the case of anisotropic molecules, whose polarizability is specified not by a scalar $\alpha$, but by a (symmetrical) tensor $\alpha_{ik}$.

Let us introduce a system of principal axes—the symmetry axes of this tensor—rigidly bound with the molecule. The component of the induced moment of the molecule in the direction of one of these axes is

$$p_i = \alpha_i \beta_i E_e, \tag{33}$$

and the total moment to

$$\mathbf{p} = \sum_i \mathbf{a}_i \alpha_i \beta_i E_e, \tag{33a}$$

where $\alpha_i$ are the principal components of the polarizability tensor, $\beta_i$ the direction cosines of the effective field $\mathbf{E}_e$, and $\mathbf{a}_i$ three unit vectors in the direction of the coordinate axes.

In the general case $\mathbf{p}$ has a direction different from that of $\mathbf{E}_e$, so that the field $\mathbf{E}_e$ not only polarizes the molecule but also produces a torque with the moment $\mathbf{M} = \mathbf{p} \times \mathbf{E}_e$, tending to orientate it in the direction of the axis $\mathbf{a}_1$, for instance, corresponding to the maximum value of the polarizability. The actual distribution of these orientations at a given temperature $T$ is determined by Boltzmann's formula $f = \text{const.}\, e^{-W/kT}$, where $W$ is the orientational potential energy of the molecule.

Just as in the case of molecules with permanent dipole moments, the effective field $\mathbf{E}_e$ can be represented as the sum of the cavity field $\mathbf{G}$ and of the reactive field $\mathbf{R}$, i.e.

$$\mathbf{E}_e = \frac{3\epsilon}{2\epsilon+1}\mathbf{E} + \frac{2(\epsilon-1)}{2\epsilon+1}\frac{\mathbf{p}}{a^3}. \tag{34}$$

In view of the anisotropy of the molecule the dipole moment induced by the reactive field is in general not parallel to the latter; hence the reactive field not only increases the total moment, as in the case of Onsager's theory, but also contributes to orientating torque.

In order to determine the resulting orientating field we must solve the equation (34) in conjunction with (33) for any given orientation of the molecule, specified by the direction cosines $\gamma_i$ of the field $\mathbf{E}$ with respect to the coordinate axes $x_i$.

Taking the component of (34) along the $x_i$ axis, multiplying by $\alpha_i$, and substituting in (33) we get

$$p_i = \frac{3\epsilon}{2\epsilon+1} E\gamma_i\alpha_i + \frac{2(\epsilon-1)}{(2\epsilon+1)a^3}\alpha_i p_i, \tag{34 a}$$

whence

$$p_i = \alpha_i'\gamma_i E. \tag{35}$$

The quantities

$$\alpha_i' = \frac{3\epsilon\alpha_i a^3}{(2\epsilon+1)a^3 - 2(\epsilon-1)\alpha_i} \tag{35 a}$$

will be described as the reduced components of the polarizability tensor.

We have further

$$W = -\frac{1}{2}\mathbf{G}.\mathbf{p} = -\frac{1}{2}\frac{3\epsilon}{2\epsilon+1}\sum \alpha_i'\gamma_i^2 E^2. \tag{36}$$

Since the component of $\mathbf{p}$ along the direction of $\mathbf{E}$ is equal to

$$p_E = \sum p_i\gamma_i = E\sum \alpha_i'\gamma_i^2, \tag{37}$$

we get
$$\frac{\overline{p_E}}{E} = \frac{\int \sum_i \alpha_i' \gamma_i^2 e^{A\Sigma\alpha_i'\gamma_i^2}\, d\Omega}{\int e^{A\Sigma\alpha_i'\gamma_i^2}\, d\Omega}, \tag{38}$$

where
$$A = \frac{3\epsilon}{2(2\epsilon+1)} \frac{E^2}{kT} \tag{38 a}$$

and $d\Omega$ denotes an element of solid angle.

For the sake of simplicity we shall limit ourselves to the case in which the polarizability tensor has a symmetry of revolution about the axis of highest polarizability, i.e. $\alpha_2 = \alpha_3$. Noting that $\sum \gamma_i^2 = 1$, we can rewrite (38) as follows:

$$\frac{\overline{p_E}}{E} = \frac{\int\limits_{-1}^{+1} [\alpha_1'\gamma_1^2+\alpha_2'(1-\gamma_1^2)] e^{A[\alpha_1'\gamma_1^2+\alpha_2'(1-\gamma_1^2)]}\, d\gamma_1}{\int\limits_{-1}^{+1} e^{A[\alpha_1'\gamma_1^2+\alpha_2'(1-\gamma_1^2)]}\, d\gamma_1}. \tag{39}$$

The exponent is very small compared with 1; the exponential function can therefore be expanded into a series of powers of $A$. In the zero approximation we get

$$\overline{p_E} = \frac{E}{2} \int\limits_{-1}^{+1} [\alpha_1\gamma_1^2+\alpha_2'(1-\gamma_1^2)]\, d\gamma_1 = \frac{E}{3}(\alpha_1'+2\alpha_2'). \tag{40}$$

In the next approximation, putting

$$e^{A[\alpha_1'\gamma_1^2+\alpha_2'(1-\gamma_1^2)]} = 1+A[\alpha_1'\gamma_1^2+\alpha_2'(1-\gamma_1^2)],$$

we get
$$\overline{p_E} = \frac{E}{3}\left[\alpha_1'+2\alpha_2'+\frac{4A}{15}(\alpha_1'-\alpha_2')^2\right], \tag{40 a}$$

or substituting here (35 a) and (38 a):

$$\overline{p_E} = \frac{E}{3}\left\{\frac{3\epsilon a^3\alpha_1}{(2\epsilon+1)a^3-2(\epsilon-1)\alpha_1} + \frac{6\epsilon a^3\alpha_2}{(2\epsilon+1)a^3-2(\epsilon-1)\alpha_2} + \right.$$
$$\left. + \frac{18E^2\epsilon^3 a^{12}(2\epsilon+1)(\alpha_1-\alpha_2)^2}{5kT[(2\epsilon+1)a^3-2(\epsilon-1)\alpha_1]^2[(2\epsilon+1)a^3-2(\epsilon-1)\alpha_2]^2}\right\}. \tag{41}$$

This formula, along with the relation $P = (\epsilon-1)E/4\pi$ yields an equation of the fifth degree for the determination of the dielectric constant $\epsilon$, which in the present case depends on the temperature and the intensity of the field $E$.

It should be noticed that the simplified form of Debye's theory for very strong local fields, given in § 2, is, in the first approximation, fully equivalent to the theory of the elastic polarization of liquid dielectrics with anisotropic molecules.

In fact, an external field parallel to the local field **F** gives no additional polarization, while a field perpendicular to **F** causes it to deviate from the direction of the latter, which is equivalent to a certain elastic polarization. Putting in (40) $\alpha_1' = 0$ and $\alpha_2' = p/F$ we obtain Debye's formula (5).

A molecule with a permanent dipole moment $p$, situated in a strong local field $F$, can be dealt with as possessing an anisotropic elastic polarizability with the above components. The random orientation of the local field corresponds to a random orientation of the molecular axes (in the first approximation).

## 6. Polarization of Dipolar Liquids in Alternating Electrical Fields

In 1912 Debye gave a generalization of his original theory of the polarization of dipolar liquids in permanent electric fields, extending it to the case of variable fields of small intensity by the application of Einstein's theory of rotational Brownian motion to the rotational motion of the molecules. The orientational mutual action between the molecules is reduced in this case to a friction torque opposing their rotation, with a moment proportional to the average value of the angular velocity $\omega$. The proportionality coefficient is determined by Stokes's formula

$$\frac{1}{\alpha} = 8\pi a^3\mu, \tag{42}$$

where $a$ is the radius of the molecule, which is treated as a small sphere, and $\mu$ the viscosity coefficient of the liquid; $\alpha$ is the 'orientational mobility', introduced in § 1 and connected with the coefficient of orientational diffusion $D$ by the relation (1 a).

This theory thus wholly ignores the orientational elasticity of the liquid, which forms the basis of Debye's new static theory (§ 2), and takes into account the orientational fluidity (or viscosity) only. As has been explained in § 1, such a treatment is admissible only in the case of liquids with sufficiently large molecules.

Besides this 'kinetic' mutual action of the molecules, which is reduced to a friction torque, Debye's theory takes into account that part of the statical interaction which is included in the orientation effect of the electric field, using for that purpose (erroneously as we now know) Lorentz's expression for the effective field.

Let us denote by $d\Omega = \sin\theta\, d\theta d\phi$ an element of the solid angle enclosing the direction of the dipole moment of one of the molecules, i.e. an element of the surface of a sphere of unit radius, containing the point where the axis of the molecule intersects this surface (all the molecules being supposed to be located at the centre of the sphere). Let further $f(\theta,\phi)\,d\Omega$ denote the relative number of molecules whose axes are contained in $d\Omega$.

The distribution function $f$ can be found from the generalized equation of two-dimensional diffusion of the 'representative points' on the surface of the sphere (see (1)):

$$\frac{\partial f}{\partial t} = D\nabla^2 f + \operatorname{div}(\alpha f \nabla U), \tag{43}$$

where

$$U = -pE_e\cos\theta \tag{43 a}$$

is the potential energy of a dipole in the effective field and

$$-\nabla U = -\frac{\partial U}{\partial \theta} = pE_e\sin\theta$$

the moment of the torque produced by it. The latter is treated as a force acting on the representative point and directed in the direction of decrease of $\theta$ (the direction of $\mathbf{E}$ defining the pole of the sphere).

In equation (43) we can limit ourselves to the case in which $f$ is a function of $\theta$ only. Setting $\alpha/D = 1/kT$, equation (43) then becomes

$$\frac{1}{D}\frac{\partial f}{\partial t} = \frac{1}{\sin\theta}\frac{\partial}{\partial\theta}\left[\sin\theta\left(\frac{\partial f}{\partial\theta} + \frac{f}{kT}\frac{\partial U}{\partial\theta}\right)\right]. \tag{44}$$

If the field is weak, the function $f$ deviates but slightly from the constant value $f_0 = 1/4\pi$ which it must have in a state of equilibrium when the field is absent. Since this deviation is of the same order of magnitude as the forces causing it, the function $f$ can be determined approximately if the product $f(\partial U/\partial\theta)$ in (44) is replaced by $f_0(\partial U/\partial\theta)$. Limiting ourselves to the case of a simple (harmonic) alternating field $E_e = E_e^0 e^{i\omega t}$ and putting accordingly $f - f_0 = \text{const. } e^{i\omega t}$, we get

$$f = \frac{1}{4\pi}\left[1 + \frac{pE_e\cos\theta}{kT(1+i\omega\tau)}\right], \tag{45}$$

where the quantity

$$\tau = \frac{1}{2\alpha kT} = \frac{1}{2D} \tag{45 a}$$

plays the role of a relaxation time.

This corresponds to the following expression for the polarization of the liquid:

$$P = \frac{np^2E_e}{3kT}\frac{1}{1+i\omega\tau}, \tag{46}$$

which differs from that of the old theory for a permanent field by the factor $1/(1+i\omega\tau)$.

It should be noted that the preceding formula can be obtained in a much simpler way as follows.

If the (permanent) electric field, which gives rise to the polarization $P = \chi E_e$ where $\chi = np^2/3kT$, is suddenly removed, the polarization must gradually decrease. Let us suppose that this decrease proceeds according to the ordinary relaxation law $P = P_0 e^{-t/\tau}$, i.e.

$$\frac{dP}{dt} = -\frac{1}{\tau}P.$$

In the presence of an electric field $E_e$ the right-hand side of this equation must be completed by a term proportional to $E_e$, i.e. giving rise to an orientational flow with a velocity $dP/dt$, proportional to the driving force. Denoting the proportionality coefficient by $1/\mu$ ($\mu$ playing the role of viscous resistance) we get

$$\frac{dP}{dt} = -\frac{1}{\tau}P+\frac{1}{\mu}E_e. \tag{47}$$

Since in the special case of a constant field the solution of this equation must be reduced to $P = \chi E_e$, we obtain the following expression for $\mu$:

$$\mu = \frac{\tau}{\chi}. \tag{47 a}$$

If the field alternates with an angular frequency $\omega$, we can put $p \sim e^{i\omega t}$, which gives

$$p = \frac{\chi}{1+i\omega\tau}E_e,$$

in agreement with (46).

Equation (47) can be interpreted as expressing the fact that a certain part $E_1$ of the field $E_e$ gives rise to an elastic effect $P = \chi E_1$, while a second part $E_2$ compensates the viscous resistance connected with a variation of $P$: $dP/dt = E_2/\mu$. The condition $E_1+E_2 = E_e$ leads to the equation (47) along with the relation (47 a).

The relaxation time $\tau$ defined by (45 a) must not be identified with the mean life of a molecule $\tau'$ in the sense of the preservation of a constant orientation. In fact the notion of the rotational Brownian motion of the 'orientational diffusion' has a physical meaning only (see § 1) if the elementary rotations $\delta\theta$ are very small (compared with $\pi$). We thus have

$$D = \frac{\overline{(\delta\theta)^2}}{2\tau'},$$

i.e. $\tau' = \overline{(\delta\theta)^2}/2D$. The relaxation time (45 a) is thus, in general, much larger than $\tau'$, the smaller the elementary rotations $\delta\theta$. A coincidence between $\tau$ and $\tau'$, with respect to the order of magnitude at least, can take place in the case of very small molecules only, with large elementary rotations (of the order of $\pi$). But in this case the very notion of orientational diffusion and of the viscous resistance connected with it loses all meaning. Under such conditions the effect of orientational flow, which forms the basis of Debye's (second) theory, is less important and must be replaced by the orientational-elastic effect, which leads to Debye's third theory, discussed in § 2 and corresponding to constant fields.

In the elementary form in which it has been presented by us for the case $pF/kT \gg 1$ this theory can easily be extended to the case of variable electric fields. Let us consider the forced vibrations of an oscillator about the equilibrium orientation, determined by $\mathbf{F}$, under the influence of an external field $E_e \ll F$. Using the same notation as in § 2 we have, if $J$ is the moment of inertia,

$$J\frac{d^2\phi}{dt^2} = pE_e \sin\theta - pF\sin\phi,$$

or, in view of the smallness of $\phi$,

$$J\frac{d^2\phi}{dt^2} + pF\phi = pE_e \sin\theta. \tag{48}$$

Remembering that $p\sin\phi\sin\theta \approx p\phi\sin\theta$ is the component of the moment of a molecule in the direction of $\mathbf{E}_e$, we obtain, after averaging over all values of $\theta$ and multiplication by $n$:

$$J\frac{d^2P}{dt^2} + pFP = \tfrac{2}{3}np^2E_e. \tag{48 a}$$

The solution of this equation for the case $E_e \sim e^{i\omega t}$ is

$$P = \frac{2}{3}\frac{np^2}{J}\frac{E_e}{\omega_0^2-\omega^2} = \frac{2}{3}\frac{npE_e}{F(1-\omega^2/\omega_0^2)}, \tag{48 b}$$

where $\omega_0 = \sqrt{(pF/J)}$ is the frequency of free vibrations. Since the latter is of the order $10^{13}$ sec.$^{-1}$, whereas $\omega$ does not exceed $10^{10}$ (ultra-short radio-waves), the preceding formula is practically reduced to the formula $P = \frac{2}{3}npE_e/F$, representing the influence of a constant field.

The preceding argument does not allow for the fact that the direction of the local field $\mathbf{F}$ does not remain fixed, but is sharply changed after a certain mean life $\tau$. The vibrations of an oscillator cannot thus reach a stationary character, for their phase is irregularly changed every now and then (the accumulated energy being transferred to the surrounding molecules). Quite analogous conditions are considered in Lorentz's well-known theory of the damping of forced electron vibrations in molecules as a result of collisions between the latter. The influence of these collisions is equivalent to a frictional resistance, proportional to the velocity, with a proportionality coefficient equal to $2m/\tau$, where $m$ is the mass of an electron and $\tau$ the average length of time between two successive collisions. These results of Lorentz's theory of 'Stossdämpfung' may be directly applied to our case. The influence of sharp changes in the direction of the local field can, accordingly, be accounted for by the introduction into the right-hand side of equation (48) of an additional frictional term $-\mu d\phi/dt$ with a frictional coefficient $\mu = 2J/\tau$. This gives

$$J\frac{d^2\phi}{dt^2}+pF\phi+\mu\frac{d\phi}{dt} = pE_e\sin\theta, \tag{49}$$

and further, after averaging over all directions of the local field,

$$\frac{Jd^2P}{dt^2}+pFP+\mu\frac{dP}{dt} = \tfrac{2}{3}np^2E_e \tag{49 a}$$

instead of (48 a). Putting $E_e \sim e^{i\omega t}$ we get in the case $\omega \ll \omega_0$

$$P = \frac{2}{3}\frac{np^2}{J}\frac{E_e}{\omega_0^2+(i\omega\mu/J)},$$

or

$$P = \frac{2}{3}\frac{np}{F}\frac{E_e}{1+(i\omega\mu/J\omega_0^2)}. \tag{49 b}$$

This formula is quite similar to Debye's formula (46).

An important difference between them relates to the definition of the relaxation time, Debye's relaxation time $\tau = \tau_D$, which is multiplied by $\omega$ in (46), being replaced in (49 b) by a relaxation time $\tau'_D = 2/\omega_0^2\tau_F$, where $\tau_F$ is the mean duration of a certain direction of the local field $\mathbf{F}$.

If the time $\tau_F$ is assumed to decrease with rise of the temperature according to a formula of the usual type $\tau_F = \text{const. } e^{U/kT}$, then $\tau'_D$ should increase with $T$, which is contradicted by the experimental data. The latter agree with Debye's definition of the relaxation time in (46), at least qualitatively, showing that this time $\tau_D$ is decreased with rise of $T$ as it should, according to Stokes's formula (42) and to the relation (45 a). Moreover, in the case of large molecules their radius, calculated from the value of $\tau_D$, turns out to be of a correct order of magnitude.

If in the expression $\tau'_D = 2/\omega_0^2\tau_F$, replacing Debye's relaxation time, we put $\omega_0 \sim 10^{13}$ sec.$^{-1}$, and $\tau \sim 10^{-10}$ sec., we get $\tau'_D \approx 10^{-16}$. This value is absurdly small and certainly insufficient for the explanation of the large value of dielectric losses in dipolar liquids found experimentally. Hence it is clear that the actual mechanism of the damping of the rotation oscillations of small dipole molecules must be quite different from that considered above.

In his last paper (in conjunction with Ramm) Debye attempts to generalize his new theory of the polarization of dipolar liquids in constant fields to cover the case of variable fields, using the notion of the local field *explicitly* as the cause of the quasi-elastic torque, holding a molecule near the equilibrium orientation, and *implicitly* as the cause of the frictional torque exerted on the rotating molecules. As has already been explained, this view involves an intrinsic contradiction, so that the results following from it hardly need to be examined in detail.

E. Kuwshinsky has expressed the opinion that the Debye–Ramm theory can be justified by assuming that the interaction between nearest neighbours gives rise to the static (elastic) effect, while the interaction with more distant molecules leads to a slow rotation of the equilibrium orientation, which corresponds to the kinetic (viscous) effect. This justification does not, however, appear convincing.

It might be thought further that the frictional force $-\mu\partial\phi/\partial t$ is due to the anharmonic character of the rotational oscillations, i.e. to the non-linearity of the dependence of the intermolecular forces on their deviation from the equilibrium orientation—just as in the case of solid bodies. This idea does not agree, however, with the rapid increase of the relaxation time with a lowering of the temperature.

It may be conjectured finally (P. Kobeko) that the effects of orientational friction are due to the fact that a change in the orientation of one molecule involves a simultaneous change in the orientation of a very large number of molecules surrounding it, i.e. a kind of structure relaxation of a large volume of the liquid.

Under such conditions the rapid increase of the relaxation time with a decrease of the temperature becomes intelligible. It is very difficult, however, to put this theory into a quantitative form.

## 7. Orientation of Non-polar Molecules in Variable Fields

The orientation of polar (dipole) molecules can be specified by the cosine of the angle formed by the positive direction of their electric moment with some fixed direction in space. In the case of non-polar molecules with an axis of symmetry for which the two opposite directions are equivalent (in the sequel we shall limit ourselves to the consideration of this case), it is natural to specify the orientation by a spherical harmonic of the second order $P_2(\cos\theta) = \cos^2\theta - \frac{1}{3}$, whose average value for all possible orientations, supposed to be equally probable, vanishes (just as does the average value of the function $P_1(\cos\theta) = \cos\theta$).

The degree of orientation of a liquid consisting of identical molecules of the 'quadripole type' can be defined by the average value of $P_2(\cos\theta)$, or, more exactly, by the average values of three such expressions for three mutually perpendicular axes $X_1$, $X_2$, $X_3$. Denoting by $\theta_i$ the angle between the axis of a molecule and the $i$th axis, we can specify the average distribution of the molecular axes in space by the tensor

$$s_{ik} = \overline{\cos\theta_i \cos\theta_k} - \tfrac{1}{3}\delta_{ik} \quad (i, k = 1, 2, 3)$$

whose diagonal components ($i = k$) are equal to the average values of the functions $P_2(\cos\theta_i)$, their sum being equal to zero (since, by definition, $\delta_{ik} = 1$ if $i = k$ and 0 if $i \neq k$).

This tensor will be denoted by the term *anisotropy tensor*.

If the forces causing the anisotropy of the liquid suddenly vanish, the anisotropy must likewise vanish, not instantly, however, but gradually. We shall assume that it vanishes according to the usual relaxation law

$$\frac{ds_{ik}}{dt} = -\frac{1}{\tau}s_{ik}, \tag{50}$$

where $\tau$ is the relaxation time, which we shall leave indeterminate.

In the presence of a factor giving rise to the anisotropy we must add to the right-hand side of this equation a term $f_{ik}$ specifying the influence of this factor, so that the equation for $s_{ik}$ assumes the form

$$\frac{ds_{ik}}{dt} = -\frac{1}{\tau}s_{ik} + f_{ik}. \tag{50 a}$$

If $f_{ik}$ does not depend upon the time (constant field of force), this equation can be solved by putting $s_{ik} = \tau f_{ik}$. Thus, for example, if we have to deal with the orientation of the molecules of the liquid in a permanent electric field $\mathbf{E}$ with the components $E_i$, we can put

$$f_{ik} = \lambda E_i E_k + \mu\delta_{ik} E^2,$$

where $\lambda$ and $\mu$ are certain proportionality coefficients. From the condition $\sum s_{ii} = 0$ it follows that $\mu = -\frac{1}{3}\lambda$, so that the preceding expression is reduced to

$$f_{ik} = \lambda(E_i E_k - \tfrac{1}{3}\delta_{ik} E^2). \tag{51}$$

In order to determine $\lambda$ let us assume that $\mathbf{E}$ is directed along the first axis ($E = E_1$, $E_2 = E_3 = 0$) and let us consider the quantity $s_{11} = \overline{\cos^2\theta_1} - \frac{1}{3}$. If the molecules are orientated by the field independently (i.e. if they exert no mutual influence on each other) the energy of a molecule, making an angle $\theta_1$ with the direction of the electric field, is equal to

$$W = -\tfrac{1}{2}\alpha_1 E^2 \cos^2\theta_1 - \tfrac{1}{2}\alpha_2 E^2 \sin^2\theta_1$$
$$= -\tfrac{1}{2}(\alpha_1-\alpha_2)E^2\cos^2\theta_1 - \tfrac{1}{2}\alpha_2 E^2.$$

Hence the average value of $\cos^2\theta_1$,

$$\overline{\cos^2\theta_1} = \frac{\int\limits_0^\pi \cos^2\theta_1\, e^{-W/kT}\sin\theta_1\, d\theta_1}{\int\limits_0^\pi e^{-W/kT}\sin\theta_1\, d\theta_1} = \frac{\int\limits_{-1}^{+1} e^{\gamma\xi^2}\xi^2\, d\xi}{\int\limits_{-1}^{+1} e^{\gamma\xi^2}\, d\xi},$$

where $\gamma = (\alpha_1-\alpha_2)E^2/kT$, is found to be, if $\gamma \ll 1$,

$$\overline{\cos^2\theta_1} = \frac{1}{3}\left(1+\frac{4}{15}\gamma\right),$$

so that

$$\tau f_{11} = \frac{4(\alpha_1-\alpha_2)}{45kT}E_1^2,$$

whence

$$\lambda = \frac{4}{45}\,\frac{\alpha_1-\alpha_2}{kT\tau}. \tag{51 a}$$

The preceding equations enable one to determine the anisotropy due to the action on the liquid of a field with a variable intensity or direction. Putting, for example, $E = E_1 = A\cos\omega t$, we obtain the following expressions for the non-vanishing components of the tensors $s_{ik}$ and $f_{ik}$ ($i = k = 1$):

$$\frac{ds}{dt}+\frac{s}{\tau} = \tfrac{2}{3}\lambda A^2\cos^2\omega t = \tfrac{1}{3}\lambda A^2(1+\cos 2\omega t).$$

Replacing $\cos 2\omega t$ by $e^{i2\omega t}$ we obtain in the stationary case

$$s = \tfrac{1}{3}\tau\lambda A^2\left(1+\frac{e^{i2\omega t}}{1+i2\omega\tau}\right) = \tfrac{1}{2}s_0\left(1+\frac{e^{i2\omega t}}{1+i2\omega\tau}\right), \tag{52}$$

where $s_0$ is the static value of $s$ (for $\omega = 0$) considered above. If the field $E$ has a constant intensity, but a variable direction, rotating uniformly in the (1, 2) plane with an angular velocity $\omega$, we have: $E_1 = A\cos\omega t$, $E_2 = A\sin\omega t$, $E_3 = 0$, so that the non-vanishing components $s_{ik}$ are found to be

$$\left.\begin{aligned} s_{11} &= \tfrac{1}{2}s_0\left(1+\frac{e^{i2\omega t}}{1+i2\omega\tau}\right)\\ s_{22} &= \tfrac{1}{2}s_0\left(1-\frac{e^{i2\omega t}}{1+i2\omega\tau}\right)\\ s_{12} = s_{21} &= -\frac{3i}{2}s_0\frac{e^{i2\omega t}}{1+i2\omega\tau} \end{aligned}\right\}, \tag{52 a}$$

the real parts of these expressions being of course alone taken into account. The presence of the complex denominator $1+i2\omega\tau$ corresponds to a phase shift, i.e. to a retardation of the average direction of the orientation of the molecules with respect to the direction of the field. This retardation must give rise to a torque $M$, exerted on the molecules of the liquid and balanced by the forces of friction.

In the case of a molecule whose axis makes an angle $\theta$ with the (instantaneous) direction of the field $\mathbf{E}$, the moment $M$ of the torque is equal to $-\partial W/\partial\theta$, i.e.

$$M = -\tfrac{1}{2}(\alpha_1-\alpha_2)A^2\sin 2\theta. \tag{53}$$

In order to calculate its average value, corresponding to the expression (52 a) for the components of the anisotropy tensor, we shall transform these components to a coordinate system $X_1'$, $X_2'$, rotating with the electric field in such manner that the latter remains parallel to the $X_1'$ axis. If the angle between this axis and the field axis $X_1$ is denoted by $\phi = \omega t$, we have, according to the general formula for the transformation of tensor components, $s'_{i'k'} = \sum_i \sum_k \alpha_{i'i}\alpha_{k'k}s_{ik}$, where $\alpha_{i'i} = \cos(X'_{i'}, X_i)$:

$$s'_{11} = s_{11}\cos^2\phi+2s_{12}\cos\phi\sin\phi+s_{22}\sin^2\phi$$

$$s'_{12} = s'_{21} = (s_{22}-s_{11})\sin\phi\cos\phi+s_{12}(\cos^2\phi-\sin^2\phi)$$

$$s'_{22} = s_{11}\sin^2\phi-2s_{12}\cos\phi\sin\phi+s_{22}\cos^2\phi.$$

On the other hand, according to the definition of $s'_{ik}$,

$$s'_{11} = \overline{\cos^2\theta}-\tfrac{1}{3}, \qquad s'_{12} = \overline{\cos\theta\sin\theta}, \qquad s'_{22} = \overline{\sin^2\theta}-\tfrac{1}{3}.$$

Comparing $s'_{12}$ with (53) we see that the average value of $M$ can be represented as follows:

$$\bar{M} = -\Delta\alpha A^2 s'_{12}. \tag{53 a}$$

Putting here $s'_{12} = \frac{1}{2}(s_{22}-s_{11})\sin 2\phi+s_{12}\cos 2\phi$ and using (52 a) we get

$$\bar{M} = \Delta\alpha E^2\frac{s_0}{2}\left[\frac{e^{i2\phi}}{1+i2\omega\tau}\sin 2\phi+3i\frac{e^{i2\phi}}{1+i2\omega\tau}\cos 2\phi\right].$$

The real part of this expression is equal to

$$\frac{\Delta\alpha A^2 s_0}{2[1+(2\omega\tau)^2]}[2\omega\tau(\sin^2 2\phi+3\cos^2 2\phi)-2\cos 2\phi\sin 2\phi].$$

After taking its mean value with respect to the time (i.e. to $\phi$) we get

$$\bar{\bar{M}} = \Delta\alpha A^2 s_0\frac{4\omega\tau}{1+(2\omega\tau)^2},$$

or since $s_0 = \frac{2}{3}\lambda\tau A^2$ and $\lambda\tau = 4\Delta\alpha/45kT$

$$\overline{\overline{M}} = \frac{16}{135}\frac{(\Delta\alpha)^2}{kT}A^4\frac{2\omega\tau}{1+(2\omega\tau)^2}. \tag{53 b}$$

The average value of $M$ thus proves to be proportional to the fourth power of the intensity of the field (which is explained by the fact that for a given degree of the orientation of the molecules $M$ is proportional to $A^2$, while the degree of orientation is itself proportional to $A^2$). If $\omega\tau \ll 1$, $\overline{\overline{M}}$ increases in direct proportion to the angular frequency $\omega$; in the contrary case ($\omega\tau \gg 1$) it is decreased inversely as $\omega$.

The rotation of the molecules of a liquid about their own axes, perpendicular to their symmetry axis (and to the plane containing the field), will be denoted in the sequel as the *spin* of the molecules. Since such a spin involves a friction torque exerted on each molecule by the surrounding liquid (and balancing the driving torque in the stationary case), the liquid cannot remain at rest and must finally come into a state of rotation in the same direction.

This 'drag' of a liquid by a rotating field, whose action consists in the orientation of the molecules, was observed for the first time by V. N. Zwetkov,† who, however, applied a magnetic field instead of an electric one, and used in his experiment anisotropic liquids. In this case the orientational effect, and, along with it, the rotational one, is strongly enhanced by the orientational mutual action between the molecules, which causes them to combine into more or less homogeneous groups, called 'swarms' (see below). In the case of ordinary liquids a rotational effect similar to that of Zwetkov has not hitherto been observed—probably because of the smallness of the relaxation time $\tau$, which necessitates large rotation velocities. It may be mentioned that a similar effect should also be observed in liquids with *polar* molecules, where it must be proportional to the square of the electric intensity and not the fourth power, as in the case of non-polar liquids with anisotropic molecules.

In the classical hydrodynamics of Navier–Stokes the molecules of a liquid body are treated as material points devoid of any spin motion. The only type of rotational motion envisaged in classical hydrodynamics reduces to a translation of the molecules with non-vanishing vorticity $\text{curl}\,\mathbf{v}$, where $\mathbf{v}$ is the translational velocity, the angular velocity of a volume element containing a large number of molecules being equal to $\boldsymbol{\omega} = \frac{1}{2}\text{curl}\,\mathbf{v}$.

† V. N. Zwetkov, *Acta Physicochimica U.R.S.S.* **10**, 555 (1939).

In the case of liquids whose molecules cannot be regarded as material points, but must rather be treated as small rigid bodies, the total angular momentum of a volume element is equal to the sum of the part due to the ordinary vorticity and of a part due to the spin—in the above sense.

The introduction of the internal degrees of freedom corresponding to this spin involves a far-reaching modification and generalization of classical hydrodynamics, the main point referring to the establishment of the mutual action between the spin motion and the translational motion. This mutual action must be characterized by a tendency to an equalization of the vortex angular velocity $\boldsymbol{\omega} = \frac{1}{2}\operatorname{curl}\mathbf{v}$ and the spin angular velocity $\boldsymbol{\Omega}$. Hence it follows that if the components of $\boldsymbol{\omega}$ and $\boldsymbol{\Omega}$ along a certain axis (say $Z$) are different, a frictional force, or rather torque, must arise with a moment (about the $z$-axis) proportional to the difference $\omega_z - \Omega_z$. Strictly speaking, we must distinguish two equal and opposite torques, one of them with the moment $dM'_z = \mu(\omega_z - \Omega_z)\,dV$ acting on the spins (i.e. tending to accelerate or decelerate the rotation of the molecules in the volume element $dV$ about their own axes, parallel to $Z$), and the other with the moment $dM''_z = \mu(\Omega_z - \omega_z)\,dV$ acting on the centres of gravity of the molecules and tending to accelerate (or decelerate) their vortex motion.

In the presence of external forces tending to orientate the molecules the total moment acting on the spins $d\mathbf{M}^{(s)}$ is equal to the sum of $d\mathbf{M}'$ and of a vector $d\mathbf{M}_e = \overline{\mathbf{M}}\,dV$, where $\overline{\mathbf{M}}$ is given by (53 b). Denoting the average moment of inertia of the molecules about an axis parallel to $z$ by $j_z$ and the number of molecules in unit volume by $n$, we obtain the following equation for the spin motion:

$$nj_z\frac{d\Omega}{dt} = \overline{M}_z - \mu(\Omega_z - \omega_z). \tag{54}$$

The corresponding equation for the rate of change of the part of the angular momentum of $dV$ which is due to the translational motion can be written as follows:

$$nm(dV)^{\frac{2}{3}}\frac{d\omega_z}{dt} \approx nm\overline{r^2}\frac{d\omega_z}{dt} = \mu(\Omega_z - \omega_z) + T_{xy} - T_{yx},$$

where $m$ is the mass of a molecule and $T_{xy}$, $T_{yx}$ the components of the stress tensor, which in classical hydrodynamics (just as in classical elasticity theory) is assumed to be symmetrical.

This symmetry follows from the fact that in the limit $dV \to 0$ the left-hand side of the preceding equation vanishes, if the frictional torque, represented by the first term of the right-hand side, is not taken into account. In the presence of this term the usual symmetry condition $T_{xy} = T_{yx}$ is replaced by the following more general relation:

$$T_{xy} - T_{yx} = \mu(\omega_z - \Omega_z). \tag{54 a}$$

It should be mentioned that the vector of spin velocity $\mathbf{\Omega}$ has in general no connexion whatsoever with the average orientation of the molecules, as specified by the polarization vector $\mathbf{P}$ or the anisotropy tensor $s_{ik}$. The molecules can rotate in a similar way about the same axis ($\Omega_z \neq 0$), while the direction of their average orientation as well as the magnitude of the latter remains constant (see next section).

## 8. Orientation and Rotation of Anisotropic Molecules in a Flow of Liquid

We shall not attempt to develop in more detail the theory of the connexion between the spin of the molecules and their translational motion and shall now proceed to an examination of the connexion between the orientation of the molecules, or rather between the degree of anisotropy of the liquid due to this orientation, and the rate of change of the strain of the liquid, no account being taken of the rotation. This rate, i.e. the rate of the deformation of a liquid, is specified by a tensor with the components

$$e_{ik} = \frac{1}{2}\left(\frac{\partial v_i}{\partial x_k} + \frac{\partial v_k}{\partial x_i}\right)$$

which can be denoted as the tensor of velocity gradient.

The deformation described by such a tensor is reduced, as is well known, to three extensions or compressions in the direction of three mutually perpendicular axes, denoted as the principal axes of the tensor. It is natural to expect that such a deformation will be accompanied by a partial orientation of the molecules; if the latter are rod-shaped, their axes must tend to be orientated preferentially in the direction corresponding to the maximum velocity of extension. This orientating action must cease as soon as the deformation velocity vanishes; the resulting orientation must, however, persist for a certain time $\tau$, vanishing exponentially as $e^{-t/\tau}$. Hence it is clear that the dependence of the anisotropy tensor $s_{ik}$ on $e_{ik}$ must be expressed by an equation of the type (50 a), where the tensor $f_{ik}$ can be assumed to be connected with $e_{ik}$ by the linear relation

$$f_{ik} = \lambda(e_{ik} - \tfrac{1}{3}\delta_{ik}\, e), \tag{55}$$

following from $\sum s_{ii} = 0$. In the case of an incompressible liquid $e = \sum e_{ii} = \operatorname{div} \mathbf{v} = 0$, so that the preceding relation is reduced to

$$f_{ik} = \lambda e_{ik}.$$

If the flow of the liquid is steady, the equation (50 a) gives

$$s_{ik} = \tau \lambda e_{ik}. \tag{55 a}$$

Let us assume, for example, that the liquid flows in the $x$ direction with a velocity $v = v_x$, changing in the perpendicular direction $y$ (such a motion actually takes place near the surface of a solid body). The only non-vanishing component of the tensor $e_{ik}$ is reduced in this case to $e_{12} = e_{21} = \frac{1}{2}\partial v_x/\partial y$. Introducing a new system of coordinates $x'$, $y'$ making an angle of 45° with the original one and referring the components of $e_{ik}$ to this system we get

$$e'_{11} = e_{12} = \frac{1}{2}\frac{\partial v_x}{\partial y}, \qquad e'_{22} = -e_{12}, \qquad e'_{12} = 0. \tag{56}$$

The deformation of the liquid connected with the type of flow under consideration thus consists in a continuous extension along the $x'$-axis and compression along the $y'$-axis. The molecules of the liquid must be orientated accordingly in the $x'$ direction as if they were acted upon in this direction by an external electric field. If the molecules are optically anisotropic this orientation must give rise to a double refraction, i.e. to an effect similar to that of Kerr. If the degree of orientation is small, the difference between the refractive indices for light vibrations parallel to the $x'$- and $y'$-axes must be given by the linear relation

$$\Delta n = c\frac{\partial v_x}{\partial y},$$

which is due to Maxwell (the proportionality coefficient $c$ is called Maxwell's constant).

This formula is verified experimentally both for pure liquids and for solutions of substances with elongated (rod-shaped) molecules up to the largest velocity gradients that can be realized (of the order of $10^{-4}$ sec.$^{-1}$). In the case of large gradients, however, one of the principal axes of the anisotropy tensor is found to make with the direction of flow ($x$) an angle $\alpha < 45°$, this angle decreasing with increase of $\partial v_x/\partial y$.

This circumstance is explained by the following considerations† which can serve as a basis for a molecular kinetic theory of these phenomena.

A molecule of a dissolved substance will be treated as a thin rod with

† W. Kuhn, *Kolloidzschr.* **62**, 269 (1933); Böder, *Z. f. Phys.* **75**, 258 (1932); see also J. M. Burgers, Second Report on Viscosity and Plasticity, Ch. III, Amsterdam, 1938.

a length $s$, and the solvent as a continuous medium formed by infinitely small particles. Let us assume further that the centre $O$ of the molecule $A$ moves with the same velocity $v_0$ as the surrounding liquid. If the axis of the molecule were inclined at a fixed angle $\theta$ to the direction of flow ($x$-axis), the velocity of the liquid with respect to its two ends $A_1$ and $A_2$ would be equal to $v-v_0 = \frac{1}{2}sg\sin\theta$, where $g = \partial u_x/\partial y$ is the

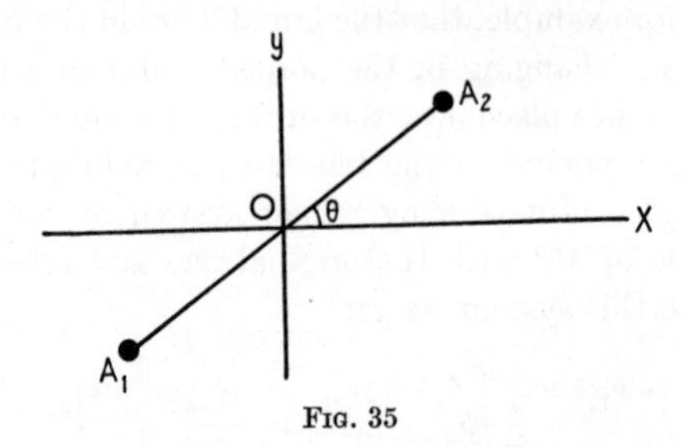


FIG. 35

velocity gradient at $O$. The components of this relative velocity at both ends in the longitudinal direction $\frac{1}{2}gs\sin\theta\cos\theta$ must give rise to a force extending or compressing the molecule (a circumstance which must be taken into account in the determination of the resulting double refraction), while the transverse components of the relative velocity $\frac{1}{2}sg\sin^2\theta$ tend to rotate the molecule in a definite direction (clockwise if $g > 0$, anti-clockwise in the opposite case). If the influence of inertia can be neglected, the molecule must rotate with an angular velocity of such a magnitude $\dot{\theta}$ that the linear velocity of its ends in the transverse direction should be equal to the corresponding relative velocity of the solvent. We thus get

$$\dot{\theta} = -g\sin^2\theta. \tag{57}$$

It should be noted that the mean value of this 'spin velocity' of the dissolved molecules $\bar{\dot{\theta}} = \Omega_z$ is equal to $\frac{1}{2}g$.

Let us denote by $\rho(\theta)\,d\theta$ the relative number of molecules $A_1A_2$ whose axes are inclined to the direction of flow at angles lying between $\theta$ and $\theta+d\theta$.

If the motion of the dissolved molecules is reduced to the non-uniform rotation, due to the flow of the surrounding liquid, the condition for a steady distribution $\rho(\theta)$ is given by the equation

$$\rho\dot{\theta} = \text{const.}, \tag{57 a}$$

whence, according to (57), we get

$$\rho = \frac{\text{const.}}{\sin^2\theta}. \tag{57 b}$$

The preferred orientation of the molecules coincides thus in this case with the direction of flow $x$.

The situation is essentially changed if account is taken of the rotational thermal (Brownian) motion of the dissolved molecules. This thermal component of the motion gives rise to an orientational *diffusion* of the molecules in the direction corresponding to a decrease of $\rho(\theta)$. Adding the corresponding diffusion term $-D\partial\rho/\partial\theta$ to the left-hand side of (57) we obtain the following generalized equation, expressing the condition of a steady distribution:

$$\rho\dot{\theta}-D\frac{\partial\rho}{\partial\theta} = \text{const.} \equiv c. \tag{58}$$

If the diffusion term is of a prevalent importance (as is actually the case for dissolved molecules of a moderate size) the distribution function $\rho$ must differ but slightly from the constant value $\rho_0 = 1/2\pi$. Putting $\rho = \rho_0+\rho_1$, where $\rho_1 \ll \rho_0$, we can rewrite equation (58) in the following approximate form:

$$\rho_0\,\dot{\theta}-D\frac{\partial\rho_1}{\partial\theta} = c, \tag{58 a}$$

whence, since $\dot{\theta} = -g\sin^2\theta$

$$\rho_1 = \left(-\frac{c}{D}-\frac{\rho_0 g}{2D}\right)\theta+\frac{\rho_0 g}{4D}\sin 2\theta.$$

The first term of this expression must obviously vanish (in the contrary case the function $\rho(\theta)$ would not be single-valued). We thus get

$$\rho = \rho_0\left(-1+\frac{g}{4D}\sin 2\theta\right). \tag{58 b}$$

This expression shows that the preferred orientation of the molecules makes an angle of 45° with the direction of flow in agreement with the result of the formal theory previously given.

A more exact expression for the function $\rho$ can be found by expanding it into a series of powers of the parameter $g/2D$ so long as the latter is small (compared with 1). In the opposite case it is more expedient to expand $\rho$ into a series of powers of $2D/g$; in this case the preferred orientation of the molecules tends to that which corresponds to $D = 0$, i.e. to (57 b).

The order of magnitude of the diffusion coefficient $D$ can be estimated with the help of the formula

$$\frac{1}{\alpha} = \pi\mu\left(\frac{s}{2}\right)^3 = \frac{\pi}{8}\mu s^3,$$

where $\alpha$ is the rotational mobility of a small rod with a length $s$ in a liquid with viscosity $\mu$. Using Einstein's relation $D/\alpha = kT$ we get

$$D = \frac{8kT}{\pi\mu s^3}.$$

This expression differs only by a numerical factor of the order 1 from Debye's formula (1 a) and (42), which is obtained for a sphere with a diameter $s$.

Coming back to the formal theory of the orientation of the molecules of a liquid in the presence of a velocity gradient, we shall now consider a motion of an essentially different character from the usual viscous flow considered above, namely the propagation through a liquid of longitudinal sound waves.

Since such waves are due to compressions and expansions in a single direction (the direction of propagation), they are connected with a variation of the *shape* of each volume element, i.e. with shears which give rise to an orientational effect. If the period of sound vibration is very large compared with the relaxation time $\tau$ appearing in equation (50 a), the orientational effect can be determined with the help of the relations

$$\frac{1}{\tau}s_{ik} = \lambda(e_{ik} - \tfrac{1}{3}e\delta_{ik})$$

referring to the steady state, and reducing in the case of longitudinal waves propagated in the $x$ direction to

$$s_{11} = \tfrac{2}{3}\lambda\tau e_{11}, \qquad s_{22} = s_{33} = -\tfrac{1}{3}\lambda\tau e_{11}, \tag{59}$$

where $e_{11} = \partial v_x/\partial x$ is the only non-vanishing component of the tensor $e_{ik}$.

These equations show that in those places where the liquid is expanding ($s_{11} > 0$) the molecules are orientated preferentially in the longitudinal direction, but in those places where it is compressed, in the transverse directions. In both cases the maximum value of the birefringence, i.e. the largest value of the difference between the refractive indices, is obtained for those light waves whose electric vectors vibrate in directions parallel and perpendicular to the direction of propagation of the sound waves.

The appearance of a double refraction in viscous liquids with optically anisotropic molecules under the influence of progressive or standing ultrasonic waves has been experimentally observed by Lucas† and studied in more detail by Petraglia.‡ The latter author used standing ultrasonic waves, the light rays being transmitted through the liquid

† R. Lucas, *C.R.* **206**, 827 (1938). ‡ S. Petraglia, *Nuovo Cimento*, July 1940, p. 378.

in a direction parallel to the plane of the sound waves, and polarized under an angle of 45° with respect to this plane. When the transmitted light was examined in crossed nicols a set of equidistant bright fringes was observed which corresponded to the anti-nodes of the sound waves. These effects were especially sharply pronounced in the case of suspensions with needle-like crystalline particles.

The results of Petraglia's experiments are in full agreement with the approximate theory, which corresponds to the assumption of the smallness of the relaxation time $\tau$ with respect to the period of the ultrasonic vibrations. If this assumption is dropped, the equations (59) must be replaced by

$$\frac{ds_{11}}{dt}+\frac{1}{\tau}s_{11}=\tfrac{2}{3}\lambda e_{11}, \qquad s_{22}=s_{33}=-\tfrac{1}{2}s_{11}. \tag{59a}$$

In the case of harmonic vibrations with an angular frequency $\omega$, $e_{ik}$ and $s_{ik}$ are proportional to $e^{i\omega t}$, so that the first equation (59 a) is reduced to

$$\left(i\omega+\frac{1}{\tau}\right)s_{11}=\tfrac{2}{3}\lambda e_{11},$$

whence

$$s_{11}=\frac{2}{3}\frac{\lambda\tau e_{11}}{1+i\omega\tau}. \tag{59b}$$

Hence it is clear that in the case $\omega\tau \gg 1$ the effect under consideration must vanish (because the average orientation of the molecules cannot keep pace with the ultrasonic vibrations).

Since under the influence of the ultrasonic waves the degree of anisotropy of the liquids changes not only in space but also in time, modulating the *phase* of the monochromatic light vibrations with a given direction of polarization which are transmitted through the liquid, a spectroscopic investigation of the transmitted light must reveal, along with the undisplaced line $\nu'$, two lines displaced with respect to it in opposite directions by an amount equal to the frequency $\nu$ of the ultrasonic vibrations.

This effect cannot be observed in practice because of the smallness of $\nu$ compared with $\nu'$. A similar effect would, however, be expected to result from the 'hypersonic' waves, which constitute the main part of the heat motion in solid and liquid bodies, in the case of liquids with optically anisotropic molecules.

It is necessary to distinguish the *scattering* of light by these hypersonic waves, which is associated with a modulation of the *amplitude* of the scattered light vibrations (see Ch. IV, § 8) from the *transmission* of (polarized) light through the optically unhomogeneous medium, which is accompanied by a modulation of the *phase* of the transmitted light vibrations.† In both cases the modulation frequency is equal to the frequency of the sound (hypersonic) vibrations. In the former case, however, the undisplaced line is either wholly absent or is relatively weak, while in the latter case it must be more intense than the two displaced lines.

The influence of the thermal motion in solids and liquids on the transmitted (polarized) light has not hitherto been investigated.

## 9. Thermal Fluctuations of Anisotropy in Liquids and the Resulting Scattering of Light Rays

The thermal motion in a liquid body, constituted by more or less complex molecules, can be described as a superposition of translational vibrations in the form of longitudinal and of transverse waves, due to the translational motion of the centres of gravity of the molecules, and angular vibrations, or orientational waves, due to rotational oscillations about three (or in the case of diatomic molecules two) mutually perpendicular axes. These two components of the thermal motion are not wholly independent in the sense that the translational vibrations must be accompanied by secondary variations of the orientation, such as have been considered in the preceding section for the case of longitudinal waves, while the angular vibrations can be accompanied by secondary translational ones. This correlation between the two types of motion is quite similar to that which exists between the acoustic and the optical branch of the vibrations of an ionic crystal, according to Born–Karman's theory. Nevertheless, the vibrations constituting the heat motion in a body—either solid or liquid—consisting of separate undissociated molecules can be classified as essentially translational with an orientational 'accompaniment', and essentially angular with (possibly) a translational 'accompaniment'.

If the molecules are optically anisotropic their thermal motion must give rise to an additional 'angular' scattering of light (with respect to that which would result under the same condition in the absence of anisotropy), which in its turn can be divided into two parts: a part due to angular motion, irrespective of the translational one ('purely angular' part), and a part due to the angular accompaniment of the translational

† Petraglia's experiments refer to this second effect. A similar interpretation is applicable to the experiments on the diffraction of non-polarized light by ordinary ultrasonic waves. These experiments were initially interpreted from the point of view of Brillouin's old theory, which in reality refers to the scattering of light. A correct theory was given for the first time by Raman and Nagendra Nath, and later in a more complete form by Brillouin.

motion ('translational-angular' part). The second part of the light-scattering must further be divided into two portions depending on the longitudinal and the transverse components of the translational motion respectively. They will be denoted, for the sake of brevity, as $l_a$ and $t_a$.

It should be noted that the additional scattering representing both $l_a$ and $t_a$ is due to such elastic waves only as satisfy Bragg's condition $2\lambda \sin\theta = \lambda'$, just as in the case of the main component of the scattering, due to the longitudinal hypersonic waves ($l$). The portion $l_a$ must be relatively very faint and, if the incident light is polarized, must depend upon the type of polarization, the refractive index being increased for light vibrations which are parallel to the preferential orientation of the molecules, and this orientation changing from longitudinal to transverse along the normal to the wave-front (cf. the theory of the preceding section). A more interesting and instructive situation is found in the case of $t_a$, for the transverse waves alone would yield no scattering whatever if the molecules were optically isotropic. Moreover, the transverse waves with a frequency lying in the hypersonic range ($10^{10}$ sec.$^{-1}$) for which Bragg's condition can be satisfied must in the case of ordinary liquids be strongly *damped*, since this frequency is of the order of the relaxation time of the liquid $\tau$ at ordinary temperatures. Now it can easily be shown that such a damping must cause a broadening of the corresponding Rayleigh doublet; if this broadening is large enough, the doublet must be reduced to a diffuse band of a certain width. If, along with the elastic transverse vibrations of the liquid, shears of a similar kind, due to entropy fluctuations, are taken into account, a third, undisplaced Rayleigh line must be introduced, so that in reality the transverse displacements of the anisotropic molecules connected with their rotations must give rise not to a doublet but to a triplet, quite similar to that due to the ordinary Rayleigh triplet in liquids with isotropic molecules. This '$t_a$ triplet' must differ from the preceding one ($l_a$) in four respects.

(1) For a given value of the scattering angle $\theta$ and, accordingly, of the effective wave-length $\lambda = \lambda'/2\sin\theta$, the width of the $t_a$ triplet in the absence of damping should be smaller than that of the ordinary $l$ triplet, since it is equal to the frequency $\nu_t$ of the transverse vibrations, which is smaller than that of longitudinal vibrations with the same wave-length $\nu_l$ (the ratio $\nu_t/\nu_l$ being equal to the ratio of the corresponding propagation velocities).

(2) In reality all the three lines $t_a$ must be broadened, as a result of the damping, into a diffuse band.

(3) The scattered radiation, forming this band, being due to the secondary angular displacements of the anisotropic molecules, must be depolarized in exactly the same way as the radiation scattered owing to primary angular fluctuations (see below).

(4) Finally, the $t_a$ scattering must increase with the degree of optical anisotropy of the molecules.

An additional scattering of light with all these characteristics has actually been discovered experimentally in 1930 by E. Gross,† who has shown that the Rayleigh line in liquids is characterized by the presence of a depolarized background, with an intensity distribution falling off rather rapidly with increase of the distance from the centre (corresponding to the undisplaced line). This depolarized background, which is especially strong in liquids with anisotropic molecules, is usually referred to as the 'wings' of the Rayleigh line, although Gross himself reserves the latter term to indicate that portion of the scattered radiation which is shifted with respect to its frequency much farther from the centre of the line (by an amount of the order of $10^{12}$ sec.$^{-1}$) and which corresponds to low-frequency Raman lines discovered by him in the spectrum of the same substances in the crystalline state.

Gross has shown that the width of his 'background' which is usually of the order of $10^{11}$ sec.$^{-1}$ (10–20 cm.$^{-1}$ in the wave number scale) increases as the viscosity of the liquid decreases, both for the same liquid (with increase of the temperature) and for different liquids. He has shown, moreover, that the width of the background can be identified approximately with the reciprocal of the relaxation time $\tau$, as defined by Debye's formula $\tau = 4\pi\mu a^3/kT$, where $\mu$ is the viscosity of the liquid. Such an identification has been possible in the case of monochlorbenzene, the molecules of which, besides being optically anisotropic, possess permanent dipole moments revealed in the electric polarization of this substance in low-frequency alternating fields. In the case of other non-polar substances with optically anisotropic molecules (benzophenone, for example) Gross has shown that the width of the depolarized background varies with the temperature inversely as the coefficient of viscosity.

Gross himself believed that Bragg's or Brillouin's interference condition $2\lambda \sin\theta = \lambda'$, which determines the width of Rayleigh's $l$ doublet, is immaterial for the surrounding background, whose width is limited

† E. Gross and M. Vuks, *Journ. de Phys.* **6**, 457 (1935); **7**, 113 (1936). E. Gross, *Nature*, **126**, 201, 603 (1930); **129**, 722 (1932). See also Gross and Raskin and Gross and Korshunov, *Proc Ac. Sci. U.S.S.R.*, Phys. series, 1940.

by the condition $\Delta\nu' \leqslant 1/\tau$ only and can therefore greatly exceed the width of the doublet $\Delta\nu' = \nu$. As a matter of fact Brillouin's condition must apply both to the $l$ (longitudinal) and to the $t$ (or more exactly $t_a$) doublet, in a generalized form, however, accounting for the *damping* of the corresponding waves.

A system of elastic waves propagated in the direction of the $x$-axis with a damping coefficient $\alpha$ is defined by the formula

$$\psi = Ae^{-\alpha x+i(kx-\omega t)} \quad (x > 0),$$

where $k = 2\pi/\lambda$ and $\omega = 2\pi\nu$. This system can be represented, according to Fourier's theorem, as a superposition of a number of undamped waves with the same frequency $\omega/2\pi$ and with all possible wave numbers $q = 2\pi/\lambda$, the amplitudes of these waves being different from zero practically in a range $\Delta q = \alpha$ only about the mean value $q = k$. In fact, putting

$$\psi(x,t) = \int\limits_{-\infty}^{+\infty} \phi(q)e^{i(qx-\omega t)}\,dq, \tag{60}$$

we get (for a constant value of $\omega$)

$$\phi(q) = \frac{1}{2\pi}\int\limits_{0}^{\infty} \psi(x,t)e^{-iqx}\,dx = \frac{1}{2\pi}Ae^{-i\omega t}\int\limits_{0}^{\infty} e^{-[\alpha+i(q-k)]x}\,dx,$$

that is,

$$\phi(q) = \frac{A}{2\pi}\frac{1}{\alpha+i(q-k)}$$

or

$$|\phi(q)|^2 = \frac{A^2}{4\pi^2}\frac{1}{\alpha^2+(q-k)^2}. \tag{60a}$$

The maximum of this expression corresponds to $q = k$, its half-width being of the order of $\alpha$.

Hence it follows that the scattering of light by an angle $2\theta$ is due not only to the hypersonic waves for which Brillouin's condition $2\lambda\sin\theta = \lambda'$ is exactly fulfilled, but also to those hypersonic waves whose wave numbers lie within a range $\Delta k = \alpha$ about Brillouin's value $2\pi/\lambda$. The corresponding frequency range $\Delta\nu = \alpha v$, where $v$ is the propagation velocity of the ultrasonic waves, can be defined as the effective width of each component of Rayleigh's doublet. If this width is much larger than the spacing between the two components $2\nu = 2v/\lambda$, i.e. if $\alpha \gg 2\pi/\lambda$, the latter must coalesce with each other (and with the undisplaced line, due to entropy fluctuations) into a diffuse band.

It is clear that this condition can be realized in the case of transverse waves only, which in liquid bodies are strongly damped so long as their frequency does not exceed the reciprocal of Maxwell's relaxation time $\tau = \mu/G$, where $G$ is the rigidity modulus of the liquid. As has been shown in § 8 of the preceding chapter, the damping coefficient per wave-length, $\alpha\lambda = 2\pi \tan\frac{1}{2}\phi$, is equal to $2\pi$ if $\omega\tau \ll 1$, since $\tan\phi = 1/\omega\tau$. The ratio between $\Delta\nu = \alpha v$ and $\nu$ is thus approximately equal to $2\pi$, which means that for $\omega \ll 1/\tau$ the width of the background $\Delta\nu$ must be larger than the width of the Rayleigh doublet, as calculated according to Brillouin's theory. This argument does not, however, explain Gross's result that $\Delta\nu$ is approximately equal to $1/\tau$. It should

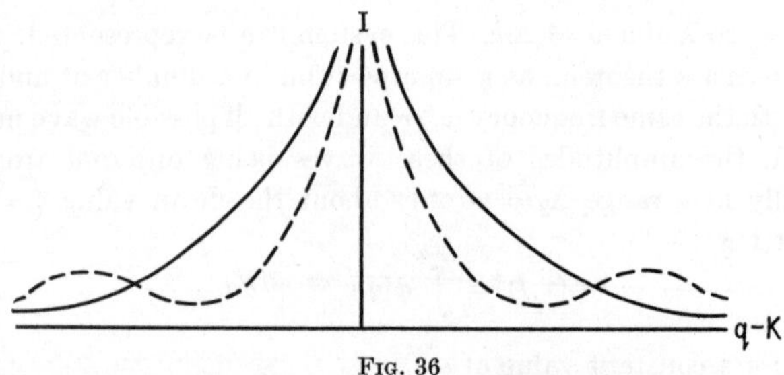


FIG. 36

be mentioned that the relaxation time defined by Debye's formula, which has been used by Gross in the interpretation of his experiments with benzophenone,† is practically identical with the relaxation time $\tau = \tau_0 e^{U/kT}$ appearing in the expression of the viscosity coefficient given by our theory (Ch. IV, § 2), namely $\mu = (kT/\pi\delta^3)\tau$, since $\delta \approx a$.

According to the preceding theory the intensity distribution in the wings of the Rayleigh line (or within the Gross 'background') is given by the formula (60 a), where $q-k$ is the distance from the centre of the line (or more exactly from one of the lines of the ideal doublet) measured in wave numbers. This formula is in agreement with the experimental results, as can be seen from Fig. 36, where the full line gives the intensity distribution observed experimentally by Bai.‡ The latter author has shown that it can be represented by an empirical formula of the exponential type

$$I \sim e^{-\gamma|q-k|}$$

with an effective width $1/\gamma$, which increases as the viscosity of the liquid decreases. Our theoretical expression seems to be in even better agreement with Bai's experiments than his own empirical expression.

The coefficient $A$ in (60 a) must be proportional to the degree of anisotropy of the molecules, which is also in full agreement with the experimental data.

† *C.R. Ac. Sci. U.S.S.R.* **28**, 786 (1940).

‡ K. S. Bai, *Proc. Ind. Ac. Sci.* A, **13**, 439 (1941).

We shall not engage in a more detailed investigation of this question and shall limit ourselves to the following remarks.

If a plane transverse wave is propagated in the $y$ direction, upwards, for instance, the vibrations of the particles being parallel to the $x$-axis in the plane of the paper, the velocity gradient $\partial v_x/\partial y$ will be alternately positive and negative, so that the preferential orientation of the molecules will be inclined at an angle of 45° to the normal of the waves, as shown by the arrows in Fig. 37. The degree of orientation in the case of slow vibrations will be given by (55 a), while in the case of rapid vibrations with a frequency of the order of or larger than the reciprocal of the relaxation time $\tau'$, which characterizes the rate of the establishment of a steady angular distribution (and which must, in general, be different from the relaxation time $\tau$, determining the ordinary viscosity), it will be proportional to $\tau'\lambda e_{ik}/(1+i\omega\tau')$ (cf. equation (59 b), $\tau'$ standing in the place of $\tau$).

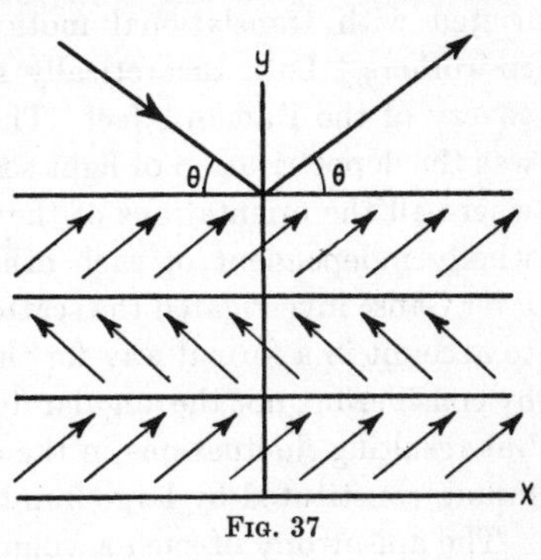

Fig. 37

If the incident light is polarized in the plane of incidence, so that the electric vibrations are perpendicular to the plane of the paper (Fig. 37), the transverse vibrations of the liquid will not give rise to any scattering, since the refractive index will preserve the same value throughout. If, on the other hand, the electric vibrations of the incident light lie in the plane of incidence, forming an angle $45°-\theta$ with the preferential orientation of the molecules in odd layers with a thickness equal to $\frac{1}{2}\lambda$, and an angle $45°+\theta$ with the preferential orientation of the molecules in the even layers, the refractive index will be different in alternating layers and a scattering will take place, provided Brillouin's relation $2\lambda\sin\theta = \lambda'$ is (approximately) satisfied. If the incident light is not polarized, the scattered light, or, more exactly, that fraction of it which is due to the 'rotational accompaniment' of the transverse vibrations, must be polarized normally to the plane of scattering. Owing to the angular fluctuations of the molecules about their mean orientation this polarization will, however, not be complete, the degree of depolarization being the same (1/7) as in the case of primary angular fluctuations. This circumstance has been verified by Bai (loc. cit.), who has shown, simultaneously, that near the centre of the Rayleigh line the degree of depolarization is much smaller (of the order of 8 per cent.).†

The scattering of light as a result of primary angular fluctuations of optically anisotropic molecules (i.e. angular fluctuations not connected with translational motion) was studied by Raman and his co-workers,‡ both theoretically and experimentally, prior to the discovery of the Raman effect. The main question studied at that time was the depolarization of light scattered by an angle $2\theta = 90^\circ$ in *gases*, where all the orientations of the different molecules can be treated as wholly independent of each other and equally probable. Somewhat later Gans§ investigated the scattering of light in liquids and attempted to account in a formal way for the mutual orientation of the molecules by considering, not the angular fluctuations of the individual molecules, but resulting fluctuations in the anisotropy of volume elements of the liquid, constituted by large numbers of molecules.

The anisotropy of such a volume element can be specified, from the point of view of its optical properties, by the deviation of the tensor of dielectric constant $\epsilon_{ik}$ from its mean value, which is reduced to the scalar $\epsilon_0$ (equivalent to the tensor $\epsilon_0 \delta_{ik}$). Gans assumes that this deviation corresponds to an increase of the free energy of the volume element $F$ by an amount $\Delta F$ which is a quadratic function of the quantities $\Delta\epsilon_{ik} = \epsilon_{ik} - \epsilon_0 \delta_{ik}$. Referring this increase to unit volume and taking into account the average isotropy of the liquid we can put:

$$\Delta F = \tfrac{1}{2}\alpha\Big(\sum \Delta\epsilon_{ii}\Big)^2 + \tfrac{1}{2}\beta \sum_i \sum_k (\Delta\epsilon_{ik})^2,$$

where $\alpha$ and $\beta$ are essentially positive coefficients, while $\sum \Delta\epsilon_{ii}$ and $\sum\sum (\Delta\epsilon_{ik})^2$ are the linear and the quadratic invariants of the tensor $\Delta\epsilon_{ik}$. The first of them is connected with a variation of the density of the liquid, so that the coefficient $\alpha$ must be proportional to the bulk modulus of the latter. As to the coefficient $\beta$, it can be partially connected with the rigidity modulus of the liquid in the case of secondary angular fluctuations associated with transverse shears,‖ but must also contain a second term, independent of the parameters

† A general mathematical theory of the scattering of light in liquids allowing for relaxation phenomena, connected with the degree of relaxation, has recently been given by M. Leontovich, who, however, did not attempt to explain Gross's background or to analyse the physical ground for the broadening of the Rayleigh doublet components, limiting himself to the introduction of a single relaxation time. See *J. of Phys. U.S.S.R.*, **4**, 499 (1941).

‡ Raman and Rao, *Phil. Mag.* **46**, 426 (1923).

§ R. Gans, *Z. f. Phys.* **17**, 353 (1923).

‖ In this case the liquid should behave as an amorphous solid with an infinitely large viscosity, and the anisotropy fluctuations should reduce to the well-known optico-elastic effect. Such treatment is applicable to vibrations for which $\omega\tau \gg 1$.

describing the translation motion, and characteristic of primary angular fluctuations.

It follows from the preceding expression for $\Delta F$ that the average value of the squares of $\Delta\epsilon_{ik}$ must be of the form

$$\overline{(\Delta\epsilon_{ii})^2} = \frac{kT}{\alpha' v}, \qquad \overline{(\Delta\epsilon_{ik})^2} = \frac{kT}{\beta' v} \quad (i \neq k),$$

where $\alpha'$, $\beta'$ are two new constants which can easily be expressed through the constants $\alpha$, $\beta$.

The results of Gans's theory differ from those of Raman's theory for gases by the fact only that the two parts of the scattered radiation—the completely polarized (due to the density fluctuations) and the partially depolarized (due to the angular fluctuations)—are proportional to the absolute temperature of the liquid, whereas in the case of gases they are both independent of the temperature. This result fully agrees with the experimental data.

The existence of an essential difference between the scattering of light by gases and by liquids (as well as by solids) was established only after the discovery of the Raman effect by a study of the spectral distribution of the intensity of the scattered radiation in the neighbourhood of a Rayleigh line.

In the case of gases this distribution corresponds to a free quantized rotation of the molecules, and is reduced to a large number of rotational lines which eventually merge into a continuous diffuse band. This band is characterized by the presence of two intensity maxima, on both sides of the central (undisplaced) line, at a distance $\pm\Delta\nu$, corresponding to the average (most frequent) angular velocity of the molecules at a given temperature. As long as the quantum effects are blurred, the average angular velocity of the molecules $2\pi\Delta\nu$ is determined by the equation

$$\tfrac{1}{2}J(2\pi\Delta\nu)^2 = \tfrac{1}{2}kT,$$

where $J$ is the moment of inertia of a molecule about the corresponding axis.

If in the liquid state the molecules were rotating just as freely as in the gaseous one, the wings of the Rayleigh line would have a shape shown by the dotted line in Fig. 36. In reality, however, in the case of liquids with anisotropic molecules these wings are represented by the full line of Fig. 36, their intensity falling off monotonically with increase of the distance from the centre. Hence it is clear that in the liquid state of a substance a free rotation of the molecules does not take place, at moderate temperatures at least.

The Rayleigh doublet has a width $\Delta\nu$ of the order $10^{10}$ sec.$^{-1}$, while the main part of the 'wings', which Gross denotes as the 'background' of the Rayleigh line, stretches to a distance of the order of $10^{11}$ sec.$^{-1}$ Still farther away—up to a distance of $10^{12}$ sec.$^{-1}$—a region is found, denoted by Gross as the 'wings' in the stricter sense, which corresponds to separate lines of an unidentified origin in the Raman spectrum of the same substance in the crystalline state. The origin of these low-frequency Raman lines discovered by Gross† is not yet clear. It may be surmised that they are due to primary angular fluctuations of the molecules in the form of rotational oscillations, which replace their free rotation in the gaseous state. In the liquid state these lines are blurred into a broad band, probably as a result of a strong damping of the waves in the form of which they are propagated. In certain cases, such as benzophenone for example, some of these low-frequency lines are practically not affected by fusion. This shows in a very conclusive way that the thermal motion of the molecules in liquid bodies is essentially similar to that in the corresponding solids—which is the main thesis of the kinetic theory of liquids.

It should be mentioned that the frequency interval between $10^{12}$ and $10^{13}$ sec.$^{-1}$—the latter figure corresponding to the end of Debye's acoustical spectrum—does not contain, as a rule, any additional low-frequency Raman lines. The ordinary Raman lines due to the intramolecular vibrations of the molecules are found near a frequency of the order of $10^{14}$ sec.$^{-1}$, being practically independent of the state of aggregation. Some of these lines are, however, slightly shifted in a direction corresponding to a decrease of frequency as we pass from the gaseous state to the liquid one. The shift is especially conspicuous in dipolar substances where it amounts to 1 per cent. It can be explained in a general way by the fact that the attraction between dipole molecules must loosen the bond between the opposite charges constituting their dipole moments (this is an example of the antagonism between inner and outer bonds, which will be discussed at a greater length in Ch. VIII, § 1).

## 10. The Mutual Orientation of Molecules in Liquid Bodies and Cybotactic Groupings

The mutual orientation of dipole molecules of a small size (such as the alkali halides) both in crystals and in liquids can be reduced to the simple dipole forces acting between them and described in Debye's new

† E. Gross, *Nature*, **135**, 100, 431 (1935).

theory with the help of the notion of the 'local field'. In the case of molecules—both polar and non-polar—of a larger size such forces are wholly insufficient to account for the phenomena of their mutual orientation. In this case it is more expedient to treat the molecules as small rigid bodies of a definite shape, with superficial fields of attractive forces tending to press them against each other as tightly as possible, so as to ensure a spatial distribution corresponding to the smallest possible volume of the whole system.

This tendency is fully realized at low temperatures only, when it gives rise to a regular crystalline structure. At higher temperatures, corresponding to the liquid state, it is in conflict with the disorganizing action of the thermal motion, resulting in a partial order, which can be described approximately by introducing the notion of molecular groupings of a finite size with approximately the same orientation. The existence of such groupings or 'swarms' in anisotropic liquids ('liquid crystals') was discussed theoretically long ago by Kast and by Ornstein on the basis of broad experimental evidence.

In the case of ordinary isotropic liquids with rod-shaped molecules it has been discovered experimentally, with the help of X-ray analysis, by G. W. Stewart, who has denoted this phenomenon by the term 'cybotaxis', the molecular groupings with a regular arrangement or orientation being described by him as cybotactic regions.

The real existence of such 'swarms' or 'cybotactic regions' in the case of liquids with strongly elongated rod-shaped molecules has been established experimentally beyond all doubt. Some authors are inclined to treat them simply as small crystallites of exactly the same type as in solid polycrystalline bodies, with somewhat blurred boundaries constituted by broad transition layers. This point of view is admissible, with great reserve, in certain cases only; the arrangement of the centres of gravity of the molecules within the cybotactic groups can be wholly irregular, provided their axes are parallel to each other.

The question of the size of the cybotactic groups, the character of their boundaries, the change of both with the time, especially when the liquid is moving under the influence of external forces, has practically not been studied hitherto.

In the case of liquid crystals the size of the cybotactic groups—which in this case are denoted as 'swarms'—may reach a few millimetres if use is made of the orientating influence of solid walls (with respect to which the molecules tend to be orientated with their axes parallel or normal to the surface of the walls), of magnetic or electric fields and so on. In the absence of such influences, i.e. in the case of a spontaneous splitting of the liquid into swarms, the latter have usually linear dimensions of the order of $10^{-5}$ cm.—so far as can be judged from their diamagnetic susceptibility if each swarm is assumed to rotate as a solid body, without any change in the relative distribution and orientation of the molecules constituting it (Kast). It is clear, however, that such a picture cannot be applied simultaneously to several contiguous swarms, for a rotation of one of them as a rigid body would lead to a formation of more or less wide gaps between them. Since in reality such gaps do not arise, a change of the orientation of the molecules constituting a swarm must be accompanied by a deformation of the latter, involving a variation of its boundaries. The preceding scheme of the swarms must therefore be rejected as soon as we turn from their geometry to their kinematics. The main fallacy of this scheme is due to the neglect of the *spin* degrees of freedom of the molecules. In reality the change in the orientation of a swarm must take place by way of a rotation of each molecule about its own axis, this 'spin rotation' being accompanied by such a translation of the centres of gravity that the neighbouring molecules remain in contact with each other.

Under such conditions a change in the orientation of a swarm must be connected with a change of its shape, the latter change being especially large in the case of a rotation through an angle of 90°.

This specific kinematics of the 'swarms' in anisotropic or ordinary liquids sharply distinguishes them from the crystallites of polycrystalline solids.

The correlation between the two types of motion in a liquid is determined by equations of the type (54) and (54 a), viscous forces (or torques) replacing rigid bonds.

The orientation of the molecules within the same swarm can gradually change from point to point, which must obviously correspond to an additional 'elastic' energy. In a transition from one swarm to the next the orientation of the molecules must change more or less sharply, in correspondence with a rotation of their axes, by an angle of the order of 90°.

The corresponding additional energy can be treated as the *surface energy* of the swarms, since it is proportional to the area of contact between them.

In the case of anisotropic liquids the swarms, in the absence of external influences, maintain a practically constant structure, as follows from the permanence of the picture observed through a polarization microscope. Hence it follows that the swarms have in this case an 'athermic origin', i.e. do not represent thermodynamically stable groupings, arising spontaneously as a result of thermal fluctuations. In this respect they are similar to the crystallites of an ordinary solid body. In the latter case the microcrystalline structure is determined not by the condition of thermodynamical equilibrium but by the kinetics of the crystallization process, which is connected with a simultaneous appearance and growth of crystal nuclei in the volume of the melt, and the existence of a large activation energy for the recrystallization of the polycrystalline aggregate thus formed.

In the case of an anisotropic liquid a thermodynamically stable structure corresponds probably to the formation of a single swarm by all the mass of the liquid (such a single swarm is actually realized by pressing a drop of the liquid between the object-glass and the cover-glass of a microscope). The splitting up of this mass into a large number of smaller swarms with different orientations is probably connected with the kinetics of the transition into the anisotropic liquid state from the ordinary liquid state on cooling, or from the crystalline on heating.

An entirely different situation is found in the case of the 'cybotactic groups' of ordinary liquids with rod-shaped molecules. These groups differ from the swarms of liquid crystals not only by their small size but also by their spontaneous origin and thermodynamically stable character. The splitting up of a simple organic liquid, such as molten paraffin, into a large number of 'micro-swarms' (which must not be confused with micro-crystals because of the kinematical peculiarity of their rotations and deformations) is not due to extraneous causes and must arise as a result of the tendency of the molecules to be arranged in an energetically most advantageous way, i.e. in a tight contact with each other, in spite of the thermal agitation, which tends to distribute them in an absolutely irregular manner.

Hence it follows that the average size of the cybotactic regions must gradually decrease as the temperature is raised.

In order to estimate this average size as a function of the temperature the following roughly approximate reasoning may be used.

Let us imagine that the liquid under investigation, consisting of $N$ molecules, is split up into $z = N/g$ homogeneous regions (cybotactic groups) containing $g$ molecules each. The orientations of the molecules in contiguous regions will be assumed to be sharply different, their contact being connected with a surface energy $\sigma$ per unit area. If the total volume of the liquid is $V$, the surface of each region has an area of the order $(V/z)^{\frac{2}{3}}$. The splitting of the liquid into $z$ regions with sharply different orientations thus requires an additional surface energy $E = \sigma(V/z)^{\frac{2}{3}}z$, that is,

$$E = \sigma V^{\frac{2}{3}} z^{\frac{1}{3}}. \tag{61}$$

This splitting is connected, on the other hand, with an increase of the entropy of the liquid, since the distribution of the molecules over the different regions can be effected in a number of different ways. This number is obviously equal to

$$\frac{N!}{[(N/z)!]^z},$$

which, with the help of the approximate formula $x! = (x/e)^x$, is reduced to $z^N$. The additional entropy connected with the splitting is thus found to be

$$S = kN \log z. \tag{62}$$

The free energy $F = E - TS$, as a function of $z$, has a minimum at

$$z = \left(\frac{3NkT}{\sigma V^{\frac{2}{3}}}\right)^3. \tag{63}$$

This equilibrium value of $z$ corresponds to the following average number of molecules in a single region

$$g = \frac{N}{z} = \frac{\sigma^3 V^2}{N^2 (3kT)^3} \tag{63a}$$

or

$$g = n\left(\frac{\sigma}{3kTn}\right)^3, \tag{63b}$$

where $n = N/V$ is the number of molecules in unit volume of the liquid.

As would be expected, $g$ increases as the temperature is lowered although not very rapidly. Putting $\sigma = 100$ erg/cm.$^2$ and $n = 10^{21}$ cm.$^{-3}$ we get for $T = 300$, $g \simeq 10^3$. If $\sigma = 10$, then, for the same values of $n$ and $T$, $g$ drops to 1, which means that in this case the liquid would be wholly disorientated at room temperatures.

The size of the cybotactic regions can be determined experimentally from the width of the intensity maxima in the X-ray diagrams of the corresponding liquids. The available data are, however, insufficient for a quantitative check of the above theory.

Liquids composed of rod-shaped molecules, and in particular liquid crystals, display, owing to the extremely strong mutual orientation of their molecules, extraordinarily strong orientation effects under the influence of external forces—elastic, magnetic, and mechanical; in the last case we mean the tangential stresses connected with the viscous flow of liquid bodies and tending to orientate the molecules in the direction of flow (or at a certain angle $\leqslant 45°$ to the latter).

The orientation of the molecules of liquid bodies in an electric or magnetic field is revealed experimentally by their electric or magnetic polarization and also by the corresponding optical birefringence (Kerr effect); it has been, moreover, found by Zwetkov that an anisotropic liquid is 'dragged' by a horizontal magnetic field slowly rotating about a vertical axis. The existing theories of these effects are all based on the Ornstein–Kast conception of a swarm as a rigid body, capable of rotating as a whole. In view of the erroneous character of this conception we shall not discuss these theories here. A correct formal theory of the Zwetkov effect has been given in § 7.

# VI

# SURFACE AND ALLIED PHENOMENA

## 1. The Surface Tension of Liquids and its Dependence on the Temperature

THE surface tension of liquids $\sigma$ is usually measured (in the absence of adsorbed layers, see below) by the free energy of their surface referred to unit area.

It is connected with the total surface energy $w$ and the surface entropy $s$ by the relation

$$\sigma = w - Ts, \tag{1}$$

or, since $s = \partial\sigma/\partial T$,

$$\sigma = w - T\frac{\partial\sigma}{\partial T}. \tag{2}$$

The surface energy of a liquid can be defined, generally speaking, as the additional potential energy per unit surface due to the fact that the particles of the surface layer lack neighbours on the external side. It is therefore practically independent of the temperature. The temperature dependence of the surface tension is thus represented by the second term of the expression (1).

The character of this dependence can be determined on the basis of the conception of a specific type of heat-motion associated with the free surface of a liquid body, which can be treated as a superposition of a set of *surface capillary waves* of all directions and lengths (up to a certain maximum length of the order $2\delta$, where $\delta$ is the average distance between neighbouring particles). This conception, which was introduced in 1912 by L. Mandelstam in connexion with his theory of the diffuse scattering of light reflected by the surface of a liquid,† is quite similar to Debye's conception of elastic waves, by a superposition of which the thermal motion in the volume of solids and—to a certain extent—of liquids can be described.

Just as in Debye's theory, that part of the free energy of the surface due to its thermal motion can be represented by the formula

$$\psi = -n'kT\log\frac{kT}{h\bar{\nu}}, \tag{3}$$

where $n'$ is the number of particles per unit area of the surface layer (which is identified with the number of degrees of freedom of the latter).

† L. Mandelstam, *Ann. d. Phys.* **41**, 609 (1913).

In the case of capillary waves the vibration frequency is connected with the wave-length by the formula

$$\nu = \sqrt{\frac{\sigma}{\lambda^3 \rho}} = k^{\frac{3}{2}} \sqrt{\frac{\sigma}{\rho}}, \tag{4}$$

where $k = 1/\lambda$ is the wave number.

The number of different surface vibration modes in the range between $k$ and $k+dk$ per unit area is equal to $2\pi k\,dk$ (cf. Ch. III, § 4). The maximum value of $k$ is consequently given by the equation

$$\pi k_{\max}^2 = n'. \tag{4 a}$$

Hence it follows that the shortest waves have a length of the order $\sqrt{(\pi/n')} \approx \sqrt{\pi}\delta$. The corresponding maximum value of the frequency is thus equal to

$$\nu_{\max} = \left(\frac{n'}{\pi}\right)^{\frac{3}{4}} \left(\frac{\sigma}{\rho}\right)^{\frac{1}{2}}. \tag{4 b}$$

As to the average frequency $\bar{\nu}$, it is defined by the formula

$$\log \bar{\nu} = \frac{1}{n'} \int_0^{k_{\max}} \log\left[k^{\frac{3}{2}} \left(\frac{\sigma}{\rho}\right)^{\frac{1}{2}}\right] 2\pi k\,dk,$$

that is,

$$\log \bar{\nu} = \log \nu_{\max} - \tfrac{3}{4}. \tag{4 c}$$

The energy $w$ which has been defined above as the additional potential energy of the particles forming the surface of the body can be considered as independent of the temperature (explicitly, at least). Hence it follows that the quantity $\psi$ can be identified with the second term of equation (1), i.e. with $-sT$ and that, consequently, the surface entropy is equal to

$$s = -n'k \log \frac{kT}{h\overline{\nu'}}. \tag{5}$$

Since, however, the surface entropy (just as the surface energy) is defined as a *correction* to the volume entropy (or energy) of the body, calculated without taking into account the effects due to its free surface, $s$ must be determined not by $\psi$ but by the difference $\Delta\psi$ between this quantity and that part of the free energy of the body which is replaced by $\psi$. Since this part must correspond to the same number of degrees of freedom, it must be represented, when referred to unit area, by an expression of the same type (3) as $\psi$, with $\overline{\nu'}$ replaced by $\bar{\nu}$, the mean value of the vibration frequency, calculated without taking into consideration surface effects. We thus obtain the following expression for the surface entropy

$$s = n'k \log \bar{\nu}/\overline{\nu'}, \tag{5 a}$$

which leads to the formula

$$\sigma = w - n'kT\log\bar{\nu}/\overline{\nu'} \tag{5b}$$

for the surface tension, as a function of the temperature.

The result is in good agreement with the experimental law established by Eötvös

$$\sigma = \gamma(T_0 - T)$$

for the surface tension of a liquid in equilibrium with its saturated vapour at temperatures sufficiently removed from the critical point $T_0$.

The coefficient $\gamma$ can be calculated for different liquids with the help of the Ramsay–Shields formula

$$\gamma = \frac{2\cdot12}{(Mv)^{\frac{2}{3}}},$$

where $M$ is the molecular weight of the liquid and $v$ its specific volume. The product $Mv$ is connected with the number of particles per unit area $n'$ by the relation

$$n' = \left(\frac{N}{Mv}\right)^{\frac{2}{3}},$$

where $N = 6\times10^{23}$ is Avogadro's number. We thus have

$$\gamma = \frac{2\cdot12}{N^{\frac{2}{3}}}n' \cong 3\times10^{-16}.$$

This empirical value lies close to the theoretical one

$$\gamma = n'k\log\bar{\nu}/\overline{\nu'},$$

since $k = 1\cdot34\times10^{-16}$ while the factor $\ln\bar{\nu}/\overline{\nu'}$ is of the order 1.

It should be remarked that the critical temperature, if it is defined by the condition $\sigma = 0$, turns out to be given by the formula

$$T_0 = \frac{w}{n'k\log\bar{\nu}/\overline{\nu'}},$$

which also agrees with the experimental data, with respect to the order of magnitude at least (cf. Ch. III, § 2). For a more accurate determination of the critical temperature it is necessary to take into account the influence of the saturated vapour on the free energy of the boundary surface between it and the liquid phase.

The preceding theory was developed by the author as a modification of a theory proposed earlier by Born and Karman,† who identified the surface waves with ordinary elastic waves serving to describe the

† Born and Karman, *Phys. Z.* **15,** 361 (1913). This theory has been improved by Brillouin (*C.R.* **180,** 1248 (1925)), who limited himself to an alteration of the vibration frequency of the surface particles, without introducing the conception of surface waves for the calculation of the surface entropy.

thermal motion in the volume of a body. It can be applied, however, only if relatively long surface waves are considered, with a frequency which is smaller than the reciprocal of the relaxation time of the corresponding liquid at the temperature under consideration, $\tau = \tau_0 e^{U/kT}$. With respect to vibrations of a higher frequency the liquid must behave in exactly the same way as a solid body. Under such conditions the capillary waves must be replaced by surface waves of the Rayleigh type, which are propagated without dispersion with a velocity $v_s$ closely approaching that of the ordinary transverse waves in the corresponding solid. According to Rayleigh's theory

$$v_s \cong 0{\cdot}9\sqrt{\frac{G}{\rho}},$$

where $G$ is the rigidity modulus of the body.

The frequency spectrum of the surface waves, constituting the heat motion of the free surface of a liquid body, must thus be separated into two parts: (1) the low-frequency or capillary part $\nu < 1/\tau$, and (2) the high-frequency or Rayleigh part $\nu > 1/\tau$.

The frequency of the capillary waves is connected with their length by the relation (4), which in the case of the Rayleigh waves is replaced by $\nu = v_s/\lambda = 0{\cdot}9/\lambda\sqrt{(G/\rho)}$. In a solid body the rigidity modulus $G$ and the compressibility modulus $K$ are of the same order of magnitude as the evaporation energy per unit volume $Q$ (cf. Ch. III, § 1), whereas the surface energy $w$ and consequently the surface tension $\sigma$ is of the order of the product $Q\delta$ (see below). Hence it is seen that in the limiting case of the shortest waves with a length $\lambda$ of the order of $\delta$, the frequency $\nu$ given by (4) becomes practically identical with that given by Rayleigh's formula.

A certain difficulty arises in connexion with the transition region $\nu \sim 1/\tau$ where neither formula is strictly applicable. The course of $\nu$ as a function of $k = 1/\lambda$ in this region can be determined approximately by interpolation as shown by the dotted line in Fig. 38.

It should be noticed that the complication arising in connexion with the existence of a transition region from capillary to Rayleigh waves does not alter in the least the distribution of the modes of vibration with respect to the wave numbers or wave-lengths, the shortest value of the latter remaining, as before, $\sqrt{(\pi/n')} = \sqrt{\pi}\delta$ according to (4 a). As to the wave-length corresponding to the transition region (or more exactly to its middle part), it can be defined approximately as a certain mean value, lying between $\{\tau\sqrt{(\sigma/\rho)}\}^{\frac{2}{3}}$ and $0{\cdot}9\tau\sqrt{(G/\rho)}$. Putting $\tau = 10^{-11}, \rho = 1,$

$\sigma = 100$, $G = 10^{11}$ dyne/cm.$^2$ (which roughly corresponds to the case of ordinary liquids at room temperatures) we find $\lambda_c = 2\times10^{-6}$ cm. in the former case and $10^{-6}$ cm. in the latter. We thus see that even in this case the major part of the vibration spectrum, as judged by the *number* of modes of vibration contained in the whole range between 0

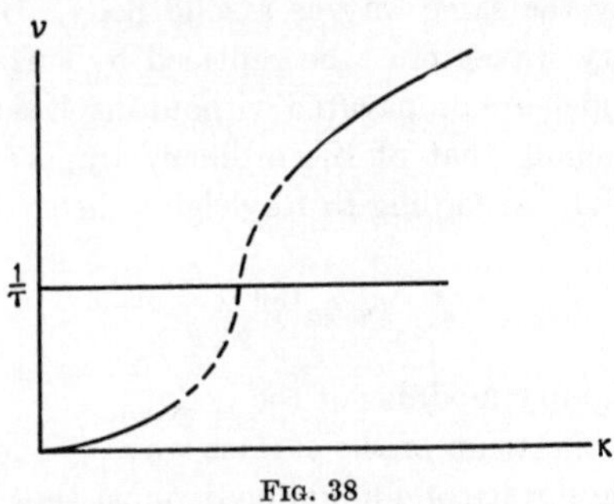


FIG. 38

and $k_{\max}$, belongs to the Rayleigh region. It is therefore more correct to define the average frequency $\overline{\nu'}$ in (5 a) as the average frequency of Rayleigh's spectrum, and not as that of the capillary waves. It should be mentioned that under such conditions the quantity $\bar{\nu}/\overline{\nu'}$ must approximately be equal to the ratio of $\frac{1}{3}\sqrt{(E/\rho)}+\frac{2}{3}\sqrt{(G/\rho)}$ to $0{\cdot}9\sqrt{(G/\rho)}$, i.e. to $\{\sqrt{(E/G)}+2\}/2{\cdot}7$, which for $E/G \approx 3$ gives 1·4 and corresponds to a theoretical value of the Eötvös constant $\gamma$, which is a little smaller than the empirical one (for non-metallic liquids; in the case of molten metals the new value of $\gamma$ is in better agreement with the experimental data than the old one).

It has been assumed hitherto that the presence of a free surface does not influence the character of the volume vibrations of a solid or liquid body, apart from replacing a certain part of these vibrations by vibrations corresponding to surface waves. A closer investigation shows, however, that this conception is incorrect. If account is taken of the boundary condition which must be satisfied on the free surface of an elastic solid body (absence of normal and tangential stresses), it becomes clear that longitudinal (or 'potential') waves cannot exist alone. The same applies to transverse (or 'solenoidal') ones. In fact, the reflection of a potential wave from the free surface of an elastic body gives rise to a potential and a solenoidal wave, and the reflection of a solenoidal wave gives rise to a solenoidal and a potential one. The two reflected waves have the same frequency (equal to that of the incident wave) but *different lengths*, which are proportional to their respective propagation velocities.

Hence it follows that each normal (or 'free') vibration of a *limited* solid body must be described by a certain *combination* of longitudinal and transverse waves.

In the simplest case of a semi-infinite body, limited by a plane surface, this combination, satisfying the condition of vanishing normal and tangential stress at the free surface, can be reduced to a system of four progressive waves, two of which (a longitudinal $L_1$ and a transverse $T_1$) may be treated as incident, and the other two ($L_2$ and $T_2$) as reflected. The waves formed by the superposition of $L_1$ and $L_2$ or $T_1$ and $T_2$ can be dealt with as progressive in a direction parallel to the surface of the body (provided it is supposed to be unbounded in this direction) and as standing in a direction perpendicular to it. Besides such combined longitudinal-transverse, progressive-standing waves, the presence of the free surface leads to the existence of Rayleigh surface waves which are travelling in a tangential direction and are exponentially damped in the normal direction. Each Rayleigh wave can be regarded as a superposition of two waves, a potential wave connected with density variations exactly as an ordinary longitudinal wave, and a solenoidal one connected with torsions or shears as an ordinary transverse wave. Each of these two waves corresponds to a pair of longitudinal or of transverse waves of the volume type in the same way as the wave formed in the case of total reflection corresponds to a combination of an incident and a reflected wave.

The meaning of the preceding considerations for the statistical theory of solid and liquid bodies, and especially for the theory of their surface tension, consists in the fact that they lead to an important modification of the frequency spectrum of the free vibrations which constitute the heat motion in such bodies. Whereas, according to the simple theory which has been discussed above, this spectrum consists of three independent spectra referring, respectively, to longitudinal (potential), transverse (solenoidal), and surface (Rayleigh) waves with different maximum frequencies and (approximately) identical minimum lengths (of the order of $2a$, where $a$ is the interatomic distance), according to the new conception this spectrum must be regarded as corresponding to a single system of combined density-shear vibrations with a common maximum frequency, each value of the frequency being associated with waves of two or even three kinds: a volume wave formed by the superposition of two incident and two reflected potential and solenoidal waves, a surface wave of the Rayleigh type exponentially decaying with increase of depth, and a volume-surface wave formed by the superposition of a volume solenoidal wave (incident+reflected) with a surface potential wave.

The question as to the minimum length of the waves becomes here meaningless (even in the case of purely volume waves); as for the maximum vibration frequency, it is determined in the usual way by the condition that the total number of free vibrations of the volume, surface, and volume-surface type should be identical with the number of degrees of freedom of the body, i.e. with $3N$ in the case of a simple body consisting of $N$ atoms.

A rather complicated analysis which will not be reproduced here† shows that in the case of a body having the shape of a plate, or film, of a finite thickness and practically unbounded in the lateral directions, the number of normal vibration modes with a frequency not exceeding a given value $\nu$ is given by the formula

$$Z_\nu = \frac{4\pi}{3}V\left(\frac{2}{v_t^3}+\frac{1}{v_l^3}\right)\nu^3+\frac{\pi A}{v_s^2}\nu^2, \tag{6}$$

where $v_l$, $v_t$, and $v_s$ denote the velocities of propagation of longitudinal, transverse, and surface (Rayleigh) waves respectively:

$$v_l = \sqrt{(E/\rho)}, \qquad v_t = \sqrt{(G/\rho)}, \qquad v_s = 0{\cdot}9\sqrt{(G/\rho)}.$$

Here $E$ denotes Young's modulus, $G$ the shearing modulus, $V$ the volume, and $A$ the area of the plate (film).

Equating the expression (6) to $3N$ we obtain the maximum value of the frequency $\nu = \nu_{\max}$. In view of the smallness of the second (surface) term in (6) in comparison with the first one, this value can be determined by the following approximate formula:

$$\nu_{\max} = \left(\frac{9N}{4\pi Vf}\right)^{\frac{1}{3}}-\frac{f_1 A}{4fV}, \tag{6 a}$$

where
$$f = \frac{2}{v_t^3}+\frac{1}{v_l^3} \quad\text{and}\quad f_1 = \frac{1}{v_s^2}.$$

Hence it is clear that the presence of a free surface leads to a decrease of the maximum vibration frequency and consequently of its mean value $\overline{\nu'}$.

In order to determine the thermal part of the free energy of the body $\psi$ we must calculate the mean value of the frequency of all its normal vibrations according to the formula

$$\log\overline{\nu'} = \frac{1}{3N}\int\limits_0^{\nu_{\max}} \log\nu\frac{dZ_\nu}{d\nu}\,d\nu.$$

† See J. Frenkel and A. Gubanov, *Journ. of Phys. U.R.S.S.*, 1945 (in the press).

Using the expression (6) and (6a) for $Z_\nu$ and $\nu_{max}$, we get

$$\log \bar{\nu} = \frac{1}{3}\left(\log \frac{9N}{4\pi V f} - 1\right) - \frac{f_1 A}{4(Vf)^{\frac{2}{3}}}\left(\frac{3\pi}{2N}\right)^{\frac{1}{3}},$$

whence it follows

$$\Psi = VnkT \log \frac{9n}{4\pi e f kT} - \tfrac{3}{4}An^{\frac{2}{3}}kT \frac{(3\pi/2)^{\frac{1}{3}}}{\xi[2+(G/E)^{\frac{3}{2}}]^{\frac{2}{3}}}.$$

Here $n$ denotes the number of atoms per unit volume $N/V$ and $\xi = (v_s/v_l)^2$ a numerical constant lying close to 0·8.

The second term of the right-hand side represents the correction corresponding to the presence of the free surface of the body. Dividing it by $A$, i.e. referring it to unit area, and adding to the surface energy $w$, we obtain $\sigma = w - \gamma T = \gamma(T_0 - T)$, with the following expression for the coefficient $\gamma$:

$$\gamma = \frac{3}{4}\left(\frac{3\pi}{2}\right)^{\frac{1}{3}} \frac{kn'}{\xi[2+(G/E)^{\frac{3}{2}}]^{\frac{2}{3}}},$$

where $n' = n^{\frac{2}{3}}$ is the number of surface atoms per unit area.

This expression for $\gamma$ is but slightly different from that which has been found above and which can be written down in the form

$$\gamma = kn' \frac{\log\{2+\sqrt{(E/G)}\}}{2 \cdot 7}.$$

The new expression agrees more with the experimental data than the old one. As A. Gubanov has shown, the agreement is further improved if account is taken of the decrease of the surface energy $w$ with a rise of the temperature (due to the thermal expansion of the body).

In conclusion a few words must be added about the theory of the surface tension of liquid bodies which has been worked out by van der Waals and his school on the basis of the analogy between the liquid and the *gaseous* state. This theory assumes that the boundary between the liquid and the gaseous phase is vague, corresponding to a continuous decrease of the density from the value $\rho$, characteristic of the liquid to the value $\rho_2$ specifying the saturated vapour. This assumption is known at the present time to be incorrect, except, perhaps, in the vicinity of the critical temperature.†

On this assumption the pressure in the transition layer must be anisotropic, i.e. must have different values in the normal direction ($x$) and in the tangential ones ($y$ or $z$). The difference between these two

† And also with the exception of metallic bodies, for which it remains valid even at $T = 0$, for the gas formed by the free electrons.

pressures $P_{xx}-P_{yy}$ ($P_{yy} = P_{zz}$) can be defined as the 'differential surface tension' in the transition layer, referred to unit thickness. The total value of the surface tension is equal to the integral

$$\sigma = \int_{-\infty}^{+\infty} (P_{xx}-P_{yy})\, dx.$$

We shall give later (§ 7) an interesting example of the application of this formula to the theory of electrocapillary phenomena.

In the case when the density of the liquid (or solid) body is decreased in a discontinuous way as we pass to the gaseous phase, the preceding formula is inapplicable.

## 2. Monomolecular Adsorbed Layers

Substances dissolved in a liquid and tending to concentrate near its surface or to become 'adsorbed' by the latter are known to lower its surface tension. This refers in particular to 'surface active' substances which are practically insoluble in the volume of the liquid but are strongly adsorbed on its surface. To this class belong, in the case of water, various fatty acids, in the case of mercury, alkali metals, etc. If the surface concentration of the adsorbed particles, i.e. their number $n$ per unit area, is small compared with the maximum value, corresponding to a compact monomolecular layer, so that the adsorbed particles form a kind of two-dimensional gas, the resulting decrease of the surface tension is equivalent to a 'plane pressure', determined by the formula

$$p = nkT \tag{7}$$

similar to Clapeyron's formula for an ordinary three-dimensional gas.

This formula can be derived in the simplest way as follows.

Let us imagine that the surface particles are acted upon by external forces directed parallel to the surface along the $x$-axis, with a potential energy $U$ which is a certain function of $x$. Under such conditions the distribution of the adsorbed particles will not be uniform; their concentration will be increased in those portions of the surface where the energy $U$ is small at the cost of other portions where it is large. The dependence of the surface concentration $n$ on $x$ is given by Boltzmann's formula $n = ce^{-U/kT}$. Differentiating this equation with respect to $x$ we get

$$\frac{d(nkT)}{dx} = -n\frac{dU}{dx} = -nF_x,$$

where $F_x$ is the force acting on an adsorbed particle in the $x$ direction.

This equation can thus be interpreted as expressing the condition of the balance between the external force acting on the adsorbed particles per unit area and the internal force reducing to the (negative) gradient of a 'pressure' $p$, determined by formula (7). This pressure must be revealed by a decrease of surface tension according to the formula

$$\sigma = \sigma_0 - p = \sigma_0 - nkT, \tag{7 a}$$

where $\sigma_0$ is the value of $\sigma$ for $n = 0$.

It is interesting to note that in the case of a pure liquid or of a compact monomolecular layer of the adsorbed substance the surface tension $\sigma = \sigma_0$ is obtained by subtracting from the surface energy $w$ the quantity $n'kT \log kT/h\bar{\nu}$, approximately equal to the two-dimensional pressure, which would be produced by the surface molecules if they behaved as an ideal two-dimensional gas.

The entropy of a three-dimensional ideal gas is given as a function of its temperature and volume $V$ by the well-known expression

$$S = c_V \log T + kN \log V + \text{const.}$$

A similar expression, viz.

$$\Delta S = c_A \log T + kN \log A + \text{const.},$$

may be used for the additional entropy of the liquid surface when it is covered by a two-dimensional ideal gas consisting of a fixed number $N$ of adsorbed particles distributed over the variable area $A$ of the surface of the adsorbent; $c_0$ is the specific heat of this gas at constant area.

It is clear that by adding the specific entropy of such a gas per unit area $s' = S'/A$ to the specific entropy $s$ of the pure liquid and introducing the corresponding correction $w'$ for the surface energy $w$ in the formula (1) we shall obtain an entirely wrong value for the change of surface tension due to the adsorbed particles. This is explained by the fact that the identification of the surface tension with the free energy of the surface per unit area $\Psi/A = \psi$ is possible only when $\psi = w - Ts$ is independent of $A$. This condition holding for pure liquids does not apply to the case of the presence of adsorbed films. In this case the surface tension is connected with the free energy by the general relation

$$\sigma = \frac{\partial \Psi}{\partial A}, \tag{8}$$

which is quite similar to the formula $p = -\partial\Psi/\partial V$ for the pressure of a three-dimensional body, and which directly follows from the fact that $\sigma\, dA$ is the work done against the inner (capillary) forces when the area of the surface is increased by the amount $dA$ at a constant temperature.

Inasmuch as the presence of the adsorbed layer affects the surface energy $W$ in a way independent of the area of the surface (being, in the case under consideration, simply proportional to $N$), the resulting change of the surface tension is given, according to (8), by the formula $\Delta\sigma = \partial\Delta\psi/\partial A$, where $\Delta\psi$ is the corresponding change of the free energy. Since only that part of $\Delta\psi$ which depends on $A$ must be retained, we can put

$$\Delta\psi = -T\Delta S, \tag{8 a}$$

or, according to (7),

$$\Delta\psi = -kNT\log A. \tag{8 b}$$

We thus get

$$\Delta\sigma = -\frac{kNT}{A} = -knT,$$

in agreement with the conception of the pressure of the two-dimensional gas introduced above.

The possibility of treating a diluted adsorbed layer as an ideal two-dimensional gas is supported by the following interesting consideration.† If the surface of the liquid is spherical, convex or concave, with a radius $R$, the surface tension is known to produce a capillary pressure $2\sigma/R$ which is positive in the former case and negative in the latter. Putting here $\sigma = \sigma_0 - nkT$, we see that each adsorbed particle changes this capillary pressure by an amount

$$\frac{2kT}{R} = \frac{m\overline{v^2}}{R},$$

where $\overline{v^2}$ is the mean square of the velocity of its thermal motion parallel to the surface. Now this quantity is nothing but the centrifugal force produced by the particle when it is moving with its average thermal velocity on the spherical surface of the liquid meniscus.

A closer examination shows that a diluted adsorbed layer must be treated not as an ideal gas but rather as a diluted two-dimensional *solution*. The lowering of the surface tension, produced by it, is from this point of view a measure of its two-dimensional *osmotic pressure*, the equation (7) representing an analogue of van 't Hoff's law for ordinary diluted solutions.

The conception of an adsorbed layer as a two-dimensional solution follows immediately from the fact that the adsorbed particles, being attached to the molecules of the adsorbent, cannot move along the surface quite freely as in a gas; their thermal motion must rather be similar to the motion of particles dissolved in an ordinary three-dimensional liquid.

† Due to J. B. Chariton (unpublished).

This circumstance does not affect the validity of the preceding expressions $2kT/R$ for the average value of the capillary pressure produced by an adsorbed particle, since its centrifugal force, equal to this pressure, is not altered if, instead of sliding freely along the surface of the liquid, it performs a more complicated motion of an oscillatory type with the same average value of $\overline{mv^2}$. This shows that this complication does not invalidate the expression for the two-dimensional pressure given above, and determined according to (7 a) by the lowering of the surface tension.

This lowering can be studied experimentally by measuring the tangential force acting on a movable barrier, separating the surface of the pure liquid (with a tension $\sigma_0$) from the contaminated one, i.e. from that part of the surface of the liquid which contains the adsorbed particles. This force is directed from the contaminated to the pure part and is equal, per unit length of the barrier, to the difference $\sigma_0 - \sigma$.

So long as the adsorbed particles are firmly bound to the surface of the liquid, i.e. cannot penetrate inside the latter, the barrier, referred to above, is wholly impermeable with respect to them.

It has, on the other hand, no influence whatever on the molecules of the adsorbent, which can easily pass to and fro underneath it. The surface barrier used for the detection of the difference between the surface tensions of the pure and the contaminated part of the free surface of a liquid body is thus seen to play with respect to the 'surface solution', forming this contamination, the same role as a semi-permeable membrane in the detection of the ordinary three-dimensional osmotic pressure.

Coming back to the equation

$$kT\frac{dn}{dx} = nF_x,$$

with the help of which the notion and value of the surface osmotic pressure, as a statical inner force, has been introduced, we can give it an essentially different—kinetic—interpretation, connected with the phenomenon of *surface diffusion*.

Under the action of an external force $F_x$ an adsorbed particle 'swimming', as it were, on the surface of the liquid, just as a dissolved particle immersed in the latter, must move preferentially in the direction of this force with an average velocity proportional to it, i.e.

$$\overline{v_x} = qF_x,$$

where $q$ is the 'mobility' or, more exactly, the surface mobility of the particle. On this orderly 'drift' motion an irregular thermal agitation, or diffusion motion, must be superimposed, which in the presence of a concentration gradient in the direction of the $x$-axis must give rise to a diffusion current $-D\,\partial n/\partial x$ per unit length of a line perpendicular to $x$, where $D$ is the surface diffusion coefficient. In a state of statistical equilibrium this surface diffusion current must be balanced by the two-dimensional drift current due to the action of the external forces and equal to $n\overline{v_x} = nqF_x$.

Multiplying equation (7) by $q$, we see that it can be considered as the condition expressing the existence of such a kinetic balance, if the surface diffusion coefficient is connected with the surface mobility by Einstein's relation

$$D = qkT,$$

just as in the three-dimensional case.

It should be noted that in the absence of statistical equilibrium the concentration of the adsorbed particles must vary with the time according to the two-dimensional equation

$$\frac{\partial n}{\partial T} = D\nabla^2 n - \mathrm{div}(qn\mathbf{F}),$$

where $\nabla^2 n = \partial^2 n/\partial x^2 + \partial^2 n/\partial y^2$ and $\mathrm{div}(qn\mathbf{F}) = \partial(qnF_x)/\partial x + \partial(qnF_y)/\partial y$.

Extending to the two-dimensional diffusion motion the results referring to the three-dimensional case, we can put

$$D = \frac{\delta^2}{4\tau} = \frac{\delta^2}{4\tau_0} e^{-U/kT},$$

where $\delta$, $\tau_0$, $\tau$, and $U$ have their usual meaning; the parameters $\delta$ and $\tau_0$ must, moreover, have in both cases the same order of magnitude ($10^{-8}$ cm., $10^{-13}$ sec.), while the activation energy $U$ and, consequently, the 'mean life' $\tau$ must be somewhat smaller for adsorbed particles than for dissolved ones.

The existence of surface diffusion has been experimentally discovered and studied by a number of authors (especially by Volmer and by Langmuir), who have shown that the adsorbed particles—atoms and molecules—can 'creep' rather rapidly over the surface both of liquid and of solid adsorbents. In the latter case the concentration of the adsorbed particles cannot, of course, be determined from a measurement of the surface tension; it can, however, be measured in the case of electrically conducting bodies by the surface drop of potential which, as will be shown below, is strongly affected by the presence of adsorbed particles.

The decrease of the surface tension of different liquids by the absorption of surface-active substances can be reduced to a 'plane' osmotic pressure, produced by their particles, only in the case of *small* concentrations, considered above. In this case the adsorbed substance practically alters the surface *entropy* alone, increasing it and thereby lowering the surface tension by an amount proportional to the absolute temperature.

The lowering of the surface tension of various liquids under the influence of adsorbed layers can be reduced to the two-dimensional osmotic pressure produced by them in the case of dilute surface layers only. In this case the change of the surface tension depends on the variation of the surface entropy alone, being, as a result, proportional to the absolute temperature. In the general case both the additional entropy $\Delta S$ and the additional energy $\Delta W$ due to the presence of the surface layer, constituted by a given number of particles $N$, depend on the area $A$ occupied by them, so that the change of the surface tension is expressed in a more complicated way. The surface pressure $p$, defined as the difference $\sigma_0 - \sigma$, loses in this case its simple kinetic meaning and assumes the character of a static force, due to a mutual repulsion of the adsorbed molecules or, more exactly, to the difference between their mutual attraction and the stronger mutual attraction between them and the molecules of the adsorbent. Thus, for example, the surface tension of water covered by a compact monomolecular layer of a fatty acid $CH_3(CH_2)COOH$ lies close to the surface tension of paraffin, as would be expected if it is taken into account that the adsorbed molecules stand upright on the surface with their inactive methyl tails pointing upwards, while their active carboxyl ends are anchored in water. The smallness of the surface tension of water covered with such a film is thus explained by the relatively small cohesion between the methyl radicals.

Whereas diluted adsorbed layers behave as two-dimensional gases, condensed monomolecular layers can be treated as two-dimensional analogues of liquids and even to some extent, of solid bodies. This analogy refers to a number of various properties of such layers, and, in the first place, to the similarity of their equation of state, connecting the surface pressure $p = \sigma_0 - \sigma$ with the concentration $n$ and temperature $T$, to van der Waals's equation. We shall not examine this relation more closely here and shall only mention that small variations of $n$ and $p$ can be connected by a linear equation

$$-\Delta p = \Delta\sigma = K\frac{\Delta A}{A},$$

where $K$ plays the role of a two-dimensional compressibility modulus.

It is possible, furthermore, to ascribe to a condensed monomolecular layer a certain 'rigidity', specified by a two-dimensional shearing modulus $G$, which can be masked by their fluidity $1/\eta$, just as in the case of three-dimensional amorphous bodies.

The surface viscosity coefficient $\eta$ has been determined by several authors by measuring the rate of flow of a monomolecular 'liquid' film through a capillary slit on the surface of the adsorbent, and applying to this flow the two-dimensional analogue of Poiseuille's law. This theory, which leaves out of account the interaction of the adsorbed molecules with the surface of the adsorbent, or describes it as an analogue of solid friction, leads to enormous values of the surface viscosity $\eta$ which cannot be reconciled with its value for the corresponding substances in the three-dimensional liquid state.

V. Levich† has recently shown that the surface viscosity of the adsorbed layer is wholly irrelevant to the phenomena under consideration, which can be satisfactorily explained by the ordinary hydrodynamical theory of the viscous flow of a three-dimensional liquid, constituting the adsorbent, under the condition of the absence of slipping of the adsorbed layer with respect to its surface (as well as with respect to the solid walls of the capillary slit). Monomolecular oil films on the surface of the water are well known to produce a strong damping of its wave motion. It has been suggested by Rayleigh and by Lamb that this influence is an indirect one and consists in the alteration of the boundary conditions for the free surface of water. This idea has been quantitatively developed by V. Levich, who has shown that, besides altering the capillary pressure $\sigma(1/R_1+1/R_2)$, as a result of the lowering of $\sigma$, the adsorbed film gives rise to a tangential force due to its surface elasticity (compressibility), and equal per unit area to $-K(\Delta n/n)$.

In the absence of such a film the wave motion of water can preserve an irrotational character, the tangential components of the viscous stress tensor $P_{xz} = \mu(\partial v_x/\partial z+\partial v_z/\partial x)$ and $P_{yz} = \mu(\partial v_y/\partial z+\partial v_z/\partial y)$ (where $\mu$ is the volume viscosity of water) vanishing at its surface $z = 0$. If, however, the latter is covered by an elastic oil film, the boundary conditions are expressed by the equations

$$P_{xz} = -\frac{K}{n}\frac{\partial n}{\partial x}, \qquad P_{yz} = -\frac{K}{n}\frac{\partial n}{\partial y},$$

which are inconsistent with the irrotational character of the wave

† V. Levich, *On the Theory of Surface Phenomena* (Russian), 1941.

motion. The resulting vorticity, without altering the character of the waves, leads, owing to the viscosity of the liquid, to their damping, which is thus seen to be wholly independent of the surface viscosity of the oil film itself.

Of special interest from the molecular kinetic point of view are the phenomena of transition of an adsorbed monomolecular layer from a diluted (gas-like) state into a condensed (liquid or solid-like) one under an isothermic compression of the layer or as a result of lowering the temperature of the whole system. In both cases the gas-like film reaches, for a certain value of the surface tension $\sigma$, depending on the temperature, a state of saturation and begins to condense, in exactly the same way as a saturated three-dimensional vapour. The condensation point, or rather curve $\sigma(T)$, is determined by the equation

$$-\frac{d\sigma}{dT} = \frac{r}{T(A'-A'')},$$

which is the analogue of the Clausius–Clapeyron equation for the three-dimensional case, $-\sigma$ playing the role of the pressure; $r$ is the latent heat of condensation, and $A'$ and $A''$ the area occupied by a given number of adsorbed molecules $N$ in the gas-like and the condensed state.

Putting $\sigma = \sigma_0 - nkT$ and $A' = N/n' \gg A''$, we get

$$kT^2\frac{dn'}{dT} = \frac{rn'}{N},$$

that is, $$n' = \text{const.}\, e^{-U/kT},$$

where $U = r/N$ is the 'surface evaporation heat' referred to one molecule. The constant can be identified approximately with the concentration $n''$ of the adsorbed molecules in the condensed state. This result can of course be obtained without the use of the Clausius–Clapeyron equation as a direct corollary of Boltzmann's principle.

The analogy between condensed adsorbed layers and three-dimensional condensed bodies is limited by the fact that these layers are not 'free' but are deposited on the surface of a liquid or solid adsorbent. It is therefore not surprising that by further compressing or cooling a liquid-like layer, it is impossible to bring it into a crystal-like state. Such overcompressed or overcooled layers behave as two-dimensional analogues of solid amorphous bodies, or in some cases of liquid crystals. The latter refers in particular to rod-shaped molecules, such as the molecules of long-chain fatty acids, alcohols, and paraffins, which according to Langmuir are orientated, in the highly condensed state of the adsorbed layer, in a direction perpendicular to the surface of the adsorbent, without, however, long-distance order in the distribution of their centres of gravity. The surface rigidity of such layers is usually masked by the smallness of their surface viscosity.

### 3. Polymolecular Films; Thermodynamical Theory

We have limited ourselves thus far to a consideration of monomolecular adsorbed layers. In the case of immiscible liquids one of them can be covered by a thick polymolecular layer of the other (usually lighter) liquid. The boundary surface between the two liquids (1, 2) is characterized by a certain tension $\sigma_{1,2}$, which, in the absence of contaminations (in the form of monomolecular layers with a variable concentration, depending on the area), can be identified with the free energy $w_{1,2}-Ts_{1,2}$ per unit area, $w_{1,2}$ and $s_{1,2}$ denoting the corresponding specific energy and entropy. The energy $w_{1,2}$ is practically independent of the temperature, being determined by the interaction forces between the particles of the two liquids, while the entropy term $-Ts_{1,2}$ depends on the thermal motion of the boundary surface, represented by a superposition of surface—capillary and Rayleigh—waves.

Let us imagine a liquid or a solid body (1) with a practically infinite (plane) surface, covered over an area $A$ by a thin uniform film of a second liquid (2) consisting of a given number of molecules $N$. The thickness of this film $h$ can be supposed to be inversely proportional to $A$, the product $Ah$ being equal to the volume $V_2$ of (2).

If $h$ is large enough, the change of the free energy of the system (1, 2) due to the presence of the film can be represented by the formula

$$F = [(\sigma_{2,0}-\sigma_{1,0})+\sigma_{1,2}]A,$$

where $\sigma_{i,0}$ is the surface tension of the $i$th liquid against air.

If $A$ is increased by the amount $dA$, the quantity of the liquid (2) forming the film remaining constant, the free energy is increased by $\sigma_0\,dA$, where

$$\sigma_0 = \sigma_{2,0}-\sigma_{1,0}+\sigma_{1,2}.$$

We thus see that, so long as this quantity is independent of the thickness $h$, it plays the role of the surface tension of the film.

When the latter is spread over a sufficiently large area, the film becoming very thin, its free energy is no longer proportional to $A$ but depends on it in a more complicated way. Under such conditions the surface tension of the film is determined by the formula

$$\sigma = \frac{\partial F}{\partial A}.$$

This quantity, which is a certain function of the thickness of the film $h$, must not be confused with the ratio $f = F/A$, that is, with the free energy of the film per unit area, which is connected with $\sigma$ by the relation

$$\sigma = f + A\frac{\partial f}{\partial A}.$$

Replacing here $A$ by $V/h$, where $V$ is the constant volume of the film, we get

$$\sigma = f - h\frac{\partial f}{\partial h}. \tag{9}$$

It is sometimes convenient to consider, instead of the free energy, the thermodynamical potential $\phi$, which in the case under consideration is connected with it by the formula

$$\phi = F - A\sigma,$$

whence it follows that $$A = -\frac{\partial \phi}{\partial \sigma}.$$

If $\sigma = \partial F/\partial A$ is negative for all values of $A$, the film, in the absence of external forces, must tend to spread over the whole surface of 1, until it becomes monomolecular, and then it can be split up into two phases—the condensed and the gas-like one—in a ratio depending on the available area. If, on the contrary, $\sigma$ is positive for all values of $A$, the film must tend to contract into a single drop, forced to remain in contact with 1 over a certain minimum area $A_0$ by the influence of gravity.

The behaviour of the film is characterized, however, not only by the sign of $\sigma$, but also by that of its derivative with respect to $A$, i.e. $\partial\sigma/\partial A = \partial^2 F/\partial A^2$, which determines its *compressibility* under the influence of external forces. In the case of a three-dimensional liquid the condition of dynamical stability requires that the pressure should decrease with increase of the volume, which corresponds to a positive value of the compressibility modulus $K = -V(\partial p/\partial V)$. In the case of a two-dimensional film the analogous stability condition requires that the surface tension (which corresponds to a negative pressure) should *increase* with increase of the area, i.e. that $\partial\sigma/\partial A > 0$. The physical meaning of this condition can be seen from a consideration of the equilibrium of the film under the influence of an external force, which we shall describe as a tension of a constant magnitude $\alpha$ (applied to its perimeter). In a state of equilibrium this tension must be balanced by the inner tension $\sigma$. Now when $A$ is increased or decreased by $dA$, the film will tend to return to the initial state (size) if in the former case $\sigma$

becomes larger than $\alpha$, and in the latter if it becomes smaller, which means that $\partial\sigma/\partial A > 0$. The same result can be obtained from a consideration of the free energy of the film. In the presence of the constant external tension its inner free energy $F$ must be decreased by the quantity $-\alpha A$. The condition that in a state of equilibrium $F-\alpha A = \phi$ would have a *minimum* value gives $\frac{\partial}{\partial A}(F-\alpha A) = 0$, i.e. $\frac{\partial F}{\partial A} = \sigma = \alpha$ and $\frac{\partial^2(F-\alpha A)}{\partial A^2} > 0$, i.e. $\frac{\partial \sigma}{\partial A} > 0$. Replacing $A$ by $v/h$ and using the expression (9) for $\sigma$, we get

$$\frac{\partial \sigma}{\partial h} = -h\frac{\partial^2 f}{\partial h^2}.$$

The condition of dynamical stability of a film $\partial\sigma/\partial h < 0$ is thus reduced to

$$\frac{\partial^2 f}{\partial h^2} > 0, \tag{9 a}$$

which means that the curve representing the dependence of $f$ on $h$ must be convex with respect to the $h$-axis.

We thus see that irrespective of the sign of the surface tension $\sigma$ (i.e. of the tendency of the film to expand or to contract) it must increase monotonically with increase of the area $A$ (i.e. decrease of the thickness) so long as the film is capable of remaining in a state of *stable* equilibrium under the influence of external forces.

If this condition is realized for all values of $A$ (i.e. of $h$), then three cases must be distinguished:

(1) $\sigma > 0$ *for all values of* $h$. The film tends to contract into a drop of the smallest possible size, limited by the influence of gravity. The film can be said to be 'non-wetting'.

(2) $\sigma < 0$ *for all values of* $h$. The film tends to spread over the whole available area. In this case the liquid (2) is said to 'completely wet' the surface of (1).

(3) $\sigma < 0$ *for* $h > h_0$ *and* $> 0$ *for* $h < h_0$. In this case the liquid film, in the absence of external forces, assumes an equilibrium thickness for which $\sigma = 0$.

If within a certain range of $h$-values $\partial\sigma/\partial A < 0$ (i.e. $\partial\sigma/\partial h > 0$), a stable film can exist only outside this range. More than that, from the *thermodynamical* point of view, the range of instability will stretch on both sides beyond the corresponding limits, just as in the case of the van der Waals theory of an amorphous 'gas-liquid' body.

The fact that there can exist a close analogy between the isotherms

$p(V)$ of such a body and the isotherms $-\sigma(A)$ of a liquid film has been recently pointed out by Frumkin.† This analogy cannot be complete in the region of small values of $A$, for $\sigma$ tends with decrease of $A$, i.e. increase of $h$, to a constant finite value $\sigma_0 = \sigma_{2,0} - \sigma_{1,0} + \sigma_{1,2}$, whereas $-p$ tends to $-\infty$ for $V \to 0$. If $\sigma$ is assumed to be negative for all values of $h$ (case of wetting), its dependence on $A$ can be represented by one of the following curves (Fig. 39):

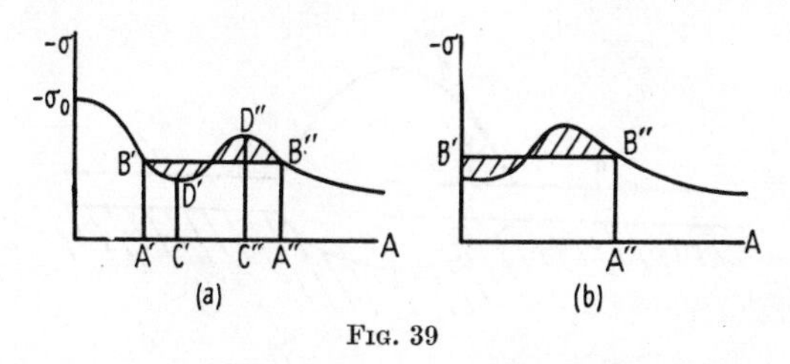


FIG. 39

The curve 39*a* is an exact replica of a van der Waals isotherm with the only difference that $-\sigma(0) = -\sigma_0$ is finite. By the application of a two-dimensional external pressure to a thin film initially spread over a sufficiently large area the latter will gradually diminish until a certain point $A''$ corresponding to a certain thickness $h'' = V_2/A''$ is reached when a second 'phase' in the form of a film of a much greater thickness $h' = V_2/A'$ will appear, the decrease of $A$ from $A''$ to $A'$ being accompanied by the growth of the thick film at the cost of the thin one until the latter is wholly exhausted; a further decrease of $A$ will cause a gradual thickening of the resulting homogeneous film.

This process is an exact analogue of the process of the condensation of a vapour into a liquid; the horizontal line $B'B''$ corresponding to the equilibrium between the thinner and the thicker film, just as the analogous horizontal line in the isotherms of the van der Waals theory must bisect the theoretical isotherm in such a way as to cut its wave-like portion into two equal halves (shaded areas on Fig. 39*a*). Fig. 39*b* differs from the preceding one only in that the lower limit of stability $A'$ practically vanishes.

The values of the potential $\phi$ of the film in the points $A'$ and $A''$ are easily seen to be equal, which is the thermodynamic criterion of the possibility of the coexistence of the corresponding two phases in equilibrium with each other. It should be emphasized that the states lying in the range $A'C''$ on the one side and in the range $C''A''$ on the other,

† A. Frumkin, *Acta Physicochimica U.R.S.S.* **9**, 313 (1938).

without being dynamically unstable (since $\partial\sigma/\partial A > 0$), are, nevertheless, unstable, or rather only relatively stable, from the thermodynamical point of view, just as an overheated liquid or a supersaturated vapour.

The preceding relations, according to Frumkin, can be used to explain the frequently observed phenomenon of the spontaneous disintegration of an originally uniform film covering a given area (if the latter lies in the range $A'A''$) into a number of small lenses (if the body 1 is liquid)

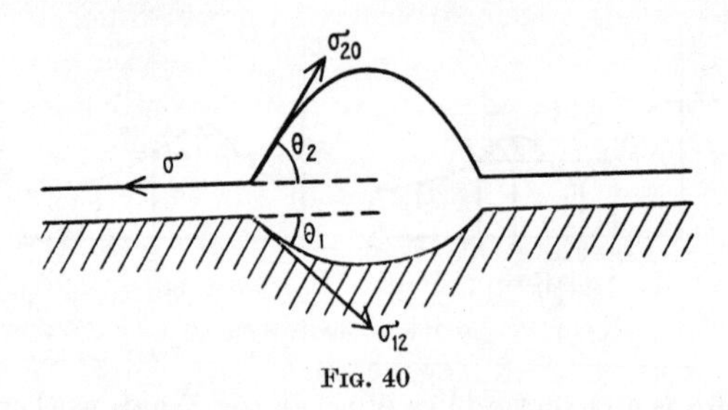


Fig. 40

or droplets (if it is solid). The latter are characterized by a definite value of the contact angle $\theta$, which is determined by Neumann's formula

$$\cos\theta = \frac{\sigma - \sigma_{1,2}}{\sigma_{2,0}}.$$

The quantity $\sigma$ in this formula is erroneously identified by many authors with the surface tension of the body 1 against air ($\sigma_{1,0}$), whereas in reality it is equal to the surface tension of the thin film remaining on the surface of this body, with the equilibrium thickness $h''$ corresponding to the temperature of the system.

In the case of liquid lenses on a liquid surface the preceding formula must be replaced by

$$\sigma = \sigma_{1,2}\cos\theta_1 + \sigma_{2,0}\cos\theta_2,$$

$\theta_1$ and $\theta_2$ being the angles between the surface of the film and the two tangent planes at the edges of the lens as shown in Fig. 40.†

It should be mentioned that in the case corresponding to Fig. 39 *a* the drops or lenses formed tend to have a certain equilibrium thickness $h'$, which as a rule is very small, and is therefore practically not influenced by gravity, whereas in the case corresponding to Fig. 39 *b* the

† A complete theory must take into account the additional free energy of the linear boundary of the drops or of the lenses. The existence of this linear free energy plays an essential role in the kinetics of lens formation in an 'over-pressed' film—just as does the existence of the surface free energy of liquid droplets in the condensation of a supersaturated vapour.

size and, in particular, the thickness of the drops is limited by the influence of gravity alone.

The phenomenon of drop (or lens) formation just described can take place not only in the case of wetting films $\sigma < 0$, but just as well in that of non-wetting films $\sigma > 0$, which require an external tension in order to be spread over the surface of the corresponding body (under the condition of a strong adherence to the barrier limiting this surface). In fact, the preceding relations, illustrated by the Figs. 39 *a*, *b*, are not altered in their essential features by adding to $\sigma$ an arbitrary positive value of constant magnitude, i.e. by shifting the curves parallel to themselves below the $A$-axis.

It should be mentioned, further, that the shape of the isotherms $\sigma(A)$, just as the shape of the isotherms of van der Waals's theory, must depend upon the temperature. It seems natural to expect that above (or below) a certain critical temperature the surface tension becomes a monotonic increasing function of $A$, corresponding to the stability of films of any thickness.

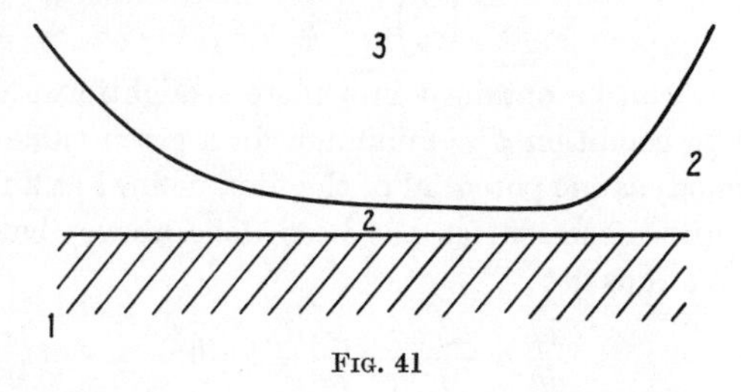


Fig. 41

We have supposed thus far that the film 2 is in contact with the free surface of the body 1, lying on the top of it as a flat drop, and being held in equilibrium by an external tension distributed over its borderline (due, for example, to its adherence to a linear solid barrier).

We shall now consider the opposite case of a thin film in contact with a thick mass of the same liquid 2. This case can be realized approximately by introducing into the liquid 2 a gas bubble and pressing it against the surface of 1. A similar result is obtained if the gas bubble is replaced by a drop of some other liquid 3, or by a solid body with a plane lower surface pressed against the surface of the body 1 in such a way as to leave a uniform layer of the liquid 2 with a constant thickness $h$ between 1 and 3.

In this case it is convenient to measure the free energy of the system shown in Fig. 41, starting from a state corresponding to a thick film.

Let us assume that the area of the film remains constant ($= A_0$) while its thickness is varied. The corresponding variation of the free energy $F = A_0 f$ is equal to $dF = A_0(\partial f/\partial h)\,dh$. If $\partial f/\partial h < 0$, the film tends to get thicker and produces accordingly a pressure $p$, *normal* to its surface, of a magnitude given by $A_0 p\,dh = -dF$, i.e.

$$p = -\frac{\partial f}{\partial h}. \tag{10}$$

Now, since in the case of a variable area $A = V/R$, $f$, the free energy per unit area, is connected with the surface tension by the formula $\sigma = f + A(\partial f/\partial A) = f - h(\partial f/\partial h)$, we have $\partial f/\partial h = (f-\sigma)/h$ and consequently

$$p = \frac{\sigma - f}{h}. \tag{10a}$$

Differentiating this equation with respect to $h$, we get

$$\frac{\partial p}{\partial h} = \frac{1}{h}\left(\frac{\partial \sigma}{\partial h} - \frac{\partial f}{\partial h}\right) - \frac{\sigma - f}{h^2} = \frac{1}{h}\frac{\partial \sigma}{\partial h} + \frac{-\sigma + f - h(\partial f/\partial h)}{h^2} = \frac{1}{h}\frac{\partial \sigma}{\partial h},$$

that is,

$$\left(\frac{\partial p}{\partial \sigma}\right)_T = \frac{1}{h}. \tag{10b}$$

This relation can be obtained in a more straightforward way from the equilibrium condition $\phi =$ minimum for a given value of $h$, where $\phi$ is the thermodynamic potential of the film, defined as a function not only of its surface tension (as has been done above) but also of its pressure $p$. We thus get

$$\frac{d\phi}{dh} = \frac{\partial \phi}{\partial \sigma}\frac{d\sigma}{dh} + \frac{\partial \phi}{\partial p}\frac{dp}{dh} = 0,$$

or since $\partial \phi/\partial \sigma = -A$ and $\partial \phi/\partial p = +V = Ah$

$$d\sigma - h\,dp = 0.$$

This equation† has a very simple physical meaning. If for a given value $h_0$ of $h$ the pressure $p$ of the film is balanced by an external pressure $p_0$, while its tension is balanced at the same time by an external tension $\sigma_0$, then for an infinitesimal variation of $h$ we must have

$$p - p_0 = \frac{\sigma - \sigma_0}{h}.$$

It should be mentioned that in the case of a gas bubble or of a drop of

† Strictly speaking, the pressure $p$ must be active not only in the normal direction but along the edges of the film—in the tangential direction also, the effective value of the surface tension being equal to the difference between $\sigma$ and $ph$, that is

$$\sigma_{\text{eff}} = \sigma - (\sigma - f) = +f,$$

so that $p = -d\sigma_{\text{eff}}/dh$.

liquid 3, the external tension $\sigma_0$ is equal to $\sigma_{1,3}+\sigma_{2,3}\cos\theta$, where $\theta$ is the contact angle. This expression can be used for measuring $\sigma$ and for checking the validity of the relation (10a).

Noting that $p = 0$ for $h \to \infty$ we see that $p$ is positive if $\sigma$ increases with a decrease of $h$, as it should, so long as the film is dynamically stable. If there exists a region of instability between $h'$ and $h'' < h'$, then in this region $p$ must decrease along with $\sigma$, and can even become negative for small values of $h$. If a gas bubble or liquid drop 3 is pressed against 1 until the film 2 underlying it reaches the upper stability limit, corresponding to a thickness $h'$, the film will spontaneously 'collapse', i.e. become in a discontinuous way much thinner; under such conditions the bubble or drop will, eventually, adhere to the surface of 1 without the help of an external pressure.

This mechanism of the adherence of gas bubbles or oil drops to the boundary surface between two liquids or between a liquid and a solid body has been proposed by A. Frumkin† as a result of an experimental investigation of the influence of an electric potential difference between the two bodies (one of them being a metal, liquid mercury for example, and the other a solution of an electrolyte) on the contact angle of the bubble or drop. By varying this potential difference $\phi$ it was possible to change the value of the surface tension $\sigma_{1,3}$ and consequently the value of the contact angle $\theta$ according to the relation $\sigma_{1,3}+\sigma_{2,3}\cos\theta = \sigma$. A direct measurement of this angle has shown that the surface tension $\sigma$, which was usually interpreted as the tension of the clean surface of the body 1 (mercury) or of the boundary surface between it and the liquid 3 (oil drop), did not remain constant, but varied with $\phi$ in a way similar to $\sigma_{1,3}$, though to a much smaller extent, displaying a normal type of electrocapillary curve (see below). Hence it could be concluded that the surface (1, 0) or (1, 3) was not actually clean but that there remained upon it a very thin layer of the electrolytic solution (2). The latter was usually invisible; in certain cases, however, its presence was manifested by the appearance of coloured interference fringes (the thickness of the film being of the order of $10^{-5}$ cm.).

The fact that the film remains in equilibrium with the gas filling the bubble implies the existence of a pressure balancing the pressure of the gas. This inference has been drawn by B. Derjaguin,‡ who generalized

† A. Frumkin, Gorodetzkaya, Kabanov, and Nekrassov, 'Kapillaelektrische Benetzung von Metallen durch Elektrolytlösungen, I', *Sow. Phys.* (1932); Frumkin and Gorodetzkaya, II, *Sow. Phys.* **5**, 419 (1934).

‡ B. Derjaguin and M. Kussakov, *Bull. Acad. Sci. U.R.S.S.*, série chimique, **5**, 1119 (1937); *Acta Physicochimica U.R.S.S.*, **10**, 25 (1939).

it to the case of a thin liquid film between two solid surfaces, and introduced in this way the important conception of a 'disjoining pressure', suffered by two solid bodies immersed in a liquid medium when they are pressed together, and exerted by the liquid layer remaining between them.† The magnitude of this disjoining pressure and its dependence on the thickness of the layer has been determined experimentally by the same author with the help of the gas-bubble method, the pressure of the gas (or more exactly the excess of its pressure with respect to the atmospheric pressure) being measured by the quantity $2\sigma_{2,0}/R$, where $R$ is the radius of the spherical portion of the bubble (its base being flattened practically to a plane parallel to the surface of 1, the underlying layer of the liquid 2 displaying a set of Newton's rings which were used to determine its thickness).

## 4. Molecular-kinetic Theory of Liquid Films

Derjaguin has shown that the phenomenon of disjoining pressure is displayed by thin films of practically all liquids in contact with any other substances in the solid, liquid, or gaseous state. It reaches a value of the order of 1 gm./cm.$^2$ for a thickness of the order of $10^{-5}$ cm., rapidly increasing with a further decrease of the thickness, as shown by the curve of Fig. 42 (taken from Derjaguin's paper). It is strongly influenced in the case of water by the presence of electrolytes dissolved in the latter. Derjaguin has shown that the presence of a diffuse electric double layer at the boundary surface between the metal and the electrolyte causes by itself a disjoining pressure, which, for small values of the electric potential difference, is proportional to the square of the latter and depends on the thickness of film in an exponential way.‡ This dependence does not contradict in any way the experimental results; the calculated magnitude of this electric pressure is found, however, to be about 1,000 times smaller for $h = 10^{-5}$ than the experimental values. It is thus clear that the pressure due to the diffuse electric double layer can represent but a small addition to the main effect; according to Frumkin§ this additional effect explains the influence of the concentration of the electrolyte and of the potential difference between it and the surface of the metallic electrode on the disjoining pressure of very thin films underlying a gas bubble, while the main part of the disjoining pressure is due to forces of non-electric

† B. Derjaguin, *Acta Physicochimica U.R.S.S.* **5**, 1 (1936); **10**, 333 (1937).

‡ B. Derjaguin, *Trans. Farad. Soc.* **56**, 204 (1940); *Acta Physicochimica, U.R.S.S.* **10**, 333 (1939); *Bull. Ac. Sci. U.R.S.S.*, série chimique, **5**, 1153 (1937).

§ Frumkin and Gorodetzkaya, *Acta Physicochimica U.R.S.S.* **9**, 327 (1938).

origin. This conclusion is supported by the fact that the phenomenon of disjoining pressure is observed just as well in the case of non-conducting liquid films not containing any ions.

It seems natural to trace the origin of the disjoining pressure to the action of ordinary cohesive forces between the molecules of the film and those of the body underlying it. A calculation of this effect yields,

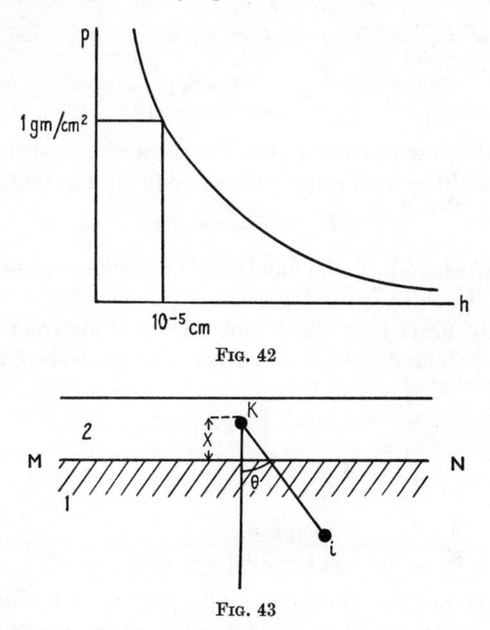


FIG. 42

FIG. 43

however, values which are likewise too small by one or two orders of magnitude.† Because of the great theoretical interest of this question we shall reproduce here the corresponding calculation. Let the mutual potential energy of the molecules of the kind $i$ and $k$ at a distance $r$ from each other be $u_{ik}(r)$. The potential energy of a body consisting of molecules $i$ and limited by a plane surface $MN$ (Fig. 43) with respect to a molecule $k$ at a distance $x$ from this surface, is equal to

$$U_{ik}(x) = \iint n_i u_{ik}(r) 2\pi r^2 \, dr \sin\theta \, d\theta,$$

where $n_i$ denotes the number of $i$ molecules per unit volume, the integration being extended over the corresponding half-space. For a given value of $r$ the angle $\theta$ between the radius vector $r_{ki}$ and the normal to

† B. Derjaguin, *Koll. Z.* **69**, 155 (1934); see also Frumkin and Gorodetzkaya.

the surface is changed from 0 to a value $\theta_2$ for which $\cos\theta_2 = x/r$. We thus get $\int\limits_0^{\theta_2} \sin\theta\, d\theta = (1-(x/r))$ and consequently

$$U_{ik}(a) = 2\pi n_i \int\limits_a^\infty u_{ik}(r) r^2 \left(1-\frac{a}{r}\right) dr.$$

In the case of a simple power law, $u_{ik} = -c_{ik}/r^m$, where $m > 3$ we find

$$U_{ik}(x) = -\frac{2\pi c_{ik} n_i}{(m-2)(m-3)} \frac{1}{x^{m-3}}.$$

A plane layer of $k$ molecules with a thickness $dx$ at a distance $x$ from the surface $MN$ has with respect to the body (1) a potential energy

$$de_{ik} = U_{ik}(x) n_k\, dx$$

per unit area, where $n_k$ is the number of molecules per unit volume of the layer.

If the body formed by the $k$ molecules extends from $x = -a$ to $x = -\infty$ its potential energy with respect to the body $k$ is equal per unit area to

$$e_{ik}(a) = \int\limits_a^\infty U_{ik}(x) n_k\, dx,$$

which in the case $u_{ik} = -c_{ik}/r^m$ reduces to

$$e_{ik} = -\frac{2\pi c_{ik} n_i n_k}{(m-2)(m-3)(m-4)} \frac{1}{a^{m-4}} \equiv -\frac{\gamma_{ik}}{a^{m-4}}.$$

The validity of this expression implies that $m > 4$. In the case of most substances the mutual potential energy of two molecules depends upon their van der Waals attraction and is inversely proportional to the sixth power of their distance. In this case ($m = 6$) $\gamma_{ik} = \frac{1}{12}\pi c_{ik} n_i n_k$. The smallest admissible value of $a$ is the distance $\delta_{ik}$ between two molecules $i$, $k$ 'in contact' with each other; it is of the order of $2\text{–}3 \times 10^{-8}$ cm.

Putting $i = k$ and $a = \delta_{ii}$ we obtain the mutual potential energy between two parts of a single body separated (mentally) by a plane surface. This energy taken with the opposite sign is obviously equal to the work which must be done in order actually to separate the two halves of the body (i.e. to bring them to a sufficiently large distance apart), referred to unit area. This work $-e_{ii}(\delta_{ii})$ can be identified with the double of the surface energy of the body with respect to air $w_{i0}$. In the same way the quantity $-e_{1,2}(\delta_{1,2})$ is seen to be equal to the surface energy of the two bodies 1 and 2 in contact with each other decreased by the sum of their surface energies (with respect to air) $w_{1,2}-w_{1,0}-w_{2,0}$.

Let us finally calculate the potential energy of the system (1, 2) when the second body is present in the form of a film with a finite thickness $h$, lying upon the surface of 1. Its mutual potential energy with respect to 1 is equal per unit area to

$$\int_{\delta_{1,2}}^{h} u_{1,2}\, n_2\, dx = \int_{\delta_{1,2}}^{\infty} u_{1,2}\, n_2\, dx - \int_{h}^{\infty} u_{1,2}\, n_2\, dx$$

$$= e_{1,2}(\delta_{1,2}) - e_{1,2}(h) = -\frac{\gamma_{1,2}}{\delta_{1,2}^{m_{1,2}-4}} + \frac{\gamma_{1,2}}{h^{m_{1,2}-4}}$$

if the potential energy of two molecules 1 and 2 is inversely proportional to the $m_{1,2}$th power of their distance. Instead of calculating the self-energy of 2, which must be added to the preceding expression in order to obtain the total energy of the system 1+2 (or rather that part of it which depends upon $h$), we can subtract from it the mutual potential energy of 2 with respect to the half-space 1 filled with the substance of 2, instead of 1. We thus get

$$w = -\gamma_{1,2}\left[\frac{1}{\delta_{1,2}^{m_{1,2}-4}} - \frac{1}{h^{m_{1,2}-4}}\right] + \gamma_{2,2}\left[\frac{1}{\delta_{2,2}^{m_{2,2}-4}} - \frac{1}{h^{m_{2,2}-4}}\right],$$

or

$$w = \frac{\gamma_{1,2}}{h^{\mu_{1,2}}} - \frac{\gamma_{2,2}}{h^{\mu_{2,2}}} + \text{const.}, \tag{11}$$

where $\mu_{1,2} = m_{1,2}-4$ and $\mu_{2,2} = m_{2,2}-4$; the constant is irrelevant for the sequel and can be dropped.

If a layer of 2 is enclosed between two different bodies 1 and 3, the preceding expression must be replaced by

$$w = \frac{\gamma_{1,2}}{h^{\mu_{1,2}}} + \frac{\gamma_{2,3}}{h^{\mu_{2,3}}} - \frac{\gamma_{2,2}}{h^{\mu_{2,2}}} + \frac{\gamma_{1,3}}{h^{\mu_{1,3}}}, \tag{11 a}$$

the last term representing the variable part of the mutual potential energy of 1 and 3.

If the entropy of the layer is left out of account, $w$ can be identified with its free energy per unit area $f$. The disjoining pressure, or rather its statical part, depending on the potential energy only, can thus be calculated according to the formula $p_{st} = -dw/dh$ (cf. eq. 10). Taking the case of equation (11) and putting for the sake of simplicity $m_{1,2} = m_{2,2} = 6$ (London dispersion forces), we get

$$p_{st} = 2(\gamma_{1,2}-\gamma_{2,2})/h^3. \tag{12}$$

The disjoining pressure is thus inversely proportional to the cube of the thickness of the layer. It turns out, however, that it is not necessarily positive; if $\gamma_{1,2} < \gamma_{2,2}$ it must be negative for all values of $h$. Taking the derivative of $p$ with respect to $h$, we get

$$\frac{dp_{st}}{dh} = -\frac{d^2w}{dh^2} = -6(\gamma_{1,2}-\gamma_{2,2})/h^4.$$

Now, according to (9a) this expression must be negative if the film is to be stable. We thus see that if the film is stable it must produce a positive pressure; a negative disjoining pressure could be produced by an unstable film only.

These results show that the disjoining pressure can, in principle, be produced by cohesive forces. An estimate of its numerical value shows, however, that this cause is insufficient. As has been pointed out above, $\gamma_{ii}/\delta_{ii}$ is equal to the double of the surface energy which is equal to the surface tension at the zero point of the temperature. We can thus put $\gamma_{ii}/\delta^2 \approx 100$ dyne/cm., whence it follows that $p \approx \frac{\gamma}{h^3} \approx \frac{\gamma}{\delta^2}\frac{\delta^2}{h^3} = 10^{+2}\frac{\delta^2}{h^3}$. Putting here $\delta \approx 2.10^{-8}$ and $h = 10^{-5}$ cm., we get $p \cong 40$ dyne/cm.$^2$, which is about 20 times smaller than the value found experimentally by Derjaguin in the case of a number of liquids.

The results are not essentially changed if we assume that the exponents $\mu_{1,2}$ and $\mu_{2,2}$ in (11) are different from each other. In this case, however, $p$ and $\sigma$ lose their monotonic character as functions of $h$. Thus, for example, if $\mu_{1,2} > \mu_{2,2}$, the curve $p(h)$ assumes a shape shown in Fig. 44*a*, while in the contrary case it assumes a shape shown in Fig. 44*b*, which is just the reverse of the preceding one.

Using the formula $d\sigma = p\,dh$ we obtain for $\sigma(h)$ a dependence which is represented by the dotted lines in the corresponding figures, the value of $\sigma$ for $h \to \infty$ (thick layers) being assumed to be positive. We thus see that in the case 44*a* the film is unstable for small thicknesses. Both cases cannot correspond to the actual conditions, for sufficiently thick films on the one hand, and monomolecular (adsorbed) layers on the other, are known to be always stable.

It has been shown above that in the case of *diluted* monomolecular layers the surface tension is always decreased with respect to the value $\sigma_0$, corresponding to the clean surface, by the amount $p = nkT$, where $n$ is the number of adsorbed molecules per unit area. Since $n$ can be treated as an equivalent for $h$ in the region $h \to 0$, we thus see that in this region $\sigma$ must always increase with a decrease of $h$, tending to a finite limiting value $\sigma_0$. This course of $\sigma$ as a function roughly corresponds to the initial portion of the dotted curve in Fig. 44 *b*. Such a coincidence is, however, purely accidental, since the effect we are now considering is due not to the variation of the potential energy, which has been taken into account in drawing the curve 44 *b*, but to a variation of the *surface entropy*, which represents the temperature dependent term in the surface free energy $f = w - Ts$.

By taking into account this entropy term it is possible to stabilize

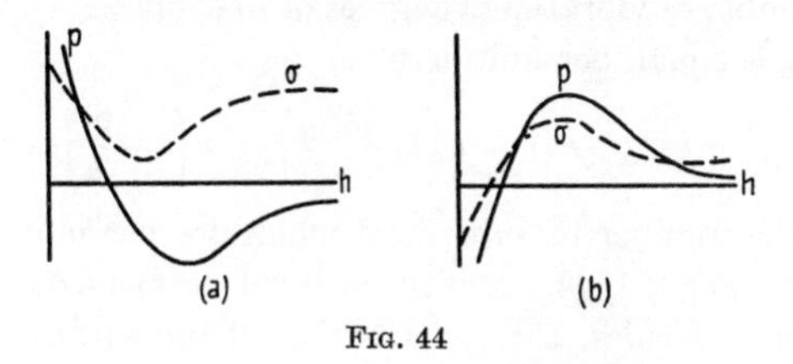


FIG. 44

a thin film in the case corresponding to Fig. 44 *b*. It seems natural to expect that a similar entropy effect must be responsible for the stability of thicker films, corresponding to the case of Fig. 44 *a*.

As has been shown in § 1, the surface entropy of a liquid or solid body of a practically infinite thickness depends on the heat motion of its free surface, which can be represented as a superposition of capillary and Rayleigh waves and is equal per unit area to $kn \log \bar{\nu}/\bar{\nu}'$, where $\bar{\nu}$ and $\bar{\nu}'$ are the geometrical means of the vibration frequencies associated with all volume and surface waves respectively, and $n$ the number of superficial molecules per unit area.

Let us imagine a layer of liquid with a finite thickness $h$, supported by an absolutely rigid body. Under such conditions, implying that the lower surface of the liquid film remains fixed, capillary or Rayleigh waves will be propagated on its upper (free) surface only if the length of these waves is small compared with the thickness of the film. In fact, the fundamental characteristics of surface waves consist in the rapid decrease of their amplitude with increase of the distance from the surface. In the case of capillary waves (or gravity waves on the surface of deep water) the dependence of the amplitude on the depth $Z$ below the surface is described by the exponential expression $e^{-\alpha Z}$, where $\alpha$ is equal to $2\pi/\lambda$. In the case of Rayleigh waves the amplitude of the vibration is proportional to the sum of two exponential terms of the preceding type with slightly different exponential factors $\alpha_1$ and $\alpha_2$ of the same order of magnitude, $2\pi/\lambda$, as before. Although such waves can, in principle, exist in very thin layers (just as gravity waves in shallow water), yet in this case they cannot be treated as *surface* waves, since the motion constituting them is not limited to the free surface of the layer, its amplitude decreasing with the depth in an approximately linear way.

Hence it is clear that in estimating the surface entropy of a liquid film with a thickness $h$ we must limit ourselves to surface waves with a length not exceeding a certain critical value $\lambda_h$, of the order of $h$. Since the number of vibrational degrees of freedom with a wave number exceeding $k_h$ is equal, per unit area, to

$$\pi(k_{\max}^2 - k_h^2) = n\left(1 - \frac{\lambda_{\min}^2}{\lambda_h^2}\right) = n\left(1 - \frac{\delta^2}{h}\right),$$

where $n$ is the number of superficial molecules per unit area and $\delta$ a length of the order of $1/\sqrt{n}$, i.e. of the order of the mean distance between neighbouring molecules, the contribution of the surface waves to the entropy per unit area is equal to

$$s = kn\left(1 - \frac{\delta^2}{h^2}\right)\log\frac{\bar{\nu}}{\bar{\nu}_h'}. \tag{13}$$

The dependence of $\bar{\nu}_h$—the geometrical mean of the vibration frequencies—on the thickness $h$ can be neglected and $\bar{\nu}_h$ can be identified with $\nu_{\max}$. Noting that $kn \log \bar{\nu}/\bar{\nu}' = s_\infty$ is equal to the surface entropy of a thick layer, we can rewrite (13) as follows:

$$s = s_\infty\left(1 - \frac{\delta^2}{h^2}\right). \tag{13 a}$$

The kinetic or entropy part of the surface tension $\sigma_k = -T(s - h\,\partial s/\partial h)$ is thus equal to

$$\sigma_k = -s_\infty T\left(1 - \frac{3\delta^2}{h^2}\right). \tag{14}$$

This expression increases with a decrease of $h$, as it should in order to ensure the stability of sufficiently thick films.

If the surface energy of the film is given by (11), which corresponds to a monotonic variation of the pressure (12), the statical part of the surface tension is equal to

$$\sigma_s = w_\infty + \frac{3\gamma}{h^2}, \tag{14 a}$$

where $\gamma = 2(\gamma_{1,2} - \gamma_{2,2})$. It is interesting to note that in this case, i.e. the case of ordinary van der Waals forces between the molecules with a potential energy inversely proportional to the sixth power of the distance, the dependence of the statical part of the surface tension of a film on its thickness is the same as that of the kinetic part, both varying with $h$ as $1/h^2$. Adding the two parts of the surface tension we get

$$\sigma = \sigma_\infty + \left(\frac{3\gamma}{\delta^2} + 3s_\infty T\right)\frac{\delta^2}{h^2}. \tag{15}$$

The two terms in the brackets are of a comparable magnitude, $\gamma/\delta^2$ being approximately equal to $w_\infty$ (if $\gamma > 0$). If $\gamma < 0$, the second term must certainly outweigh the first, so that $\sigma$ should increase with a decrease of $h$; the same relationship must be expected to hold in the opposite case.

We thus see that the introduction of the entropy part of the surface tension, inasmuch as it is due to capillary or Rayleigh waves on the outer surface of the film, enables one to secure the stability of thick films, and at the same time improves the agreement between theory and experiment so far as the numerical values of $\sigma$ and $p$ are concerned. As has been pointed out above, $p$ is found experimentally to be of the order of 1 gm./cm.² for $h = 10^{-5}$, whereas according to (15) we have

$$p = 6\left(\frac{\gamma}{\delta^2} + s_\infty T\right)\frac{\delta^2}{h^3}$$

which for $h = 10^{-5}$, $\delta = 3.10^{-8}$, and $\gamma/\delta^2 \approx s_\infty T \approx 50$ dyne/cm., gives $p = 60$ dyne/cm.²

Similar results are obtained in introducing the entropy contribution to the surface tension in the case of the more complicated expressions for the surface energy given by (11) or (11 a). The dotted curve of Fig. 44 *b* acquires a more or less pronounced maximum on the side of larger thickness, the region of instability being thus limited to a certain range of intermediate thickness. In the case of the curve of Fig. 44 *a* the main contribution of the entropy term must be in the region of small values of $h$, where without the influence of heat motion, which is represented by this term, it would be unstable.

It must be noted that in the case of the thinnest monomolecular films, especially of the rarefied gas-like type, the character of the heat motion, which has been considered above (§ 2) in connexion with the surface tension, is entirely different from that which can be described as a superposition of surface capillary or Rayleigh waves. In the latter case the motion has a component normal to the surface, and vanishes at a fixed boundary (lower surface), while in the former it takes place at the fixed boundary in a tangential direction, the adsorbed molecules slipping, as it were, along it. In reality the molecules vibrate about certain equilibrium positions both in the tangential and in the normal direction, jumping every now and then from one equilibrium position to the next. The surface entropy essentially depends, however, only on the latter component of the thermal motion, reducing to a two-dimensional diffusion of the adsorbed molecules.

If their number per unit area is increased until they form a condensed monomolecular layer, the character of the thermal motion parallel to the surface must be fundamentally altered. It seems natural to assume that it is transformed into a two-dimensional wave motion consisting of longitudinal waves and transverse waves, the latter being similar to some extent to the Rayleigh waves considered above, while the former resemble the surface waves introduced by Lamb. A macroscopic description of this type of wave motion is hampered by the fact that it involves a breakdown of the usual continuity conditions which require that the molecules of a surface layer remain fixed if the surface of the adsorbent is supposed to be fixed. If the latter assumption, which represents only a rough simplification of the reality, is dropped, then it is possible to consider, not only in the case of a monomolecular layer but also in that of thicker film, surface waves of the Rayleigh and of the Lamb type as giving a second contribution to the surface entropy, along with the free surface waves considered above.

We shall not engage in a more detailed discussion of these questions and shall confine ourselves to a few concluding remarks concerning the external manifestation of the properties of thin liquid film.

These properties have an important bearing on a number of capillary and colloidal phenomena connected with the stability of gas bubbles and foams, the stability of colloidal solutions the particles of which are kept apart by the action of the disjoining pressure of the liquid films separating them (electrical forces alone being insufficient), and finally on the explanation of the mechanical properties of gel-like systems.

The specific elasticity of thin films (which has been described by Derjaguin in terms of the 'disjoining pressure' produced by them) seems to have been discovered for the first time by D. Talmud and S. Bresler, who noticed in 1931 that two drops of mercury freely moving on the bottom of a glass vessel filled with molten paraffin did not coalesce but remained separated from each other by a very thin paraffin film. The thickness of this film has been determined by measuring the electric capacity of the minute condenser formed by the two drops when they were slightly pressed together and was found to be of the order $10^{-6}$ cm. Under such conditions the capillary attraction between the mercury drops must be balanced by the disjoining pressure of the paraffin layer separating them. Later P. Rehbinder applied this principle for the purpose of cutting the surface of liquid mercury, covered with an aqueous solution of saponin, into pieces which remain separated from each other for a relatively long time by extremely thin water films, extending from the surface of mercury to the bottom of the glass vessel containing it.

These experiments clearly show that the stability of emulsions and suspensions can be explained by the elasticity (disjoining pressure) of thin films of the dispersive medium which prevent their coalescence (coagulation). From this point of view, introduced by Derjaguin, the influence of various agents affecting the stability of colloidal solution, and, in particular, of ions, appears in an entirely new light. According to the current view, the stabilizing action of electrolytic ions is reduced to the Coulomb repulsion of the colloidal particles to which these ions are attached (forming the inner surface of the electric double layer covering them); the coagulative action produced by ions of the opposite sign is explained, from this point of view, by the fact that they neutralize the surface of the particles.

From our point of view the influence of the ions on the stability of colloidal solutions is not directly connected with their mutual repulsion (or attraction) but depends upon the stabilizing effect which is produced by them on a liquid film which is the seat of the diffuse side of the electric double layer, while the opposite side is concentrated on the surface of the adjacent solid. It has been shown by Derjaguin† that the presence of such a double layer increases the disjoining pressure of the film and eventually wholly removes its instability for moderate values of the thickness.

This effect is beautifully demonstrated by Frumkin's experiments on the adhesion of gas bubbles to the surface of mercury (cf. Ch. VI). If this adhesion can be regarded as a macroscopic illustration of the process of coagulation, then it follows that in the case of coagulation of colloidal solutions the colloidal particles remain attached to each other by extremely thin films of the dispersive medium, the process of coagulation being due to the instability of the liquid films of intermediate thickness.

One thing remains, however, obscure, namely the stabilizing influence of monomolecular layers of certain surface active substances, serving, in particular, as emulsifying agents. The difficulty consists in the fact

† B. Derjaguin, *Bull. Acad. Sci. U.R.S.S.*, série chimique, **5**, 1153 (1939); *Acta Physicochimica U.R.S.S.*, **10**, 333 (1939).

that the influence of such layers is extended to films with a thickness of the order of $10^{-5}$ cm., i.e. lying far beyond the range of the field of force directly due to the layer. Its influence must accordingly also be of an indirect nature (just as in the case of an ionic double layer). It may be due either to the orientation of the molecules of the liquid, extending, by the action of one molecular layer on the next, through relatively large distances (as in the case of liquid crystalline films orientated between two parallel plates), or to an alteration of the character of the surface heat waves, which are responsible for the entropy part of the surface tension of a liquid film. The latter effect can be illustrated by the damping of capillary waves on the free surface of a liquid, due to the presence of a thin oil film, and can be reduced to an alteration of the boundary conditions which determine the character of the surface waves (irrotational or rotational, longitudinal or transverse).

In all these cases the unusual properties of thin liquid films are due to their characteristic 'elasticity', which they acquire as a result of the dependence of their tension, and pressure, on their thickness. It should be mentioned that the quenching influence of oil film on water waves is by no means limited to monomolecular films, which are considered in Levich's theory (§ 3); stable polymolecular films, with a tension increasing as their thickness is decreased, must be still more effective in this respect owing to their higher elasticity.

## 5. Reduction of Cohesive Forces between Molecules to their Surface Energy, and Application of this Method to the Distribution of Molecules in Solutions

Since the molecular forces fall off very rapidly with the distance, it is usually possible, in calculating various quantities connected with cohesive forces in liquid bodies, to limit oneself to the consideration of the mutual action between neighbouring molecules only. This refers, in particular, to the surface energy of liquids ($w$), which has been defined in § 1 as the 'excess potential energy per unit area, due to deficiency in the number of nearest neighbours about the molecules of the superficial layer'.

Denoting the number of nearest neighbours for inner molecules of the liquid by $z$, and the number of such neighbours for a superficial molecule by $z'$, we can put

$$w = u_1(z-z')n', \tag{16}$$

where $u_1$ is the mutual potential energy of two neighbouring molecules at a mean distance of the order of $10^{-8}$ cm. from each other, and $n'$

the number of superficial particles per unit area, which is a quantity of the same order of magnitude as $1/r^2$ ($r =$ mean distance between nearest neighbours).

On the other hand, the quantity

$$W = \tfrac{1}{2}nzu_1, \tag{16a}$$

where $n$ is the number of particles per unit volume (equal approximately to $1/r^3$), is equal to the evaporation energy of the liquid (i.e. the latent heat of evaporation at $T = 0$) referred to unit volume. We thus obtain the following relation:

$$\frac{w}{W} = \frac{2(z-z')}{z}r \approx r \approx 10^{-8}. \tag{16b}$$

This result is verified experimentally for practically all liquids. Thus, for example, in the case of water we have $W = 500$ cal./cm.$^3 = 2 \times 10^{10}$ erg/cm.$^3$, while $w \cong \sigma \approx 100$ erg/cm.$^2$, so that $w/W = 5 \times 10^{-9}$ cm.

The relation between the surface energy of a liquid and the latent heat of its evaporation can also be approached in a somewhat different way, indicated by Langmuir.†

Let us imagine that a prismatic rod of a liquid with a cross-section $A$ is divided along this section into two halves. This process is accompanied by the appearance of a new free surface with an area $2A$, which is connected with an additional surface energy $2Aw$. If the subdivision of the liquid into smaller and smaller elements is continued until it is separated into single molecules, the surface energy will be increased by the amount $Nqw$, where $N$ is the number of molecules and $q$ the area of the surface of each molecule (treated approximately as a volume element of a continuous medium).

This quantity does not admit of an unambiguous determination. Langmuir defines it, for instance, as the surface $4\pi r^2$ of a sphere with a volume $\frac{4}{3}\pi r^3$ equal to the volume of the liquid per molecule $V/N = 1/n$. This gives

$$q = 4\pi\left(\frac{3}{4\pi n}\right)^{\frac{2}{3}} \approx 5n^{-\frac{2}{3}}.$$

Now, it is clear that the surface energy $Nqw$ required for dissociating the liquid into separate molecules is equal to its evaporation energy (at $T = 0$). Putting

$$W = nqw \tag{17}$$

we thus get

$$\frac{w}{W} = \frac{1}{nq} \approx \frac{1}{5n^{\frac{1}{3}}},$$

which agrees with respect to the order of magnitude with (16b).

† I. Langmuir, *Chem. Rev.* **13**, 147 (1933).

We give below a table (taken from Langmuir's paper) illustrating the relation considered in a number of examples:

| *Substance* | $V/N$ | $4\pi r^2$ | *Boiling point* | $W$ | $\frac{W}{4\pi r^2}$ | $w$ |
|---|---|---|---|---|---|---|
| | (A.U.)$^3$ | (A.U.)$^2$ | °K. | erg $\times 10^{-14}$ | erg/cm.$^2$ | erg/cm.$^2$ |
| He | 52† | 68 | 4·3 | 0·24 | 0·35 | 0·59 |
| $H_2$ | 47† | 63 | 20·5 | 1·67 | 2·7 | 5·4 |
| $H_2O$ | 30 | 48 | 373 | 67 | 140 | 118 |
| A | 47 | 63 | 88 | 11·3 | 18 | 35·3 |
| $CH_4$ | 64 | 78 | 112 | 16·3 | 21 | .. |
| $C_8H_{18}$ | 266 | 200 | 398 | 56 | 28 | 50·7 |
| $C_8H_{17}HO$ | 260 | 198 | 467 | 82 | 41·5 | 50·7 |

If it is assumed that the energy of a molecule immersed in a liquid consisting of molecules of the same sort is equal to zero, then an isolated molecule in the gas phase, for instance, must possess a surface energy $wq$. If, on the other hand (which is, in principle, more correct), the energy of an isolated molecule is taken for zero, then to a molecule situated inside the liquid must be ascribed a surface energy $wq$. Inasmuch as we are interested only in the *change* of the energy connected with a change in the aggregation state of a substance, the two treatments are wholly equivalent. The former is, however, practically more convenient and we shall adopt it, following Langmuir, in the sequel.

The energy $2Aw$ which is required to break up a liquid over an area $A$ is made up of two parts: the work $2A\sigma$ which must be done for this purpose if the temperature is to remain constant (and which is equal to the increase of the free energy), and the quantity of heat which must be communicated to the region of rupture in order to ensure the maintenance of a constant temperature (latent heat of disruption). Since to effect a rupture it is sufficient to increase the gap between the corresponding surface layers by an amount of the order of $r$, the minimum value of the work of rupture (at $T$ = const.) per unit area $2\sigma$ must be equal to the product of $r$ with the corresponding value of the breaking strength, i.e. the maximum value of the negative pressure $p_{\max}$, which the liquid can bear without splitting up. We thus get the following expression for this pressure:

$$p_{\max} \approx \frac{2\sigma}{r}. \tag{18}$$

† It should be mentioned that the gas-kinetic radius of a He atom is equal to 1·9 A. and of a hydrogen molecule to 2·4 A, which corresponds to a volume 3·6 A. in the former case and 7·2 A. in the latter. The fact that these volumes are much smaller than those actually occupied by the corresponding particles is explained by the smallness of their mutual cohesion.

Putting here $r \approx 2\times10^{-8}$ we obtain in the case of water ($\sigma \approx 100$ dyne/cm.) $p_{\max} \approx 10^{10}$ dyne/cm.$^2 = 10^4$ kg./cm.$^2$, i.e. about 10,000 atmospheres. For mercury the corresponding figure is found to be five times as high. This calculation shows that the breaking strength of liquid mercury found in Meyer's experiments (Ch. IV, § 1) is equal to 1 per cent. only of the theoretical value.

The force of adhesion of a liquid to the surface of a solid body can in principle be either smaller or larger than its internal cohesion as measured by the breaking strength $p_{\max}$; in ordinary circumstances, when the walls of the vessel are contaminated by adsorbed layers, especially by oil films, the surface tension and, consequently, the force of adhesion can fall far below the normal value.

The minimum work required to detach at a constant temperature a liquid (1) from another body (2) to which it adheres is equal per unit area to $f_{1,0}+f_{2,0}-f_{1,2}$, where $f_{i,k}$ is the free energy of a boundary surface between the bodies $i$ and $k$ (the index 0 referring to air).

If the separated surfaces are clean, i.e. not covered by a thin film of some other liquid, $f_{i,0}$ can be identified with the value of the surface tension $\sigma_{i,0}$, so that in this case the isothermal work of separation per unit area can be defined as

$$L_{1,2} = \sigma_{1,0}+\sigma_{2,0}-\sigma_{1,2}. \tag{18}$$

The quantity $L_{1,2}$ thus represents the minimum work necessary for an isothermal and reversible separation of the two bodies over 1 cm.$^2$ of their contact surface (in the case of two identical bodies $\sigma_{1,2} = 0$ and $L_{1,2} = 2\sigma$ in agreement with the preceding results). The quantity (18) which specifies the adhesion between the two bodies should be distinguished from the quantity $\sigma_0 = \sigma_{2,0}-\sigma_{1,0}+\sigma_{1,2}$, (3), which characterizes the wetting of the body 1 by the liquid 2, i.e. the tendency of the latter to spread over the surface of the former. Unlike adhesion, wetting is not a reciprocal property.†

Replacing in (18) $\sigma$ by $w$ we obtain the quantity

$$K_{1,2} = w_{1,0}+w_{2,0}-w_{1,2}, \tag{19}$$

representing the total or adiabatic work of separation of the corresponding bodies per unit area of the boundary surface.

This quantity, just as in the special case of a homogeneous liquid,

† It should be noted that the adhesion $L_{1,2}$ can be written in the form $\sigma_{0,2}(1+\cos\theta)$, (cf. Fig. 40), so that it can be determined by measuring the contact angle $\theta$ and the surface tension $\sigma_{2,0}$ of the liquid against air.

can be applied to single molecules of the respective substances. Thus, for example, in the case of a diluted solution of 2 in 1 the product $K_{1,2} q_2$ is equal to energy which is required for the extraction of a molecule of the second kind from the solution under the condition that the hole, left by it, is not closed. If it is closed by the coalescence of the liquid 1 (as is actually the case) the energy $w_{1,0} q_2$ is gained, so that the energy required for the removal of the molecule under consideration is reduced to $(K_{1,2}-w_{1,0})q_2 = (w_{2,0}-w_{2,1})q_2$. This energy can obviously be defined as the latent heat of evaporation of a molecule of the second substance from a diluted solution of this substance in the first liquid. A similar meaning can be attributed to the product

$$(K_{1,2}-w_{2,0})q_1 = (w_{1,0}-w_{1,2})q_1$$

in the case of a diluted solution of 1 in 2.

Noting that $w_{2,0} q_2$ is equal to the latent heat of evaporation per molecule of the second liquid, we see that the quantities

$$w_{1,2} q_2, \qquad w_{1,2} q_1 \tag{19a}$$

can be defined as the molecular latent heats of solution of the second liquid in the first or of the first in the second respectively at high dilution; these heats being reckoned positive if the process of solution is accompanied by the *absorption* of heat.

The preceding definition does not take into account the change of entropy accompanying the process of solution (outside the irreversible portion due to the mixing); the corresponding contribution can be neglected so long as the energy $w_{1,2}$ is not too small.

The values of the latent heat of solution calculated by Langmuir with the help of the expressions (19a) are in satisfactory agreement with those found experimentally if the surface areas of the molecules $q_1$ and $q_2$ are determined as has been indicated above (using the formula $W_i = n_i q_i w_{i,0}$ for the latent heat of evaporation).

The preceding formulae can easily be generalized in the case of concentrated solutions, i.e. binary liquid mixtures.

Let the molecular concentrations of the two components (i.e. numbers of molecules of the first and second kinds per unit volume) be denoted by $n_1$ and $n_2$. If the molecules of both kinds are distributed irregularly, then the molecules 1 must be in contact with the molecules 2, not over their whole surface but only over a fraction of it, $q_{1,2}$, equal, on the average, to $q_1 n_2/(n_1+n_2)$, whereas the remaining fraction $q_{1,1} = q_1 n_1/(n_1+n_2)$ remains in contact with the molecules of the same kind 1.

The total energy of the mixture, in so far as it depends on the contact between the molecules of the two kinds, is thus equal to

$$Q_{1,2} = w_{1,2}(q_{1,2}n_1+q_{2,1}n_2) = w_{1,2}\frac{n_1 n_2}{n_1+n_2}(q_1+q_2), \tag{20}$$

or

$$Q_{1,2} = nw_{1,2}c_1 c_2(q_1+q_2), \tag{20 a}$$

where

$$c_1 = \frac{n_1}{n_1+n_2}, \quad c_2 = \frac{n_2}{n_1+n_2}$$

are the molecular concentration of the two liquids and $n = n_1+n_2$ the total number of molecules per unit volume. Since in the pure liquids the corresponding quantities ($Q_{11}$ and $Q_{22}$) are equal to zero, $Q_{1,2}$ can be defined as the latent heat of mixing the two liquids in the corresponding proportion.

It follows from (20) that the quantities

$$\left.\begin{aligned}\left(\frac{\partial Q_{1,2}}{\partial n_1}\right)_{n_2=\text{const.}} &= w_{1,2}(q_1+q_2)c_2^2\\ \left(\frac{\partial Q_{1,2}}{\partial n_2}\right)_{n_1=\text{const.}} &= w_{1,2}(q_1+q_2)c_1^2\end{aligned}\right\} \tag{21}$$

can be defined as the increase of energy connected with a transfer of a single molecule of a pure liquid (1 or 2) into the mixture of the given composition.

In the derivation of the preceding formulae we have ignored the possibility of the existence of a certain degree of order in the relative arrangement of the molecules of different kinds in the mixture. If the cohesion between unlike molecules is stronger than that between like ones, i.e. if

$$w_{1,2} < 0,$$

a molecule of each kind will tend to be surrounded by molecules of the other kind; their proportion will, accordingly, exceed the average value of the ratio

$$\frac{n_1}{n_2} \quad \text{or} \quad \frac{n_2}{n_1}.$$

If, on the other hand, the cohesion between like molecules is larger than between unlike ones, i.e. if

$$w_{1,2} > 0,$$

then the molecules of the same kind will tend to segregate from those of the other kind. It should be mentioned that this case corresponds to the majority of liquid solutions and is characterized by an increase of the solubility with rise of the temperature. In the case of solutions of gases in liquids the opposite, as a rule, occurs ($w_{1,2} < 0$); and this is characterized by a decrease of the solubility with rise of the temperature.

The fraction of the surface of the molecules of the first kind, which is in contact with the surface of the molecules of the second kind, is increased (or decreased) according to the value $q_{1,2} = q_1 c_2$, given above, by a factor proportional to the Boltzmann expression $e^{-w_{1,2}q_{1,2}/kT}$. We thus get

$$q_{1,2}/q_{1,1} = (c_2/c_1)e^{-w_{1,2}q_{1,2}/kT}/e^{-w_{1,1}q_{1,1}/kT},$$

or, since $w_{1,1} = 0$ and $q_{1,1}+q_{1,2} = q_1$,

$$q_{1,2} = \frac{q_1}{1+(c_1/c_2)e^{w_{1,2}q_{1,2}/kT}}; \tag{22}$$

and in the same way

$$q_{2,1} = \frac{q_2}{1+(c_2/c_1)e^{w_{1,2}q_{2,1}/kT}}. \tag{22 a}$$

If $w_{1,2}q/kT$, where $q$ is of the order of $q_1$ or $q_2$, has a large negative value, the equations (22) and (22 a) yield $q_{1,2} = q_1$ and $q_{2,1} = q_2$ respectively, which corresponds to a practically complete alternation between unlike molecules when the concentrations $c_1$ and $c_2$ are comparable with each other (as in the case of binary solid solutions with alternation order). In the opposite case $w_{1,2}q/kT \gg 1$, $q_{1,2}$ and $q_{2,1}$ practically vanish, which means that the two liquids are immiscible at the corresponding temperature.

At sufficiently high temperatures any pair of liquids must, in principle, become miscible with each other in arbitrary proportions. This temperature may, however, in the case of liquids with complex molecules, lie above the limit of their chemical stability.

Let us consider the dependence of the miscibility on the temperature somewhat more closely (neglecting, for the sake of simplicity, the complications connected with a variation of $q_{1,2}$ and $q_{2,1}$ with a change of the temperature). Let us assume to begin with that the liquid I is completely insoluble in II, but is itself capable of dissolving a small amount of II. If, in such conditions, the two liquids are brought in contact with each other, the first liquid is converted into a diluted solution of II in I which will be denoted as $I_2$ or simply as I. The concentration of 2 in this solution (I) can be calculated approximately according to the formula

$$n_{I,2} = n_{II,2}\, e^{-U_2/kT}, \tag{23}$$

where $n_{II,2}$ is the number of molecules per unit volume in the pure liquid II, and

$$U_2 = w_{1,2}q_2$$

according to (19 a).

If the finite solubility of the first liquid in the second one is also taken into account, then its concentration in the solution II ($2_1$) can be calculated with the help of a similar formula

$$n_{\mathrm{II},1} = n_{\mathrm{I},1}\, e^{-U_1/kT} \tag{23 a}$$

with

$$U_1 = w_{1,2}\, q_1.$$

The expressions (23) and (23 a) remain valid in the case of higher concentrations if the energies of solution $U_1$ and $U_2$ are determined with regard to the presence in I ($1_2$) and II ($2_1$) of molecules of both kinds. The energy $U_1$ can be represented in this case as the difference between the change of energy involved in the transfer of a molecule of the first kind from the pure liquid into the solution II with the relative concentrations $c_{\mathrm{II},1}$, $c_{\mathrm{II},2}$, and the solutions I with the relative concentrations $c_{\mathrm{I},1}$, $c_{\mathrm{I},2}$. We thus get

$$U_1 = w_{1,2}(q_1+q_2)(c_{\mathrm{II},2}^2 - c_{\mathrm{I},2}^2) \tag{24}$$

and

$$U_2 = w_{1,2}(q_1+q_2)(c_{\mathrm{I},1}^2 - c_{\mathrm{II},1}^2). \tag{24 a}$$

Substituting these expressions into the equations (23), (23 a), and putting

$$n_{\mathrm{I},1} = n_{\mathrm{I}}\, c_{\mathrm{I},1}, \qquad n_{\mathrm{I},2} = n_{\mathrm{I}}\, c_{\mathrm{I},2}, \qquad n_{\mathrm{II},1} = n_{\mathrm{II}}\, c_{\mathrm{II},1}, \qquad n_{\mathrm{II},2} = n_{\mathrm{II}}\, c_{\mathrm{II},2},$$

where $n_{\mathrm{I}}$ and $n_{\mathrm{I}}$ denote the total numbers of molecules in unit volume of the two liquids (which can be considered as known and approximately constant), we obtain two equations for the relative concentrations which, along with the equations

$$c_{\mathrm{I},1} + c_{\mathrm{I},2} = 1, \qquad c_{\mathrm{II},1} + c_{\mathrm{II},2} = 1,$$

define these concentrations as functions of the temperature $T$.

To every given value of the temperature two pairs of values of the relative concentrations $c_{\mathrm{I},1}$, $c_{\mathrm{I},2}$ and $c_{\mathrm{II},1}$, $c_{\mathrm{II},2}$ for the solutions I and II in equilibrium with each other generally correspond. If the temperature is raised, the ratios $c_{\mathrm{I},2}$ and $c_{\mathrm{I},1}$ gradually increase until, at a certain temperature $T_c$, they become equal. These relations are represented graphically in Fig. 45 (solubility diagram), where the concentrations $c_2$ and $c_1$ are plotted on the abscissa, the former in the positive and the latter in the negative directions. The highest value of the temperature represents the critical temperature of the molecular miscibility of the two liquids (Fig. 45).

The preceding calculations are, of course, not exact. In particular, they do not take into account the fact, discussed above, that the *relative* arrangement of like and unlike molecules, i.e. the fractions of their surfaces $q_1$, $q_2$ in contact with the molecules of the same or of a different kind, are functions of the temperature, determined by (22) and (22 a). This involves the replacement of the solution energies (24), (24 a) by more complicated expressions, which can be defined as the free energies of dissolving a molecule 2 in 1 and a molecule 1 in 2. We shall not investigate this question in greater detail, and shall now turn to a discussion of the somewhat unexpected fact, discovered in recent years, that a large number of binary mixtures which at the temperature of the experiment appear to be perfectly homogeneous consist in reality of more or less extended groups of molecules of the same kind. This fact can be ascertained by an X-ray examination of such mixtures; their X-ray diagrams display broad diffraction maxima characteristic of each of the two components taken separately. This method has been applied to a variety of organic mixtures at a temperature above what was believed to be their critical miscibility temperature, to mixtures of fused metals,† and to complex glasses (mixtures of silicate and borate glasses).‡

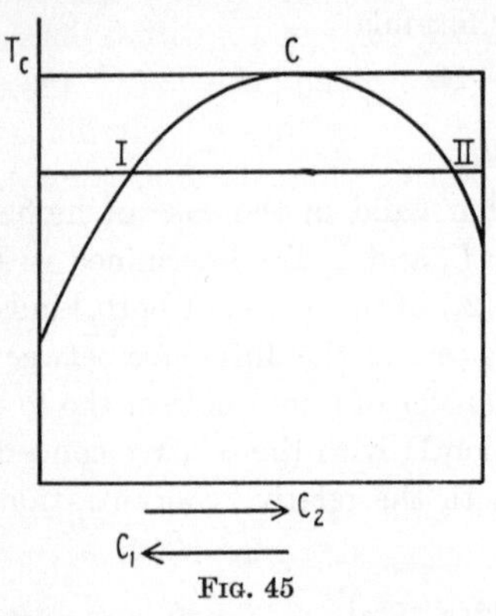

FIG. 45

It has not yet been possible, however, to determine in this way the average size of the homogeneous groups, to check their homogeneity (they can in reality represent solutions of the type $1_2$ and $2_1$ with a relatively small concentration of 2 or 1), and to ascertain their topological relationship, i.e. mutual arrangement in space. It seems natural to expect that this arrangement is of the type found in the case of ordinary emulsions, one of the components II, for instance (with a small admixture of 1), being distributed in the form of drops (with an eventually irregular shape) within a continuous medium formed by I (with a small admixture of 2).

By investigating the scattering of polarized light in a number of transparent liquid mixtures (water and phenol, hexane and $CS_2$, nitrobenzene and methyl alcohol), Krishnan§ was able to show in 1934 that, up to temperatures lying about 25° C. higher than the conventional

† Danilow and Radtschenko, *Sow. Phys.* **12**, 756 (1937).

‡ E. Porai-Koshitz, Dissertation, Karan, 1943.

§ Krishnan, *Ind. Inst. of Sc.* i. 211 (1934), 732 (1935), 915 (1935); ii. 221 (1935); iii. 126 (1936).

value of the critical miscibility temperature $T_0$, these mixtures remain markedly unhomogeneous from the molecular point of view, and consist of homogeneous regions of different composition (I or II) with a linear extension of the order of the wave-length of visible light.

These phenomena of molecularly incomplete or 'macro' miscibility can be explained in a formal way by considering the surface tension $\sigma_{1,2}$ between two liquids I and II—pure, or containing a relatively small admixture of the other component in a concentration corresponding to their mutual saturation—as a function of the concentration, taking into account the increase of the surface tension of thin layers with a decrease of their thickness.

In considering the boundary surface between two immiscible or partially miscible molecularly homogeneous liquids it is usually assumed, without sufficient justification, that this surface is stable, i.e. that the surface tension $\sigma_{1,2} = w_{1,2} - Ts_{1,2}$ has a positive value, which is gradually lowered with a rise of the temperature as a result of the decrease of the difference in the compositions of the two liquids, and vanishes when these compositions become identical, i.e. at the critical miscibility temperature $T_c$, both the surface energy $w_{1,2}$ and the surface entropy $s_{1,2}$ vanishing simultaneously.

Now, the surface tension between two liquids must decrease with rise of the temperature even when these liquids remain practically immiscible, as a result of the increase of the entropy term $Ts_{1,2}$ in the expression $\sigma_{1,2} = w_{1,2} - Ts_{1,2}$.

It is thus perfectly natural to expect that in certain cases, which may be of very frequent occurrence, the surface tension between two liquids can vanish at (and above) a certain temperature $T_0$, lying much below the critical miscibility temperature $T_c$ and defined by the equation

$$T_0 = \frac{w_{1,2}(T)}{s_{1,2}(T)}, \tag{25}$$

while $w_{1,2}$ and $s_{1,2}$ are different from zero (and positive). Here $s_{1,2}$ is determined by the formula of the same type

$$s_{1,2} = kn \log \frac{kT}{h\bar{\nu}_{1,2}}$$

as in the case of the free surface of a liquid (against air), being due to surface waves of a similar kind,† while $w_{1,2}$ can be calculated with the help of equation (11), and must, as a rule, be much smaller than both

† Capillary waves on the boundary surface between two liquids are well known; Rayleigh waves travelling along the surface between two different solids firmly adhering to each other have not been studied hitherto either experimentally or theoretically.

$w_{1,0}$ and $w_{2,0}$. In this case the temperature $T_0$ can be much lower than the critical temperature of the two liquids, taken separately, and than their critical miscibility temperature.

If this is the case, the plane boundary surface between the two liquids will become unstable at $T \geqslant T_0$, and they will mix with each other not molecularly but in such a way as to form an emulsion of one of them in the other (the roles can be interchanged between the two in different parts of the volume occupied by them). This 'macro-mixing' cannot, however, go on indefinitely, for it would lead to a true molecular mixing, which is inconsistent with the assumption that $T_0 < T_c$. It is thus seen that the process of macro-mixing must stop when the size of the homogeneous regions formed by the two components of the mixture, i.e. the linear dimensions of the liquid drops of I (or II) and the thickness of the liquid films of II (or I), separating them from each other, reaches a certain equilibrium value $h$, depending on the temperature (so long as the latter lies between $T_0$ and $T_c$). The existence of an equilibrium degree of dispersion, measured by a finite value of $h$, is a natural consequence of the fact, discussed in the preceding section, that the surface entropy of a thin film (or a small drop) must decrease with a decrease of its thickness (or radius); this decrease must lead to the stabilization of the resulting emulsoidal system. The equilibrium value of $h$ can be estimated with the help of the expression (13 a) for the surface entropy of a film with a thickness $h$. Putting accordingly

$$s_{1,2}(h) = \left(1-\frac{\delta^2}{h^2}\right)s_{1,2}(\infty)$$

and neglecting the variation of $w_{1,2}$ with $h$, we get from the condition $\sigma_{1,2}(h) = w_{1,2}-Ts_{1,2}(h) = 0$, in conjunction with $w_{1,2}-T_0 s_{1,2}(\infty) = 0$

$$1-\frac{\delta^2}{h^2} = \frac{T_0}{T}, \tag{26}$$

i.e.

$$h = \delta\sqrt{\frac{T}{T-T_0}}.$$

This formula cannot be applied to those cases in which the mutual action between the molecules of the two kinds is described by attraction forces with a potential energy inversely proportional to the sixth power of the distance, for in such cases the energy $w_{1,2}$ varies with $h$, according to (11) in a way similar to $s_{1,2}$. If the parameters $\delta_{1,2}$ and $\delta_{2,2}$ appearing in (11) are identical with $\delta$, the factor $1-(\delta^2/h^2)$ is cancelled out. If it is assumed, however (which seems to correspond to the actual facts), that they are smaller than $\delta$, we get, putting for the sake of simplicity $\delta_{2,2} = \delta_{1,2}$:

$$w_{1,2}(h) = w_{1,2}(\infty)\left(1-\frac{\delta_{1,2}^2}{h^2}\right),$$

and consequently
$$T\left(1-\frac{\delta_{1,2}^2}{h^2}\right) = T_0\left(1-\frac{\delta^2}{h^2}\right)$$

instead of (26), which if $\delta_{1,2} < \delta \ll h$ gives

$$h = \sqrt{\left[(\delta^2-\delta_{1,2}^2)\frac{T}{T-T_0}\right]}.$$

## 6. Orientation of Molecules in the Surface Layer of Liquids and Surface Electric Double Layers

In the preceding sections the molecules were treated as small solid bodies of a spherical or some other shape, with a perfectly homogeneous surface, characterized by a constant value of the specific surface energy $w$. This treatment can be applied to the simplest molecules only. In the case of molecules with a more complicated chemical constitution (of organic substances in particular) the surface of a molecule $q$ can, according to Langmuir, be subdivided into a number of regions $q_1$, $q_2$,..., which correspond to different constituent parts of the molecules, i.e. to different radicals, from which it is built up, with different values of the specific surface energies with respect to air $w_{1,0}$, $w_{2,0}$, etc., or with respect to some other homogeneous medium $a$, $w_{1,a}$, $w_{2,a}$, etc.

Thus, for example, a molecule of an organic acid

$$CH_3(CH_2)_nCOOH$$

can be divided into two parts: the active end COOH with a surface $q_1$ and an inactive paraffin-like 'tail' $CH_3(CH_2)_n$ with a surface $q_2$. Let the specific surface energy of the former and the latter, with respect to water, be denoted by $w_{1,a}$ and $w_{2,a}$ respectively. The energy required for bringing such a molecule from the gas phase (i.e. practically from a vacuum) into water is equal to

$$(w_{1,a}-w_{1,0})q_1+(w_{2,a}-w_{2,0})q_2.$$

The two terms of this expression can be determined experimentally, since the second term, referring to the paraffin tail of the molecule, is proportional to the number of links $(n+1)$. It has been found in this way that the surface of each link has an area $q_2/(n+1) = 25$ A.$^2$, if the specific energies $w_{2,0}$ and $w_{2,a}$ are identified with the values corresponding to macroscopic conditions. The large positive value of the quantity $(w_{2,a}-w_{2,0})q_2$ corresponds to the practical insolubility of paraffin in water. It is but partially compensated by the negative value of the quantity $(w_{1,a}-w_{1,0})q_1$ which characterizes the strong affinity of the carboxyl radical with respect to water.

As a result of this incomplete compensation of the 'hydrophobic' character of the 'tails' of the molecules $CH_3(CH_2)COOH$ by the 'hydrophil' character of their active ends, the ordinary volume solubility of these molecules is extremely small; they possess, however, with respect to water a very large *surface solubility*. This means that they are strongly adsorbed by the surface of water, their active ends being dipped in the latter while the inactive tails remain outside it. Under such conditions an energy gain $(w_{1,0}-w_{1,a})q_1$ is obtained for each adsorbed molecule, obviously equal to the latent heat of adsorption from the gas phase. The adsorption energy from the (volume) solution is equal to the much larger value $(w_{2,a}-w_{2,0})q_2$.

The adsorption of such 'surface active' molecules is accompanied, as has already been indicated in § 3, by a considerable lowering of the surface tension from the value 70 dyne/cm. for clean water down to 20–15 dyne/cm. for condensed layers. Langmuir's investigations have shown that in such layers the adsorbed molecules are perfectly orientated, like trees, with their active ends playing the role of roots, and the inactive group that of trunks, and pressed against each other to the limit corresponding to their cross-section (about 4 A.$^2$). The surface energy of water covered by such an orientated compact monolayer is equal to the sum of the quantity $w_{2,0}$, referring to the outer surface of paraffin, and the quantity $w_{1,a}\,q_1\,n$, referring to the active ends dipping in water; $n$ denotes the number of adsorbed molecules per unit area, so that $q_1\,n \approx 1$. The calculation of the surface tension is complicated by the fact that the character of the (capillary or Rayleigh) surface waves is altered by the presence of an adsorbed monomolecular film.

The surface layer of any pure liquid can be considered as a monomolecular film adsorbed on the surface of that same liquid. There naturally arises the question whether, under such conditions, the molecules of a homogeneous liquid can be partially orientated on its surface.

In the case of molecules with a complex structure and asymmetrical shape such a 'self-orientation' must be of frequent occurrence. Let us assume, for example, that the molecule consists of two parts with partial surfaces $q_1$ and $q_2$. Let the specific energy of two molecules which are in contact with each other along unlike parts of their surfaces be denoted by $w_{1,2}$ (per unit area of contact; $w_{1,1} = w_{2,2} = 0$). If $w_{1,2} > 0$ the molecules tend to be arranged inside the liquid in such a way as to be in contact with each other along like parts of their surface. In the contrary case each part of one molecule tends to be in contact with the unlike part of the other molecules.

Let the fraction of the surface $q_1$ of a molecule which is in contact with the like and unlike parts of the surface of the surrounding molecules be denoted by $q_{1,1}$ and $q_{1,2}$ respectively. If $w_{1,2} = 0$, these fractions must be proportional to the total areas of the corresponding regions of the surface of a molecule, i.e.

$$\frac{q_{1,2}}{q_{1,1}} = \frac{q_2}{q_1}.$$

If $w_{1,2} \neq 0$, it is necessary to introduce into the right-hand part the Boltzmann factor $e^{-w_{1,2}q_{1,2}/kT}$. We thus get

$$\frac{q_{1,2}}{q_{1,1}} = \frac{q_2}{q_1} e^{-w_{1,2}q_{1,2}/kT},$$

whence, in conjunction with the condition $q_{1,1}+q_{1,2} = q$, there follows

$$q_{1,1} = \frac{q_1}{1+q_2/q_1\, e^{-w_{1,2}q_{1,2}/kT}}, \qquad q_{1,2} = \frac{q_1}{1+q_1/q_2\, e^{w_{1,2}q_{1,2}/kT}}.$$

In a similar way the fractions of the area of the second surface region, which are in contact with like and unlike regions of the neighbouring molecules, are found to be

$$q_{2,2} = \frac{q_2}{1+q_1/q_2\, e^{-w_{1,2}q_{2,1}/kT}}, \qquad q_{2,1} = \frac{q_2}{1+q_2/q_1\, e^{-w_{1,2}q_{2,1}/kT}}.$$

These formulae are quite similar to the formulae (22) and (22 a) of the preceding section for binary mixtures of simple molecules, the partial areas of the surface $q_1$, $q_2$ replacing the concentrations $n_1$ and $n_2$.

With the help of these formulae the volume energy of the liquid can be calculated as a function of the temperature. Subtracting it from the surface energy of isolated molecules $n(w_{1,0}\, q_1+w_{2,0}\, q_2)$ we obtain the latent heat of evaporation.

Leaving this question aside, we shall return to the question of the 'self-orientation' of the molecules on the free surface of a homogeneous liquid.

Let the area of the surface of a molecule which projects from the surface of the liquid in contact with air be $q_0$. It must make a certain fraction $\gamma$ of the total area of the surface of a molecule $q$; in the simplest case one can put $\gamma = \frac{1}{2}$. Further, let $q_{0,1}$ and $q_{0,2}$ denote those parts of the area $q_0$ which correspond to the superficial regions of the first and second kind. If the mutual action between the 'immersed' parts of the superficial molecules is neglected, the ratio between $q_{0,1}$ and $q_{0,2}$ can be determined by the equation

$$\frac{q_{0,2}}{q_{0,1}} = \frac{q_2\, e^{-w_{2,0}q_{2,0}/kT}}{q_1\, e^{-w_{1,0}q_{1,0}/kT}},$$

which, in conjunction with $q_{0,1}+q_{0,2} = q_0$, gives

$$q_{0,1} = q_0 \frac{q_1\, e^{-w_{1,0}q_{1,0}/kT}}{q_1\, e^{-w_{1,0}q_{1,0}/kT}+q_2\, e^{-w_{2,0}q_{2,0}/kT}},$$

$$q_{0,2} = q_0 \frac{q_2\, e^{-w_{2,0}q_{2,0}/kT}}{q_1\, e^{-w_{1,0}q_{1,0}/kT}+q_2\, e^{-w_{2,0}q_{2,0}/kT}}.$$

The degree of orientation of the molecules of the surface layer could be defined by the ratio

$$\xi = \frac{q_{0,1}}{q_0} = \frac{1}{1+(q_2/q_1)\, e^{(w_{1,0}q_{1,0}-w_{2,0}q_{2,0})/kT}},$$

which tends to 1 if $w_{1,0} < w_{2,0}$ when the temperature is lowered.

The situation is complicated by the fact that a variation of the ratio $q_{0,1}/q_0$ is accompanied by a variation of the interaction energy between the 'immersed' halves of the molecules and the surrounding molecules.

In the case of relatively simple molecules with a pronounced asymmetry it is more expedient to treat them as points or spheres of a small radius, capable of being orientated on the surface of various liquids (which must be treated as continuous media), and in particular of the liquid constituted by themselves, owing to the presence of permanent electric moments—dipole, quadripole, or of a still higher order.

If the dipole moment only is considered, the surface molecules can take two equally advantageous orientations corresponding to an outward and inward direction of the moment. If, however, the quadripole moment is also taken into account, one of these orientations must, generally speaking, be more advantageous than the other. As a result of its predominance the surface of the liquid will be covered by an electric double layer which will give rise to a certain potential difference between the interior of the liquid and the external space. The existence of such electric double layers on the surface of polar liquids is revealed by a preferential 'affinity' displayed by them with respect to negative or positive ions. This affinity leads to the absorption of ions of a given sign by small drops of a liquid, which arise in a condensing supersaturated vapour, and become stabilized by these ions as a result of a lowering of the vapour pressure due to them.

In the presence of adsorbed molecules of some foreign substance with active dipole groups (such as the organic acids considered above), the orientation of these molecules leads to the formation of electric double layers with a much larger potential drop than that existing at the surface of homogeneous polar liquids.

If the effective length of the dipoles is denoted by $d$ ($\approx 10^{-8}$ cm.), their charges by $\pm e$, and their number per unit area by $n$, then the magnitude of the potential drop is given by the expression

$$\phi = 4\pi edn = 4\pi\bar{p}n,$$

where $\bar{p} = ed$ is the mean value of the dipole moment. Putting $\bar{p} = 10^{-18}$ and $n \approx 10^{15}$ cm.$^{-2}$, we get $\phi = 10^{-2}$ c.g.s., i.e. 3 volts. The actual value of $\phi$ which is observed experimentally, is usually smaller than this figure by an order of magnitude.

As a result of partial dissociation of the active groups (e.g. the dissociation of the $H^+$ or $OH^-$ ions) one side of the double layer can become 'diffuse', the ions forming it being distributed in a layer of considerable thickness, decreasing as the concentration of the dissociated ions is increased, while the oppositely charged side remains attached to the surface.

Such double layers are somewhat different from those which have been considered in Ch. I, § 6, in connexion with the distribution of positive and negative holes near the surface of an ionic crystal, since in the present case we have to do with ions of one sign only. The density of electric charge is thus equal to

$$\rho = en,$$

where $n$ is the number of ions with a charge $e$ per unit volume at a given distance $x$ from the surface. Putting $n = n_0 e^{-e\phi/kT}$ we obtain the following equation for the potential:

$$\frac{d^2\phi}{dx^2} = -\frac{4\pi e n_0}{\epsilon} e^{-e\phi/kT} \quad \text{or} \quad \frac{d^2\psi}{d\xi^2} = -e^{-\psi}, \tag{27}$$

where $\psi = e\phi/kT$, $\xi = \kappa x$, and $\kappa = \sqrt{(4\pi e^2 n_0/\epsilon kT)}$; $\epsilon$ denotes the dielectric constant of the liquid and $n_0$ the concentration of the ions at the point of zero potential, which may be identified with the surface of the liquid $x = 0$.

It follows from (27) that the potential at infinity ($x = \infty$), where $n$ must obviously vanish, becomes infinite, while in the case of diffuse electric double layers formed by ions of two opposite kinds it remains always finite.

Integrating (27) and noting that $d\psi/d\xi = 0$ for $\xi \to \infty$, we get

$$\frac{1}{2}\left(\frac{d\psi}{d\xi}\right)^2 = e^{-\psi}, \tag{27a}$$

and consequently, since $\psi = 0$ for $\xi = 0$,

$$e^{\frac{1}{2}\psi} = \frac{1}{\sqrt{2}}\xi + 1,$$

that is,

$$\psi = 2\log\left(1+\frac{\xi}{\sqrt{2}}\right). \tag{27b}$$

It follows from (27a) that the maximum value of the electric field strength (at $x = 0$) is equal to

$$E_0 = \left(\frac{d\phi}{dx}\right)_0 = \frac{\kappa kT}{e}\left(\frac{d\psi}{d\xi}\right)_0 = \frac{\sqrt{2}\kappa kT}{e},$$

that is,

$$E_0 = \sqrt{\left(\frac{8\pi n_0 kT}{\epsilon}\right)},$$

which must be identical with $4\pi\eta$, where $\eta$ is the electric charge of the surface per unit area.

In the case of a solution of an electrolyte where ions of two opposite signs are present in equal numbers ($\bar{n}$ per unit volume) at a sufficiently large distance from the surface of a metallic electrode, or from the boundary surface of some other liquid, their concentrations are in general different in the neighbourhood of this surface, as a result of a preferential adsorption of the ions of one particular sign on it, or—in the case of a metallic electrode—of a partial dissolution of the latter (in the form of positive ions) in the electrolyte. The surface charge arising in this way and formed by the ions or electrons adsorbed on the boundary surface is compensated by the charge of the ions present in excess in the adjacent layer of the solution.

Their concentration is determined by the equations

$$n_+ = \bar{n}e^{-e\phi/kT}, \qquad n_- = \bar{n}e^{+e\phi/kT}$$

in connexion with Poisson's equation for the potential

$$\frac{d^2\phi}{dx^2} = -\frac{4\pi e}{\epsilon}(n_+ - n_-).$$

Putting $e\phi/kT = \psi$, $\xi = \kappa x$, and $\kappa^2 = 4\pi e^2\bar{n}/\epsilon kT$ (with $\bar{n}$ standing in the place of $n_0$), as before, we get

$$\frac{d^2\psi}{d\xi^2} = e^{\psi} - e^{-\psi}. \tag{28}$$

If the boundary conditions are now chosen in such a way that $\psi = 0$

and $d\psi/d\xi = 0$ for $\xi \to \infty$ (where the solution is neutral), the first integral of (28) is obtained in the form

$$\frac{1}{2}\left(\frac{d\psi}{d\xi}\right)^2 = e^{\psi}+e^{-\psi}-2 = (e^{\frac{1}{2}\psi}-e^{-\frac{1}{2}\psi})^2,$$

that is,
$$\frac{d\psi}{d\xi} = \pm\sqrt{2}(e^{\frac{1}{2}\psi}-e^{-\frac{1}{2}\psi}). \tag{28a}$$

If $\psi$ is supposed to be positive ($=\psi_0$) for $\xi = 0$, the minus sign must be taken, which gives

$$\log\tanh\frac{\psi}{4} = -\sqrt{2}(\xi-\xi_0),$$

that is,
$$\frac{e^{\frac{1}{4}\psi}-e^{-\frac{1}{4}\psi}}{e^{\frac{1}{4}\psi}+e^{-\frac{1}{4}\psi}} = e^{-\sqrt{2}(\xi-\xi_0)}, \tag{28b}$$

where the constant $\xi_0$ is determined by the value $\psi_0$ of $\psi$ for $\xi = 0$. If the charge $\eta$ adsorbed per unit area of the boundary surface is known, then from (28 a) we get

$$4\pi\eta = E_0 = -\left(\frac{d\phi}{dx}\right)_{x=0} = \frac{\kappa kT}{e}\left(\frac{d\psi}{d\xi}\right)_0,$$

that is,
$$\sqrt{2}(e^{\frac{1}{2}\psi_0}-e^{-\frac{1}{2}\psi_0}) = 4\pi\eta e/kT. \tag{28c}$$

This equation can be used for the determination of $\psi_0$.

In the limiting case $\psi \ll 1$, considered in the approximate form of the Stern or Debye–Hückel theory, the equation (28 b) reduces to the simple exponential formula

$$\psi = \psi_0 e^{-\sqrt{2}\xi},$$

where $\psi_0 = e^{\sqrt{2}\xi_0}$. This result is obtained directly if, in the equation (28), the right-hand side is replaced by $2\psi$. Putting $\kappa\sqrt{2} = 1/\delta$, we get in this case

$$\phi = \phi_0 e^{-x/\delta} \tag{29}$$

and
$$E_0 = \frac{\phi_0}{\delta}. \tag{29a}$$

The surface charge is determined by the formula

$$\eta = e(n'_+-n'_-),$$

where $n'_+$ and $n'_-$ denote the numbers of positive ions adsorbed per unit area of the boundary surface. If these surface concentrations of the ions are small, they must be connected with their volume concentrations near the surface $n'_\pm$ by the relations

$$n^0_+ = \frac{n'_+}{\delta'_+}e^{-U_+/kT}, \qquad n^0_- = \frac{n'_-}{\delta'_-}e^{-U_-/kT}, \tag{30}$$

where $\delta'_{\pm}$ denotes the effective thickness of the adsorbed layer and $U_{\pm}$ the adsorption energy of the corresponding ions. The quantities $\delta_{\pm}$ are of the order of $10^{-8}$ cm. and can be expressed through the coefficients of the quasi-elastic force holding the adsorbed ions near their equilibrium positions $f_{\pm}$ by the formula

$$\delta'_{\pm} = \sqrt{\frac{2\pi kT}{f'_{\pm}}}$$

(cf. Ch. I, § 1).

Substituting in (30) the expressions $n^0_{\pm} = \bar{n}e^{\mp e\phi_0/kT}$ we get

$$n'_{+} = \bar{n}\delta'_{+}\, e^{(U_{+}-e\phi_0)/kT}, \qquad n'_{-} = \bar{n}\delta'_{-}\, e^{(U_{-}+e\phi_0)/kT}. \tag{31}$$

The condition that the surface charge $\eta$ is compensated by the volume charge (per unit area of the boundary surface) $\int\limits_0^\infty \rho\, dx$ gives, if the approximate formula (29) for $\phi$ is used, in connexion with $\rho = -(\epsilon/4\pi)(d^2\phi/dx^2)$,

$$e(n'_{+}-n'_{-}) = \frac{\epsilon}{4\pi\delta}\phi_0. \tag{31a}$$

This equation can be regarded as the expression of the fact that the capacity of the double layer per unit area $C$ is equal to $\epsilon/4\pi\delta$, i.e. to the specific capacity of a plane condenser filled by a homogeneous dielectric medium with an effective thickness $\delta = \sqrt{(\epsilon kT/8\pi e^2\bar{n})}$. So long as $e\phi_0$ is assumed to be small compared with $kT$, the factors $e^{\pm e\phi_0/kT}$ in (31) can be replaced by $1 \mp e\phi_0/kT$, which gives, if $\delta'_{+} \simeq \delta'_{-} = \delta'$,

$$en_0\,\delta'\left[e^{U_{+}/kT} - e^{-U_{-}/kT} - \frac{e\phi_0}{kT}(e^{U_{+}/kT}+e^{U_{-}/kT})\right] = \frac{\epsilon}{4\pi\delta}\phi_0 = \frac{\epsilon kT}{4\pi\delta e}\frac{e\phi_0}{kT},$$

that is,
$$\frac{e\phi_0}{kT} = \frac{e^{U_{+}/kT} - e^{U_{-}/kT}}{(2\delta/\delta') + e^{U_{+}/kT} + e^{U_{-}/kT}},$$

or finally,
$$\frac{e\phi_0}{kT} = \frac{\sinh(U_{+}-U_{-})/kT}{(\delta/\delta')e^{-(U_{+}-U_{-})/kT} + \cosh\{(U_{+}-U_{-})/kT\}}. \tag{31b}$$

This expression is reduced to $\tanh(U_{+}-U_{-})/kT$ if the difference between the two adsorption energies $U_{+}-U_{-}$ is large compared with $kT$.

The preceding results are easily generalized to the case in which $e\phi_0$ is not small compared with $kT$ and the surface concentrations of the adsorbed ions are large, so that their mutual action cannot be neglected.

We shall not engage, however, in a discussion of these details, and shall now turn to a consideration of the influence of surface electric double layers on the surface tension of the boundary between two liquids. This influence is revealed in the case of diffuse layers by the fact that the surface tension between a liquid electrode (mercury) and a solution of an electrolyte depends on the external electric potential difference which is established between them (electrocapillary curve).

It may seem, at first sight, that the presence of a surface electric double layer of any type and origin must increase the surface free energy and along with it the surface tension by an amount equal to the electric energy per unit area

$$f_e = \int_0^\infty \frac{\epsilon E^2}{8\pi}\,dx. \tag{32}$$

In reality, however, this relation is found to hold (approximately) in the case of monomolecular double layers, formed, for example, by adsorbed molecules with orientated electric moments (Helmholtz layers). In the case of double layers, considered above, i.e. with one diffuse side formed by dissolved ions, the surface tension is not increased but on the contrary *decreased* by the amount $f_e$.

This circumstance is explained as follows. A diffuse (or rather 'half-diffuse') double layer of the type under consideration is formed at the boundary surface between a metal and an electrolytic solution, for instance, *spontaneously*, as a result of the difference in the adsorption energies of the positive and negative ions. In this respect the adsorption forces are equivalent to an external electromotive force $\phi_0$, applied to a plane condenser with a capacity $c = \epsilon/4\pi\delta$ per unit area. The work done by this force when the condenser is charged is equal to $\phi_0\eta$, where $\eta$ is the magnitude of the electric charge per unit area, i.e. $c\phi_0^2$, if $\eta$ reaches the equilibrium value $c\phi_0$. On the other hand, when the condenser is charged, a work $\int_0^{\eta_0} \phi\,d\eta = \int_0^{\phi_0} c\phi\,d\phi = \frac{1}{2}c\phi^2$ must be done *against the electrostatic forces* arising in this process, the electric energy of the charged condenser being just equal to this work. The total change in the free energy of the boundary surface (per unit area) due to the redistribution of ions (between the surface of the electrode and the adjacent layer of the electrolyte), which leads to the formation of the half-diffuse electric double layer, is thus equal to the algebraic sum of $-\phi_0\eta$ (work done by the electromotive force, representing the effect of adsorption) and of $\frac{1}{2}c\phi_0^2$ (work done against the electrostatic forces).†

† A similar situation is found when a molecule, deprived of a permanent electric moment, is polarized under the action of an external electric field $E$. If the moment induced by the latter is equal to $p = \alpha E$, then the potential energy of the molecule with respect to the source of the field is decreased by $-pE$, while its own potential energy increases by the amount $\frac{1}{2}pE$, which gives a net decrease equal to $\frac{1}{2}pE = -\frac{1}{2}\alpha E^2$.

If, therefore, the change of the surface tension must be equal to the resulting change of the free energy per unit area it must be *decreased* and not increased by the amount $\frac{1}{2}c\phi_0^2$.

A clearer insight into the nature and origin of this decrease of the surface tension is obtained from a consideration of the electrical tensions which are acting in the solution near its boundary with the metal electrode and which amount to a positive pressure in the lateral direction $(y, z)$ and to a negative pressure in the normal one $(x)$. These electrical tensions are numerically equal (per unit area) to the volume density of the electrical energy $\epsilon E^2/8\pi$. The resulting change of the surface tension is expressed by the formula (cf. § 1)

$$\Delta\sigma = \int_0^\infty (T_{yy} - T_{xx})\, dx, \tag{33}$$

or, since $T_{xx} = -T_{yy} = \epsilon E^2/8\pi$,

$$\Delta\sigma = -\frac{\epsilon}{4\pi}\int_0^\infty E^2\, dx. \tag{34}$$

Putting here $E = -\partial\phi/\partial x = \phi/\delta$, we get, according to (28 b),

$$-\Delta\sigma = \frac{\epsilon}{4\pi\delta^2}\int_0^\infty \phi^2\, dx = \tfrac{1}{2}c\phi_0^2, \tag{35}$$

in agreement with the preceding argument. It should be noticed that, if we took into account the lateral pressure only $(T_{yy})$, we should obtain a value for $\Delta\sigma$ half as large. Another point of interest (indicated by A. Frumkin) is the coincidence of the effect of the lateral electrical pressure with that due to the additional osmotic pressure of the ions of both signs, corresponding to the excess $\Delta n$ of their total concentration, near the boundary between the metal and the electrolytic solution, over the mean value. In fact we have

$$\Delta n = (n_+ + n_- - 2\bar{n}) = \bar{n}[e^{-e\phi/kT} + e^{e\phi/kT} - 2],$$

or, if $e\phi/kT \ll 1$,

$$\Delta n = \left(\frac{e\phi}{kT}\right)^2 \bar{n} = \bar{n}\left(\frac{e\phi_0}{kT}\right)^2 e^{-2x/\delta}; \tag{36}$$

which corresponds to an additional osmotic pressure at a depth $x$

$$\Delta n\, kT = \frac{\bar{n}e^2\phi_0^2}{kT} e^{-2x/\delta}, \tag{37}$$

and consequently to a surface pressure

$$p' = \frac{\bar{n}e^2\phi_0^2\,\delta}{2kT} = \frac{\epsilon\phi_0^2}{16\pi\delta} = \tfrac{1}{4}c\phi_0^2. \tag{38}$$

Since, however, the osmotic pressure is isotropic, the influence on $\sigma$ produced by the additional osmotic pressure in the lateral direction is compensated by that due to the additional pressure in the normal direction, so that the excessive osmotic pressure of the solution near the boundary with the electrode does not alter the value of the surface tension.

The fact that the quantity $f = \frac{1}{2}c\phi_0^2$ representing the *free energy* of the surface connected with its electrical charge $Q = c\phi_0$ is twice as large as its electrical energy $w = \int\limits_0^\infty E^2/8\pi \, dx$ is in full harmony with the thermodynamical relation $w = f - T(\partial f/\partial T)_{Q=\text{const.}}$ between the energy and the free energy, if account is taken of the dependence of the latter on the temperature (for a constant value of the surface charge $Q$). Noting that $\delta \sim \sqrt{T}$ (according to (25 a)) and that $c = \epsilon/4\pi\delta \sim 1/\sqrt{T}$, we see that for $Q =$ const. the dependence of $f$ on $T$ is reduced to a proportionality with $T (f = \frac{1}{2}c\phi_0^2 = Q^2/2c \sim \sqrt{T})$. We thus get, putting $f = A\sqrt{T}$:

$$w = A\sqrt{T} - \frac{T}{2}\frac{A}{\sqrt{T}} = \tfrac{1}{2}A\sqrt{T} = \tfrac{1}{2}f. \tag{39}$$

If an external potential difference $V$ is introduced between the metallic electrode and the solution of the electrolyte, the electric double layer is changed in exactly the same way as if the adsorption potential difference $\phi_0$ was increased by $V$; the resulting change in the surface tension is thus given by the equation

$$\sigma_0 - \sigma = \tfrac{1}{2}c(\phi_0 + V)^2. \tag{40}$$

If $V$ has a sign opposite to that of $\phi_0$, the surface tension $\sigma$ must increase with $V$ until it reaches the maximum value $\sigma_0$, when $V = -\phi_0$, the surface double layer vanishing at the instant. With a further increase of $V$ in the same direction, $\sigma$ must fall off again owing to the formation of a double layer with the opposite sign of the electric charge. This dependence of $\sigma$ on $V$ is in full agreement with the experimental facts.

In 1917 the present writer proposed a theory of the surface tension and contact potential drop of metals based on the conception that the surface of a metallic body is covered by an electric double layer of atomic thickness, with an outer side formed by the electrons (because of their external position in the atoms with respect to the positive nuclei), and an inner side by the uncompensated charge of the positive nuclei of the superficial atomic layer.†

† J. Frenkel, *Phil. Mag.*, April 1917.

The electric charge of this natural 'surface condenser' per unit area is equal to $zen' \approx ze/r^2$, where $e$ is the charge of an electron, $z$ the valency of an atom (i.e. the number of outer electrons per atom), and $n' \approx 1/r^2$ the number of atoms per unit area ($r$ = distance between neighbouring atoms).

The electrical field within this condenser is $E \approx 4\pi\eta$. Hence in a transition through the surface layer of the metal the electric potential is changed by the amount $\phi \approx Er = 4\pi\eta r$, i.e.

$$\phi_0 = \frac{ze}{r}. \tag{41}$$

The capacity of the double layer per unit area is equal to $1/4\pi r$ and its energy to

$$w = \frac{ze^2}{8\pi r^3} \approx \frac{z^2e^2n}{8\pi}, \tag{41 a}$$

where $n \approx 1/r^3$ is the number of atoms per unit volume of the metal.

The 'contact potential' defined by (41) is of the order of a few volts, while the energy $w$ is of the order of a few hundred ergs/cm.$^2$ The potential difference, arising between two metals when they are brought into contact with each other, can be identified with the difference of their 'contact' (or 'intrinsic') potentials $\phi_0$ and the surface electric energy of a metal (41 a) with its surface tension (at $T = 0$). The values of $w$ obtained in this way are of the correct order of magnitude.

This theory stands in contradiction with the theory of electrocapillary phenomena previously discussed, for it identifies the surface tension of a metal (at $T = 0$) with its surface electric energy, while the presence of a surface electric double layer on the boundary surface metal solution decreases the surface tension by the same amount. This contradiction is due to the fact that in the above treatment of the surface energy of a metal the conditions of dynamical equilibrium for the electrons of the superficial layer have been wholly disregarded. In reality the surface electric field produced by them (in conjunction with the positive ions) and pulling them inside the metal must affect their concentration and their kinetic energy so that the electric force should be balanced by the resulting normal pressure. The situation is here similar to that discussed in the case of electrocapillary phenomena with the difference that Boltzmann's statistics must be replaced by that of Fermi. This question has recently been discussed in detail by A. Samoylovich.† Starting with an expression for the surface tension $\sigma$, which contains the electric (potential) energy of the surface layer $\int E^2/8\pi \, dx$ and the

† Dissertation, Gorky, 1944.

associated change of the kinetic energy $\Delta \int \frac{1}{2}mr^2n\,dx$, and taking into account the equilibrium condition for the forces in the direction of the normal to the surface, he obtains a final expression for $\sigma$, to which the electric field contributes a negative term, corresponding to a surface pressure, of exactly the same form as in the case of electrocapillary phenomena, namely $-\int E^2/4\pi\,dx$; this term is outweighed, however, by a positive one, electric in origin, but non-electric in its external form, the resulting value of $\sigma$ being of approximately the same magnitude as in my original approximate theory where it is defined as $\int E^2/8\pi\,dx$.

# VII

# KINETICS OF PHASE TRANSITIONS

## 1. Thermodynamical Theory of the Equilibrium between a Supersaturated Vapour and a Drop of Liquid

SURFACE phenomena play an important role in processes connected with phase changes, i.e. with transitions from one aggregation state to another. These include, in the first place, transitions from the gaseous state to the liquid one (condensation of a vapour) and vice versa (evaporation or rather boiling of a liquid); further, transitions from the liquid to the solid state (crystallization) and from the solid to the liquid (fusion); the dissolution of some substance—solid or liquid—in a liquid medium and its 'precipitation' from the solution in the form of crystals or liquid drops, which can subsequently coalesce into a continuous mass, and so on.

The usual thermodynamical theory of phase transitions deals not with the *course* of these transitions, i.e. the velocity with which they progress under given conditions, but with the conditions under which this velocity is exactly equal to zero—which means that the two phases can remain in stable equilibrium with each other for any length of time.

It is clear that the growth of a new phase B after it has made its appearance can proceed with a finite velocity at the cost of the initial phase A only if they are *not* in equilibrium with each other. This deviation from equilibrium can be very minute when the new phase is sufficiently developed. Much larger deviations are, however, necessary at the initial stages of the development of the new phase, in the form of an embryonic 'nucleus' (*b*), i.e. a very small element of volume that has suffered the transition.

The initial phase A, when it is being transformed into B, is in a condition not envisaged by the ordinary thermodynamical theory, which deals with equilibrium states only.

This condition can be described as unstable or rather 'metastable', which means that it can be preserved for a certain time (very short or, on the contrary, indefinitely long, as the case may be), because the velocity of the generation and growth of the new phase is sufficiently small.

Examples of such metastable states are found in a supersaturated (i.e. overcooled or overcompressed) vapour; in an overheated liquid, which does not start to boil although its temperature is raised above the thermodynamical boiling-point (corresponding to the equality between the pressure of the saturated vapour and the external pressure); in an overcooled liquid, which can eventually behave as a practically stable amorphous solid body (glass); in a superheated solution, and so on.

The new phase B is generated amidst the 'metastable' phase A in the form of 'nuclei' which are usually considered as very small vapour bubbles, liquid droplets, or crystalline bodies, that is, generally speaking, as complexes of particles, which differ from ordinary macroscopic bodies in an aggregation state, corresponding to the phase B, by their small size only. This point of view, as will be shown in detail below, cannot be regarded as correct, for it does not provide us with a solution of the question of the mechanism of the generation of a new phase, but simply shifts the problem from macroscopic to microscopic (i.e. very small) elements of volume.

If we leave aside, for a moment, the question of the origin of a nucleus of the B phase and consider the conditions which determine the rate of its further growth, we must take into account, in the first place, the fact that its smallness implies an abnormally large ratio of its surface to its volume, compared with the case of ordinary macroscopic bodies. Its surface energy and free energy (or surface tension) must accordingly constitute an important part of the total change of energy or the free energy of the whole system involved in the process of the formation of a nucleus.

If the surface energy (or free energy) of the nuclei of the B phase with respect to the metastable A phase, in which they are 'suspended' as particles of a colloidal solution, is taken into account, the notion of thermodynamical equilibrium between A and B can be extended in such a way that the nucleus of B, with a given size and shape, should remain in equilibrium with the 'medium' A, in spite of the fact that the latter is not in equilibrium with respect to a fully developed B phase, separated from it by a plane boundary surface.

This extension of the notion of equilibrium between two phases has been applied by J. J. Thomson to the problem of the condensation of a supersaturated vapour. It can be shown that the pressure of a vapour (A) in equilibrium with a small drop of the liquid (B) at a given temperature $T$ is larger the smaller the radius $r$ of this drop. A vapour which is supersaturated in the usual sense, i.e. with respect to a 'drop' of liquid with an infinitely large radius (i.e. with a plane boundary surface), can be 'non-saturated' with respect to a drop with a sufficiently small radius.

If the latter is not too small (see below), the surface free energy of the drop can be represented as the product of its surface $4\pi r^2$ with the ordinary surface tension $\sigma$ corresponding to $r = \infty$ (and to a given vapour pressure).

The thermodynamical potential of the whole system, consisting of the vapour A and of the liquid drop B, is expressed, under such conditions, by the formula

$$\Phi = N_A \phi_A + N_B \phi_B + 4\pi r^2 \sigma, \tag{1}$$

where $N_A$ and $N_B$ denote the number of particles constituting A and B, while $\phi_A$ and $\phi_B$ are the 'chemical' potentials, referred to one particle of the corresponding phase, at the given temperature $T$ and *external* pressure $p$, equal to the pressure of the vapour (it should be noted that the pressure inside the liquid drop $p'$ must be larger than $p$ by the amount $2\sigma/r$).

The thermodynamic equilibrium of the system under consideration is determined by the condition $\delta\Phi = 0$, which, in connexion with $N_A + N_B =$ const., leads to the equation

$$\phi_B - \phi_A + 4\pi\sigma \frac{dr^2}{dN_B} = 0.$$

Denoting the volume occupied by one particle in the liquid phase by $v_B$, we have $N_B = \dfrac{4\pi r^3}{3v_B}$, and consequently

$$\phi_B - \phi_A + \frac{2\sigma}{r} v_B = 0. \tag{1 a}$$

In the limiting case $r \to \infty$ this equation is reduced to the ordinary equilibrium condition $\phi_A = \phi_B$. If at the temperature $T$ the latter is satisfied for a certain value $p_\infty$ of the pressure, the equation (1 a) will be satisfied for a somewhat different value $p$, depending on the radius of the drop $r$. Differentiating the equation (1 a) for a fixed value of $T$ and noting that in this case $d\phi_A = v_A\, dp$ and $d\phi_B = v_B\, dp$ (where $v_A$ is the volume per molecule in the gas phase), we get

$$(v_A - v_B)\, dp = 2\sigma v_B\, d\left(\frac{1}{r}\right).$$

If $v_B$ is neglected compared with $v_A$ and if the vapour is treated as an ideal gas, for which $v_A = kT/p$, this equation can be rewritten in the form

$$kT d(\log p) = 2\sigma v_B\, d\left(\frac{1}{r}\right),$$

whence

$$\log \frac{p}{p_\infty} = \frac{2\sigma v_B}{rkT}. \tag{2}$$

It is interesting to note that the same result is obtained if the surface free energy is not introduced in the expression $\Phi$ for the potential of the system (A, B), while it is taken into account that the pressure within the drop $p_r$ is equal to $p+2\sigma/r$ and this pressure is treated as the external pressure for the liquid phase. In fact, putting

$$\Phi = N_A \phi_A(T,p)+N_B \phi_B(T,p_r)$$

we find from the equilibrium condition $\delta\Phi = 0$ in conjunction with $N_A+N_B = \text{const.}$, that

$$\phi_A(p) = \phi_B\left(p+\frac{2\sigma}{r}\right) = \phi_B+\frac{\partial\phi_B}{\partial p}\frac{2\sigma}{r},$$

i.e.
$$\phi_A(p) = \phi_B(p)+v_B\frac{2\sigma}{r}.$$

The increase of the vapour pressure about a liquid drop can be considered, from the molecular-kinetic point of view, as a direct consequence of the decrease of the evaporation energy in connexion with the increasing contribution of the surface energy of the drop with a decrease of its size.

If this surface energy could be left out of account, the evaporation energy of the drop would be equal to $U_\infty N_B$, where $U_\infty$ is the evaporation energy of a large mass of liquid referred to one molecule and equal, according to Langmuir, to $w_B q_B$. Since, however, a liquid drop possesses a surface energy $w_B 4\pi r^2$, the total energy required for its evaporation is diminished by this amount, being thus equal to

$$N_B U_\infty - w4\pi r^2.$$

The energy $U_N$, required for the evaporation of one molecule from a drop consisting of $N_B = N$ molecules, is obtained by differentiating this expression with respect to $N$; we thus have

$$U_N = U_\infty - 4\pi w\frac{d}{dN}r^2,$$

or, since $\frac{4}{3}\pi r^3 = v_B N$,
$$U_N = U_\infty - \frac{2w}{r}v_B. \tag{3}$$

According to Boltzmann's law the vapour pressure about a drop consisting of $N$ molecules must be proportional to $e^{-U_N/kT}$. Hence

$$\frac{p_N}{p_\infty} = e^{-(U_N-U_\infty)/kT} = e^{2wv_B/rkT}. \tag{3 a}$$

This formula differs from that of Thomson by the substitution of the surface energy $w$ for the surface tension $\sigma$. For small values of the radius this substitution is fully justified, from the point of view of the general theory developed in § 4 of the preceding chapter; for large values of $r$ it is practically irrelevant, for the corresponding corrections become insignificant.

It must be borne in mind that $r$ cannot be smaller than the average distance between neighbouring molecules (in the liquid phase). This limiting value $r_0$ of $r$ corresponds to an embryonic drop consisting of a small number (2–8) of molecules. It is clear that the preceding macroscopic theory cannot be strictly applied to such small 'drops'. Its application enables one, however, to estimate the limiting degree of supersaturation, i.e. the maximum value of $p_N/p_\infty$ corresponding to the smallest possible values of $N$. Putting $N \approx 8$ and $v_B \approx 4r^3$ we get

$$\log \frac{p_{\max}}{p_\infty} \cong \frac{8wr^2}{kT}.$$

This gives, if we take $w = 100$ erg/cm.$^2$, $r = 4.10^{-8}$ cm., and $T = 300$, $\log p_{\max}/p_\infty = 4$, i.e. $p_{\max} \approx 100 p_\infty$.

For such high degrees of supersaturation embryonic droplets, consisting of but a few molecules and arising accidentally as a result of density fluctuations in the vapour, are capable not only of existing in the presence of the vapour (which is saturated with respect to them) but to develop rapidly and thus cause its condensation.

It should be noted that, for any degree of supersaturation, the equilibrium of the drops, having a radius $r_p$ connected with the pressure by the formula (2) or (3 a), with the vapour is an *unstable* one. In fact, the vapour, being saturated with respect to such drops, is unsaturated with respect to smaller and supersaturated with respect to larger ones. Hence the former must have a tendency to evaporate and the latter to grow up more and more (until the pressure of the remaining vapour decreases to the normal value $p_\infty$).

The preceding considerations can be applied with a few minor modifications to the converse process of the boiling up of a superheated liquid, that is of a liquid subject to a pressure which is smaller than the equilibrium pressure of the saturated vapour at a given temperature $T$ with respect to a plane surface $p_\infty$. Of special interest is the case of a *negative* pressure $p < 0$, tending to 'break up' the liquid. With respect to such a pressure the latter is unstable, or rather *metastable*, at any temperature.

It may be imagined (which, as will be seen below, is not actually the fact), that the breakdown of the liquid takes place in the form of an embryonic gas bubble which rapidly grows to macroscopic dimensions. It thus becomes necessary to investigate the relation between the radius of the bubble and the vapour pressure $p_r$ in it, which corresponds to an equilibrium with respect to the surrounding liquid phase, if the latter is subjected to an external pressure $p$.

The condition of mechanical equilibrium between the bubble and the liquid is expressed by the same equation

$$p_r = p+\frac{2\sigma}{r}$$

as in the case of the equilibrium between a liquid drop and a vapour. The condition of thermodynamic equilibrium between the two phases is likewise given by the equation (1 a), if the index A is understood to refer to the liquid and B to the gaseous phase (and not vice versa, as before).

If the difference $|p-p_\infty|$ is small, we can put

$$\phi_B(p)-v_A(p) = (v_B-v_A)(p-p_\infty) \cong v_B(p-p_\infty),$$

since $v_B \gg v_A$, whence

$$p_\infty - p = \frac{2\sigma}{r}. \tag{4}$$

The same result is obtained from the exact equation

$$\phi_A(p) = \phi_B\left(p+\frac{2\sigma}{r}\right).$$

Differentiating both sides of this equation with respect to $p$ we get

$$v_A\,dp = v'_B\left(dp+2\sigma d\frac{1}{r}\right),$$

where $v'_B$ is the value of $v_B$ for a pressure $p+2\sigma/r$, that is, since $v'_B \gg v_A$, $dp+2\sigma d(1/r) = 0$, which is equivalent to (4).

A comparison of this equation with the equation of mechanical equilibrium shows that $p_r = p_\infty$. The vapour pressure inside the bubble, in a state of thermodynamic equilibrium with the liquid, is thus independent of its size, that is, equal to the pressure exerted at the same temperature against a plane surface.

Since, however, according to (4) it is larger than the pressure of the surrounding liquid in inverse proportion to the radius of the bubble, this equilibrium proves to be unstable with respect to a variation of the radius. In fact, so long as $p_\infty$ remains constant, this inner pressure must become larger than the outer (mechanical-capillary) pressure $p_r = p+(2\sigma/r)$ when $r$ is increased above the value defined by (4), which we shall denote by $r_p$, and smaller than $p_r$ when $r < r_p$. In the former case the bubble must expand and in the latter collapse.

The expansion of a bubble means a breakdown of the liquid, that is, in other words, its 'cavitation' or 'boiling up'. We thus see that the condition for the breakdown is the existence at a given temperature, corresponding to a (normal) vapour pressure $p_\infty$, of an embryonic bubble or cavity with a critical radius defined by (4), that is

$$r_p = \frac{2\sigma}{p_\infty - p}. \tag{4a}$$

The usual condition which serves to determine the boiling-point of a liquid is given by $p_\infty = p$. We see that in reality $p_\infty$ must be larger than $p$ for the boiling process to start, the maximum possible value of the difference $p_\infty - p$ being of the order $2\sigma/\delta$, where $\delta$ is the mean distance between neighbouring molecules, i.e. a length of the order of $10^{-8}$. Putting $\sigma \sim 100$, we get $(p_\infty - p)_{\max} \cong 10^{10}$ dyne/cm.$^2$ = $10^4$ kg./cm.$^2$ This means that at moderate temperatures for which $p_\infty$ is relatively small the liquid can be broken apart or, in other words, forced to boil up, by the application of a negative pressure of the order of 10,000 atmospheres. This result has already been obtained before (see Ch. VI, § 5).

The process of boiling (or cavitation) is usually considered not for a given value of the temperature (i.e. of $p_\infty$), but of the external pressure $p$. Under such conditions the preceding results can be stated in a somewhat different form, namely, that the temperature at which the process of boiling can start must be higher than the standard temperature of the boiling-point $T_0$, determined by the condition $p_\infty = p$. In the presence of an embryonic bubble with a radius $r$ this 'starting' temperature $T$ must exceed $T_0$ by an amount corresponding to an excess of the value $p_\infty$ with respect to $p$ by the capillary pressure $2\sigma/r$. If the latter is small, the difference $T - T_0$ can be calculated with the help of the thermodynamical equation of Clausius–Clapeyron

$$\frac{dp}{dT} = \frac{\lambda}{T(v_B - v_A)},$$

where $\lambda$ is the latent heat of evaporation referred to one molecule; we need only replace in this equation $dp$ by $2\sigma/r$ and $dT$ by $T - T_0$. This gives

$$T - T_0 = \frac{T(v_B - v_A)}{\lambda}\frac{2\sigma}{r} \cong \frac{T_0 v_B}{\lambda}\frac{2\sigma}{r},$$

or, since $v_B \cong kT_0/p$,

$$T - T_0 = \frac{2\sigma k T_0^2}{p\lambda r}. \tag{5}$$

This equation connects the initial radius of the gas bubble with the 'overheating' of the liquid with respect to the normal point, $T-T_0$.

In the case of large overheatings the relation

$$p = \text{const. } e^{-\lambda/kT},$$

which is obtained by integrating the Clausius–Clapeyron equation, under the assumption $v_B - v_A \cong v_B \cong kT/p$, can be used. We then get

$$\log\frac{p+2(\sigma/r)}{p} = +\frac{\lambda}{k}\left(\frac{1}{T_0}-\frac{1}{T}\right),$$

that is,

$$T-T_0 = \frac{kT_0 T}{\lambda}\log\left(1+\frac{2\sigma}{pr}\right). \tag{5 a}$$

This expression reduces to (5) if $2\sigma/r \ll p$. For a given degree of overheating $T-T_0$ (or $T/T_0$) this equation determines the minimum size of a gas bubble whose pre-existence is a necessary condition for the boiling process to start.

It should be noted that a similar transition, from the variable pressure as determining the state of the system A+B for a given temperature $T_0$, to a variable temperature as determining its state at a given pressure $p_0$, can be performed in the case of a supersaturated vapour previously considered. If, at a given temperature, the supersaturation of the vapour is due to its overcompression as measured by the ratio $p/p_\infty$, then at a given pressure $p_0$ it can be due to its *undercooling*, as measured by the difference $T_0-T$ (or the ratio $T_0/T$). The relation between the two is obtained, just as in the case of a superheated or undercompressed (extended) liquid, with the help of the Clausius–Clapeyron equation, or the equation $p = \text{const. } e^{-\lambda/T}$. Using the latter equation and replacing in (2) $\log p/p_\infty$ by $\lambda/k\{(1/T)-(1/T_0)\}$ we get

$$T_0-T = \frac{2\sigma T_0 v_B}{\lambda r}, \tag{5 b}$$

where $v_B$ is the molecular volume of the liquid phase, and $r$ the radius of a drop which is in a state of (unstable) equilibrium with the vapour cooled by $T_0-T$ degrees below the conventional condensation point.

It should be mentioned that both in the case of an overcooled vapour and of an overheated liquid $r$ tends to infinity when $T$ tends to $T_0$ or $p$ to $p_\infty$.

We shall illustrate the preceding results by a few figures, referring to water. Putting in (5) $T_0 = 373$ and $p = 1$ atm. $= 10^6$ dynes/cm.$^2$ (conventional boiling-point), we get with $\sigma = 70$ and $\lambda = 7.10^{-13}$ erg (500 cal./gm.).

$$r \cong 10^{-5}\frac{T_0}{T-T_0} \cong \frac{4.10^{-3}}{T-T_0}\text{cm.},$$

i.e. $r = 4.10^{-3}$ cm. for an overheating by 1° C. Under the same conditions equation (5 b) gives

$$r = 6\times10^{-9}\frac{T_0}{T-T_0} \cong \frac{2\times10^{-6}}{T-T_0}\text{ cm.},$$

that is, $r \cong 2\times10^{-6}$ cm. for a water drop in equilibrium with a vapour with a pressure of 1 atm., undercooled by 1° C.

## 2. Embryos of the Liquid Phase in a Vapour near the Saturation Point

The instability of the equilibrium between a supersaturated vapour and a liquid drop, or between an overheated (extended) liquid and a gas bubble of the corresponding radius $r^*$ with respect to a variation of the latter is expressed, in a formal way, by the fact that the thermodynamical potential $\Phi$ of the system formed by them has for $r = r^*$ $(= r_p)$ not a minimum value, as in the case of ordinary stable equilibrium, but, on the contrary, a *maximum* value. In fact, denoting the value of $\Phi$ corresponding to the absence of the drop (or bubble) by $\Phi_0$, we have, according to (1):

$$\Delta\Phi = \Phi-\Phi_0 = \phi_A N_A+\phi_B N_B+4\pi r^2\sigma-\phi_A(N_A+N_B),$$

i.e.

$$\Delta\Phi = -(\phi_A-\phi_B)N_B+4\pi r^2\sigma$$

or

$$\Delta\Phi = -\frac{\phi_A-\phi_B}{v_B}\frac{4\pi}{3}r^3+4\pi\sigma r^2. \tag{6}$$

Putting here, according to (1 a), $(\phi_A-\phi_B)/v_B = 2\sigma/r^*$, we get

$$\Delta\Phi = 4\pi\sigma\left(-\frac{2}{3}\frac{r^3}{r^*}+r^2\right). \tag{6 a}$$

When $r$ is increased (starting from zero), this expression increases until, for $r = r^*$, it reaches a maximum value

$$\Delta\Phi_{\max} = \frac{4\pi}{3}\sigma r^{*2}, \tag{6 b}$$

decreasing monotonically with a further increase of $r$, as shown by the full line in Fig. 46. If the initial phase (A) is in a thermodynamically stable condition, i.e. if $\phi_A < \phi_B$, $\Delta\Phi$ is a monotonically rising function of $r$ represented by the dotted curve in Fig. 46 (for small values of $r$ it must practically coincide with the full line, corresponding to $\phi_A > \phi_B$, because of the prevalence of the surface term, which is quadratic in $r$).

Now, even in a thermodynamically stable system *fluctuations*, i.e. local and transient deviations from the normal state, must take place, which bring it into a state of higher potential and smaller probability.

In the usual statistical theory of a homogeneous molecular system, in particular of a gas or liquid, fluctuations of the *density* are considered which lie within the limits compatible with the preservation of a given aggregation state of the system. These ordinary density fluctuations may be denoted as 'homophase'. Along with them it is, however, necessary to take into account density fluctuations transcending the

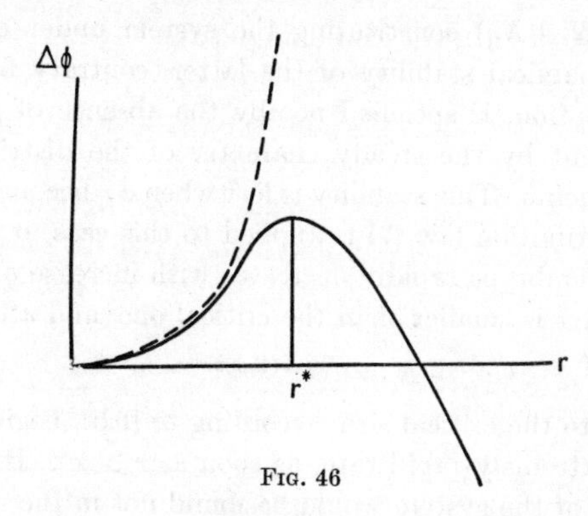


FIG. 46

above limit and giving rise to small embryos of another phase of the same substance (e.g. liquid droplets in a gas, or vapour bubbles in a liquid). Such fluctuations will be denoted in the sequel as 'heterophase'. They must become especially important in the neighbourhood of the equilibrium curve $\phi_A(p,T) = \phi_B(p,T)$ between the main phase A (corresponding to the given aggregation state) and some other phase B of the same substance. So long as the main phase is thermodynamically stable in the sense that $\phi_A < \phi_B$, embryos of the new phase will remain abortive, i.e. they will arise, reach a relatively small size, and decay again, without a pronounced tendency for further growth. If, however, the initial phase is thermodynamically unstable or rather *metastable* ($\phi_A > \phi_B$), such a tendency will become prevalent in the case of those embryos of the new phase which have been able to reach the critical size, corresponding to the maximum of the potential $\Delta\Phi$. Such embryos, which may be likened to new-born babies, capable of further growth and development, are often denoted as the 'nuclei' of the new phase. We thus see that as soon as $\phi_A$ becomes larger than $\phi_B$ a transformation $A \rightarrow B$ must begin, its rate being, however, limited by the necessity of passing through the 'potential barrier' $\Delta\Phi$, which plays a role similar to that of the activation energy in the process of diffusion or in chemical reactions. In the case $\phi_A < \phi_B$ the embryos of the B phase must form a population characterized by a steady distribution with respect to their size. This distribution is determined by Boltzmann's (or rather Gibbs's) formula

$$N_r = Ce^{-\Delta\phi(r)/kT}, \tag{7}$$

where $C$ is a proportionality constant which, so long as the number of embryos remains relatively small, is of the order of the total number of molecules $(N_A+N_B)$ constituting the system under consideration. The thermodynamical stability of the latter, contrary to the usually accepted conception, is specified not by the absence of any traces of the B phase, but by the steady character of the distribution of its embryonic elements. This stability is lost when $\phi_A$ becomes larger than $\phi_B$. If the distribution law (7) is applied to this case, it is found that the number of embryos rapidly decreases with increase of their size so long as the latter is smaller than the critical one, and after reaching a minimum value

$$N_{r^*} = Ce^{-(4\pi/3)\sigma r^{*2}} \tag{7 a}$$

corresponding to the critical size, according to (6 b), begins to increase again, at an extremely rapid rate, as soon as $r > r^*$. If this were so, the main mass of the system would be found not in the initial state A but in the final one B. Although this agrees in a formal way with the ordinary view of the transition $A \to B$, yet the picture obtained of a disperse system, constituted by isolated B elements (small and large) suspended in a continuous medium formed by the remains of A, is just the reverse of what would actually be found in a *stable* equilibrium of the system A+B when $\phi_A > \phi_B$, the phase B playing the role of the continuous medium and the phase A being represented by separate embryos, distributed according to the law (7).

Thus, for example, if A denotes the gas phase and B the liquid phase, we should find, according to (7), in the case $\phi_A > \phi_B$, that the major part of all the molecules are combined into drops of macroscopic size, which do not coalesce into a continuous liquid phase. This paradoxical result is explained by the fact that the distribution law (7) does not take into account the mutual action between the elements of the new phase, which are treated as if they were wholly isolated from each other.

We shall come back to this question in the next section, dealing with the kinetics of the condensation process and other processes of the same sort (e.g. kinetics of the phase transition $A \to B$), and shall examine here in more detail and from a somewhat different point of view the question of the distribution of B embryos amidst the A phase, when the latter is assumed to be thermodynamically stable, i.e. when $\phi_A < \phi_B$.

We shall consider first the special case of 'heterophase fluctuations', consisting of the combination of the molecules of a gas or vapour near the saturation point into complexes, which, when they are large enough, can be described as liquid drops. The combination of gas molecules into smaller complexes, consisting of two, three, or more units, can be described more adequately as their chemical combination or 'association' under the influence of van der Waals's cohesive forces. The fundamental distinction of these forces from genuine chemical forces consists not so much in their relative weakness as in the *absence of saturation* and in the resulting absence in the degree of association. This character of the molecular forces leads to an increase of the association energy with the increase of the degree of association from a relatively low value in the case of two molecules to a certain limit (reached practically for a complex of a few hundreds or thousands of molecules), equal to the macroscopic latent heat of condensation (per molecule). So long as the degree of association is high, the decrease of the association energy with a decrease of the size of the associated complex, treated as a small drop, can be referred to the surface energy of the latter. This notion is, however, inapplicable to low degrees of association; in this case the notion of 'drops' must be replaced by that of associated molecular complexes.

If the energy set free in the formation of a double molecule is equal to $U$, then the energy released in the formation of a condensed (solid or liquid) body, where each molecule is surrounded by twelve neighbours (tight-packed arrangement, which is found in the case of condensed argon, for example), is equal to $6U$, on the assumption that the distance between the nearest neighbours is practically independent of their number and that the interaction with more distant molecules can be neglected. It is clear that, under such conditions, the number of complexes of a low degree of association in a vapour—both under- and oversaturated—must be relatively small, i.e. much smaller than it would have been if the association energy were independent of the degree of association.

Turning to a quantitative formulation of the theory, let us denote by $N_g$ the number of complexes, consisting of $g$ simple molecules having a similar structure, corresponding to the least possible value of the potential energy $U_g$ compatible with the given value of $g$. If the associated complexes are treated as complex molecules, our assumption reduces to a neglect of the phenomenon of isomerism (out of all possible isomers with a given value of $g$, only that isomer is considered for which $U_g = \min.$). It can easily be shown that an allowance for 'isomerism', i.e. for a possible variation of the shape and size of the complexes consisting of the same number of molecules, is practically irrelevant so far as the results are concerned.

In order to determine the relative number of complexes with different degrees of association, we shall treat the system constituted by them (including the single molecules) as an ideal gas mixture and shall make use of the equations of statistical mechanism serving to describe the chemical equilibrium in such a mixture.

Let us consider an elementary chemical reaction, consisting of the combination of a single molecule $A_1$ with a complex $A_{g-1}$ consisting of $g-1$ molecules and thus giving rise to a complex $A_g$. The condition of equilibrium between this reaction and the reciprocal reaction of the dissociation of $A_g$ into $A_{g-1}$ and $A_1$ is expressed, as is well known, by the equation:

$$\frac{N_{g-1}N_1}{N_g} = \frac{Z_{g-1}Z_1}{Z_g}, \tag{8}$$

where $Z_g$ denotes the partition function $\sum_{W_g} e^{-W_g/kT}$, the summation being extended over all possible states of the corresponding complex. In the case of high temperatures this sum can be replaced by the integral

$$Z_g = \frac{1}{h^{3gs}g!}\int e^{-W_g/kT}\,d\Gamma_g = e^{-\psi_g/kT}, \tag{8 a}$$

where $s$ is the number of atoms in a single molecule $A_1$, $\psi_g$ the free energy of the complex $A_g$, and $\Gamma_g$ the corresponding extension in phase. Replacing in (8) $g$ by $g-1$, etc., and multiplying the resulting equations, we get

$$\frac{N_1^g}{N_g} = \frac{Z_1^g}{Z_g}. \tag{9}$$

This equation can be regarded as the condition of the equilibrium with respect to the reaction.

If the volume occupied by the whole system is equal to $V$, then

$$Z_1 = V\left(\frac{2\pi mkT}{h^2}\right)^{\frac{3}{2}} Z_1' e^{-U/kT}, \tag{9 a}$$

where $Z_1'$ is the partition function corresponding to the rotation and vibration motion of the molecule $A_1$, and $U$ its potential energy in the absence of this motion, i.e. at $T = 0$. In the case of complexes consisting of a large number of molecules $A_1$ (say, 1,000), i.e. representing minute drops (or crystals), the free energy $\psi_g$ can be assumed to be proportional to $g$ and practically independent of the volume $V$ of the whole system. Putting $\psi_g = \psi_0 g$, we get, according to (8 a),

$$Z_g = (e^{-\psi_0/kT})^g,$$

and further, according to (8),

$$N_g = \xi^g, \tag{10}$$

where
$$\xi = \frac{N_1 e^{-\psi_0/kT}}{Z_1} = \frac{N_1}{VZ_1'}\left(\frac{h^2}{2\pi mkT}\right)^{\frac{3}{2}} e^{-(\psi_0-U)/kT}. \tag{10 a}$$

If $\xi < 1$, the values $N_g$ form a decreasing geometrical series, which corresponds to a stable state of the vapour, i.e. to lack of saturation. If $\xi > 1$ the vapour tends to condense, the number of complexes increasing with $g$. The case $\xi = 1$ must obviously correspond to a *saturated* vapour. Its density, or rather the concentration of the non-associated fraction of its molecules, is thus given by the formula

$$n_1 = \frac{N_1}{V} = \left(\frac{2\pi mkT}{h^2}\right)^{\frac{3}{2}} Z_1' e^{-(U-\psi_0)/kT}. \tag{11}$$

This result exactly agrees with that which is obtained in the usual way, i.e. from a consideration of the condition of equilibrium between a saturated vapour and a liquid on the assumption that any intermediate degrees of association between $g = 1$ and $g = \infty$ are absent.

For the sake of illustration we shall consider the case of a substance which in the gaseous state is, or rather is assumed to be, monatomic, for instance argon, or some metallic vapour. We have in this case $Z_1' = 1$ and

$$\psi_0 = U_0 - 3kT\log\frac{kT}{h\bar{\nu}}, \tag{11 a}$$

where $U_0$ is the energy of one particle (atom) in the condensed phase, and $\bar{\nu}$ the average vibration frequency. Substituting this expression in (11) we get

$$n_1 = \left(\frac{2\pi m\bar{\nu}}{kT}\right)^{\frac{3}{2}} e^{-(U-U_0)/kT} \tag{11 b}$$

in agreement with the usual method, which does not take into account the association phenomenon.

We have limited ourselves thus far to a consideration of complexes of such a large size that their free energy could be treated as strictly proportional to the number of single particles constituting them. We shall now take into account smaller complexes, for which the deviation from this proportionality can be reduced to the influence of the surface energy. This method can be applied to complexes with $g > 30$, for example. Assuming the area of the surface to be proportional to $g^{\frac{2}{3}}$

(which corresponds to the independence of the density of a complex on its size), we can represent its free energy in the form

$$\psi_g = \psi_0 g + \mu g^{\frac{2}{3}}, \tag{12}$$

where $\psi_0$ is given by (11 a) and $\mu$ is a constant proportional to the surface tension or rather to the surface energy. Substituting this expression in (8 a) and (9) we get

$$N_g = \xi^g e^{-\mu g^{\frac{2}{3}}/kT}. \tag{12 a}$$

If $\xi < 1$ (unsaturated vapour) the series $N_g$ decreases monotonically with increase of $g$, as before. If, however, $\xi > 1$ (supersaturated vapour), we obtain at first a decrease of $N_g$ due to the prevailing influence of the second factor and thereafter an increase. The value $g = g^*$ corresponding to the minimum of $N_g$ is determined by the equation $\partial \log N_g/\partial g = 0$, i.e.

$$\log \xi = \frac{2}{3}\frac{\mu}{kTg^{\frac{1}{3}}}. \tag{12 b}$$

Since for a given temperature the quantity $\xi$, according to (10 a), is proportional to the concentration, and, consequently, to the pressure $p$ of the unsaturated vapour, and since for $p = p_\infty$ (saturation) $\xi = 1$, $\xi$ can be replaced in this equation by the ratio $p/p_\infty$. If, further, the complexes are treated as droplets with a radius $r_g$, defined by $\frac{4}{3}\pi r_g^3 = v_1 g$ ($v_1 = v_B$ the volume occupied by a single molecule in the liquid phase), then putting $\mu g^{\frac{2}{3}} = 4\pi r^2\sigma$ we have

$$\frac{3\sigma}{r} = \frac{\mu}{v_1 g^{\frac{1}{3}}}.$$

Hence in the case of drop-like complexes the preceding formula can be written in the form

$$\log\frac{p}{p_\infty} = \frac{2\sigma v_1}{kTr},$$

which coincides with Thomson's formula (2).

Substituting from (12 b) in (12 a) we get $N_{g^*} = (\xi e^{-\mu/kTg^{*\frac{1}{3}}})^{g^*}$, i.e.

$$N_{g^*} = e^{-\frac{1}{3}(\mu g^{*\frac{2}{3}}/kT)} = e^{-4\pi r^{*2}\sigma/3kT}.$$

This expression differs from (7) by the factor $C$ which in our case turns out to be equal to 1. Owing to this circumstance the values of $N_g$ obtained by us prove to be smaller than 1. This result is, of course, devoid of physical meaning. It is due to the fact that in the calculation of $Z_g$ we did not take into account the translation and rotation degrees of freedom of the complex. We have thereby simplified the statement of our results, without essentially altering the dependence of $N_g$ on $g$

and the other parameters, but have reduced the corresponding expressions to a form which cannot be applied for the calculation of the absolute number of complexes of various compositions.

In reality, in calculating $Z_g$, just as in the special case $g = 1$ (formula (9 a)), we must put

$$Z_g = V\left(\frac{2\pi mgkT}{h^2}\right)^{\frac{3}{2}} Z'_g \, e^{-U_g/kT},$$

where $Z'_g$ is the partition function corresponding to the rotation and vibration motion of the complex and $U_g$ denotes its potential energy, which can be taken as equal to zero.

In calculating the partition function $Z'_g$ we must separate a factor corresponding to the rotation motion of the complex as a whole; the remaining part only can be represented in the form corresponding to the expression (12) for the free energy with the factor $g$ replaced by $g-2$, as a consequence of the elimination of the six translational and rotational degrees of freedom.

Neglecting the latter circumstance and noting that the rotational factor of $Z'_g$ is equal to

$$\left(\frac{8\pi^2 J_g kT}{h^2}\right)^{\frac{3}{2}},$$

where $J_g$ is the moment of inertia of the complex with respect to one of its axes, we have approximately, since $J_g \simeq mg(v_1 g)^{\frac{2}{3}}$

$$Z_g = V\left(\frac{2\pi mgkT}{h^2}\right)^{\frac{3}{2}}\left(\frac{8\pi^2 mg^{\frac{5}{3}} v_1^{\frac{2}{3}} kT}{h^2}\right)^{\frac{3}{2}} e^{-(\phi_0 g + \mu g^{\frac{2}{3}})/kT},$$

and consequently
$$N_g = C_g \xi^g e^{-\mu g^{\frac{2}{3}}/kT},$$

where
$$C_g = 64\pi^{\frac{9}{2}} V v_1 g^4 \left(\frac{mkT}{h^2}\right)^3.$$

The quantity $h/\sqrt{(mkT)}$ is equal to the de Broglie wave-length corresponding to the average value of the thermal velocity of a single molecule; in the case of particles with a molecular weight 10–100 at $T = 300$, $\lambda$ is of the order of $10^{-8}$–$10^{-9}$ cm., i.e. of the same order as $v_1^{\frac{1}{3}}$. The coefficient

$$C_g = 64\pi^{\frac{9}{2}} \frac{V v_1}{\lambda^6} g^4$$

is thus of the order of $10^4 g^4 V/v_1$, where $V/v_1$ is the number of molecules which would fill the volume $V$ in the liquid state of the substance. This is a very high figure; the absolute number of complexes, consisting of $g$ ($\gg 1$) molecules, can therefore be very large, while remaining small compared with the total number of molecules.

## 3. General Theory of Heterophase Fluctuations and Pre-transition Phenomena

We shall now turn to a generalization of the preceding theory to the case of heterophase fluctuations of any kind.†

We shall assume, in contradistinction from the rough thermodynamic treatment, that even in the range of thermodynamic stability of the phase A, the latter is not strictly homogeneous, but contains embryos of a second phase B (in the form of liquid drops, gas bubbles, small crystals, etc.) which become especially numerous in the 'pre-transition' state of A.

Our problem consists in the determination of the statistical distribution of the B embryos in the phase A at a given temperature $T$ and pressure $p$ (other parameters which may influence the equilibrium condition of the system will be left out of account).

Under such conditions the B embryos can be characterized by their volume $v$ or by the number of simple molecules $g$ constituting them, while their statistical distribution is described by the function $N_g$ equal to the number of embryos of a given size.

This description is, of course, incomplete, for embryos of the same size can have different shapes, etc. We shall, however, limit ourselves to a definite shape corresponding to the minimum of the free energy of the surface for a given volume. (In the case of liquid embryos in a gas or embryonic gas bubbles in a liquid this most advantageous shape is of course a spherical one.) The results of the simple theory are not substantially altered by the introduction of other shapes, or densities, besides the most advantageous one.

Under such simplifying conditions the problem of the determination of the distribution function $N_g$ can be solved as follows:

Let $\phi_A(p, T)$ and $\phi_B(p, T)$ denote the thermodynamical potentials referred to a single molecule of the corresponding phases. The transformation point, or rather curve $(p, T)$, is determined by the condition $\phi_A = \phi_B$. We shall assume that the pressure has a given value $p_0$, corresponding to a definite transition temperature $T_0$; we shall assume, further, that the actual temperature $T$ is different from $T_0$, so that $\phi_A(p_0, T) < \phi_B(p_0, T)$.

The transition of $g$ molecules of the A phase into an embryo of the B phase is accompanied by a change of the potential of the whole system by an amount equal to the sum of $g[\phi_B(p_0, T) - \phi_A(p_0, T)]$ and

† See J. Frenkel, *J. of Phys.* **1**, 315 (1939). A similar theory was proposed simultaneously by Bijl, Dissertation, Leiden, 1939.

of the surface free energy between A and B, which can be represented as $\alpha g^{\frac{2}{3}}$.

The total increase of the thermodynamic potential $\Phi$ is thus equal to

$$\Delta\Phi = (\phi_B - \phi_A)g + \alpha g^{\frac{2}{3}}.$$

This formula is a generalization of formula (12) referring to the association of gas molecules, $\phi_B - \phi_A$ standing for $\psi_0$.

The embryos can be treated, in the general case, as particles of a *diluted solution* of a number of different substances constituted by embryos of the same size, the phase A playing the role of the solvent. The thermodynamic potential of such a solution is given by the formula

$$\Phi = N_A\phi_A + \sum_g N_g(\phi_B g + \alpha g^{\frac{2}{3}}) + kT\left(N_A \log\frac{N_A}{F} + \sum_g N_g \log\frac{N_g}{F}\right), \quad (13)$$

where

$$F = N_A + \sum N_g \quad (13\,a)$$

denotes the total number of 'molecules' in the generalized sense, the nuclei of different size being treated as molecules of different kinds.

The last term in (13 a) corresponds to the entropy increase associated with the process of mixing. If this term were dropped, the equilibrium condition $\delta\Phi = 0$ along with the accessory condition

$$N_A + \sum gN_g = N = \text{const.} \quad (13\,b)$$

($N$ total number of simple molecules) would lead to a system of equations $\phi_B - \phi_A = \mu g^{-\frac{1}{3}}$ which are incompatible with each other for different values of $g$.

Coming back to the formula (13) we must complete the condition (13 b) by a set of equations of the type

$$\delta N_A : \delta N_{g-1} : \delta N_g = 1:1:(-1), \quad (14)$$

which describe a 'chemical reaction' consisting of the transition of one simple molecule from an embryo $A_g$ (which is thereby transformed into $A_{g-1}$) to the 'solvent' A.

Taking the variation of $\Phi$ corresponding to the 'reaction' (14), we get

$$\phi_A - (\phi_B g + \mu g^{\frac{2}{3}}) + [\phi_B(g-1) + \mu(g-1)^{\frac{2}{3}}] + kT\left(\log\frac{N_{g-1}}{N_g} + \log\frac{N_A}{F}\right) = 0,$$

i.e.

$$\frac{N_g}{N_{g-1}} = \frac{N_A}{F} e^{-(1/kT)\{(\phi_B - \phi_A) + \mu[g^{\frac{2}{3}} - (g-1)^{\frac{2}{3}}]\}} \cong \frac{N_A}{F} e^{-[(\phi_B - \phi_A) + \frac{2}{3}\mu g^{-\frac{1}{3}}]/kT}. \quad (15)$$

If $g$ is replaced here by $g-1$, $g-2$,..., $g_0$ and the resulting expressions are multiplied by each other, the following expression for $N_g$ is obtained:

$$N_g = \left(\frac{N_A}{F}\right)^{g-g_0} N_{g_0} e^{-(1/kT)[(g-g_0)(\phi_B - \phi_A) + \mu(g^{\frac{2}{3}} - g_0^{\frac{2}{3}})]}. \quad (15\,a)$$

Here $g_0$ denotes the smallest value of $g$ for which the notion of B embryos preserves a physical meaning. In the case of liquid drops in a gas one can put $g_0 = 2$; in the case of drops in crystals, or crystalline nuclei and gas bubbles in liquids, $g_0$ must be much larger. The condition (14) must be altered in the case $g = g_0$, since an embryo of the smallest size can be destroyed, according to the definition, by a simultaneous transition of all the $g_0$ molecules constituting it, into the phase A. This process is characterized by the relation

$$\delta N_{\mathrm{A}} : \delta N_{g_0} = g_0 : (-1),$$

which gives

$$\phi_{\mathrm{A}} g_0 - (\phi_{\mathrm{B}} g_0 + \mu g_0^{\frac{2}{3}}) + kT\left(g_0 \log \frac{N_{\mathrm{A}}}{F} - \log \frac{N_{g_0}}{F}\right) = 0,$$

that is,

$$N_{g_0} = F\left(\frac{N_{\mathrm{A}}}{F}\right)^{g_0} e^{-(g_0/kT)[(\phi_{\mathrm{B}}-\phi_{\mathrm{A}})+\mu g_0^{-\frac{1}{3}}]}. \tag{15 b}$$

Combining this with (15 a) we find

$$N_g = F\left(\frac{N_{\mathrm{A}}}{F}\right)^{g} e^{-[(\phi_{\mathrm{B}}-\phi_{\mathrm{A}})g+\mu g^{\frac{2}{3}}]/kT}, \tag{16}$$

or

$$N_g = F\xi^g e^{-\mu g^{\frac{2}{3}}/kT}, \tag{16 a}$$

with

$$\xi = \frac{N_{\mathrm{A}}}{F} e^{-(\phi_{\mathrm{B}}-\phi_{\mathrm{A}})/kT}. \tag{16 b}$$

This result is essentially similar to the expression (7) obtained by the method of fluctuations for the special case of the condensation of a vapour. The constant $C$ which was left undetermined there is replaced by the factor $F$, determined by the expression (13 a), and the definition of the parameter $\xi$ is modified by the introduction of the factor $N_{\mathrm{A}}/F$. So long as $\sum_{g>g_0} N_g \ll N_{\mathrm{A}}$, this factor can be dropped since it does not practically differ from 1 and $F$ can be replaced by $N$.

If the temperature $T$ lies sufficiently close to the 'equilibrium' temperature $T_0$ which corresponds to the equilibrium pressure $p_0$ between the phases A and B, i.e. $\phi_{\mathrm{A}}(p_0, T_0) = \phi_{\mathrm{B}}(p_0, T_0)$, the potential difference $\phi_{\mathrm{B}}(p_0, T) - \phi_{\mathrm{A}}(p_0, T)$ is reduced approximately to

$$\left[\left(\frac{\partial \phi_{\mathrm{B}}}{\partial T}\right)_0 - \left(\frac{\partial \phi_{\mathrm{A}}}{\partial T}\right)_0\right](T-T_0) = (s_{\mathrm{A}}^0 - s_{\mathrm{B}}^0)(T-T_0),$$

where $s_{\mathrm{A}}^0$ and $s_{\mathrm{B}}^0$ are the entropies of the corresponding phases, referred to one molecule, for the equilibrium point $T = T_0$. Putting $s_{\mathrm{B}}^0 - s_{\mathrm{A}}^0 = \lambda/T_0$, where $\lambda$ is the latent heat of the transition $\mathrm{A} \rightarrow \mathrm{B}$ (per molecule), we find

$$\phi_{\mathrm{B}} - \phi_{\mathrm{A}} = -\lambda \frac{T-T_0}{T_0}. \tag{17}$$

In the pre-transition state of A, $\phi_B$ must be larger than $\phi_A$, that is, $T < T_0$ if $\lambda > 0$ (or $T > T_0$ if $\lambda < 0$), while in the 'metastable' (supercooled or superheated) state of A, $\phi_B$ must be smaller than $\phi_A$, that is, $T > T_0$ if $\lambda > 0$ (or $T < T_0$ if $\lambda < 0$). Substituting (17) in (16 b) we get

$$\xi = \frac{N_A}{F} e^{\lambda(T-T_0)/kT_0^2} \simeq e^{\lambda(T-T_0)/kT_0^2}. \tag{17 a}$$

If the temperature has a fixed value, while the pressure is supposed to deviate from the corresponding equilibrium value $p_0$ ($= p_\infty$), we can put

$$\phi_B(p, T_0) - \phi_A(p, T_0) = \left(\frac{\partial \phi_B}{\partial p} - \frac{\partial \phi_A}{\partial p}\right)_0 (p - p_0),$$

that is,

$$\phi_B - \phi_A = (v_B^0 - v_A^0)(p - p_0),$$

where $v_A^0$ and $v_B^0$ are the molecular volumes of the two phases in a state of equilibrium $p_0$, $T_0$.

We thus get, instead of (17 a),

$$\xi = \frac{N_A}{F} e^{\{(v_B^0 - v_A^0)/kT_0\}(p-p_0)}.$$

If A denotes the vapour and B the liquid phase, and if $p$ is supposed to be smaller than the equilibrium (saturation) value $p_0$, we have $v_B^0 - v_A^0 \approx -v_A^0 = -kT_0/p_0$, and consequently

$$\xi \approx e^{-(p_0-p)/p_0}.$$

The same result is obtained in the opposite case, in which A represents the liquid and B the gaseous phase. In the case of a supersaturated vapour the relation between $p$ and $g^*$, the critical value of $g$, corresponding to a minimum of $N$, is found to be, according to (16 a),

$$\frac{p - p_0}{p_0} = \frac{2}{3} \frac{\mu}{kTg^{*\frac{1}{3}}}.$$

This relation is nothing but the approximate form of Thomson's formula (2) with $p_0$ standing for $p_\infty$ and $\log(p/p_\infty)$ replaced by $(p/p_\infty)-1$, while $\mu/3g^{*\frac{1}{3}}$ corresponds to $2\sigma v_B/r^*$. The latter relation follows from the definition of the surface energy $4\pi r^2\sigma = \mu g^{\frac{2}{3}}$ in conjunction with $4\pi r^3 = gv_B$. In order to obtain Thomson's formula in its exact form, the above equation for $\phi_B - \phi_A$ must be replaced by

$$\phi_B - \phi_A = \int_{p_0}^{p} (v_B - v_A)\, dp \approx -kT \log \frac{p}{p_0}.$$

In a similar way the approximate formula (17), which is valid for small values of $(T - T_0)$ only, must be replaced by $\phi_B - \phi_A = -\int_{T_0}^{T} \lambda/T\, dT$.

The existence of heterophase fluctuations in a thermodynamically stable system in the vicinity of the corresponding transition point $A \rightarrow B$ has not yet been studied experimentally. The experimental proof of the fact that such a system (A) is not fully homogeneous, but rather 'quasi-homogeneous', is a difficult task, for the relative amount of the new phase (B), existing in it in an embryonic form, remains very small. The liquid embryos which are present in a nearly saturated vapour can be detected in the simplest way by a study of the Raman effect, the liquid phase being distinguished from the gaseous one by its Raman spectrum. An experiment of this kind with a vapour under very high pressure—and at a temperature near the critical point (which is necessary to secure a high density without macroscopic condensation) —has actually been performed, with results which fully support the theory of heterophase fluctuations, in a qualitative way at least.† The gaseous embryos in a liquid near the boiling-point can be detected by a study of the extinction of sound or rather ultrasonic waves, which, owing to the relatively high compressibility of such bubbles (compared with the liquid phase), must suffer an abnormally large scattering. This fact has been verified by several authors in the case of liquids containing absorbed foreign gases, while it has not been observed in carefully purified liquids. As will be shown later (§ 5), this circumstance is due to the sharp increase in the number and size of embryonic gas bubbles when they are filled not only with the vapour of the main substance but with other gases contained in it in an occluded form.

In the case of liquids near the crystallization point or crystals near the melting-point the presence of the crystalline or liquid embryos has not been detected, hitherto, in a direct way. Their existence, or rather the increase of their number and average size, with an approach to the conventional transition point $A \rightarrow B$, seems to be manifested in an indirect way by an abnormal increase of the specific heat and of the thermal expansion coefficient, both of the liquid just above the crystallization point—and of the solid (crystal) just below the melting-point. In the latter case these phenomena have been denoted by Ubbelohde‡ as phenomena of 'pre-melting'. Generalizing this notion we shall denote the analogous phenomena, which must be observed in other cases near the transition point $A \rightarrow B$, as *pre-transition phenomena*.

It should be noted that such pre-transition phenomena can be due, partly at least, to other causes.

† J. Landsberg, *Bull. Ac. Sci. U.S.S.R.* ser. phys., 373 (1938); Landsberg and Uhholmin, *C.R. Ac. Sci. U.S.S.R.* **16**, 399 (1937) (Russian).

‡ Ubbelohde, *Trans. Farad. Soc.* **34**, 292 (1938).

Even if the system A (gas, liquid, or crystal) is treated as strictly homogeneous, i.e. if heterophase fluctuations are wholly left out of account, an abnormal increase of the specific heat $C$ must be expected to take place with approach to the conventional transition point A $\rightarrow$ B (defined by the condition of thermodynamical equilibrium $\phi_A = \phi_B$). In fact, if the discontinuous character of this transition is due to the thermodynamical instability of the intermediate states, as is certainly the case for transitions between the gaseous and the liquid states (in both directions) and as must be expected to be true with respect to transitions between the liquid and solid (crystalline) states, according to the theory of the virtual continuity between the two states which has been set forth in Ch. III (§ 6), then the isotherms $(p, v)$ and the isobars $(T, S)$ must display within the range of the corresponding virtually continuous transition the characteristic wave-like shape shown in Figs. 25 and 26. Now, such a course of $p$ as a function of $v$ for $T = \text{const.}$ or of $S$ as a function of $T$ for $p = \text{const.}$ means that the isothermal compressibility modulus $-(\partial p/\partial v)_T$ must decrease to zero (and even become negative in a certain range of $v$ values, see Fig. 25), causing thus an abnormal increase (up to infinity) of the thermal expansion coefficient,† and that the specific heat $c_p = T(\partial S/\partial T)_p$ must rise up to infinity (and even jump to negative values). These conclusions are qualitatively verified in the case of a vapour near the condensation point (and especially beyond it) and of a liquid near the boiling-point; in this case they can be regarded as a direct consequence of van der Waals's theory. A more exact quantitative study is, however, required for the separation of the 'homophase' part of the total effects, as described by this theory, from the contribution due to the heterophase fluctuations.‡

Similar considerations apply to the transitions between the solid and liquid states.

An abnormal rise of $c_p$ and $\alpha$ within a range of a few (3–5) degrees from the conventional melting-point has been observed in the case of a number of crystalline bodies by several authors, the two quantities reaching sometimes values exceeding their normal values outside this

† The thermal expansion coefficient $\alpha$ is inversely proportional to the compressibility modulus, as follows from the relation $\left(\frac{\partial v}{\partial T}\right)_p \left(\frac{\partial T}{\partial p}\right)_v \left(\frac{\partial p}{\partial v}\right)_T = -1.$

‡ It should be mentioned that both the homophase and the heterophase contributions are due to the same cause, namely, to the action of the intermolecular forces leading to an extra compression of the gas in the former case and to the formation of liquid embryos in the latter.

range by a factor of 10, 20, and even more. Fig. 47 shows the variation of the thermal expansion coefficient $\alpha$ of various metals near the melting-point, according to the experiments of Strelkov and Gatchkovsky;† a similar curve has been obtained by Ubbelohde‡ for the specific heat of paraffin (the latter shows an abnormal rise of $c_p$ on both sides of the conventional melting-point).

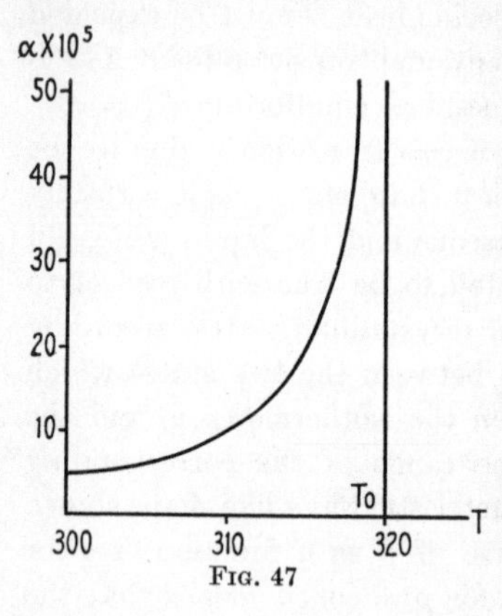

FIG. 47

These 'pre-melting phenomena' were explained, prior to Ubbelohde's experiments, by the influence of impurities, which are practically always present in any body, on the assumption that they are non-uniformly distributed over its volume (as a result of spontaneous fluctuations) and that, accordingly, they produce a lowering of the fusion temperature of variable magnitude in different places. Ubbelohde has shown, however, that by adding to paraffin foreign substances in amounts certainly greatly exceeding the amount of impurities present in it under ordinary conditions, no appreciable lowering of the melting-point nor any change in the course of the curve $c_p(T)$ could be produced. Thus the impurity hypothesis must be rejected.

The magnitude of the 'homophase' contribution to the $c_p$ and $\alpha$ anomaly cannot be established theoretically so long as we have no reliable equation of state of a condensed 'solid-liquid' body which could describe its behaviour near and beyond the thermodynamical stability limits. I do not think, however, that the sharp increase of $c_p$ and $\alpha$ near the melting-point could be explained in this way. It is possible, however, to give a satisfactory quantitative account of the pre-melting phenomena on the basis of the general theory of heterophase fluctuations, developed at the beginning of this section.

The formation in a crystal of a liquid embryo consisting of $g$ atoms requires a quantity of heat equal to $g\lambda$ (if surface effects are neglected).

The additional value of the specific heat, due to the increase of the number and size of these embryos with approach to the melting-point ($T_0$), can be defined by the formula

$$\Delta c = \sum_g \lambda g \frac{dN_g}{dT} = N\lambda \frac{dJ}{dT}, \tag{18}$$

† Strelkov, *Sow. Phys.* **12**, 58 (1937). ‡ Ubbelohde, *Trans. Farad. Soc.* **34**, 292 (1938).

where
$$J = \frac{1}{N}\sum_{g>g_0} gN_g = \int_{g_0}^{\infty} e^{-\beta g-\gamma g^{\frac{2}{3}}}g\,dg. \tag{18 a}$$

Here $\beta = (\phi_B-\phi_A)/kT$, that is, since $T$ lies sufficiently close to $T_0$,
$$\beta = \frac{\lambda(T_0-T)}{kT_0^2}$$
(cf. (17)), while $\gamma = \mu/kT$. In carrying out the integration in (18 a) the latter quantity can be replaced by its value at $T = T_0$, i.e. treated as independent of the temperature. We thus get
$$\frac{dJ}{dT} = -\frac{d\beta}{dT}\int_{g_0}^{\infty} e^{-\beta g-\gamma g^{\frac{2}{3}}}g^2\,dg = \frac{\lambda}{kT_0^2}\int_{g_0}^{\infty} e^{-\beta g-\gamma g^{\frac{2}{3}}}g^2\,dg. \tag{18 b}$$

If in (18 b) $\lambda$ is replaced by $v_B-v_A$ we obtain after dividing by $g^2\,dg\,v_A\,N$ the additional value of the thermal expansion coefficient
$$\Delta\alpha = \left(\frac{v_B}{v_A}-1\right)\frac{dJ}{dT}.$$
A comparison of this expression with (18) gives
$$\frac{\Delta\alpha}{\Delta c} = \frac{(v_B/v_A)-1}{L},$$
where $L = \lambda N$ is the latent heat of melting of the whole crystal.

The absolute magnitude of $\Delta c$ (or $\Delta\alpha$) depends in an essential way on the value of $g_0$, i.e. the smallest number of molecules which are necessary to make a drop of liquid in a crystalline medium. It is clear that this number must be very large compared with 1. It is necessary, however, in an approximate calculation of (18 b) to ascertain whether this number is small or large compared with the value $g = \bar{g}$, which corresponds to the maximum of the integrand. This value is determined by the equation
$$\frac{2}{g} = \beta+\tfrac{2}{3}\gamma g^{-\frac{1}{3}},$$
which is reduced to $g = (3/\gamma)^{\frac{3}{2}}$ if $\beta = 0$, i.e. if $T = T_0$. Since $\mu g^{\frac{2}{3}} = 4\pi\sigma r_g^2$, where $\sigma$ is the surface tension between the liquid and the solid phase of the same substance, we have $\mu = 4\pi\sigma(r_g^3/g)^{\frac{2}{3}} \cong \sigma v_B^{\frac{2}{3}}$, where $v_B^{\frac{2}{3}}$ is the area occupied by one molecule on the surface of the liquid phase. If this surface were free, $\sigma v_B^{\frac{2}{3}}$ would be of the same order of magnitude as the *evaporation* heat of the liquid, referred to one molecule, which is about 10–30 times larger than the latent heat of fusion $\lambda$, and hence about 20–60 times larger than $kT_0$, according to Trouton's rule.

In reality, however, the surface tension between a liquid and the solid phase of the same substance must be much smaller than in the case of a free liquid surface. We thus see that in our case $\mu = \sigma v_B^{\frac{2}{3}}$ must be of the same order of magnitude as $kT_0$, or perhaps still smaller. For $\mu = 1$, $\bar{g}$ is of the order of a few units. Putting $\mu = \frac{1}{10}$ we get $\bar{g} = 160$, which is probably of the same order of magnitude as $g_0$. The value of $g_0$ and of $\mu$ (i.e. $\sigma$) can be determined from a comparison of theory with the experimental data, referring to the maximum value of $\Delta c$, and of the rate of its increase with $T$ (for $T = T_0$).

It is known that $\Delta c$ becomes markedly different from zero at a distance of but a few degrees from the melting-point $T_0$, its maximum value for simple substances being of the order of 100 cal./mole and more. Hence it is seen that the factor $e^{-\beta g_0}$ in the integrand of (18 b) must reduce $\Delta c$ with respect to its maximum value about 100 times if the difference $T_0 - T$ is equal to, say, 5. Putting $T_0 = 500$, we get $\beta \simeq 3.10^{-2}$. Hence $g_0$ must be of the order of 150. Assuming that at $T = T_0$ $\bar{g}$ does not exceed this value, we can calculate $(\Delta c)_{\max}$ with the help of the approximate formula

$$(\Delta c)_{\max} = \frac{N\lambda^2}{kT_0^2}\tfrac{3}{2}g_0^{\frac{7}{6}}\int_{g_0}^{\infty} e^{-g\gamma^{\frac{2}{3}}}\,dg^{\frac{2}{3}},$$

which is obtained from (18) and (18 b) if the factor $g^{\frac{7}{6}}$ is replaced by its maximum value in the range of integration. We thus get

$$\Delta c_{\max} = \tfrac{3}{2}Nk\left(\frac{\lambda}{kT_0}\right)^2 \frac{g_0^{\frac{7}{6}}}{\gamma}e^{-\gamma g_0^{\frac{2}{3}}}.$$

The product $N\lambda$ in cal./mole is equal to 2, while $(\lambda/kT_0)^2$ is approximately equal to 6 according to Trouton's rule. Hence it follows that the factor $(g_0^{\frac{7}{6}}/\gamma)e^{-\gamma g_0^{\frac{2}{3}}}$ must be of the order of 10. In conjunction with $g_0 = 150$ this gives $\gamma = \frac{1}{3}$, which corresponds to a surface tension of the order of 1 dyne/cm.

This figure is probably of a correct order of magnitude. It can be checked by a quite independent method, based on the consideration of the velocity of crystallization of an overcooled liquid. Unfortunately, the surface tension between a crystal and its melt has never yet been measured directly.

## 4. The Kinetics of Condensation and Other Phase Transitions in Metastable Systems

The application of thermodynamical or statistical methods to a system A+B in a metastable pre-transition state ($\phi_A > \phi_B$) can yield results which are valid for a limited lapse of time only, and for a limited range of admissible configurations of the molecules, with the exclusion of those configurations which correspond to the macroscopically most probable, i.e. stable state (cf. Ch. IV, § 7). Taking into account these limitations, we can apply the general results of the preceding section, and in particular the formula (16) for the number of embryos of the B phase, to the metastable state of the quasi-homogeneous system A+B, striking out, however, all those embryos which markedly exceed the critical size $g = g^*$, defined by the maximum of the expression

$$\Delta\Phi = (\phi_B - \phi_A)g + \mu g^{\frac{2}{3}},$$

i.e.

$$g^* = \left(\frac{2}{3}\frac{\mu}{\phi_A - \phi_B}\right)^3. \tag{19}$$

The number of such 'critical' embryos, or nuclei of the B phase, is given by

$$N_{g^*} = F\left(\frac{F}{N}\right)^{g^*} e^{-(\Delta\Phi)_{\max}/kT},$$

or, approximately,

$$N_{g^*} = Ne^{-\frac{1}{3}(\mu g^{*\frac{2}{3}}/kT)}. \tag{19 a}$$

The formula (16) can be applied approximately even to values of $g$ somewhat larger than $g^*$; starting, however, from a certain value $g = G$ we must put $N_g = 0$.

These considerations have been used by Volmer in the special case of a supersaturated vapour, as a basis for the determination of the velocity of its condensation.†

Since all the drops which arise in such a vapour must, in the process of their gradual growth (partially neutralized by the reverse process of re-evaporation), pass through the critical size, which forms, as it were, a narrow gate to the process of a rapid macroscopic condensation, the velocity of this process must be proportional to the number of drops of the critical size existing in the vapour, at any given instant, in a state of unstable equilibrium, and given by (19 a). If it is assumed that these drops do not evaporate, but continue to grow and are eliminated from the system, being replaced by an equivalent number of single molecules, so that the vapour remains in a stationary state, the velocity of its condensation can be obtained by multiplying the number of such drops $N_{g^*}$ by the number of single molecules of the vapour striking their surface in unit time. Referred to unit area this number is equal to

$$\beta = n_A\sqrt{\frac{kT}{2\pi m}} = \frac{p}{\sqrt{(2\pi mkT)}}, \tag{20}$$

† O. Volmer, *Zs. f. phys. Chem.* **119**, 277 (1926).

where $n_A = 1/v_A$ is the concentration of the molecules in the gas phase (cf. Ch. I, § 1).

The velocity of condensation, defined above as the product $g^* N_g \cdot 4\pi r^{*2}\beta$, is thus represented by the formula

$$Q = Ng^* e^{-4\pi\sigma r^{*2}/kT} 4\pi r^{*2} \frac{p}{\sqrt{(2\pi mkT)}}, \tag{20 a}$$

where $r$ and $\mu$ are connected with $g$ and $\sigma$ by the relations $\mu g^{\frac{2}{3}} = \sigma 4\pi r^2$ and $g = v_B \frac{4}{3}\pi r^3$.

Volmer's theory has been subsequently improved by Farkas,† Kaishew and Stranski,‡ and especially by Becker and Döring,§ who have rejected the thermodynamical considerations on which it is based and have derived the velocity of condensation by a purely kinetic argument, taking into account not only the condensation of the vapour on the surface of the drops but also the reverse process of their re-evaporation.

The description of the resulting process is greatly simplified if it is assumed, as has already been done above, that all the drops of a certain size $G$, slightly exceeding the critical one, are eliminated from the system and replaced by an equivalent number ($GN_G$) of single molecules. Under such conditions the number of drops of any size, including the individual molecules (which in a purely formal way can be treated as drops of the smallest possible size), must remain constant.

Let $\alpha_g$ denote the number of molecules which are evaporated from the surface of the drops, consisting of $g$ molecules ($g \geqslant 2$) per unit time and area. In other words $s_g \alpha_g \, dt$ denotes the probability that such a drop, with a surface $s_g = 4\pi r_g^2$, will lose one molecule by evaporation during the time $dt$. In a similar way the product $s_g \beta \, dt$ denotes the probability that it will gain one more molecule, during the same time, owing to the condensation of the surrounding vapour.

If the system A+B is in a stable state ($\phi_A > \phi_B$), the following relation must hold:

$$N_g s_g \alpha_g = N_{g-1} s_{g-1} \beta \tag{21}$$

according to the principle of detailed balance. Substituting here the expression (15) for the ratio between $N_g$ and $N_{g-1}$, corresponding to the equilibrium distribution, we get

$$\alpha_g = \frac{F}{N_A} e^{(\phi_B - \phi_A + \frac{2}{3}\mu g^{-\frac{1}{3}})/kT} \frac{s_{g-1}}{s_g} \beta, \tag{21 a}$$

† Farkas, *Zs. f. phys. Chem.* **125**, 236 (1927).
‡ Kaishew and Stranski, ibid. B, **26**, 317 (1934).
§ Becker and Döring, *Ann. d. Phys.* **24**, 719 (1935).

which is applicable, in principle, down to $g = 1$, since in this case $s_{g-1} = 0$. If $g \gg 1$ the ratio $s_{g-1}/s_g$ can be replaced by 1; the same refers to the ratio $F/N_A$ so long as the total number of drops is relatively small. Writing $2\sigma v_B/r_g$ for $\frac{2}{3}\mu g^{-\frac{1}{3}}$, we can thus put

$$\alpha_g = \beta e^{(1/kT)(\phi_B-\phi_A+2\sigma v_B/r_g)}. \tag{21 b}$$

This expression for $\alpha_g$, although derived from thermodynamical considerations referring to the state of stable equilibrium, can be used just as well for the metastable states, characterized by a negative value of $\phi_B-\phi_A$. It should be noticed that in the latter case the coefficient $\alpha_g$ turns out to be equal to $\beta$ for drops of the critical size

$$\alpha_{g^*} = \beta \tag{21 c}$$

as follows, for example, from Thomson's formula (2). This result can be considered as a direct corollary from the condition (21), in conjunction with the fact that in the neighbourhood of $N_g = \text{min.}$, $N_g \cong N_{g-1}$.

The preceding expression for $\alpha_g$ is valid independently of the existence or non-existence of an equilibrium in the distribution of the B embryos with respect to their size, so long as the velocities (and coordinates) of the molecules—both in these embryos and in the gas phase—preserve an equilibrium distribution characterized by Maxwell's law. Now, the relaxation time required for the establishment of this distribution is always very short, much shorter than the time necessary for the establishment of an equilibrium distribution of the embryos with respect to their size (under the condition $\phi_B > \phi_A$), or in general for a marked change of this distribution.

The rate of this change can therefore be calculated with the help of the expressions for $\beta$ and $\alpha_g$ given by the preceding formulae, with modified values of the numbers $N_g$. To avoid confusion we shall denote these modified values, corresponding, in general, to a non-equilibrium distribution, by $f_g$. Replacing $N_g$ by $f_g$, we must no longer expect the equation (21) to be satisfied.

The difference
$$I_g = f_{g-1}s_{g-1}\beta - f_g s_g \alpha_g \tag{22}$$

is equal to the excess of the number of drops which, owing to condensation of the vapour on their surface, pass per unit time from the class $g-1$ to the class $g$ over the number, which, owing to evaporation, pass from the class $g$ to the class $g-1$.

Taking into account the equations (21) we can rewrite (22) as follows:

$$I_g = N_{g-1}s_{g-1}\beta\left(\frac{f_{g-1}}{N_{g-1}} - \frac{f_g}{N_g}\right). \tag{22 a}$$

The rate of change of the number of drops of a given class is obviously determined by the equation

$$\frac{\partial f_g}{\partial t} = I_g - I_{g+1}. \tag{22 b}$$

This is the fundamental kinetic equation of our problem. It has been introduced and solved by Becker and Döring† on the assumption of a steady distribution with the boundary condition $f_G = 0$.

If small values of $g$ of the order of a few units are left aside, the quantities appearing in this equation must be only slightly varied if $g$ is changed by 1. We can treat them, accordingly, for $g \geqslant g_0$ (where $g_0 \approx 10$, say) as functions of a continuous variable $g$—which will be indicated by writing $f(g)$ instead of $f_g$ etc.—and replace the finite differences in (22 a) and (22 b) by differential coefficients of the corresponding quantities with respect to this variable. Writing, for the sake of brevity,

$$s(g-1)\beta \cong s(g)\beta = D(g), \tag{23}$$

we thus get

$$I(g) = -D(g)N(g)\frac{\partial}{\partial g}\left(\frac{f(g)}{N(g)}\right), \tag{23 a}$$

that is,

$$I = -D\frac{\partial f}{\partial g} + Df\frac{\partial \log N}{\partial g},$$

or, finally, since $N(g) = Ce^{-\Delta\Phi(g)/kT}$,

$$I = -D\frac{\partial f}{\partial g} - \frac{D}{kT}f\frac{\partial \Delta\Phi(g)}{\partial g}, \tag{23 b}$$

where

$$\Delta\Phi = (\phi_{\mathrm{B}} - \phi_{\mathrm{A}})g + \mu g^{\frac{2}{3}}.$$

The expression (23 b) is formally identical with the usual expression for the flow of particles distributed over the axis $g$ with a density $f(g)$, owing to diffusion and to the action of an external force $F$, corresponding to a potential energy $\Delta\Phi(g)$, the mobility of the particles $q$ being connected with their diffusion coefficient by Einstein's relation $q = D/kT$, while the diffusion coefficient is itself a function of $g$ given by (23) or

$$D = (4\pi)^{\frac{1}{3}} 3^{\frac{2}{3}} v_{\mathrm{B}}^{\frac{2}{3}} g^{\frac{2}{3}} \beta.$$

Substituting the expression (23 b) in (22 b) and replacing $I_{g-1} - I_g$ by $-\partial I/\partial g$ we obtain the following kinetic equation:

$$\frac{\partial f}{\partial t} = \frac{\partial}{\partial g}\left(D\frac{\partial f}{\partial g}\right) + \frac{1}{kT}\frac{\partial}{\partial g}\left(Df\frac{\partial \Delta\Phi}{\partial g}\right), \tag{24}$$

† Loc. cit.

which differs from the equation of this type previously used for the motion in ordinary space only by the dependence of $D$ on $g$.

It should be noticed that this dependence is very weak compared with that which characterizes the distribution function $f(g)$. It can accordingly be neglected in the approximate treatment of the problem —especially if we are interested in the variation of $f$ within a relatively narrow range of $f$-value, near its maximum at $g \approx g^*$, for instance.

The preceding equations have been obtained in a practically equivalent form by Zeldovich.† They enable one to find an approximate solution of Becker–Döring's problem which is just as accurate as that obtained by these authors (after a number of approximations, consisting in replacing summations with respect to $g$ by integrations), but in a much simpler and more straightforward way.

A steady distribution considered by Becker and Döring ($\partial f/\partial t = 0$) is equivalent to the condition $I = \text{const}$. If, following Zeldovich, we write $I$ in the form (23 a), the distribution function $f$ is immediately found by a simple integration, namely

$$f(g) = IN(g) \int_g^G \frac{dg}{D(g)N(g)}, \tag{25}$$

the integration constant being determined by the boundary condition $f = 0$ for $g \equiv G$, where $g$ lies near to the value $g^*$, which corresponds to the minimum of $N(g)$. Replacing the latter by $Ce^{-\Delta\Phi/kT}$ we get

$$f(g) = Ie^{-\Delta\Phi(g)/kT} \int_g^G \frac{e^{\Delta\Phi/kT}}{D(g)}\, dg. \tag{25 a}$$

Since the function $e^{\Delta\Phi/kT}$ has a very sharp maximum near $g = g^*$, we can replace here $D(g)$ by its value for $g = g^*$, and $\Delta\Phi$ by its expansion with respect to the difference $g = g^*$, viz.

$$\Delta\Phi = \Delta\Phi_{\max} - \gamma \frac{(g-g^*)^2}{2}, \tag{26}$$

where
$$\gamma = -\left(\frac{\partial^2 \Delta\Phi}{\partial g^2}\right)_{g=g^*}. \tag{26 a}$$

Substituting this in (25 a) we get

$$f(g) = \frac{I}{D(g^*)} e^{[\Delta\Phi(g^*)-\Delta\Phi(g)]/kT} \int_{-(g^*-g)}^{G-g^*} e^{-\gamma\xi^2/2kT}\, d\xi, \tag{27}$$

where $\xi = g - g^*$.

† J. Zeldovich, *J. Exp. Theor. Phys.* (Russ.), **12**, 525 (1942).

The quantity $\sqrt{(kT/\gamma)}$ is a measure of the width of the maximum of the function $1/N(g)$ near $g = g^*$. If $G-g^*$ and $g^*-g$ are both large compared with $\sqrt{(kT/\gamma)}$ the integration limits can be extended to $\pm\infty$, which gives, if $e^{-\Delta\Phi(g)/kT}$ is replaced by $N(g)/C$,

$$\frac{f(g)}{N(g)} = \frac{I}{CD(g^*)} e^{\Delta\Phi(g^*)/kT} \sqrt{\frac{2\pi kT}{\gamma}} = \text{const.} \tag{27 a}$$

This relation holds of course for $g < g^*-\sqrt{(kT/\gamma)}$ only. Now, it is clear that for $g \ll g^*$ the actual distribution function $f(g)$ must be

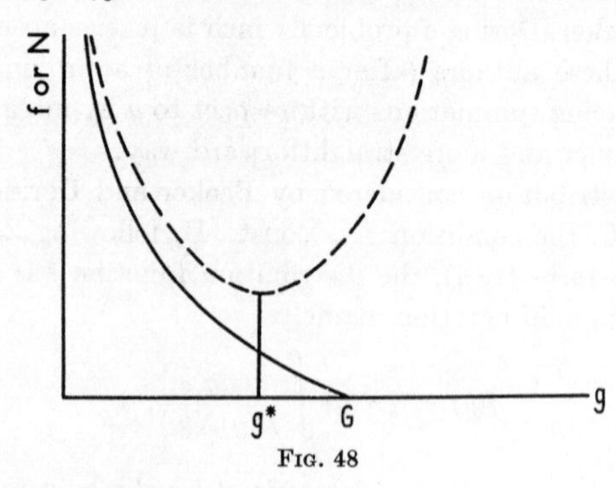


FIG. 48

practically identical with $N(g)$. Hence it follows that it must be practically identical with it in the whole range from $g \approx 1$ to $g \simeq g^*-\sqrt{(kT/\gamma)}$, while above this value the ratio $f/N$ must rapidly fall off down to zero for $g = G$, as shown in Fig. 48 (where $f$ is represented by the full line and $N$ by the dotted line). It should be mentioned that for $g = g^*$ $f = \frac{1}{2}N$.

Noting that the constant in (27 a) is equal to 1, we obtain the following expression for $I$:

$$I = CD(g^*)e^{-\Delta\Phi(g^*)/kT} \sqrt{\frac{\gamma}{2\pi kT}} = N(g^*)D(g^*) \sqrt{\frac{\gamma}{2\pi kT}}. \tag{27 b}$$

The coefficient $C$ can be identified with the total number of molecules $N$ in the supersaturated vapour.

The expression (27 b) has a very simple physical meaning.

Near the critical value of $g$ the second term of (23 b) vanishes, since by the definition of $g^*$, $(\partial\Delta\Phi/\partial g)_{g=g^*} = 0$, so that the expression for $I$ reduces to $-D(g^*)(\partial f/\partial g)_{g=g^*}$. Now $-(\partial f/\partial g)_{g=g^*}$ can be replaced by the ratio $f(g^*)/\Delta g$, where $\Delta g$ is the effective width of the critical region, the width of the Gaussian curve by which it is possible to replace the actual curve $1/f(g) = 1/N(g) = (1/C)e^{\Delta\Phi/kT}$. This width is measured by the factor $\sqrt{(2\pi kT/\gamma)}$ in (27 a). We thus get

$$I = D(g^*)f(g^*)\Big/\sqrt{\frac{2\pi kT}{\gamma}},$$

which is identical with (27 b).

Using the expression $-(\phi_A-\phi_B)g+\mu g^{\frac{2}{3}}$ for $\Delta\Phi$, we get

$$\gamma = -\left(\frac{\partial^2\Delta\Phi}{\partial g^2}\right)_{g=g^*} = \tfrac{2}{9}\mu g^{*-\frac{4}{3}},$$

or, since $\phi_A-\phi_B = \frac{2}{3}\mu g^{*-\frac{1}{3}}$,

$$\gamma = \tfrac{1}{3}(\phi_A-\phi_B)/g^*. \tag{28}$$

Substituting this in (27 b) and replacing $\Delta\Phi(g^*)$ by $\frac{4}{3}\pi\sigma r^{*2}$ we obtain the following final expression for the relative rate of condensation of a supersaturated vapour:

$$\frac{Q}{N} = \frac{Ig^*}{C} = e^{-4\pi\sigma r^{*2}/3kT}2\pi r^{*2}\frac{p}{kT}\Big/\sqrt{\left(\frac{1}{3}\frac{\phi_A-\phi_B}{m}g^*\right)}. \tag{28 a}$$

This expression is practically identical with that obtained by Becker and Döring, but somewhat different from the roughly approximate expression (20 a) given by Volmer.

The critical radius is given, as a function of $\phi_A-\phi_B$, by the formula (2), i.e.

$$r^* = \frac{2\sigma v_B}{\phi_A-\phi_B},$$

while the potential difference can be expressed in the form

$$\phi_A-\phi_B = kT\log\frac{p}{p_\infty}$$

if the vapour is 'overcompressed' at a given temperature $T$, or

$$\phi_A-\phi_B = \int_T^{T_0}\frac{\lambda}{T}\,dT \cong \frac{\lambda}{T}(T_0-T)$$

if it is overcooled with respect to the condensation point $T_0$, corresponding to a given pressure.

We shall illustrate these results by a few figures, referring to water vapour at room temperature ($T = 300$). Taking a degree of supersaturation $p/p_\infty$ equal to $e = 2{\cdot}7,...$, we get $\phi_A-\phi_B = kT$, and consequently, since $\sigma = 70$ dyne/cm.$^2$, and $v_B = 18/6.10^{23} = 3.10^{-23}$,

$$r^* \cong 10^{-7}\text{ cm.}$$

The corresponding value of $g^*$ is found to be equal to 100.

We get further $4\pi\sigma r^{*2}/3kT = 150$, i.e. $e^{-4\pi\sigma r^{*2}/3kT} \cong 10^{-63}$

$$\frac{Q}{N} = 10^{-72} n_{A\infty},$$

where $n_{A\infty} = p_\infty/kT$ is the concentration of the saturated vapour.

It thus turns out that for the degree of supersaturation we are considering the velocity of condensation is negligibly small. Let us now take a degree of supersaturation equal to 7, i.e. to the square of the preceding one ($\log p/p_\infty = 2$). The critical radius $r^*$ is in this case only one-half that in the preceding one; this leads, however, to an enormous increase of the exponential factor $e^{-4\pi\sigma r^{*2}/3kT}$, which is now equal to $10^{-16}$ instead of $10^{-63}$. The corresponding value of $Q/N$ is now of the order of $10^{-25} n_{A\infty}$. A somewhat more accurate calculation yields a much larger figure which shows that a superposition of the above degree (and even of a somewhat smaller degree—of the order of 6) is sufficient for the condensation process to proceed with a marked velocity. For still higher degrees of supersaturation the latter becomes so large that the condensation must take place practically instantly. These results are in satisfactory agreement with the experiments of Volmer and Flood on the condensation of carefully purified water vapour.

It should be mentioned that in view of the smallness of the critical radius which is obtained on the basis of the above theory, the latter must be considered as a rather crude approximation and must be modified to account for the discontinuous character of the variable $g$. Moreover, the surface tension $\sigma$ in the expressions of $r^*$ and $\Delta\Phi^*$ must be replaced by a larger value, lying close to the surface energy $w$.

We shall not stop to discuss these refinements more closely and shall now consider how the preceding theory should be modified when applied to the converse process of the cavitation (rupture) or boiling up of a liquid, which is in a metastable state owing to a negative (or, in general, algebraically too small) pressure, or to overheating.

The notation $f_g$ will now be used for the number of gas bubbles, containing $g$ molecules of the vapour at the equilibrium pressure $p_\infty$ and $N_g$ for the value of $f_g$, in the corresponding equilibrium distribution.

Since in this case the increase of $g$ is due to the evaporation of the liquid, and its decrease to the condensation of the vapour, the coefficients $\beta$ and $\alpha_g$ in the equation (21) and in the expression (22) for the 'flow' of bubbles in the direction of increasing size between $g-1$ and $g$, must be interchanged.

We thus get, instead of (22 a),

$$I_g = N_{g-1} s_{g-1} \alpha_{g-1} \left( \frac{f_{g-1}}{N_{g-1}} - \frac{f_g}{N_g} \right),$$

and so on. This brings us to exactly the same equations as before, with an altered definition of the diffusion coefficient, namely,

$$D(g) = s(g)\alpha_g. \tag{29}$$

Now according to the modified equation (21) (with $\alpha_g$ and $\beta$ interchanged) and the general relation (15) we have

$$\alpha_g = \beta \frac{N_g s_g}{N_{g-1} s_{g-1}} \cong \frac{\beta s_g}{s_{g-1}} \frac{N_A}{F} e^{-[(\phi_B - \phi_A) + \frac{2}{3}\mu g^{-\frac{1}{3}}]/kT},$$

where the index A refers to the liquid and B to the gas phase, or with a sufficient degree of accuracy

$$\alpha_g = \beta e^{-[(\phi_B - \phi_A) + \frac{2}{3}\mu g^{-\frac{1}{3}}]/kT}, \tag{29 a}$$

$\beta$ being given, as before, by (20).

Noting that $\phi_B - \phi_A = -\frac{2}{3}\mu g^{*-\frac{1}{3}}$, we can rewrite this expression in the form

$$\alpha_g = \beta e^{-\frac{2}{3}(\mu/kT)(1/g^{\frac{1}{3}} - 1/g^{*\frac{1}{3}})}. \tag{29 b}$$

The decrease of $\alpha_g$ with decrease of $g$ is explained in the same way as its increase in the converse case of the evaporation of small drops, the evaporation energy being decreased by $2\sigma v_{\text{liq}}/r$ in the latter case, and increased by $2\sigma v_{\text{liq}}/r$ in the former, owing to the negative curvature of the surface. It should be mentioned that for bubbles of the critical size $\alpha_g$ must according to (29 b) have the same value as for drops of the critical size, both being equal to $\beta$.

The velocity of cavitation or of the boiling up of a liquid can be calculated in exactly the same way as the velocity of condensation of a supersaturated vapour. If the process is again imagined to be rendered steady by a removal of all the bubbles with $g \geqslant G$ and their replacement by an equivalent amount of the liquid phase, the formulae (25), etc., can be applied to the present case with practically no modifications. The dependence of $D(g)$ on $g$ can be taken into account by replacing the product $D(g)N(g) = s(g)\alpha(g)N(g)$ in the integrand of (25) with $s(g+1)\beta N(g+1)$, which, if $g^* \gg 1$, is practically irrelevant. We thus arrive at the same formula (27 b) for $I$ with a different value for the coefficient $\gamma$, however, given as before by (28), with A and B interchanged.

For the purpose of illustration we shall again consider the case of water. If the latter is under normal pressure, but superheated by 1 degree, say, over the standard boiling-point $T_0 = 373$, the critical radius of the bubbles is equal to $4 \times 10^{-3}$ cm. (cf. § 1).

This gives $4\pi\sigma r^{*2}/3kT = 8.10^{10}$, which corresponds to a vanishingly small value of $N(g^*) = Ce^{-4\pi\sigma r^{*2}/3kT}$. It is thus seen that boiling could be started with much larger superheatings only, corresponding to values of $r^*$ of the order of $10^{-7}$ cm. as before; since $r^*$ is inversely proportional to $T-T_0$, this means that the superheating required should be of the order of 1,000 degrees. It is clear that under such conditions the approximate expression (5 b) for $r^*$ as a function of $T$ is no longer applicable. Replacing it by the more exact formula (5 a), we get with $p = 10^6$, $2\sigma/rp = 1{\cdot}5 \times 10^3$, and consequently,

$$\frac{1}{T_0} - \frac{1}{T} \cong \frac{k}{\lambda}\log(1{\cdot}5 \times 10^3) \approx 10^{-3}$$

(since $k/\lambda \approx 2.10^{-4}$), which leads to a negative value of $T$. This means that the formula (5 a) is not sufficiently exact to be applied to the case under consideration. We shall not attempt to derive here a more exact formula, and shall be satisfied with the remark that water under normal pressure in the absence of some factors facilitating the beginning of cavitation cannot be brought to boiling by any reasonable overheating. The fact that in reality a very small overheating is usually sufficient to start the boiling process in any liquid shows that factors of the above type (corresponding to nuclei in the condensation of a supersaturated vapour) are actually always present (see next section). If such factors were not operative, then boiling—or cavitation—could be started only by application of a large negative pressure. Formula (4 a) shows that in order to lower the critical radius of the bubbles down to $10^{-7}$ cm. at the temperature of the normal boiling-point (corresponding to $p_\infty = 10^6$) it is necessary to apply to the liquid water a negative pressure of the order of $10^9$ dyne/cm.$^2 \cong 10^3$ atmospheres, which is about one-tenth of the maximum negative pressure which it can withstand without breaking up. Similar figures are obtained for all the other liquids.

We thus see that the kinetic theory of the process of condensation of a supersaturated vapour and especially of the boiling up of an overheated liquid possesses only a very limited practical significance, unless the factors facilitating it, and actually always present, are duly taken into account.

## 5. Role of Solid Surfaces and of Foreign Colloidal Particles in the Cavitation and Condensation Processes

We shall inquire first into the causes of the lowering of the tensile strength of a liquid, as revealed by the impossibility of obtaining large degrees of overheating under normal (positive) pressures, contrary to the results of the schematic theory of the preceding section.

It is well known that in the case of a boiling liquid the vapour bubbles arise, as a rule, not in the interior of the liquid, but on the bottom and walls of the vessel containing it.

This is obviously explained by the fact that the surface free energy $\sigma_{1,0}$ of the liquid with respect to the vapour is much larger than its surface energy with respect to the substance of the walls, or more exactly that the quantity

$$\Delta\sigma = \sigma_{1,0}+\sigma_{2,0}-\sigma_{1,2},$$

equal to the work which must be done per unit area in detaching the liquid from the wall to which it adheres, is much smaller than $2\sigma_{1,0}$ —the work required to separate one part of the liquid from the other over the same area.

This interpretation is supported by the fact, which has already been mentioned in Ch. III, § 1, that when liquid mercury filling a glass vessel is extended by cooling (owing to its adherence to the walls of the vessel in connexion with a larger value of the thermal expansion coefficient), it never suffers an internal rupture, but is finally detached from the walls at some place where its adherence is especially weak. The adherence of a liquid to a solid surface, as measured by the quantity $\Delta\sigma$, can be lowered by a monolayer of some surface active substance or by a thin oil film by which this surface is contaminated. Such contaminations must be carefully removed in order to obtain a more or less marked degree of superheating.

If these contaminations are not distributed uniformly over the whole surface, but are concentrated over certain isolated portions of the latter, the cavitation of the liquid, on extension or heating, must start on these portions, spreading beyond them in the same way as a crack on the surface of a solid body. The process of rupture of a solid body, as is well known, is greatly facilitated by the presence, on its surface or inside it, of embryonic cracks; according to Griffith's well-known theory, a tensile stress directed normally to the plane of the crack is concentrated near its edge, where it can reach the theoretical value of the tensile strength, while its mean value over a large area may be much smaller. According to Griffith's view, supported in particular by the experiments of Joffé on rock-salt, these 'over-tensions' due to small local cracks lead to a rupture of a solid body under the action of tensile stresses which are, on the average, much smaller than would be expected from the theory (the theoretical strength per unit area being of the order of $2\sigma_{1,0}/\delta$, where $\delta$ is of the order of $10^{-8}$ cm.; see Ch. VI, § 5).

These considerations can be equally applied to the rupture of the contact between a liquid and a solid surface, under a relatively small tensile stress due to a negative pressure, or to a tendency of the liquid to evaporate, if $2\sigma_{1,0}$ is replaced by $\Delta\sigma$ and if small particles of the wall, contaminated by substances, causing a marked lowering of $\Delta\sigma$, give rise to initial 'embryonic' cracks.

The latter are often found to be pre-existing in the form of minute bubbles of some gas absorbed in the liquid or in the walls of the vessel containing it; such bubbles can be seen on the surface of a glass of water after standing for some time under normal conditions (atmospheric pressure and room temperature).

The role of the surface of the vessel can be played by the surface of dust particles and any other solid colloidal particles which are usually contained in the liquid, and which can be removed only after a very careful purification. It is sometimes believed that such particles can serve as 'nuclei' for the ebullition process in the same way as for the condensation of a supersaturated vapour (see below), and that their capacity of acting as such nuclei depends mainly on their *size*. In our view the latter is practically irrelevant, the action of the nuclei being due to their surface properties, as specified by a small value of the adhesion $\Delta\sigma$. In other words, the surface of the nuclei must be not wetted or rather imperfectly wetted by the liquid. The same refers to the surface of the walls, or those patches of this surface where the embryonic bubbles are most easily formed. The degree of wetting can be ascertained from a measurement of the contact angle $\theta$ in the case of a bubble or of a liquid drop. If this angle is reckoned from the surface of the solid to the boundary surface between the liquid and gas *throughout the liquid phase*, then the wetting is more complete the smaller $\theta$. Complete wetting corresponds to $\theta = 0$, complete non-wetting to $\theta = 180°$. Using Neumann's formula

$$\sigma_{1,2}+\sigma_{1,0}\cos\theta = \sigma_{2,0},$$

we see that if $\theta = 180°$, $\sigma_{2,0}+\sigma_{1,0}-\sigma_{1,2} = \Delta\sigma = 0$, which means that the liquid does not adhere at all to the solid (of course $\Delta\sigma$ can have even a negative value). If $\theta < 90°$, the surface of the solid remains covered by a thin film of the liquid, forming the bottom of the gas bubble adhering to it. For the latter to be detached it is necessary that this thin film should be converted into a thick one by a discontinuous process, the converse of the process of the adhesion of a bubble to a solid surface, which has been examined in § 4 of the preceding chapter.

The modification of the kinetics of the ebullition process which follows from the preceding considerations may be reduced to a replacement of the surface tension $\sigma$ ($= \sigma_{1,0}$) between the liquid and the vapour, which determines the critical size of the embryonic bubbles, by the adhesion $\Delta\sigma$ to the surface of the walls or of dust particles present in the liquid, those portions of this surface being active in furthering the cavitation or ebullition process which are imperfectly wetted by the liquid, i.e. for which $\Delta\sigma \approx 0$ or even $< 0$.

It may seem at first sight that in the latter case the contact between the liquid and the solid surface must be broken spontaneously irrespective of the thermal motion, since this involves a *decrease* of the free energy by the amount $-|\Delta\sigma|A$, where $A$ is one-half of the area of the arising gas bubble or rather 'lens'. In reality, however, so long as the latter is limited by a certain boundary line it is necessary to take into account the linear free energy of this boundary $\alpha L$, which must always have a positive value ($\alpha$ being the linear tension along $L$), i.e. the free energy per unit length.

Now, it is clear that for small values of $A$ and $L$ the linear term must be more important than the surface one, since $C$ is of the second order of smallness compared with $L$. Thus, for example, if the arising cavity is a disk with a radius $r$, we have $L = 2\pi r$ and $A = \pi r^2$; the resulting change of the free energy (or thermodynamic potential)

$$\Delta\Phi = \Delta\sigma \, . \, \pi r^2 + \alpha 2\pi r$$

must therefore be positive for sufficiently small values of $r$ even in the case when $\Delta\sigma < 0$.

The situation is here quite similar to that which is met with in the case of ordinary (volume) cavitation in a superheated liquid, the volume of the embryonic gas bubble being replaced by the area of the embryonic lens $A$, and its surface cavitation in the case $\Delta\sigma < 0$ requires an activation (free) energy equal to the maximum value of the preceding expression for $\Delta\Phi$, namely $\Delta\Phi = \frac{1}{2}\alpha 2\pi r^* = \alpha\pi r^* = \pi\alpha^2/|\Delta\sigma|$, where $r^* = \alpha/|\Delta\sigma|$ is the corresponding critical value of the radius. The probability that such a cavitation will actually take place referred to unit time must thus be proportional to $e^{-\pi\alpha^2/|\Delta\sigma|kT}$ (i.e. tend to zero as the temperature is lowered).

In reality the situation is complicated by the fact that the arising cavity is filled up by some gas—partially by the vapour of the liquid, but mainly, as a rule, by foreign gases dissolved in the latter. If this solution is supersaturated (as is usually the case when the temperature is sufficiently raised), the formation of this gas phase is accompanied by a decrease of the free (thermodynamic) potential by an amount proportional to the volume of the cavity, which is an additional factor furthering its formation. The total change of the free energy, including the volume term, is thus equal to

$$\Delta\Phi = \Delta\phi\, V + \Delta\sigma\, A + \alpha L,$$

where $\Delta\phi = \phi_B - \phi_A$ is the difference between the thermodynamic potential of unit volume of the gas phase and the equivalent quantity of the dissolved phase. In the case of a supersaturated solution $\Delta\phi < 0$. Putting $V = Ah$, where $h$ is the mean width of the cavity, which at the instant of its origin must be of the order of $10^{-8}$ cm., we can treat the volume term as a simple addition to the surface one, corresponding to a change of the effective value of $\Delta\sigma$ by the product $\Delta\phi\, h$.

The secretion of foreign gases dissolved in a liquid through the volume of the latter or on the surface of the vessel containing it is a process quite similar to the process of the boiling of the liquid, and well known to be a factor helping, or even starting, this boiling. Its connexion with pre-boiling phenomena is illustrated by the rapid increase of the absorption (damping) of ultrasonic waves propagated through a liquid containing large amounts of dissolved gases when its temperature is approaching the boiling-point, this damping being due to the scattering of the waves by the embryonic gas bubbles originating in the volume of the liquid on the surface of dust particles and other colloidal contaminations.

It should be mentioned that the cavitation, and especially surface cavitation, must be greatly facilitated by strong ultrasonic vibrations since they are associated with negative pressures (alternating with positive ones) of a very large magnitude.

Since the contact surface between a liquid and a solid is, as a rule, the seat of an electric double layer, surface cavitation, which means a rapid separation between the positive and negative halves of such a layer, must involve the appearance of high potential differences corresponding to electric fields of the same magnitude ($10^7$ volt/cm.) as those initially confined to the contact surface. When the thickness of the gas lens becomes a few times larger than the mean free path of electrons in the gas filling it, an electric discharge, due to cumulative ionization by collision of the electrons, must take place (unless it is growing so slowly that the opposite charges have a chance of getting neutralized by an electric current flowing in the solid-liquid 'container' of the gas lens). The fact that such micro-electric discharges actually take place in a liquid as a result of cavitations due to powerful ultrasonic vibrations has not yet been ascertained by direct experiment. The latter shows, however, in a conclusive way that the propagation of strong ultrasonic vibrations in a liquid gives rise to chemical action (formation of atomic oxygen, hydrogen peroxide, etc.), which on the preceding theory can be treated as a direct result of electric discharges in the gas bubbles or as a photochemical action, due to ultra-violet light, emitted as a result of such discharges.†

We shall now turn to a discussion of the factors which facilitate the converse process of the condensation of a supersaturated vapour. It is usually assumed that this condensation is facilitated (in the sense of a lowering of the degree of supersaturation which is required for a sufficiently rapid rate of this process) by the presence of dust particles, which serve as condensation nuclei owing to the fact that they set a lower limit, different from zero, to the size (radius) of the embryonic liquid drops. In fact, if a solid sphere of radius $r_0$ is covered by a thin film of the liquid with a thickness $h \ll r_0$, this film must behave in the same way as a liquid drop with a radius $r_0+h$, if the influence of the solid is assumed to be immaterial (which in reality is not true, see below). Hence, in order to ensure the rapid condensation of the vapour it is sufficient to overcompress or overcool it in such a way that $r_0+h \approx r_0$ should be equal to the critical radius $r^*$ of the simple theory developed in the preceding sections; for a given temperature $T$ the minimum pressure necessary for a rapid condensation is thus given by equation (2), that is,

$$\log\frac{p}{p_\infty} = \frac{2\sigma v_B}{kTr_0},$$

or the minimum degree of overcooling by (5 b), i.e.

$$T_0 - T = \frac{2\sigma T_0 v_B}{\lambda r_0}.$$

As a matter of fact the degree of supersaturation can be even somewhat

† This theory was initially proposed by the writer in a somewhat different form, based on the consideration of the volume-cavitation only. See J. Frenkel, *Acta Physicochimica.*

smaller, i.e. the critical radius $r^*$ somewhat larger than $r_0$, by an amount corresponding, according to (27) and (28), to a range

$$\sqrt{\frac{2\pi kT}{\gamma}} = \sqrt{\left(\frac{6\pi kT}{\phi_A - \phi_B} g^*\right)}$$

of $g$ values in the vicinity of critical one $g^*$. Noting that $\frac{4}{3}\pi r^3 = v_B g$, we have

$$\Delta r = \frac{v_B}{4\pi r^2}\Delta g \simeq \frac{v_B}{4\pi r^{*2}}\sqrt{\frac{2\pi kT}{\gamma}},$$

or, if $r^*$ is here approximately identified with $r_0$, $\phi_A - \phi_B$ replaced by $2\sigma v_B/kTr_0$, and $g^*$ by $\frac{4}{3}\pi r_0^3/v_B$,

$$\Delta r \approx \frac{1}{2}\sqrt{\frac{kT}{\sigma}},$$

which is of the order of $10^{-8}$ cm.

The preceding argument, in spite of its apparent simplicity and conclusiveness, is in reality only partially correct. In fact, if the size of the dust particles were the sole factor determining their capacity to act as condensation nuclei, then it would be utterly incomprehensible why the condensation process should not begin, in the absence of any such nuclei, on the walls of the vessel containing the vapour, since these walls are practically flat ($r = \infty$), so that from the purely geometrical point of view no supersaturation should be required at all.

If this geometrical approach to the problem were fully correct, it would be impossible to obtain even the smallest supersaturation of a vapour in a closed space, which is obviously wrong. The fallacy of the preceding argument consists in neglecting the physico-chemical factors which determine the adsorption of the vapour on the solid surface (of the walls, or of the dust particles) in the form of a monomolecular layer or a polymolecular film and its equilibrium with thicker films and with the gas phase. Now these factors are of decisive importance for the effectiveness or non-effectiveness of the geometrical factor represented by the curvature of the solid surface. Generally speaking, if the latter is not wetted by the liquid ($\Delta\sigma \leqslant 0$), condensation will not take place without a sufficient degree of supersaturation, even upon a flat surface ($r = \infty$); in the best case a monomolecular adsorbed layer will be formed which, however, will not be able to develop into a thicker film. But even in the case of strong wetting ($\Delta\sigma > 0$, contact angle $\theta < 90°$) a certain degree of supersaturation of the vapour is, in general, required for the condensation process to start with a measurable velocity.

This result is a consequence of the fact that the range of molecular forces is in reality larger than the distance between the nearest neighbours in the liquid (or solid) phase, and that, consequently, the evaporation energy per molecule in the case of a thin liquid film is smaller than in that of a thicker one, the thickness of the film $h$ thus playing a role similar to that of the radius in the case of small drops.

A quantitative estimate of the influence of $h$ on the evaporation energy can be obtained as follows.

The potential energy of a molecule in the external (superficial) layer of a thin film $U(h)$ is equal to its energy with respect to a liquid extending practically to infinity $U(\infty)$ decreased by the energy $U(\infty, h)$ with respect to the same liquid, when the particle is removed from the surface of the latter at a distance $h$. Now, $U_\infty$ is obviously equal to the normal value of the evaporation energy, while $U(\infty, h)$ can be represented according to § 4, Ch. VI, by the formula

$$U(\infty, h) = \frac{\gamma}{h^\mu} = U(\infty)\frac{\delta^\mu}{h^\mu}$$

if the potential energy of two molecules is assumed to be inversely proportional to the $(\mu+3)$th power of their distance apart. This expression does not take into account the molecular forces due to the presence of the solid surface; they can be neglected if the latter is not wetted by the liquid.

We thus get

$$U(h) = U_\infty\left(1-\frac{\delta^\mu}{h^\mu}\right). \tag{30}$$

This formula is similar to the expression (3) for the evaporation energy per molecule of a drop with a radius $r$

$$U_r = U_\infty - \frac{2\sigma v_B}{r},$$

which can be written in the form

$$U_r = U_\infty\left(1-\frac{\delta}{r}\right),$$

since $2\sigma v_B$ is practically equal to $U_\infty$.

Hence it is clear that in the case of a liquid which does not wet, or wets only imperfectly, the walls of the vessel, or the surface of the dust particles present in the vapour, the condensation of the latter requires a certain degree of supersaturation, just as in the case of the Thomson–Volmer theory, with $\delta/r$ replaced by $(\delta/r)^\mu$, where in the case of the London forces $\mu = 3$.

Since the vapour pressure in a state of statistical equilibrium can be represented as a function of the evaporation energy $U$ and the temperature by the formula $p = \text{const.}\, Te^{-U/kT}$, we see that in the case of a thin film the vapour pressure is increased with respect to the value $p_\infty$, corresponding to a thick layer, according to the formula

$$p_h = p_\infty\, e^{U_\infty \delta^\mu / kTh^\mu}, \tag{31}$$

which can be rewritten in the form

$$\log\frac{p_h}{p_\infty} = \frac{U_\infty\, \delta^\mu}{kTh^\mu}, \tag{31 a}$$

similar to Thomson's formula (2).

Just as in the latter case the equilibrium between the vapour and the film turns out to be unstable with respect to a variation of the thickness, a film with a thickness smaller than that which corresponds to the vapour pressure $p = p_h$ according to (31 a) tending to get still thinner (its evaporation rate $\alpha_h$ being larger than the rate of condensation $\beta$), while a thicker film tends to increase in thickness ($\alpha_h < \beta$).

In order to account for the mutual action between the molecules of the liquid (or the gas) and those of the solid body when the surface of the latter is wetted, it is necessary to replace $\gamma/h^\mu$ by the difference $\gamma/h^\mu - \gamma'/h^{\mu'}$, where the second term represents the potential energy of the forces due to the solid body at a distance $h$ from its surface.

The expression (30) for the evaporation energy is replaced in this case by

$$U(h) = U_\infty\left(1 - \frac{\delta^\mu}{h^\mu} + \epsilon\frac{\delta^{\mu'}}{h^{\mu'}}\right), \tag{31 b}$$

where $\epsilon$ is a numerical coefficient, equal to the ratio between the adsorption energy of a molecule of the liquid (or gaseous) phase on the surface of the solid and the evaporation energy $U_\infty$. If $\mu' = \mu$, the introduction of the additional term accounting for the mutual action of the molecules with the solid body is equivalent to a diminution of the constant $\delta$ referring to the liquid alone. If, moreover, $\epsilon > 1$, which means that the solid surface is wetted fairly well by the liquid, a supersaturation of the vapour must either be impossible at all or be reduced to the degree corresponding, in the sense of Thomson's formula, to the size of liquid drops having a critical radius equal to the radius of the dust particles acting as condensation nuclei.

It should be mentioned that in the latter case, just as in the case of the absence of any nuclei and of surface effect due to the walls, it is necessary to introduce a correction in Thomson's formula in order to account more accurately for the dependence of the evaporation energy on the radius of the drop. This can be done if the surface tension $\sigma$ in Thomson's formula is treated not as a constant, but as a (decreasing) function of the radius of the drop. This function can be identified approximately with the surface tension of a film, having a thickness $h = 2r$, and can be written in the form

$$\sigma = w_\infty\left(1-\frac{\delta^\mu}{h^\mu}\right),$$

according to (11) and (13 a) Ch. VI.

In the case of a liquid which is wetting the surface of a solid body, the condensation of the vapour into a thin liquid film must take place at a pressure which is lower than that corresponding to a thermodynamical equilibrium between the vapour and the liquid phase (in bulk). The thickness of the resulting film $h$ is an increasing function of the vapour pressure $p$ which can be determined from an equation of the type (31 a) if $p_h$ is identified with $p$, and $U_\infty(\delta^\mu/h^\mu)$ is replaced by $U_\infty\left(\frac{\delta^\mu}{h^\mu}-\epsilon\frac{\delta^{\mu'}}{h^{\mu'}}\right)$, on the assumption that the latter expression has a negative value. Putting, for example, $\mu = \mu' = 3$ (London forces), we get

$$\frac{U_\infty(\epsilon-1)\delta^3}{kTh^3} = \log\frac{p_\infty}{p} \quad (p < p_\infty). \tag{32}$$

As $p$ approaches $p_\infty$ the thickness of the film $h$ tends to infinity.

The above considerations explain the phenomenon of multilayer adsorption, observed in the case of such substances which in the liquid state wet the surface of the adsorbent. This type of adsorption is often denoted as 'capillary condensation'. It is especially pronounced in that case when the surface of the adsorbent contains small cracks and fissures. The preceding theory can easily be extended to this case.

The equilibrium between a liquid film wetting the surface of the adsorbent and the vapour phase is stable, while in the case of a non-wetting film it is unstable, as has already been indicated above in connexion with equation (31 a). The latter circumstance is of decisive importance for the kinetic theory of the condensation of a saturated—or rather supersaturated—vapour on the walls of the container or on the surface of solid particles suspended in it. The stability or instability of the equilibrium between a liquid film and the vapour of the same substance can be inferred from the fact that the thermodynamic potential $\Phi$ of the system constituted by them, considered as a function of the thickness of the film $h$, for a fixed value of the total number of molecules in the two phases has a minimum in the former case and a maximum in the latter (just as in the case of the equilibrium between a liquid drop and its supersaturated vapour, according to Thomson's theory).

The potential $\Phi$ can be calculated as follows. According to the definition of the quantity $U(h)$ in (31 b) we see that the complete value of the evaporation energy of a film with a thickness $h$ is equal to the integral $\int\limits_{\delta}^{h} U(x)\frac{dx}{v_A}$, since $dx/v_A$, where $v_A$ is the volume occupied by one molecule of the liquid, is the number of molecules in a layer of thickness $dx$ (per unit area). The difference between this integral and the product $U_\infty h/v_A$ is the correction to the normal value of the evaporation energy due to the small thickness of the film, so that the quantity $W(h) = U_\infty \frac{h}{v_A} - \int\limits_{\delta}^{h} U(x)\frac{dx}{v_A} = U_\infty \int\limits_{\delta}^{h} \left(\frac{\delta^\mu}{x^\mu} - \epsilon\frac{\delta^{\mu'}}{x^{\mu'}}\right)\frac{dx}{v_A}$ can be defined as the corresponding correction to the potential energy of the film. Neglecting entropy effects we thus obtain the following expression for $\Phi$ as a function of $h$:

$$\begin{aligned}\Phi &= \phi_B h/v_B + \phi_A(N - h/v_B) + W(h)\\ &= (\phi_B - \phi_A)h/v_B + W(h) + \phi_A N,\end{aligned}$$

where $\phi_A$ and $\phi_B$ denote the potentials of a single molecule of the vapour and liquid phase respectively—for the limiting case of a very thick film ($h = \infty$), while $N$ is the total number of molecules.

Putting, for the sake of simplicity, $\mu = \mu' = 3$ we get

$$\Phi = (\phi_B - \phi_A)h/v_B + \frac{(\epsilon - 1)U_\infty \delta^3}{2v_B h^2} + \text{const.} \tag{33}$$

If $\epsilon > 1$, which means that the surface of the adsorbent is wetted by the liquid, then $\Phi$ has a minimum when $\phi_B > \phi_A$ (unsaturated vapour) decreasing monotonically in the contrary case. If $\epsilon < 1$ (poorly wetting liquid), then $\Phi$ increases monotonically in the latter case and has a maximum when $\phi_B < \phi_A$ (supersaturated vapour). The value of $h$ corresponding to the minimum or maximum value of $\Phi$ is determined by the equation

$$|\phi_B - \phi_A| = |\epsilon - 1|\frac{U_\infty \delta^3}{h^3},$$

which is reduced to (32) if $\phi_A$ and $\phi_B$ are treated as functions of the pressure for a given temperature $T$. If on the contrary they are considered as functions of the temperature for a given pressure $p$, we get, since $|\phi_B - \phi_A| = \frac{U_\infty}{T_0}|T_0 - T|$,

$$\frac{|T_0 - T|}{T_0} = |\epsilon - 1|\frac{\delta^3}{h^3}, \tag{33 a}$$

where $T_0$ is the temperature of the boiling-point for the pressure $p$.

The preceding results have an important bearing on the kinetics of the condensation process on the surface of a body which is not wetted or is poorly wetted by the liquid under consideration. Without going into the mathematical details we can describe this process as follows.

The surface is covered by patches of the liquid in the form of thin films which are growing in some places and getting thinner in others, until they reach a critical thickness $h = h^*$, determined by (33 a), whereafter their growth proceeds in a practically monotonic way and at an accelerated rate. The number of 'patches', or rather the fraction of the total area which is covered with a film whose thickness lies between $h$ and $h+dh$, is proportional to $e^{-\Phi/kT}\,dh$, where $\Phi$ is given by (33). This factor determines, in the main features, the rate of the condensation process in its initial stages. The situation may be complicated, as has already been mentioned by the instability of films in a certain range of thicknesses. In the case of small dust particles it is further complicated by their curvature $1/r$, which is a factor acting in the same direction as the 'thickness' $1/h$. If the dust particles contain a substance which can be partially dissolved in the liquid, the vapour pressure of the latter is decreased, according to Raoult's law, and the rate of supersaturation which is necessary for a sufficiently rapid condensation is decreased. It can even sometimes become negative in the sense that the vapour becomes condensed into a fog, while it is apparently non-saturated.

This condition is met with sometimes in the condensation of water vapour in the atmosphere, when the latter contains nuclei of salt-like substances (supposed to originate from the sea) or with dust particles containing large amounts of such soluble substances.

It is well known that the role of condensation nuclei can be played by *ions*. It seems, however, that the ions do not form the starting-points in the formation of the embryos of the liquid phase, but become attached to such embryos when they have already reached a certain size, thus converting them from subcritical ($r < r^*$) into supercritical ($r > r_e^*$), and so stabilizing the embryos at a rather early period of their development.

According to J. J. Thomson's old theory, the electrical stabilization of liquid drops in a supersaturated vapour was explained on the assumption that the electric charge $e$ was distributed uniformly over their surface. Under such conditions the surface (free) energy of the drop $4\pi r^2\sigma$ is increased by its electric energy $e^2/2r$, so that the thermodynamic potential of the system vapour (A)+liquid drop (B) turns out to be

$$\Phi = N_A \phi_A + N_B \phi_B + 4\pi r^2 \sigma + \frac{e^2}{2r}. \tag{34}$$

It reaches a maximum, corresponding to an unstable equilibrium between the vapour and the liquid drop, for a value of the radius determined by the equation

$$\frac{\phi_B - \phi_A}{v_A} + \frac{2\sigma}{r} - \frac{e^2}{8\pi r^4} = 0, \tag{34 a}$$

which is a generalization of the equation (1 a). It should be mentioned that the quantity $e^2/8\pi r^4 = E^2/8\pi$ is equal to the negative pressure due to the electric charge of the drop, so that the difference $2\sigma/r - e^2/8\pi r^4$ is equal to the resulting positive pressure.

It is seen from (34 a) that the presence of an electric charge leads to a decrease of the critical radius of the drop for a given degree of supersaturation of the vapour (i.e. for a given value of the difference $\phi_A - \phi_B$). This explains in a qualitative way the fact that the condensation of the vapour is facilitated by the presence of ions.

Thomson's theory would be exact if the charge of the drop $e$ was constituted by a large number of ions of the same sign, distributed more or less uniformly over its surface. In reality, however, as has been shown by Thomson himself in his classical experiments on the condensation of a supersaturated vapour on ions, each drop contains, as a rule, but a single ion. Under such conditions the assumption of a uniform distribution of this charge over the surface of the drop is devoid of physical meaning. If it is assumed, on the other hand, that the ion is situated at the centre of the drop, the electric energy of the latter due to its presence is given by the formula

$$W_e = \frac{1}{8\pi} \int_a^r \left(\frac{1}{\epsilon} - 1\right) D^2 4\pi r^2 \, dr,$$

where $D = e/r^2$ is the electric induction of the ion and $a$ the effective radius of the ion. Substituting the latter expression we get

$$W_e = -\frac{e^2}{2a}\left(1-\frac{1}{\epsilon}\right)+\frac{e^2}{2r}\left(1-\frac{1}{\epsilon}\right).$$

The first term represents the energy of the absorption of the ion by a liquid drop of a very large size ($r = \infty$), while the second term

$$\Delta W_e = \frac{e^2}{2r}\left(1-\frac{1}{\epsilon}\right)$$

is a correction for the finite value of the radius. It must be substituted in the expression (34) for Thomson's additional term $e^2/2r$, and thus proves to differ from the latter by the factor $1-1/\epsilon$ only. For water this factor is practically identical with 1.

The fact that supersaturated water-vapour is more readily condensed on negative ions than on positive ions could be explained, at first sight, by assuming that the water molecules in the surface layer of the drop are self-orientated in such a way that their negative ends point outwards and the positive inwards, forming a double layer with an electric potential which is larger inside the drop than outside it. If, however, the degree of orientation is independent of the radius of the drop $a$, the additional energy due to the adsorption of a negative ion by the drop would be independent of its radius, and would not, accordingly, influence the value of the critical radius. In order to explain why, in the case of the negative ions, it is reduced to a greater extent than in the case of positive ions, we must assume, either that the degree of orientation increases with increase of the radius (which is quite plausible), or take into account, besides the dipole moments of the molecules, their electrical quadrupole moments, supposed to be rigidly attached to the dipole ones.

## 6. Kinetics of the Crystallization Process

The crystallization process can take place directly from the gas phase, from a supersaturated liquid solution, or finally from the liquid phase of the pure substance. Apart from certain special features, connected with the regular polyhedral shape of the crystals, the kinetics of the first process does not differ, in principle, from the kinetics of the condensation process considered above. It should be mentioned that, according to Ostwald, the molecules of a supersaturated vapour first condense into drops of a supercooled liquid which are thereafter crystallized. It is certain, however, that in many cases the transition from the gas phase into the crystalline one takes place directly, and not via the liquid phase.

A liquid solution differs from a gas by the presence of the molecules of the solvent. In so far as the latter do not participate in the crystallization of the dissolved substance, their influence consists in preventing their free transition from the solution to the crystalline phase. This influence can be described by decreasing the rate of crystallization $\beta$ (number of dissolved molecules which pass from the solution to the crystal per unit time and area) with respect to its value $\beta_0$ for a gas by a factor $\gamma$, representing the probability that a molecule of the dissolved substance is in a 'gas-like' state, i.e. capable of moving from its initial site among the molecules of the solvent near the surface of the crystal to its final site, on this surface.

As has been shown in Ch. IV, the transition of a molecule of a liquid into such a gas-like state is a pre-requisite for its diffusion, or self-diffusion, and requires a certain activation energy $\Delta U$, which determines the temperature dependence of the diffusion coefficient $D$ according to the formula $D = Ae^{-\Delta U/kT}$, or the viscosity of the solvent (in the case of diluted solutions) according to the formula $\eta = Ce^{\Delta U/kT}$. Since the fraction of the molecules which must be found in such an 'activated' or 'movable' state at any instant of time is equal to $e^{-\Delta U/kT}$, we must put

$$\beta = \beta_0 e^{-\Delta U/kT}, \tag{34 b}$$

where $\beta_0 = n\surd(kT/2\pi m)$, $n$ being the concentration of the dissolved substance (number of molecules per unit volume). Equating $\beta$ to $\alpha$, the rate of dissolution of the crystal per unit time and area we must obtain for $n$ a value

$$n = \alpha \sqrt{\left(\frac{2\pi m}{kT}\right)} e^{\Delta U/kT},$$

which must be independent of $\Delta U$, and be determined by the energy of solution $U$ alone. Hence it follows that the rate of disintegration of a crystal in a solution must be smaller than in the case of evaporation, if the evaporation energy is equal to that of dissolution, by the same factor $e^{-\Delta U/kT}$ which gives the ratio between $\beta$ and $\beta_0$. In reality, however, the energy of solution is, as a rule, much smaller than the evaporation energy, which explains the possibility of obtaining very high values of the concentration, and corresponds to relatively very large values of $\alpha$.

Similar considerations apply to the process of crystallization from the liquid phase. The growth of the crystalline embryos in an overcooled liquid implies a preliminary release of the molecules settling down on their surface from the neighbouring molecules of the surrounding liquid. If the latter were not in contact with the crystal, then the activation energy which is necessary for this release would coincide with the evaporation energy of the liquid. In the presence of such a contact it must reduce to the same value $\Delta U$ which corresponds to the self-diffusion in the liquid or to the viscosity of the latter. Hence it follows that, other things being equal, the crystallization velocity of an overcooled liquid must decrease with increase of the degree of overcooling inversely as its viscosity.†

Assuming that the velocity of crystallization, just as that of any other transition process associated with the existence and growth of the embryos of the new phase B amidst the initial one (A), is proportional to the relative abundance of the embryos with a critical size $Z_{g^*}$, and treating them as small spheres, we obtain the following expression for the velocity of crystallization from a melt or a solution:

$$I = \text{const. } e^{-(1/kT)[\Delta U + \frac{4}{3}\pi r^{*2}\sigma]}, \tag{35}$$

or if $r^*$ is expressed as a function of the degree of overcooling, according to equation (5 b),

$$I = \text{const. } \exp\left\{-\frac{1}{kT}\left(\Delta U + \frac{4\pi\sigma}{3}\right)\left[\frac{2v_B\,\sigma T}{\lambda(T_0-T)}\right]^2\right\}. \tag{35 a}$$

Since $N_{g^*}$ increases with the degree of overcooling while $1/\eta \sim e^{-\Delta U/kT}$ decreases as the temperature is lowered, this expression must reach a maximum value for a certain degree of overcooling. The 'optimum' temperature $T_1 = T_0/x$, corresponding to this maximum, is determined by the equation

$$\frac{(x-1)^3}{x^2(x+1)} = \frac{4\pi\sigma}{3\Delta U}\left(\frac{2\sigma v_B}{\lambda}\right)^2, \tag{36}$$

the maximum value of $I$ being given by

$$I_{\max} = \text{const. } e^{-\{3x/(2x+1)\}(\Delta U/kT)}. \tag{36 a}$$

If $x$ lies sufficiently close to 1, the preceding equation reduces to

$$x-1 \equiv \frac{T_0-T_1}{T_0} = \left(\frac{2\pi}{3\Delta U}\right)^{\frac{1}{3}}\left(\frac{v_B}{\lambda}\right)^{\frac{2}{3}} \tag{36 b}$$

and (36 a) to $$I_{\max} = \text{const. } e^{-\Delta U/kT}.$$

Putting $\sigma/\lambda \approx 2\times10^{-2}$, as follows from the theory of pre-melting, developed in § 3, we get $x-1 \approx 10^{-2}$, i.e. $T_0-T = 3°$ if $T_0 = 300°$ K. This figure seems to be of the correct order of magnitude in the case

† These considerations were developed by the present author in 1932 (*Sow. Phys.* **1**, 498 (1932)).

of relatively simple substances, like metals or salts. In the case of such liquids as tend to solidify without crystallization (glasses, glycerine, etc.), the optimum overcooling must be much larger, of the order of 100 degrees and even more, and the corresponding maximum crystallization velocity must accordingly be very low. This explains the fact that when cooled down sufficiently rapidly such liquids do not crystal-

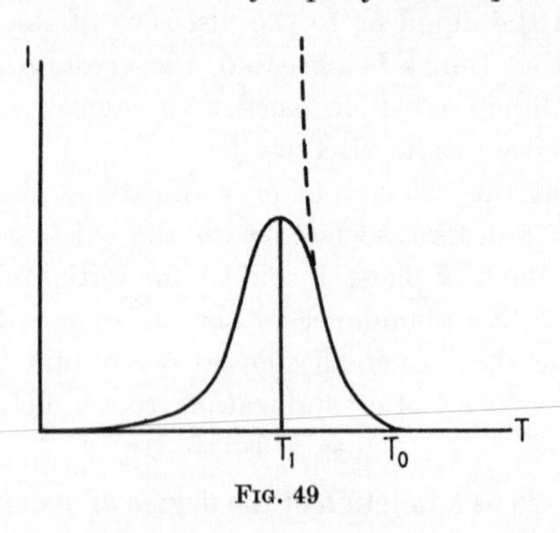


FIG. 49

lize. The decisive role, according to equation (36 a), is played by the large *viscosity* of these liquids, especially in the overcooled state, or more exactly, by the large value of the activation energy of self-diffusion $\Delta U$, whereas the surface tension between the crystalline and the liquid phase is probably only of secondary importance.

The fact that the velocity of crystallization, or, more exactly, of the formation of crystallization nuclei (i.e. of embryos, exceeding the critical size), displays a maximum, as a function of the degree of overcooling, as shown by the full curve in Fig. 49, was established experimentally long ago, especially by Tammann and his school. The correctness of our interpretation of the experimental results, as represented by the curve $I(t)$, given above, has been recently checked by Michnevitch,† who has shown, using such liquids as salol, betol, and piperine, which are liable to strong overcooling (by 60° and even more), that the product of $I$ and the viscosity $\mu$ of the liquid (at the corresponding temperature) rises monotonically as the temperature is lowered below the standard crystallization point as shown by the dotted line in Fig. 49.

† G. L. Michnevitch, Dissertation, Odessa, 1941. In his experiments Michnevitch kept the liquid for a certain length of time $t$ at the temperature under investigation $T$ and thereafter heated it for a relatively very short time $\Delta t$ to a temperature slightly below $T_0$; the submicroscopical nuclei, which had arisen during the first period, developed rapidly during the second one to a large size, when they could easily be seen through the microscope (heat 'development' of nuclei).

According to Tammann the velocity of crystallization is usually characterized by two different quantities, namely the rate of birth of crystallization centres which has been considered above ($I$), and the 'linear crystallization velocity', i.e. the velocity with which the boundary surface between the melt and the crystallized mass of the substance moves forward under macroscopic conditions (in a cooled tube, for example).

The latter velocity is devoid of a direct physical meaning, for the temperature near the boundary surface between the liquid and the crystal is raised owing to the evolution of the latent heat of crystallization, being determined by the rate of flow of heat away from this surface. In the case of the growth of crystal embryos the temperature at their surface, owing to their small size, can remain much lower than $T_0$, and practically identical with the average temperature $T$ of the whole body.

The experimental investigation of the crystallization of overcooled liquids shows that the velocity of this process is influenced by a number of factors which are left out of account by the preceding theory. In the first place we must cite the influence of the walls of the vessel containing the liquid, and of various colloidal particles serving as crystallization nuclei, just as in the case of the condensation of a supersaturated vapour. A good wetting of the solid surface by the liquid (melt) seems to be in both cases a necessary condition for the effectiveness of the corresponding bodies in furthering the crystallization process.

It has been found by a number of investigations† that the crystallization of certain organic liquids (piperine and salol, in particular) is facilitated by electric fields (sometimes by magnetic ones too), especially in the neighbourhood of the walls of the vessel, and by various ionizing agents. It seems that in both cases we have to do with a stabilization of the crystallization nuclei by the attachment of ions either formed in the liquid or penetrating into it from the solid surfaces (glass and others).

These contact and electric effects can probably be explained on the same lines as in the case of the condensation process, with due regard to the modification of the properties of a liquid in the vicinity of the surface of a solid body under the influence of its molecular field, and of the resulting alteration of the surface entropy.

The experimental investigation of the crystallization of overcooled

† See, for example, Michnevitch, *Acta Physicochimica U.R.S.S.*, **12**, 444 (1940).

liquids shows that the degree of supercooling which can be reached (i.e. for which the crystallization begins with a marked velocity) depends on the previous heat treatment of the system. The longer the liquid has been kept, before being cooled down, at a temperature $T_2 > T_0$, and the higher this temperature, the lower the temperature $T_1 < T_0$ it can withstand without crystallization. This influence of the 'pre-heating' of a liquid on its resistance to crystallization (as measured by the maximum attainable degree of overcooling) can be reduced, in principle, to a destruction (i.e. melting) of various foreign particles with a higher melting-point ($\leqslant T_2$), which, if they remained intact, could serve as crystallization nuclei for the main substance. After dissolving in the latter (at a temperature $T_2$) they can of course be regenerated when the solution is cooled down. It is conceivable, however, that the crystallization of such impurities requires a high degree of overcooling. If this is so, then their presence in a molecularly dispersed state will no longer facilitate the crystallization of the main substance when it is cooled down below the standard crystallization point $T_0$. This point of view is supported by the interesting phenomena of 'memory' which are observed under certain, not fully elucidated, conditions if the system is repeatedly fused and crystallized. The crystals which are formed during the latter portion of the cycle are found to preserve—at certain places at least, near the walls of the container—an invariable orientation, as if they 'remembered' the orientation which they acquired in the course of the preceding crystallization.

It is possible, however, that the role of such crystallization centres is played by small crystals of the main substance, which have not had enough time to get fully fused during the period of heating, especially if their melting-point is somewhat raised by the influence of the molecular field of the solid walls (or solid colloidal particles) on which they arise.†

A better understanding of the phenomenon of 'crystallization memory' requires a deeper insight into the specific features of the kinetics of the crystallization process and the role played in this process by the surface of solid bodies which are in contact with the liquid.

These specific features of the crystallization process, which distinguish it rather sharply from the process of the condensation of a vapour into a liquid, are connected with the fact that crystals, in contradistinction to liquids, have a regular polyhedral shape, being bounded, in a state of thermodynamical equilibrium, by planes which correspond

† Cf. V. Danilov and Neumark, *Sow. Phys.* **12**, 313 (1937).

to a minimum of the surface energy or, more exactly, of the surface tension.

If the shape of a crystal embryo is supposed to remain constant in the course of its growth, and if the energy of evaporation or melting is supposed to remain the same for a given crystal face irrespective of its extension, it becomes, at first sight, utterly unintelligible that a crystal embryo can be in a state of (unstable) equilibrium with an overcooled liquid, if its size has a certain critical value corresponding to this temperature. It should be remembered that in the case of equilibrium between a supersaturated vapour and an embryonic liquid drop, the dependence of the equilibrium temperature (i.e. degree of overcooling) on the size of the drop can be reduced to a change of the latent heat of evaporation per molecule as a result of a change of the fraction of the molecules in the surface layer of the drop. If the transition from the gaseous state, not into the liquid state, but into the crystalline one is considered, the variation of the equilibrium temperature (for a given temperature) must likewise be reduced to a similar cause. So long, however, as the shape of the crystal can be treated as constant, and the faces bounding it as flat, the decrease of the evaporation energy with a decrease of the crystal size can be explained by the increase of the fraction of the molecules which occupy especially disadvantageous sites, i.e. which require an abnormally small energy for their removal from the surface of the crystal. These are obviously those molecules which constitute the edges and the corners of the crystal.

We shall consider, by way of illustration, a crystal of a cubical shape, constituted by cubical particles linked together by their faces. Let the energy required for separating two such particles from each other be denoted by $U_1$. The energy required for removing a particle from the interior of the crystal, where it is surrounded by 6 neighbours, must in this case be equal to $6U_1$. If all the $N$ particles of the crystal could be treated in the same way, i.e. as if they were situated in its interior, the total energy of the crystal (with respect to the vapour) would be equal to $-\frac{1}{2}N6U_1 = -3NU_1$. Hence it follows that the evaporation energy per molecule would be equal to a constant value $3U_1$.

This result is, however, correct in the limiting case only of an infinitely large crystal. In the case of a crystal of a cubical shape, constituted by a finite number $N = G^3$ of cubic particles, we must take into account the existence of external particles, which have a smaller number of neighbours and, accordingly, an abnormally small evaporation energy.

The total number of these external particles is obviously equal to $G^3-(G-2)^3$ (since the surface layer formed by them limits a cube with an edge by two units smaller than that of the whole cube). Out of these, $6(G-2)^2$ particles form the 6 faces of the cube, without belonging either to its edges or to its corners, $12(G-2)$ constitute the edges without belonging to the corners, and 8 are situated at the 8 corners.

The latter particles have only 3 neighbours each; those situated on the edges have 4, while the remaining particles, forming the bulk of the faces, have 5 neighbours each.

The total energy of the crystal is thus equal to

$$W_N = -\tfrac{6}{2}U_1(G-2)^3-\tfrac{5}{2}U_1\,6(G-2)^2-\tfrac{4}{2}U_1\,12(G-2)-\tfrac{3}{2}U_1\,8,$$

that is,

$$W_N = -3(G^3-G^2)U_1 \equiv -3(N-N^{\frac{2}{3}})U_1.$$

If the shape of the crystal did not change in the process of its evaporation, the evaporation energy, referred to one particle, would be equal to

$$U_N = -\frac{dW_N}{dN} = 3U_1-2\frac{U_1}{N^{\frac{1}{3}}} = U_\infty-\frac{2}{3}\frac{U_\infty}{N^{\frac{1}{3}}},$$

which would correspond to an increase of the vapour pressure in the ratio

$$\frac{p_N}{p_\infty} = e^{\frac{2}{3}U_\infty/kTN^{\frac{1}{3}}}.$$

In reality, however, the evaporation of the crystal must be accompanied by at least a temporary deviation from the regular cubical shape considered above. The course of this process must be influenced by the fact that the actual evaporation energy, instead of being equal to the mean value computed above, must vary between the limits $5U_1$ for the most firmly bound particles on the faces of the crystal, before they begin to disintegrate, and $U_1$ for the last particle left on a given face, after the removal of the surface layer to which it originally belonged.

These circumstances were taken into account for the first time by Kossel, who used them as a basis for the kinetic theory of the crystallization process and of the converse process of evaporation.† According to this theory these processes do not proceed smoothly, as usually assumed, but in a jerky way. Thus, for example, in the case of an ideal crystal considered above, the evaporation must start on one of its corners and thereafter develop along one of the edges. After this preliminary stage it can assume a more or less steady character, being

† W. Kossel, *Ann. d. Phys.* **21**, 457 (1934).

propagated along subsequent rows of particles parallel to one of the edges and constituting a given face, until the whole outermost layer, corresponding to this face, is removed. After the close of such an evaporation cycle a new cycle of the same type must begin (several cycles can, of course, proceed simultaneously on different faces).

From this point of view the process of evaporation of a crystal can be likened to an inversion of the process of writing a book, by a subsequent addition of new characters to each line, of new lines to each page, and a transition to a new blank page after the preceding one has been filled.

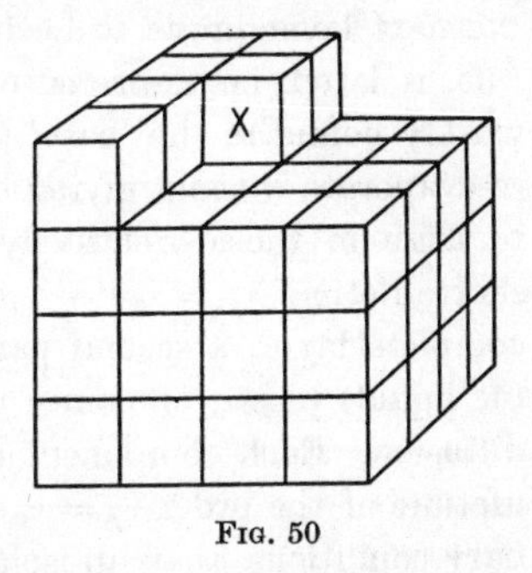


FIG. 50

This process of writing a book can serve, according to Kossel's theory, as an illustration of the process of the growth of a crystal by a condensation of particles from the gas phase, a solution, or a melt.

Kossel's scheme is illustrated in Fig. 50, which represents a phase of the quasi-steady period of the process of crystallization or evaporation (melting, dissolution). The particle which is just going to evaporate is denoted by a cross. Since it has three neighbours, its evaporation energy is exactly equal to $3U_1$, i.e. to the average evaporation energy in a crystal of unlimited size. The last particle of each row has an evaporation energy $U_1$.

The mean life of an adsorbed particle is equal to $\tau = \tau_0 e^{W/kT}$, where $\tau_0$ is the period of its free vibrations on the surface of the adsorbent, and $W$ the adsorption energy, i.e. the work which must be done to remove the adsorbed particle. The reciprocal of $\tau$ can be defined as the probability of the evaporation of the adsorbed particle, referred to unit time. The corresponding probability for one of the particles constituting the surface layer of a crystal can be expressed by a formula of the same type

$$\alpha = \nu_0 e^{-W/kT},$$

where $\nu_0 = 1/\tau_0$. Hence it follows that this probability is much larger for the last atom of a face or of a row than for the initial one (even if the latter occupies a corner position).

This circumstance must lead to an acceleration of the evaporation process towards the end of each subcycle (consisting of the evaporation of a row of particles) and to a pause at the beginning of each new cycle.

It must, however, exert a much more pronounced influence on the converse process of crystallization.

After the formation of a new layer of particles on one of the faces of the crystal has been completed, a certain, possibly long, pause must ensue, owing to the fact that the particles beginning the formation of the next layer prove to be in an unfavourable condition, being, as a rule, isolated, i.e. deprived of any side neighbours and but relatively weakly bound to the 'base' ($W = U_1$). As a result, most of them will re-evaporate without giving birth to a new layer. The latter can begin to arise in those—relatively rare—cases only in which, during the short lifetime $\tau_2 = \tau_0 e^{U_1/kT}$ of an isolated particle on the top of a complete layer, a second particle is deposited beside it from the gas (or liquid) phase, or comes to its aid, as it were, by way of surface diffusion. Each component of the doublet formed in this way has a lifetime of the order $\tau_2 = \tau_0 e^{2U_1/kT}$, i.e. enormously larger, under ordinary conditions, than an isolated atom, and accordingly an immensely larger chance of developing into a new surface colony. We thus see that a new layer of particles can begin to grow on the top of the preceding one only after an embryonic colony, consisting of two, three, or more particles, has arisen somewhere, as a result of a lucky fluctuation. The kinetics of this process is essentially similar to the kinetics of the adsorption of a monolayer of particles on the surface of a foreign body, which was considered by the author in 1924, in connexion with the experimental investigation of the phenomenon of 'critical condensation temperature' by the method of 'doublets'.† This method consisted in calculating the number of doublets corresponding to a given total number of adsorbed particles, for a random distribution of the latter, on the assumption that these doublets can give rise to stable colonies of a larger size.

Similar results can be obtained in a stricter form by the application to the problem under consideration of the method of heterophase fluctuations, the isolated particles adsorbed on a completed layer being treated as a two-dimensional gas phase, while doublets, triplets, and larger groups of particles occupying neighbouring sites, i.e. forming a compact colony, are treated as embryos of the condensed phase (B).

The concentration of the isolated particles, i.e. their number per unit area $n'$, can be calculated as a function of their volume concentration in the vapour $n$, and of the temperature, according to the formula

$$n' = n\delta e^{U_1/kT} \tag{37}$$

† J. Frenkel, *Z. f. Phys.* **26**, 117 (1924).

which has been derived in Ch. I, § 1, and where $\delta = \sqrt{(kT/2\pi f)}$ (effective thickness of the adsorbed layer). If all the two-dimensional colonies are assumed to have the same shape (circular or rectangular, for instance), corresponding to the smallest value of the potential energy for a given number $g$ of particles constituting them, then the number of embryonic colonies of a given size can be determined by the general formula

$$n'_g \cong n' e^{-\Delta\Phi'/kT}, \tag{37 a}$$

where

$$\Delta\Phi'_g = (\phi'_B - \phi'_A)g + \mu' g^{\frac{1}{2}} \tag{37 b}$$

is the increase of the thermodynamical potential of the system and adsorbed particles, connected with the formation of a compact colony of $g$ particles; $\phi'_A$ and $\phi'_B$ are the chemical (molecular) potentials of the gas-like and the compact two-dimensional phase, and $\mu'$ a coefficient which determines the 'linear tension' $\sigma'$ over the boundary of a plane embryo, referred to unit length of the boundary line.

If the embryo is treated as a disk with a radius $r$, we must put

$$\mu' g^{\frac{1}{2}} = 2\pi r\sigma',$$

where

$$g = \frac{\pi r^2}{\sigma_B},$$

$\sigma_B$ being the area occupied by a particle in a compact layer (for a cubical crystal considered above $\sigma_B = a^2$).

In the case of a stable thermodynamic equilibrium between the crystal (with fully developed faces) and the surrounding three-dimensional phase C (vapour, solution, or melt) the potentials $\phi'_A$ and $\phi'_B$ must have the same value. If, however, this three-dimensional phase C is supersaturated, then $\phi'_B$ must be smaller than $\phi_C$ and also smaller than $\phi'_A$ (since the 'adsorption' of an isolated particle is an approach to the crystalline phase). It can easily be found, in the same way as this has been done for three-dimensional embryos, that for a given value of $\phi'_A - \phi'_B > 0$ the two-dimensional gas phase formed by the pioneers of the new crystal layer is in unstable equilibrium with a 'colony' of the critical size

$$g'^* = \frac{1}{2}\left(\frac{\mu'}{\phi'_A - \phi'_B}\right)^2, \tag{38}$$

which corresponds to the maximum value of $\Delta\Phi'_g$:

$$\Delta\Phi'^* = \tfrac{1}{2}\mu' g'^{*\frac{1}{2}}. \tag{38 a}$$

In the case of small deviations from a condition of stable equilibrium (for which $g'^* = 0$) one can put approximately

$$\phi'_A - \phi'_B = \frac{\lambda}{T}(T_0 - T),$$

or

$$\phi'_A - \phi'_B = (\sigma_A - \sigma_B)(p' - p'_0) = (\sigma_A - \sigma_B)(\sigma'_0 - \sigma'),$$

where $T_0$ denotes the equilibrium temperature (the same for the two-surface and the two-volume phases), $\lambda'$ the heat of two-dimensional condensation (which in our case can be identified with $2U_1$, since each cubic particle in a compact layer has 4 side-neighbours), and $\sigma' = -p'$ the linear tension ($\sigma'_0 = -p'_0$ being its equilibrium value for $T = T_0$).

The velocity of the formation of a compact monomolecular layer on the top of the preceding one can be obtained by multiplying the expression (37 a) for $g = g^*$, i.e. the probable number of embryonic colonies of the critical size (per unit area), by the velocity of the growth of such a colony as a result of the condensation of the two-dimensional 'vapour', both from the supersaturated volume phase and by way of surface diffusion, partially compensated by the converse processes. In both cases (unless the volume phase is gaseous) we must take into account a certain activation energy $\Delta U'$, so that the resulting velocity of the surface condensation is expressed by the formula

$$I' = \text{const. } e^{-(1/kT)(\Delta U' + \Delta\Phi'_{g^*})},$$

i.e.

$$I' = \text{const. } e^{-(1/kT)[\Delta U' + \frac{1}{4}\mu'^2 T_0/\lambda'(T_0 - T)]}. \tag{39}$$

Just as in the case of a direct growth of three-dimensional embryos of a solid phase from a liquid solution or melt, which has been considered at the beginning of this section, this expression attains a maximum value for a certain degree of overcooling, determined by the formula

$$\frac{T_0 - T}{T_0} = \frac{\mu'}{2\sqrt{(k\lambda'\Delta U')}}.$$

The preceding theory refers, strictly speaking, to the kinetics of the two-dimensional condensation of an adsorbed gas-like monolayer below the corresponding equilibrium temperature. In applying it to the growth of crystals from a vapour, solution, or melt, a number of further complications must be taken into account, which are connected with linear effects on the one hand and with volume effects on the other. The former reduce to the fact that the plane embryos on the surface of the growing crystal faces must have a regular polygonal contour, corresponding to the regular polyhedral shape of the crystal. The growth of such embryos must take place by a process of formation of linear embryos on their contour line. The kinetics of this linear growth is quite similar to that of the surface and volume growth, and will not be considered here in more detail.

The process of growth of a crystal becomes complicated in the way described above, i.e. by the formation of surface and linear embryos, after they have reached a sufficiently large size—in two dimensions, at least. In dealing with the *embryos* of the crystalline phase, arising in the interior of a liquid phase, the surface and linear effects need not be considered, so far as concerns the number of embryos exceeding the critical size, i.e. capable of further growth and development, which arise in unit time.

Such effects can, however, influence the linear velocity of crystallization considered in Tammann's experiments, and determining the shape acquired by freely growing crystals. This shape is usually quite different from that which is determined by the condition of thermodynamic equilibrium (minimum surface free energy for a given value), the rate of growth of each face in a direction normal to its surface being a function not of its surface free energy, but of the activation energy $\Delta U'$, connected with the surface diffusion of the particles which serve as pioneers in the formation of a new layer on the top of the preceding one (and also to some extent of the linear tension $\sigma'$ on the boundary line of compact pioneer settlements).

Surface effects must also play an important role in the kinetics of crystallization when the latter starts, not in the interior of the liquid (or gaseous) phase, but on the walls of the vessel containing it or on the surface of foreign particles serving as crystallization nuclei, as is usually the case. The degree of overcooling (or supersaturation) which is necessary for a sufficiently rapid crystallization must essentially depend in this case on the difference between the surface free energy of the liquid and of the crystal with respect to the solid surfaces with which they are in contact (provided that this contact is preserved on solidification).

An interesting example of such surface effects is found in the converse case of the *melting* of a crystal. It is well known that under ordinary conditions an overheating of the latter, similar to the overheating of a liquid, is impossible. This peculiarity is connected with the fact that the melting of a crystal, which is kept at a homogeneous temperature, always begins on its *free* surface. The role of the latter must, accordingly, consist in lowering the activation energy, which is necessary for the formation of a flat embryo of the liquid phase, i.e. of a thin liquid film, down to zero. This result is a natural consequence of the fact that the free energy (surface tension) of a liquid is smaller than that of any face of the corresponding crystal and that the surface tension between the two phases is very small.

If the crystal is cooled down from its surface so that the temperature of the latter lies below the melting-point, then its internal temperature can be raised (by concentrating radiant heat with the help of a lens) far above the melting-point without any trace of internal melting. This fact, which has been established experimentally by Khaikin† by passing for a short time an electric current of adequate strength through a thin metallic wire and which has been found by other authors with certain silicates, shows that in the absence of surface effects the liquid phase must arise within the crystal in exactly the same way as the crystalline phase arises within the liquid one, i.e. by way of the formation of three-dimensional embryos. It should be mentioned that in the case of melting these embryos must have the same polyhedral shape as in that of crystallization, with the difference that the liquid phase is contained within them and not outside. Such liquid regions could be conveniently denoted as 'negative crystals'. Their existence has not hitherto been ascertained.

† S. Khaikin, *C.R. Ac. Sci. U.R.S.S.*, **23** (1939).

# VIII
# PROPERTIES OF SOLUTIONS AND HIGH POLYMERIC SUBSTANCES

## 1. Antagonism between External and Internal Bonds

THE investigation of the mutual action between atoms, molecules, and other simple systems discloses the general principle that the establishment of bonds between such systems always entails a weakening of the bonds between the simpler particles or systems which constitute them. This strengthening of the external bonds at the cost of the internal ones often leads to a complete dissociation of the units of higher order (molecules, atoms), constituting the system in the gaseous state, into units of lower order (atoms, or electrons and ions) when it is condensed into a liquid or solid body.

Such extreme cases of the antagonism between outer and inner bonds can be illustrated by the condensation of a metallic vapour, or of the vapour of some ionic (heteropolar) substance, like NaCl. In the former case the binding between the metallic atoms is realized through the mutual action between the external electrons and the positive nuclei (or ions), and leads to a complete ionization of the atoms when the vapour is condensed into a liquid or solid metallic body. The spontaneous ionization or 'self-ionization' of the vapour in the process of its condensation is revealed by the appearance of electrical conductivity (which is wholly absent in the gaseous phase). The electrical conductivity of liquid and solid metals is usually ascribed to 'free' electrons, capable of moving over the whole volume of the metal. This freedom is, however, quite different from that complete freedom which is possessed by the electrons released from the atoms in the gas phase by the action of some ionizing agents. In the latter case the free electrons could fly away if not prevented by the walls of the vessel containing the metallic vapour, whereas in the case of a liquid or solid metal they cannot escape into the surrounding space—unless the metal is heated to a high temperature, or acted on by ultra-violet or X-rays—being firmly bound to the whole community which is formed by the metallic atoms. This condition can be described by saying that the electrons are not wholly released but are 'collectivized', i.e. they are free to move from one atom or positive ion to another, belonging to all of them and, at the same time, acting as a bond between them. The usual conception of the condensation process as a simple return to proximity of the separate atoms, resulting in an increase of their mutual attraction, is entirely erroneous—at least in the case of a metallic body, whose atoms cease to exist as separate units when they come close to each other and are dissociated into a system of positive ions, swimming, as it were, in a negative fluid formed by the collectivized electrons. This collectivization process must be considered as the essence of the characteristic metallic bond, the different ions being bound together by the electrons which they share (in the same way as in the case of the homopolar or valence bond).

A quite similar situation is met with in the condensation of a NaCl vapour into a molten or rigid rock-salt. This process is accompanied by a loss of the segregation which characterizes the behaviour of the molecules in the gas phase, the molecules being mutually torn apart into positive and negative ions. As a result of this 'self-dissociation' a compound system is formed where each positive ion is surrounded by negative ions and each negative ion by positive ones.

When the condensation of a vapour does not lead to a self-ionization of its atoms or a self-dissociation of the molecules, it is always accompanied by a loosening of the bond between the positive ions and the electrons (as measured by the difference between the ionization potential of the gas and the threshold of the *inner* photo-electric effect of the condensed substance), or between the ions of different signs, the atoms or radicals which form the sub-units of the molecular structure.

Thus, for example, the crystallization of the vapour of sulphur, selenium, and of a number of metallic oxides and sulphides ($Cu_2O$, PbS, etc.) leads to the formation of electronic semi-conductors, which are characterized by a relatively low value of the 'collectivization potential', i.e. of the energy required to bring an electron into the conductivity band. In a similar way, the condensation of the alkali halides is accompanied by a weakening of the molecules, caused by their mutual action and, in its turn, causing a strengthening of the latter. Thus, for example, each $H^+Cl^-$ molecule, being orientated (in the condensed phase) in the direction of the electric field **F** created by the surrounding molecules, must suffer a certain extension, connected with a decrease of its dissociation energy into $H^+$ and $Cl^-$ ions (under the condition that these ions remain within the community and are not expelled from it). This extension must be associated with an increase of their dipole moment by a certain value $\Delta p = \alpha F$, where $\alpha$ is the corresponding polarizability. It must be associated, further, with a decrease of the frequency of the intramolecular vibrations by a certain value, which in the first approximation must likewise be proportional to $F$. This decrease of $\nu$ can be calculated, if the anharmonicity coefficient $g$ in the formula $\Delta U = \frac{1}{2}fx^2 - \frac{1}{3}gx^3$ for the potential energy of a molecule is known as a function of its extension $x$.

The coefficient $f$ can serve for the definition of the polarizability according to the formula $\alpha = e^2/f$, and is connected with the normal value of the vibration frequency (in an isolated molecule) by the relation $\nu_0 = (1/2\pi)\sqrt{(f/m)}$, where $m$ is the reduced mass of the two ions.

Under the influence of the extending force $eF$, due to the local electric field, the vibration frequency becomes

$$\nu = \frac{1}{2\pi}\sqrt{\frac{f-2g\xi_0}{m}} \cong \nu_0\left(1-\frac{g\xi_0}{f}\right),$$

where $\xi_0 = eF/f$ is the average value of the extension (cf. eq. (20), Ch. III), so that

$$-\frac{\Delta\nu}{\nu_0} = \frac{geF}{f^2}.$$

The decrease of the frequency of the free vibrations of a molecule in the condensed state, compared with the gaseous one, can be determined experimentally by the shift of the corresponding line (or lines) in the infra-red or in the Raman spectrum. Such shifts—to the long-wave side—are actually observed in the case of practically all dipole substances, for some of the Raman lines, at least.

A few data referring to this question are collected in the following table:†

| *Substance* | $\nu$ *(gas)* | $\nu$ *(liquid)* | $\nu$ *(solid)* |
|---|---|---|---|
| $H_2O$ | 3,650 | 3,216; 3,435 | 3,090; 3,135 |
| $NH_3$ | 3,334 | 3,300 | 3,203 |
| HCl | 2,886 | 2,800 | .. |

Quite similar effects of a 'mutual weakening' could doubtless be observed in the case of non-polar molecules, in a less pronounced form, inasmuch as the mutual action between the homopolar molecules, due to the van der Waals forces alone, is much weaker—in accordance with our general principle of the antagonism between inner and outer bonds.

We have limited ourselves thus far to the discussion of the mutual

† The frequencies are given in wave numbers. See Breit and Salant, *Phys. Z.* **31**, 871 (1930); Buchheim, ibid. **36**, 694 (1935), and especially Nielsen and Ward, *Journ. Chem. Phys.* **10**, 81 (1942).

weakening of *like* particles (molecules or atoms) in their combination into a condensed (liquid or solid) body. Perfectly similar results are obtained in the case of the mutual action between unlike particles, for example in the process of the solution of one substance in another (liquid or solid). The most common example of the weakening of the dissolved molecules as a result of their mutual action with the molecules of the solvent is the electrolytic dissociation of various ionic compounds in water or some other polar liquid with a high dielectric constant. The decrease of the dissociation energy due to this action is usually so large (owing partly to the hydration of the ions) that in the case of the so-called strong electrolytes a practically complete dissociation is found at room temperatures (and moderate concentrations).

A similar effect of a sharp decrease of the ionization energy is observed in the solutions of alkali metals in liquid ammonia.

Such solutions in the case of high concentrations of the dissolved metal are known to possess a metallic conductivity, rapidly increasing, according to a nearly exponential law, with increase of the concentration. Analogous results, which are explained by the same cause—i.e. the formation of external bonds at the cost of the internal ones—are observed in the case of many solid solutions (electronic semi-conductors with a large content of impurities) and of solutions of the oxides of alkali metals in glasses (see below).

The weakening of the atoms or molecules under their mutual action with other like, or unlike, particles is observed not only where they are fully surrounded by these particles, i.e. immersed in the liquid or solid body constituted by them, but also where they are *adsorbed* on the surface of such a body. The antagonism between the intramolecular and the adsorption bonds forms the basis of the phenomena of heterogeneous or contact catalysis. It is quite obvious that good catalysts must strongly adsorb the corresponding molecules. Such a strong adsorption is usually accompanied by their dissociation into separate atoms or radicals, bound to the surface atoms by valence forces ('chemisorption'). It should be mentioned that the catalytic action of the surface of the adsorbent is usually due not so much to a decrease of the *dissociation* energy of the adsorbed particles, as to the parallel effect of the lowering of the *activation* energy, which is required for a reaction with the adsorbed molecules of a different kind. The very notion of activation energy or, more exactly, the fact that this energy is smaller than the dissociation energy of the corresponding molecules, can be regarded as a special case of our general principle—of the antagonism between the external and the internal bonds. In fact, in the case of chemical reactions of the simplest type,

$$AB+C \rightarrow A+BC,$$

the activation energy $E$ which is required to remove B from A proves to be lowered, with respect to the energy of the dissociation process $AB \rightarrow A+B$, owing to the presence in the neighbourhood of AB of the atom C. In other words, the B atom begins to combine with C while the latter is still partially linked with A. This circumstance is described by the theory of Polanyi, Eyring, and others with the help of the conception of the 'activated complex' ABC, formed by all the atoms which participate in the reaction, in a configuration, corresponding to an increase of the potential energy by the least possible amount $E_1$, compared with the initial configuration AB+C and by an amount $E_2$ compared with the final one A+BC.

$E_2$ is the activation energy for the inverse reaction $A+BC \rightarrow AB+C$, while the difference $E_1-E_2$ is equal to the heat of the reaction.

The displacement (self-diffusion) of atoms and molecules in liquid and solid bodies proceeds, as has been shown in Ch. IV, according to a similar activation scheme.

## 2. Self-dissociation of Dissolved Substances

We shall now consider in a somewhat more quantitative way the conceptions set forth in the preceding section for the simplest special case, namely the case of electrolytic dissociation as a function of the concentration of the dissolved substance AB (or $A^+B^-$); the molecules of the solvent will be denoted by C.

As has already been mentioned, good solvents, capable of strongly lowering the dissociation energy, are formed by polar substances whose molecules (C) possess large electric moments, and which are characterized in the liquid state by high values of the dielectric constant.

In this typical case the degree of dissociation decreases with increase of the concentration of the solute according to Ostwald's law, which is a special case of the law of mass action expressed by equation (8) of the preceding chapter for $g = 2$.

Putting $N_2 = xN$, where $x$ is the degree of dissociation and $N = N_1+N_2$ the total number of molecules, both undissociated and dissociated, we get

$$\frac{x^2}{1-x} = \frac{1}{N}\frac{Z_2^2}{Z_1} = A\frac{V}{N}e^{-U/kT},$$

i.e.

$$\frac{x^2}{1-x} = \frac{A}{n}e^{-U/kT}, \tag{1}$$

where the coefficient $A$ is practically a constant quantity,† independent both of the volume $V$ or the concentration $n = N/V$ and of the temperature, while $U$ denotes the dissociation energy of the molecules AB in the liquid C. If the mutual action between the dissociated ions is taken into account, $U$ must be increased by the free energy $\psi$ of one of the ions with respect to the surrounding ionic atmosphere; in the case of small concentrations, according to the Debye–Hückel theory

$$\psi = -\frac{2}{3}\frac{e^2}{\delta},$$

where

$$\delta = \sqrt{\frac{\epsilon kT}{8\pi e^2 nx}}$$

is the effective radius of this atmosphere.

Denoting by $U_0$ that value of $U$ which corresponds to the absence of any dissociation, we have

$$U = U_0 - \alpha\sqrt{(nx)}, \tag{1 a}$$

where

$$\alpha = \tfrac{2}{3}e^3\sqrt{\frac{8\pi}{\epsilon kT}}.$$

The decrease of the dissociation energy due to the Coulomb forces between the dissociated ions is usually characterized by the multiplication of their concentration $N_2/V$ (or $N_2/N$) by a corresponding activity coefficient $f$. This decrease can be considered as a special case of the antagonism between inner and outer bonds in a somewhat complicated form, for the loosening of the bond between non-dissociated molecules is due, in the present case, not to their mutual action but to the mutual action of their dissociation products.

Substituting (1 a) in (1) we obtain the following equation for the dependence of the degree of dissociation on the total concentration at a given temperature:

$$\frac{x^2}{1-x} = \frac{c}{n}e^{\beta\sqrt{(nx)}} \qquad \left(\beta = \frac{\alpha}{kT}\right). \tag{1 b}$$

The exponential factor, accounting for the influence of the mutual action between the ions on the degree of dissociation, for small con-

† $A$ is of the order of magnitude of $1/v$, where $v$ is the volume occupied by one of the ions ($A^+$) in its motion with respect to the other ($B^-$) in the molecules $A^+B^-$:

$$v = 4\pi r^2\sqrt{\frac{2\pi kT}{f}}.$$

centrations ($n$) or large $n$'s but small values of $x$, is easily seen to be of the order of 1 and cannot, accordingly, substantially alter the value of $x$ which is obtained if this mutual action is left out of account.†

A much more interesting and important influence of the concentration upon the degree of dissociation must be expected in non-typical or 'anomalous' cases, where the molecules of the solvent, as a consequence of their small electric moments, or large size, produce only a slight weakening of the molecules of the dissolved substance. In this case the mutual action between these molecules can become a factor of prime importance.

A direct calculation of $U$, taking into account this mutual action, as a function of the concentration, is a rather difficult problem. It can, however, be solved approximately in an elementary way starting from the consideration of the dielectric constant of the solution $\epsilon$ (which should be distinguished from that of the pure solvent $\epsilon_0$).

According to Walden's rule, the degree of dissociation of the same solute in different solvents is larger the larger the dielectric constant of the latter. A very crude explanation of this relationship is based on the application to the mutual action of the ions in the molecule $A^+B^-$ of Coulomb's law in a macroscopic form, corresponding to a large distance between these ions. In this case the dissociation energy might be expressed by the simple formula:

$$U = \frac{e^2}{\epsilon r} = \frac{\text{const.}}{\epsilon},$$

i.e. it would be inversely proportional to the dielectric constant.

If the dielectric constant of the pure solvent $\epsilon_0$ is large (as in the case of aqueous or alcoholic solutions of electrolytes), it can be identified, for moderate concentrations, with that of the solution $\epsilon$.

In those cases, however, in which $\epsilon_0$ is small (say of the order of a few units), the difference between $\epsilon$ and $\epsilon_0$ can become quite considerable, especially in the case of those dissolved substances whose mole cules possess large dipole moments.

Putting
$$U = \frac{\epsilon_0}{\epsilon} U_0, \tag{2}$$

and noting that $\epsilon$ can increase rather rapidly with increase of $n$, we

† Putting $x \ll 1$ we can rewrite (1b) in the form $x = (c/y^2)e^{\beta y}$, where $y = \sqrt{(nx)}$. This equation leads to the existence of a certain maximum value $x = 4ce^2/\beta^2$ for $y = 2/\beta$, that is, $nx = \frac{\epsilon}{8\pi}\left(\frac{kT}{e}\right)^3 \approx 10^{16}$ at room temperature.

see that in such cases the degree of dissociation must *increase* with the concentration according to a law of an exponential type.

The degree of dissociation of a solution can be ascertained experimentally by a measurement of its electrical conductivity $\sigma$. It must be expected, therefore, that in the case of solvents with a relatively small dielectric constant $\epsilon_0$ the resulting dielectric constant $\epsilon$ of the solution and its electrical conductivity must increase with the concentration, the former rather slowly, according to an approximately linear law, and the latter extremely rapidly, according to a nearly exponential law.

These relationships between the quantities $\epsilon$, $\sigma$, and $n$ are actually observed, for example, in the case of borate and silicate glasses, containing in a dissolved state large amounts of oxides of alkali metals.

When their concentration reaches a value of the order of 30 mole per cent., the dielectric constant of the glass increases from about 4 ($= \epsilon_0$) to 12, while the electrical conductivity due to the dissociated alkali ions increases by a factor of $10^4$–$10^7$.

A quite similar (nearly exponential) dependence of the electric conductivity on the concentration of 'impurities' is found in a number of electric semi-conductors, both solid (like PbS with an excess of Pb or S) and liquid (solutions of Na and K in liquid ammonia). Unfortunately the existence of the correlation between $\epsilon$ and $\sigma$, indicated above, has not yet been checked experimentally in these two cases.

Making use of the Clausius–Mossotti formula

$$\frac{\epsilon-1}{\epsilon+2} = \frac{4\pi}{3}(\alpha_0 n_0+\alpha n),$$

where $\alpha_0$ and $n_0$ denote the polarizability and concentration of the molecules of the solvent, while $\alpha$ and $n$ have the same meaning for these undissociated molecules of the solute, and assuming that $\alpha n \gg \alpha_0 n_0$, we can represent the dependence of $U$ on $n$, which follows from (2), by the formula

$$U = U_0\,\epsilon_0\frac{1-\frac{4}{3}\pi\alpha n}{1+\frac{8}{3}\pi\alpha n}, \tag{2a}$$

which along with (1) gives a qualitatively correct representation of the dependence of $\sigma$ on $n$, found experimentally.

In order to obtain a more exact representation of this dependence, making use of the resulting dielectric constant of the solution as an accessory parameter, we must investigate more closely the influence of the dielectric medium both on the non-dissociated molecules and on the ions.

We shall assume the degree of dissociation to remain small (as is actually the case in solutions displaying the anomalous increase of the electric conductivity with the concentration), and the molecules of the solvent as wholly undissociated.

A molecule of the solute will be treated as an electric dipole with a moment $p$, situated at the centre of a spherical cavity with a radius $a$ ($\approx 10^{-8}$ cm.). The polarization of the medium constituted by the undissociated molecules of the solvent and the solute, due to the action of this molecule, creates within the cavity filled by it, according to Onsager (Ch. V, § 3), an electric field

$$E = \frac{2(\epsilon-1)}{2\epsilon+1}\frac{p}{a^3}. \tag{3}$$

To this reactive field there corresponds a 'solvation' energy

$$V = -\tfrac{1}{2}Ep = -\frac{\epsilon-1}{2\epsilon+1}\frac{p^2}{a^3}. \tag{3 a}$$

When the two ions constituting the molecules are torn apart, each of them becomes solvated by the medium, the corresponding solvation energies being equal to

$$V_i = -\frac{e^2}{2a_i}\left(1-\frac{1}{\epsilon}\right) \quad (i = 1, 2). \tag{3 b}$$

The decrease of the dissociation energy, due to the influence of the surrounding medium, is equal to the difference $V-V_1-V_2$, so that

$$U = W-(\epsilon-1)\left\{\left(\frac{e^2}{2a_1}+\frac{e^2}{2a_2}\right)\frac{1}{\epsilon}-\frac{1}{2\epsilon+1}\frac{p^2}{a^3}\right\}, \tag{4}$$

where $W$ is the value of $U$ for $\epsilon = 1$, i.e. in the gas phase. In order to account for the decrease of the dissociation energy, due to the mutual action between the (undissociated) dissolved molecules, we must compare this expression with that which corresponds to an infinite dilution. Introducing the index 0 for the corresponding values of $U$, $\epsilon$, and $p$, we get

$$U_0-U = \frac{e^2}{2}\left(\frac{1}{a_1}+\frac{1}{a_2}\right)\left(\frac{1}{\epsilon_0}-\frac{1}{\epsilon}\right)+\frac{\epsilon-1}{2\epsilon+1}\frac{p^2}{a^3}-\frac{\epsilon_0-1}{2\epsilon_0+1}\frac{p_0^2}{a^3}. \tag{4 a}$$

The electrical moments $p$ and $p_0$ are somewhat different from the true or unperturbed value $\mu$ of the dipole moment of the molecules under consideration in the gas state, owing to the action produced by the reactive field $E$. Denoting the polarizability of the molecule in the direction of its axis by $\beta$ we obtain the relation

$$p = \mu+\beta E,$$

which, along with equation (3), yields

$$p = \frac{\mu}{1-\frac{2(\epsilon-1)}{2\epsilon+1}\frac{\beta}{a^3}}. \tag{4 b}$$

If the dielectric constant of the solvent is not very large, $p_0$ can be identified with $\mu$.

Turning to the calculation of $\epsilon$ as a function of the concentration we must note that in the case of large concentrations, corresponding to a strong mutual orientation of the molecules of the solute (and also eventually to a large extension, measured by the difference $p-\mu$), the equation of Clausius–Mossotti must be replaced by the more accurate equation of Onsager's theory.

For a practically non-polar solvent this equation can be written in the following approximate form:

$$\epsilon = (r^2+2)^2\frac{2\pi}{g}\frac{n\mu^2}{kT}, \tag{5}$$

where $r$ is the refractive index of the dissolved substance in the condensed state.

Substituting (5) in (4 a) we can obtain an explicit expression of $U$ as a function of $n$. It has a rather complicated form and contains several parameters $(a, a_1, a_2)$, the exact values of which are not known, and, strictly speaking, have no definite physical meaning. It can therefore hardly be used for the calculation of the electrical conductivity, which is proportional to the product $nx$, as a function of $n$.

In the limiting case of very large $\epsilon$ values, the difference $U_0-U$ is reduced to the form

$$U_0-U = \frac{e^2}{a_{1,2}\,\epsilon_0}+\frac{1}{2}\frac{p^2}{a^3}, \tag{5 a}$$

which is practically independent of $\epsilon$. Here $a_{1,2}$ denotes the mean value of the atomic radii of the two ions, while $p = \frac{\mu}{1-\beta/a^3}$. Putting $a_{1,2} = 2.10^{-8}$, $p = 10^{-18}$, and $\epsilon_0 = 4$, we obtain for $U_0-U$ 1·5 volts, i.e. 30,000 cal./mole, which is larger than the values obtained experimentally in the case of concentrated alkali glasses.

The value of $U$ given by (5 a) may prove to be negative. In this case the dissolved molecules must be totally dissociated even at very low temperatures. This spontaneous dissociation, or 'self-dissociation', which is not produced by the thermal motion, but takes place because it corresponds not to an increase but to a decrease of the potential energy, is actually observed both in the case of certain solutions and in general in the case of ionic substances in the liquid or solid state, as has been pointed out above.

If the mutual action between ionic molecules AB leads only to the loosening of the intramolecular bond and not to self-dissociation, the magnitude of this loosening can be calculated more exactly, without recourse to the dielectric constant of the body constituted by such molecules. Especially simple results are obtained for low temperatures when the molecules can be treated as orientated in the direction of the local electric field $F$ produced by the other molecules. Owing to the influence of this field the electric moment of each molecule is increased by the amount $p-p_0 = \alpha F$. Since, on the other hand, this field is itself proportional to the actual value of the electric moment, it can be represented in the form

$$F = \frac{p}{p_0}F_0,$$

where $F_0$ is its value for $p = p_0$ ($p_0$ moment of an isolated molecule). Substituting this expression in the preceding formula we get

$$p = p_0+\frac{\alpha F_0}{p_0}p,$$

which is

$$p = \frac{p_0}{1-(\alpha/p_0)F_0}.$$

The field $F_0$ is of the order of $p_0/a^3$, where $a$ is the distance between neighbouring molecules. Denoting their number per unit volume $1/a^3$ by $n$, and taking into account that $n$ can be varied by the application of an external pressure, we can rewrite $p$ as a function of $n$ in the following form:

$$p = \frac{p_0}{1-\alpha n}. \tag{6}$$

If $n$ approaches the limiting value $1/\alpha$, this expression tends to infinity, which obviously corresponds to a breaking up of the molecules, i.e. to their self-dissociation. It is clear that under such conditions the preceding equation can no longer be applied for quantitative calculations; it gives, however, a satisfactory description of the tendency of the ionic molecules to become self-dissociated when the body constituted by them is compressed to a sufficient extent.

Similar results must appear—and are actually observed—in the case of non-polar substances, the molecules of which possess an electronic polarizability only—such as compressed metallic vapours or concentrated solutions of alkali metals. Birch† has shown that the electric conductivity of mercury vapour, which under ordinary conditions is practically equal to zero, rises very rapidly in the supercritical region with increase of the pressure, approaching to the conductivity of mercury in the liquid state. The temperature does not exert a marked influence on the degree of ionization, the increase of which is due mainly to a decrease of the ionization energy $U$, which becomes negative in the case of a condensed metal. This result is equivalent to the conception of the self-ionization of the atoms, according to the same scheme as has been developed above for ionic molecules.

In fact each atom has an electric moment, which varies very rapidly with the time and polarizes the other atoms in the direction of the field created by it. To this mutual polarization are due, according to London's theory, the van der Waals forces between the atoms. The potential energy of an atom of liquid or solid argon, for instance, with respect to the surrounding atoms, can thus be equated to the average value of the quantity $-\frac{1}{2}\Delta pF$, where $\Delta p = \alpha F$ and $F \approx p/r^3$ is the local electric field, due to the spontaneous rapidly fluctuating dipole moments of the surrounding atoms. Putting $p = p_0+\Delta p$ and $r^3 = 1/n$, we again arrive at formula (6). The case $\alpha n \geqslant 1$ corresponds here to a spontaneous ionization of the atoms, i.e. to a transition of the electrons from the bound state to the free or, more exactly, the collectivized state. In other words, those simple substances, for which the product of the concentration of the atoms in the liquid or solid state and their polarizability (in the gaseous state) is equal to or larger than 1, must be defined as metallic substances, while all the other are dielectrics (or semi-conductors). This criterion of the metallic state was introduced long ago by Hertzfeld in a somewhat different form. Considering the polarization of a body in a macroscopic electric field with the mean value $E$ and using Lorentz's expression for the effective field, Hertzfeld writes:

$$\Delta p = \alpha E_{\text{eff}} = \alpha(E+\tfrac{4}{3}\pi P),$$

or, replacing $P$ by $n\Delta p$,

$$\Delta p = \frac{\alpha E}{1-\frac{4}{3}\pi n\alpha}.$$

This expression becomes infinite for $\alpha n = 3/4\pi$, which, according to Hertzfeld, is the criterion of the metallic state.

It should be mentioned in conclusion that AgCl crystals, which under normal conditions behave as electronic semi-conductors, with a

† Birch, *Phys. Rev.* **40**, 1504 (1932).

low but positive ionization energy $U$, are converted by a pressure of 4,000 atmospheres (corresponding to a 25-per-cent. diminution of the specific volume) into genuine metals, with an electric conductivity which falls with a rise of temperature. This is explained by the fact that under such pressures the ionization of the atoms becomes spontaneous and independent of the temperature, which affects the value of the conductivity only by decreasing the mean free path of the electrons.

### 3. The Electric Conductivity and Viscosity of Molten Salts and of Binary Mixtures

Although a NaCl crystal is completely dissociated into ions, yet its electrical conductivity at low temperatures is vanishingly small, in contradistinction to the electrical conductivity of metals which, on the contrary, becomes extremely large in this case. This difference is due to the fact that the free, or collectivized, electrons, which are responsible for the electrical conductivity of metals, are not bound to any equilibrium positions, and do not require for their motion through the metallic body an activation energy, either because of the absence of potential barriers, or thanks to their quantum mechanical readiness to leak through such barriers by the mechanism of the tunnel effect.

In the case of ions with their relatively huge mass the tunnel effect is impossible; the motion through the crystal requires a large activation energy which is made up of two parts: the energy of dissociation (dislocation) or hole formation $U$, and the additional activation energy $\Delta U$, which is necessary for the displacement of the holes or of the dislocated ions from one side to the next. Accordingly, in spite of its complete dissociation into ions even at $T = 0$, a NaCl crystal acquires a considerable conductivity $\sigma$ at relatively high temperatures only, the temperature dependence of $\sigma$ being expressed by the formula

$$\sigma = \text{const.}\; e^{-(U+\Delta U)/kT}.$$

With approach to the melting-point $T_0$ the energy $U$ decreases; it must, however, remain different from zero even in the closest vicinity to $T_0$, so long as the ions remain arranged in a more or less regular way, characteristic of the crystal. It is natural to assume that above the melting-point $U$ vanishes, since in the absence of regular crystal sites to speak of dislocated ions or holes is meaningless. Inasmuch as the 'self-dissociation' of the molecules is preserved in the liquid state, the electrical conductivity of the molten salt must be determined by the *mobility* of the ions, just as in the case of dilute solutions of strong electrolytes, according to the formula $\sigma = \text{const. } e^{-\Delta U/kT}$ (where $\Delta U$ may be somewhat different from its value in the solid state).

It has been shown in § 6 of Ch. I that in the case of a binary crystal of the NaCl type, out of the four possible carriers of electricity (dislocated ions of both signs and the corresponding holes) one only need be taken into account, namely that for which the energy $U+\Delta U$ has the smallest value. Since in a molten salt the holes—in the strict sense of this term—are absent, two kinds of electricity carriers only come into play, namely the positive and negative ions, the electrical conductivity being determined practically by one of them, that for which the activation energy $\Delta U$ is the smaller. As a rule, a higher mobility (smaller $\Delta U$) is displayed by the positive ions, which have a smaller radius than the negative ones, because they arise from neutral atoms by a loss of their external electrons, and not by the capture of new ones. This rule, however, admits of many exceptions. Thus, for example, in molten CsF the negative ion ($F^-$) has probably a larger mobility than the positive one. This question can be solved experimentally with the help of the same methods as are used for the determination of the mobilities of ions in solutions. In the latter case, however, the ions of both signs have a mobility of the same order of magnitude, which can be calculated approximately with the help of Stokes's formula, and which depends on the temperature in the same way, being inversely proportional to the viscosity of the solvent. In the case of molten salts, on the other hand, the activation energies $\Delta U$ can be widely different for ions of the opposite sign, so that their mobilities can have a different order of magnitude, especially at the lower temperatures.

Whereas the electrical conductivity of a molten salt must be due to the ions with the higher mobility (usually to the positive ions), their viscosity, on the contrary, must depend on the ions with the smaller mobility (negative). In fact, since ions of both signs must participate in the same way in the viscous flow of a molten salt, the rate of this flow, which from the molecular-kinetic point of view consists of a transition of the separate ions from the initial equilibrium positions to the neighbouring ones (preferentially in the direction of the flow), must be limited by the slower ions.

This relationship can be illustrated by the example of molten metals, whose electrical conductivity is due practically to the free electrons alone, while their viscosity depends upon the mobility of the positive ions.

The electrical conductivity of a molten salt must be determined by the formula

$$\sigma = q_1 ne^2, \tag{7}$$

where $n$ is the number of ions (of a given sign) in unit volume, $\pm e$ their charge, and $q_1$ the mobility of the more mobile (positive) ions. As regards the viscosity coefficient $\mu$, it can be expressed as a function of the mobility $q_2$ and radius $a_2$ of the slower (negative) ions with the help of Stokes's formula

$$\mu = \frac{1}{6\pi q_2 a_2}. \tag{7 a}$$

Taking account of the temperature dependence of $q_1$ and $q_2$, which is determined in the usual way by the activation energies $\Delta U_1$ and $\Delta U_2$, we get

$$\sigma = Ae^{-\Delta U_1/kT}, \quad \mu = Be^{\Delta U_2/kT},$$

where $A$ and $B$ are practically constant coefficients.

Hence it follows that $\sigma$ and $\mu$ must be connected with each other by the relation

$$\sigma^m \mu = \text{const.}, \tag{8}$$

where

$$m = \frac{\Delta U_2}{\Delta U_1} > 1. \tag{8 a}$$

This relation is in good agreement with the experimental data for fused salts and glasses. We give below a table of values of $m$, obtained experimentally by Evstopiev:†

| *Substance* | $m$ |
|---|---|
| $NaNO_3$ | 1·23 |
| $KNO_3$ | 1·23 |
| AgBr | 7·59 |
| AgCl | 5·26 |
| Glass C 24 | 1·55 |
| Glass N 3 | 7·17 |

It should be mentioned that in the case of dilute solutions of strong electrolytes the relationship between the electrical conductivity and the viscosity (for different temperatures and for different solvents) is expressed by the formula $\sigma\mu = \text{const.}$, which follows directly from the fact that the mobilities of the ions are in this case inversely proportional to the viscosity of the solvent. In the case of more concentrated solutions deviations from this relation are observed, which can be explained by an incomplete dissociation of the molecules.

The activation energies depend on the mutual action of the ions of each sign both on each other and on the ions of the opposite sign. This

† *Bull. Ac. Sci. U.R.S.S.*, série physique, **3**, 319 (1937).

circumstance can be checked by an investigation of the electrical conductivity and of the viscosity of the mixtures of two molten salts with the same movable ion, which determines the electrical conductivity of the mixture, or with a common slowest ion, which determines its viscosity, for different concentrations of the two components and for different temperatures.

Let us consider, for example, a molten mixture of AgCl and AgBr. Its electrical conductivity is due to the $Ag^+$ ions and can be calculated with the help of the formula

$$\sigma = qe^2(n_1+n_2),$$

where $n_1$ and $n_2$ are the molecular concentrations of AgCl and AgBr, while $q$ denotes the mobility of the $Ag^+$ ions in a mixture of its composition. The activation energy $\Delta U$, which determines the dependence of $q$ on the temperature, must be a certain function of the relative concentration $c_1 = n_1/(n_1+n_2)$ and $c_2 = n_2/(n_1+n_2)$. It seems natural to choose a linear function, not only because it is the simplest one, but also because the energy of an ion ($Ag^+$) with respect to the surrounding ions ($Br^-$ and $Cl^-$) is equal to the sum of its energies with respect to each of them. We can thus put

$$\Delta U = \Delta U_1 c_1 + \Delta U_2 c_2. \tag{9}$$

Since $q_1$ and consequently $\sigma_1$ is proportional to $e^{-\Delta U/kT}$, and the sum $n_1+n_2$ has a practically constant value, it follows that the dependence of the electrical conductivity of the mixture of the two salts on their relative concentrations must be expressed by a formula of the logarithmic type:

$$\log \sigma = \text{const.} - \Delta U_1 c_1 - \Delta U_2 c_2 = \text{const.}' + (\Delta U_2 - \Delta U_1)c_1. \tag{9 a}$$

This formula is in good agreement with the experimental results obtained by Barzakovsky.†

A similar result would be expected for the dependence on the relative concentrations of the viscosity of a mixture of two salts with the same slowest ion.

In the general case of a mixture of two salts with different anions and cations the situation becomes greatly complicated.

Somewhat simpler results are obtained in the case of a mixture of two non-ionic liquids whose molecules (or atoms) preserve their integrity in the solution. It is found experimentally that the dependence of the viscosity of the mixture on the relative concentration of one of the components (the second one, say) can be represented by curves of the

† *Bull. Ac. Sci. U.R.S.S.*, série chimique, **5**, no. 1, p. 47 (1941).

type shown in Fig. 51; the curves with a maximum, or with a tendency to a maximum ($d^2\mu/dc_2^2 < 0$) correspond to the cases in which the mixing of the two liquids is accompanied by an evolution of heat, while the curves with a minimum or a tendency to a minimum, correspond to the opposite case. In other words, a maximum on the curves $(\mu, c)$ is found when the binding between unlike molecules is stronger than between like ones, and a minimum when it is weaker.

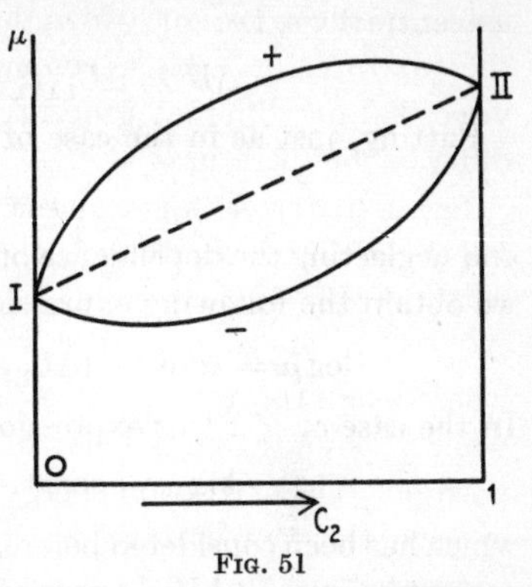

FIG. 51

This result seems quite natural from the point of view of the preceding theory. If the concentration of the second liquid is small, the viscosity of the mixture must be determined by the mobility $q_1$ of the molecules of the first liquid, with due regard, however, to the fact that the activation energy $\Delta U_1$ in the formula $q_1 = \text{const.}\, e^{-\Delta U_1/kT}$ is not constant, but is a linear function of the relative concentration of the second component

$$\Delta U_1 = \Delta U_{1,1} c_1 + \Delta U_{1,2} c_2 = \Delta U_{1,1} + (\Delta U_{1,2} - \Delta U_{1,1}) c_2.$$

If the mutual action between like and unlike molecules were the same, that is, if the activation energy $\Delta U_1$ were independent of $c_2$, the viscosity of the mixture would vary with $c_2$ according to a linear law (straight line in Fig. 51), increasing with $c_2$ if $\mu_2 > \mu_1$. If the bonding energy between unlike molecules $U_{1,2}$ is larger than that between like molecules, then the activation energy $\Delta U_{1,2}$ must also be larger than $\Delta U_{1,1}$, and consequently the mean value of the activation energy $\Delta U_1$ in the solution must increase with increase of $c_2$. Under such conditions $\mu$ must increase more rapidly than according to a linear law, which can eventually lead to the appearance of a maximum on the $(\mu, c_2)$ curve.

In a similar way it can display a minimum if $\Delta U_{1,2}$ is smaller than $\Delta U_{1,1}$ (and $\Delta U_{2,2}$).

In order to determine the dependence of $\mu$ on $c_2$, which would be valid in the whole range between $c_2 = 0$ and $c_2 = 1$, we shall come back to the theory of 'holes' or 'cavitation fluctuations' which has been developed in § 4 of Ch. IV. The mean value of the activation energy which is necessary for the formation of a hole (cavity) of a certain minimum size, ensuring an elementary displacement of the molecules of the mixture if these molecules are distributed at random, can obviously be represented by a quadratic function of the relative concentrations, i.e.

$$\Delta U = \Delta U_{1,1} c_1^2 + \Delta U_{1,2} c_1 c_2 + \Delta U_{2,2} c_2^2. \tag{10}$$

Putting, just as in the case of a simple (one-component) liquid,

$$\mu = A e^{\Delta U/kT},$$

and neglecting the dependence of the coefficient $A$ on the concentration, we obtain the following expression for $\mu$:

$$\log \mu = \text{const.} + (\Delta U_{1,1} c_1^2 + \Delta U_{1,2} c_1 c_2 + \Delta U_{2,2} c_2^2)/kT. \tag{10 a}$$

In the case $c_2 \ll 1$ this expression reduces to the linear formula

$$\log \mu = \text{const.} + (\Delta U_{1,2} - \Delta U_{1,1}) c_2/kT$$

which has been considered before. With a suitable choice of the 'mutual' activation energy $\Delta U_{1,2}$, equation (10 a) gives a satisfactory representation of the experimental data for the viscosity of binary mixtures.

It should be mentioned that Arrhenius proposed long ago the empirical equation

$$\log \mu = c_1 \log \mu_1 + c_2 \log \mu_2,$$

where $\mu_1$ and $\mu_2$ are the viscosity coefficients of the two liquids, taken separately. This equation must be considered as only a rough approximation to the theoretical equation

$$\log \mu = \text{const.} + c_1^2 \log \frac{\mu_1}{A_1} + c_2^2 \log \frac{\mu_2}{A_2} + 2 c_1 c_2 \log \frac{\mu_{1,2}}{A_{1,2}}, \tag{10 b}$$

which follows from (10 a), if it is taken into account that

$$\log \mu_1 = \log A_1 + \frac{\Delta U_{1,1}}{kT} \quad \text{and} \quad \log \mu_2 = \log A_2 + \frac{\Delta U_{2,2}}{kT},$$

and if, furthermore, an accessory coefficient of the 'mutual viscosity' of the two components is introduced, according to the formula

$$\mu_{1,2} = A_{1,2} e^{\Delta U_{1,2}/kT}.$$

The coefficient $A_{1,2}$ can be chosen arbitrarily. If $A_1$ and $A_2$ are approximately equal, then identifying $A_{1,2}$ with both of them and the const. in (10 b) with $\log A$, we get, since $c_1^2 + c_2^2 + 2c_1 c_2 = (c_1 + c_2)^2 = 1$,

$$\log \mu = c_1^2 \log \mu_1 + c_2^2 \log \mu_2 + 2 c_1 c_2 \log \mu_{1,2}. \tag{10 c}$$

It is clear that inasmuch as the viscosity of a mixture depends upon the mutual action of the molecules constituting it, the resulting viscosity coefficient $\mu$ cannot be expressed accurately with the help of the viscosity coefficients $\mu_1$ and $\mu_2$ alone, as assumed by Arrhenius, but must necessarily involve a quantity of the type $\mu_{1,2}$, specifying the mutual action between unlike molecules.

## 4. Chemically Complex Substances and their Solutions

We have limited ourselves heretofore mainly to relatively simple substances, monatomic (like metals) or diatomic (binary salts), in the solid and liquid state. We shall now investigate some of the characteristic properties of chemically complex substances having big molecules constituted by a large number of atoms.

Such 'macromolecules' (like the molecules of protein and other polymeric substances) cannot exist in the gaseous state. Even in such cases where they are bound with each other in the condensed (solid or liquid) state by relatively weak forces of the van der Waals type, their evaporation energy, which according to Langmuir's theory (discussed in § 5 of Ch. VI) is proportional to their surface ($q$), can be larger than the energy required for the breaking up of one of the chemical bonds which hold together the separate atoms or radicals out of which the molecule is built up. In such cases the evaporation of the condensed body must be accompanied—or rather preceded—by a partial dissociation of the superficial molecules. The minimum size of the latter which corresponds to this condition can easily be estimated. Let us suppose, for example, that the molecule has an approximately spherical shape with a diameter $d$. Then the area of its surface $q$ must be of the order $d^2$, and the evaporation energy of the order $\sigma d^2$, where $\sigma$ is the surface tension of the corresponding substance (in the liquid state). Evaporation without dissociation can take place only if $\sigma d^2$ is smaller than $W$, the energy of the weakest chemical bond holding together the atoms or radicals in the molecule. We thus see that $d$ must be smaller than $\sqrt{(W/\sigma)}$. Putting here $W = 10^5$ cal./mole $= 7.10^{-12}$ erg, and $\sigma = 30$ erg/cm.$^2$ we get $d < 4.10^{-6}$ cm. This is a very high limit, which is actually reached by the molecules of globular protein. In reality the disintegration of the molecules in the process of evaporation takes place at much smaller sizes. This refers, in particular, to the ionic molecules of the NaCl type, which, however, differ from the macromolecules we are discussing in this section by the loss of their integrity (self-dissociation) in the condensed state. In the case of NaCl and other somewhat more complicated ionic compounds, the dissociation of the molecules disappears in the gaseous phase at not too high a temperature.

An entirely different situation is met in the case of high molecular compounds. If the macromolecules could exist in the gas phase, they would behave as small solid particles at the corresponding temperatures. Accordingly, if the latter is not too low they would 'evaporate' individually, thus giving rise to a vapour phase consisting of the products of their partial dissociation. The degree of this dissociation can be estimated with the help of the general formulae of the theory of chemical equilibrium in gaseous systems. A more instructive way of estimating it consists in applying the thermodynamical theory of the equilibrium between the solid and the vapour phase to the individual macromolecules, treated, for the sake of simplicity, as solid bodies constituted by atoms of the same kind. It can easily be shown that the macromolecules could more or less preserve their integrity in the gas phase at very low temperatures only, when their number in the gas phase would be extremely small. Besides, under such conditions, their concentration would decrease with height so rapidly, owing to the action of gravity, that they would be found only in the close neighbourhood of the surface of the condensed body, formed by them.†

For both these reasons the high molecular compounds can exist in the condensed state only as chemically pure substances or as solutions (both liquid and solid), the solvent serving to decrease their disaggregation energy (by reducing it to the difference $q(\sigma-\sigma')$, where $\sigma'$ is the surface tension between the solvent and the solute) and to support them against gravity (just as in the case of Brownian motion of colloidal particles suspended in a liquid medium).

It must, however, be kept in mind that even in the condensed state the macromolecules must be partially dissociated. This refers, in particular, to the pure form of the corresponding high molecular substance, the degree of 'self-dissociation' of the macromolecules in a medium formed by themselves being, as a rule, larger than in a foreign solvent. This result follows from the general principle of the antagonism between the external and internal bonds which has been discussed in § 1, especially in that case when the binding between the adjacent macromolecules (specified by the surface tension of the corresponding substance) is large.

Just as in the case of simple molecules, preserving their integrity in the solid state, such as HCl, this self-dissociation gives rise to 'dislocated' atoms moving in the interstitial space between the macromolecules, i.e. creeping, as it were, over their surface, and, to some extent, even throughout their volume, and to atomic holes. If the holes lie close to

† Just as in the case of suspensions and emulsions.

atoms of the same kind (as, for example, in the case of H atoms in a paraffin chain), these holes can move within a macromolecule and travel from one of them to another in the same way as in a simple crystal. These two types of diffusion motion ensure the mixing up between all the like elements out of which the body (crystal) is built up. The important point to note is that this mixing up by the process of self-diffusion, in the case of chemically complex substances in the solid (crystalline) state, takes place not by a displacement of *whole* molecules,† but by a rambling (including dissociation and association) of the separate atoms out of which they are built up.

It is clear that the viscous flow of molecular—and especially high molecular—liquids cannot be described as due to this type of 'partial' self-diffusion motion, furthered in some direction by external forces, as in the case of simple (monatomic) bodies which has been considered in §§ 1 and 2 of Ch. IV. The only mechanism capable of ensuring the mobility of molecules as wholes in the case of large molecules is the mechanism of cavitation fluctuations discussed in § 4 of Ch. IV. As has been stressed there, these cavitations must be sharply distinguished from the atomic holes, which are found in crystalline substances at elevated temperatures, and which can also exist in the liquid state of macromolecular substances without, however, affecting their fluidity. It is clear that at a given temperature the latter must in general be smaller the larger the molecules. In fact, the cavities (holes, cracks) due to the thermal motion must have a size practically independent of the size of the molecules themselves and determined only by the surface tension (which does not vary excessively for different liquids). If the number of such cavities is identical with the number of molecules (as has been assumed in § 10 of Ch. III), then the total volume occupied by them, i.e. the free volume of the liquid, must be inversely proportional to the volume of the separate molecules. Hence it follows that the mobility of the latter must be inversely proportional to this volume, and, consequently, the viscosity coefficient of the liquid formed by them directly proportional to their volume, i.e., roughly speaking, to their molecular weight. This conclusion is in a qualitative agreement with the experimental facts. It explains, in particular, the fact that high-molecular substances are practically solid at room temperatures. While some of them with a rise of the temperature become sufficiently fluid to be treated as liquids, others are completely dissociated at such temperatures, so that they can be said to exist, as macromolecular

† In this case the process of mixing would not be complete.

substances, in the solid (amorphous or crystalline) state only. This refers especially to macromolecules with a complicated shape and internal motions (such as the polymeric chain-like macromolecules considered in the next sections). It should be mentioned that the intramolecular mobility of such bodies (due to the flexibility of their molecules) gives rise to peculiar mechanical properties, which distinguish them from common solids, and which can be described by denoting these bodies not as solid (i.e. rigid) but rather as 'soft' or 'rubber-like'.

By mixing a macromolecular substance with molecules of a relatively simple substance, the viscosity of the resulting body can be greatly lowered, until, at low concentrations of the macromolecular component, solutions with a relatively small viscosity, which remain liquid at ordinary and even low temperatures, are obtained. Such liquids display, as a rule, remarkable deviations from the behaviour of ordinary simple liquids. Their viscosity, for example, is not constant, but decreases with increase of the velocity gradient, or they begin to flow under a shearing stress exceeding a certain critical value only. Liquids with such abnormal properties are usually denoted as 'non-Newtonian'.

It should be mentioned that in the case of pure macromolecular substances, such as rubber, the process of melting consists in a transition from the crystalline to a practically *solid* amorphous state (unless the substance becomes highly dissociated or depolymerized), so that the usual conception of fusion, as a transition from the solid to the *liquid* state, is here inapplicable.

## 5. Solutions of High Polymeric Substances

When the molecules of the solute are very large compared with the solvent molecules, approaching colloidal particles, the usual conceptions of thermal motion in liquids become inapplicable to them, and their influence on the viscosity of the mixture (solution) must reduce to an alteration of the factor $A$ in the formula $\mu = Ae^{\Delta U/kT}$, while the activation energy $\Delta U$ preserves the value characteristic of the pure solvent. The mechanism of this influence consists in a change of the character of the viscous flow of the solvent, under given boundary conditions, owing to the fact that its molecules stick to the surface of the dissolved particles (in the same way as to the walls of the vessel containing the liquid, or to the surface of macroscopic solid bodies immersed in it). As a result, the smooth distribution of the velocity gradient, which would exist in the absence of the dissolved particles, under given external conditions, is modified to an extent which increases with the size of the dissolved particle (and also depends on their shape).

Leaving aside the possible rotation of these particles, and noting that their translational motion is that of a small rigid body, with no velocity gradient we see that the presence of each particle of this kind destroys the velocity gradient which would exist in the volume $\omega$ of the solvent which is occupied by it. If the velocity of the liquid (solvent) is unaltered in distant points, the destruction of the normal velocity gradient within the volume $\omega$ must be compensated by the increase of this gradient in the adjacent layer of the liquid. Let us assume, for the sake of simplicity, that this compensation takes place within a layer with the same volume $\omega$. Since the heat evolved in a unit volume of the liquid, as a consequence of its viscosity, is proportional to the *square* of the velocity gradient, the evolution of heat in the layer under consideration must be four times as large as it would have been in the volume $\omega$, were it not occupied by the 'dissolved' particle, or twice as large as the total heat which would be evolved under this condition in the total volume $2\omega$ (including that occupied by the particle and the volume of the adjacent layer).

We thus see that owing to the presence in the solution per unit volume of $n$ particles with a relatively large volume $\omega$, the heat losses due to the viscosity of the solvent must increase by a factor $n\omega$. This means that their presence must be equivalent to an increase of the viscosity of the solvent $\mu$ in the ratio $1+n\omega$.

The effective viscosity coefficient of the solution must, therefore, be determined by a formula of the type

$$\mu = \mu_0(1+\gamma n\omega), \tag{11}$$

where $\gamma$ is a numerical factor of the order of 1.

This formula was derived for the first time by Einstein in 1905 for spherical particles; the factor $\gamma$ turned out in this case to be equal to 5/2. It can be applied with fairly satisfactory results to particles of moderate size, such as the molecules of sugar (with a molecular weight of the order of 400), the size of these particles, calculated according to (11), agreeing with those obtained by various other methods.

A spherical shape can by no means be ascribed to all macromolecules, i.e. molecules of very large size. Such molecules can often be treated as rod-shaped or as prolate ellipsoids of revolution. Considerations similar to those mentioned above show that in such cases the increase of the viscosity of the solution can be represented by the same formula

(11), the value of the coefficient $\gamma$ being, however, a certain function of the *shape* of the macromolecule, and also, to some extent, of its size, or rather mass, inasmuch as the latter determines the energy of its rotational Brownian motion, which influences the average orientation of the macromolecule with respect to the direction of viscous flow (cf. Ch. V, § 8). Thus, for example, in the case of very large rod-shaped macromolecules, whose orientation is practically not influenced by the rotational Brownian motion, according to calculations of Gold and Guth,†

$$\gamma = \frac{2f}{4(\log f - \frac{3}{2})}, \tag{11 a}$$

where $f = l/d$ is the ratio of the length of a molecule to its 'thickness' $d$. For smaller molecules of the same shape with a relatively intense rotational Brownian motion Kuhn and Guth‡ obtain the expression

$$\gamma = \tfrac{5}{2} + \tfrac{1}{16} f^2. \tag{11 b}$$

The difference between these expressions is explained as follows. If the rotational Brownian motion is ineffective, then in a liquid flowing with a constant velocity gradient (in a direction perpendicular to that of flow) they are more or less parallel to the direction of flow. In this case they must perturb the latter to a much smaller extent (for given values of $l$ and $d$) than in the opposite case in which they are agitated by a violent rotational Brownian motion, so that all the orientations of their long axes have practically the same probability (with a certain tendency to an orientation at 45° to the direction of flow, cf. Ch. V, § 8). Under such conditions, the perturbation of the viscous flow of the solvent due to a strongly elongated particle must be the same as that which would be produced by a spherical particle with a radius equal to its long axis $l$, that is, with a volume of the order $l^3$. Now, since the volume of the rod-shaped particle is equal to $d^2 l$, we see that the coefficient $\gamma$ must in this case be of the order of $l^2/d^2 = f^2$, in agreement with formula (11 b).

The preceding results are of special interest in the case of solutions of high polymeric substances, forming in the condensed state natural and synthetic resins, including caoutchouc, cellulose, the keratin of hair and feather, the myosin of muscles, and a large number of various plastics.

These substances can be typified by the saturated long-chain hydrocarbons (paraffins)

$$CH_3(CH_2)_n CH_3$$

† *Koll. Z.* **74**, 266 (1936).

‡ Ibid. **62**, 269 (1933); *Z. f. phys. Chem.* A, **161**, 1 (1932).

with a very large number of links $n$, of the order of hundreds, thousands, and more (molecules of this simplest type constitute a synthetic rubber-like product called opanol). Such high polymeric molecules, or 'linear' macromolecules are usually obtained from unsaturated 'dimeric' molecules of the type $CH_2{=}CHX$ (where X denotes some radical—OH, $C_6H_5$, $OCH_3$, Cl, etc.), by a process of *polymerization*, according to the scheme

$$n(CH_2{=}CHX) \rightarrow -[(CH_2{-}CHX)_n].$$

The polymerization is thus realized by a destruction of double bonds, the free valences of the two C atoms which are released in this process being used to bind the resulting radicals $-CH_2{-}CHX-$ with each other in exactly the same way as two successive links of a chain.

If the resulting chain is very long, it can be treated as a regular one-dimensional crystal (disproving the opinion that such crystals cannot exist, cf. Ch. III, § 8).

Such linear or chain-like macromolecules cannot exist in the gas phase, for instead of evaporating they must be disintegrated or de-polymerized into smaller units, mainly monomeric or dimeric. This assertion seems fairly obvious; it can, however, be justified more strictly by means of the following simple argument. The evaporation energy $U_z$ of a chain-like macromolecule, consisting of $z$ monomeric links, must be obviously proportional to $z$, i.e. equal to $zU_1$ where $U_1$ is approximately equal to the evaporation energy of a monomer. This energy, which is due to the van der Waals forces, is much smaller than the dissociation energy $W_1$, which is due to the chemical (valence) forces, binding two monomers together into a chain. If, however, $z$ is larger than the ratio $W_1/U_1$, the dissociation of the polymeric molecule into two smaller units turns out to be easier than its evaporation. It must be expected, accordingly, that in the case of a polymeric substance the vapour phase will consist of relatively small chain fragments, containing $W_1/U_1$ links each.

While the evaporation of a polymeric substance is thus impossible, its dissolution in an adequate liquid solvent, without loss of the integrity of the molecules, can easily be achieved, if the heat of solution $U'_z$ is sufficiently small compared with the latent heat of evaporation $U_z$. Of course, a partial dissociation or depolymerization of the macromolecules must take place even in this case; it may, however, be negligible if $U'_z$ is not large compared with $W_1$.

It is found experimentally that the solubility of high-polymeric substances, like rubber, in organic solvents rapidly decreases as a rule with increase of the degree of polymerization. This result shows that the energy of solution $U'_z$ remains positive, and hence increases with $z$. Just as in the case of the evaporation energy, we can put $U'_z = zU'_1$, where $U'_1$ is the energy of solution referred to a single monomer. The latter result follows from the Langmuir theory of solutions, if the surface energy of the polymeric molecule with respect to the solvent is assumed to be positive (and small compared with its value with respect to a vacuum).

Leaving aside certain complications, which are connected with the fact that a long-chain polymeric molecule can assume a number of different configurations corresponding to the same value of the energy (see below), the solubility of a substance consisting of such molecules, i.e. the concentration of the latter in a saturated solution which is in equilibrium with the condensed phase of this substance, can be calculated, as a function of the temperature, according to the formula

$$n = ce^{-U'_1 z/kT}.$$

Hence it is seen that for a given temperature the solubility must fall off exponentially with increase of the degree of polymerization $z$. This result is in agreement with the experimental facts.

The investigations of Staudinger and his school have shown that the increase of the viscosity of dilute solutions of linear macromolecules can be represented by equation (11) with a coefficient $\gamma$ which is proportional to $z$. This result can be explained, according to Staudinger, if it is assumed that the chain-like macromolecules behave as very long straight rods, which are orientated lengthwise in a viscous flow of the solution, and to which the expression (11a) for the coefficient $\gamma$, corresponding to the non-effectiveness of the rotational Brownian motion, can be applied.

It should be noted that the neighbouring links of a carbon chain, i.e. the straight segments connecting each C atom with its two neighbours, make with each other an angle of 109°, which is characteristic of the tetrahedral scheme of the valencies, of the carbon atom (and which is met with, for example, in diamond). A linear macromolecule with a carbon backbone must therefore be likened, not to a thread (as usually assumed), but rather to a *ribbon* (band), with a symmetry plane passing through the centres of the carbon atoms. The 'trans'-position of the neighbouring C atoms with respect to the axis of the molecule in the plane of the latter, ensuring its rectilinear shape, corresponds to the largest possible distance between the side groups attached to the backbone C atoms (in Fig. 52 these side groups are shown by black dots), and to the least possible value of the potential energy of the whole system. If the chain is imagined to be rotated about one of its links with the preservation of the valence angle, these side groups must get closer together, until in a cis-configuration, corresponding to a rotation by an angle of 180°, they would lie closer than is, in general, allowed by their geometrical size. Hence it follows that a rotation of the molecular chain about its individual links must, in general, be resisted

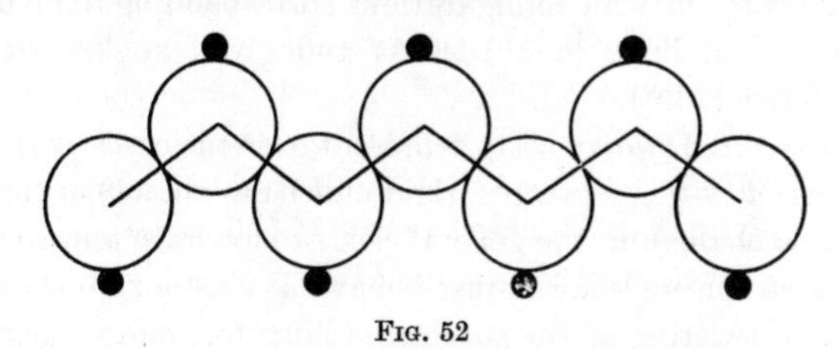

Fig. 52

by the mutual repulsion of the side groups, especially if the latter are more or less complex.

This result† is in agreement with the experimental data of Kistiakowsky‡ and of Pitzer,§ who have shown that the rotation of the carbon chain about the single bonds is not free, but 'hindered', the activation energy $\Delta U$, which is necessary for rotation by an angle of 180° (per bond), i.e. for a transition from a trans-configuration to a cis-configuration, being of the order of 3,000 cal./mole.

Staudinger has refused to accept this fact and treats the carbon macromolecules as absolutely rigid rods on the evidence of viscosity data relating to their solutions (cf. above). On the other hand, Mark, Kuhn, Guth, and a number of other authors, who have investigated the behaviour of such macromolecules, both in solution and in the condensed phase, have assumed them to be capable of a wholly free rotation about the single bonds—in apparent agreement with the results obtained from a study of relatively simple organic molecules. This assumption may be a fair approximation to the truth at sufficiently high temperatures, and it has been very useful for the understanding of the mechanical properties of high polymeric substances in the condensed state (see below). The evidence relating to the viscosity data,

† Which has been stressed by Bresler and Frenkel, *Acta Physicochimica U.R.S.S.*, **11**, 485 (1939).

‡ Kistiakowsky, Lauber, and Stitz, *J. Chem. Phys.* **7**, 289 (1939).

§ Pitzer, ibid. **5**, 469 (1939).

which seems to support Staudinger's hypothesis of absolutely rigid macromolecular chains (or ribbons), does not, in reality, contradict the opposite view of absolutely flexible chains, advocated by Mark, Kuhn, and Guth. In fact the coefficient $\gamma$ in equation (11) would be proportional not to $z$ (as found experimentally) but to $z^2$, if Staudinger's rod-like rigid molecules were supposed to be agitated by a sufficiently violent rotational Brownian motion. On the other hand, no reliable calculations of $\gamma$ exist for the case of flexible molecules, which could assume with equal probability all configurations corresponding to given lengths of the individual links ($a = 1{\cdot}52$ A) and given angles between the successive links (109°).

We believe these two views to represent extreme cases, corresponding to either very low temperatures (rigid molecular chains) or to very high ones (flexible chains); in the general case of moderate temperatures the long-chain carbon molecules must behave as elastic ribbons which can be bent by a twisting of the successive links (or, more exactly, of the planes passing through the successive pairs of links) with respect to each other, the sign and magnitude of these elementary twists varying irregularly with the time.

It should be remarked that the shape and orientation of the chain-like macromolecules in a solution is modified by the viscous flow of the latter, the molecules being partially orientated and extended in the direction of flow. This must result in a decrease of the viscosity coefficient from a value corresponding to $\gamma \sim z^2$, say, for small velocities, to a much lower value, proportional to $z$ (according to (11 a)). It is possible in this way to explain the abnormal behaviour of solutions of high polymeric substances with respect to viscous flow, which is characterized by a deviation from Newton's law in the sense of a sharp decrease of $\mu$ with the increase of the velocity gradient in a certain transition range of the latter.

## 6. Statistics and Kinetics of the Configurations of Long-chain Polymeric Molecules in Solution

The question of the configurations assumed by a linear macromolecule in a dilute solution is intimately bound up with the character of its thermal motion. In the case of small molecules the latter is reduced to a vibration-translation motion of the centre of gravity, angular vibrations interrupted by sharp changes of the equilibrium orientation, and intramolecular vibrations of small amplitude which do not affect the shape of the molecule. In the case of macromolecules, especially of the linear (chain-like) type, the main feature of the heat motion consists, on the contrary, simply in a continuous change of shape, effected by a gradual rotation of the consecutive links (along with the remaining parts of the chain) with respect to each other. This rotation (which, in general, is hindered by the mutual repulsion of the side groups—forming, as it were, the 'ribs' of the backbone) can be treated as a specific *intramolecular Brownian motion*, with an essentially oscillatory character, the equilibrium orientations of the individual links about which they perform small elastic vibrations being more or less sharply changed from time to time.

Each possible configuration of a macromolecule (which is compatible with the condition of the permanence of the length of the individual links and of the angles between the contiguous links) corresponds to a definite value of the distance between its ends $\lambda$, which will be called the 'effective length' of the molecule. This correspondence is, of course, not single valued, for the same value of $\lambda$ can be realized for a large variety of different configurations. From the point of view of the theory of 'free rotation' all these configurations are *a priori* equally probable; the probability $p(\lambda)\,d\lambda$ that the effective length of the macromolecule lies in the range between $\lambda$ and $\lambda+d\lambda$ must in this case be simply proportional to the number of different configurations, or more exactly to the volume of the configuration space, which corresponds to this range of $\lambda$ values. It is clear that under such conditions the maximum possible value of $\lambda$, which is equal to the length of the macromolecule (in the extended form), has a vanishing probability of being actually realized, and that entangled forms with a much smaller effective length must be considered, on the assumption of free rotation, as the most probable.

The situation is substantially altered, especially at low temperatures, if account is taken of the increase of the potential energy of the molecular chain (ribbon) when it is bent (or twisted) about the individual links; in this case extended configurations may prove to be the most probable.

Since the macromolecules are very complicated systems with an extremely large number of inner degrees of freedom, it is possible to apply to each of them, taken separately, the thermodynamical notions and relations. In particular a single macromolecule can be characterized by its free energy $\psi$ as a function of the effective length $\lambda$ and of the temperature $T$. Since, when a macromolecule is extended, it must, owing to the thermal motion of its links, tend to contract, this thermal motion must be imagined as causing a tension $F$ along the straight line which connects its ends. The work $F\,d\lambda$ which must be done against this tension in order to increase the effective length from $\lambda$ to $\lambda+d\lambda$ is equal to the increase of the free energy $d\psi$ at a constant temperature. The force $F$ can thus be defined with the help of the function $\psi$ according to the formula

$$F = \frac{\partial \psi}{\partial \lambda}. \tag{12}$$

Mark, Kuhn, and Guth's assumption of the free rotation of the links of the molecular chain (under the constraints imposed by the constant value of their length and of the valence angles) can be expressed, from this thermodynamical point of view, by the condition that the internal energy of a macromolecule $W$ is independent of its length $\lambda$. This hypothesis has been advanced by Wöhlisch† and independently by Meyer,‡ on the evidence obtained by an experimental study of the thermomechanical properties of rubber and similar high-polymeric substances, before the chain theory of their molecular structure had been developed by Staudinger and others.

Noting that $\psi = W-TS$, where $S$ is the entropy of the macromolecule, we see that equation (12) reduces in this case to

$$F = -T\frac{\partial S}{\partial \lambda}. \tag{12 a}$$

Using the relation

$$-\frac{\partial S}{\partial \lambda} = \frac{\partial F}{\partial T}$$

which follows from the general formula $d\psi = -S\,dT+F\,d\lambda$, and noting that, according to (12 a),

$$\frac{\partial F}{\partial T} = -\frac{\partial S}{\partial \lambda} - T\frac{\partial^2 S}{\partial T \partial \lambda},$$

we see that

$$\frac{\partial}{\partial T}\frac{\partial S}{\partial \lambda} = 0,$$

i.e. that if the energy is independent of $\lambda$, the entropy must be a function of $\lambda$ alone, not containing the temperature, and that consequently, according to (12 a), the force $F$ must be proportional to the absolute temperature. Putting

$$-\frac{\partial S}{\partial \lambda} = \phi(\lambda),$$

we can rewrite equation (12 a) in the form

$$F = \phi(\lambda)T. \tag{13}$$

† *Z. f. Biologie*, **87**, 353 (1928).

‡ Meyer, Suvich, and Valko, *Koll. Z.* **59**, 208 (1932).

With respect to the dependence of $F$ on $T$ this equation is quite similar to Clapeyron's equation for the pressure of an ideal gas, $F$ playing the role of the pressure (with a negative sign) and $\lambda$ that of the volume. As regards the dependence of $\phi$ upon $\lambda$, it can be derived theoretically on the basis of a definite mechanical model only. Leaving the latter aside for a moment, we shall assume it to be linear, i.e. shall put

$$\phi(\lambda) = A(\lambda-\bar{\lambda}), \tag{13a}$$

where $\bar{\lambda}$ is the normal value of $\lambda$, corresponding to the minimum of $\psi$ (in the absence of external forces, i.e. to $F = 0$), while $A$ is a certain proportionality coefficient, the product of which and $T$ plays the role of the elasticity modulus of the molecular chain $E = AT$.

The preceding formula corresponds to the expression

$$S = -\tfrac{1}{2}A(\lambda-\bar{\lambda})^2 \tag{14}$$

for the entropy as a function of $\lambda$. Now, since the entropy is connected with the probability $P(\lambda)$ by the relation $S = k\log P$, we see that the assumption of a free rotation, in conjunction with the assumption of Hooke's law (13a), proves to be equivalent to Gauss's law for the distribution of the effective lengths $\lambda$ of the macromolecules about the mean value $\bar{\lambda}$:

$$P(\lambda) = ce^{-A(\lambda-\bar{\lambda})^2/2k},$$

where $c$ is a proportionality coefficient which is determined by the condition $\int P(\lambda)\,d\lambda = 1$.

If $\bar{\lambda}$ is small compared with $\lambda_{\max}$ and large compared with $\lambda_{\min}$ ($= 0$), the integration with respect to $\lambda-\bar{\lambda}$ can be extended from $-\infty$ to $+\infty$, which gives $c = \sqrt{(A/2\pi k)}$. We thus get finally

$$P(\lambda) = \sqrt{\left(\frac{A}{2\pi k}\right)}e^{-A(\lambda-\bar{\lambda})^2/2k}. \tag{14a}$$

The mean value of $(\lambda-\bar{\lambda})^2$ is hence found to be

$$\overline{(\lambda-\bar{\lambda})^2} = \frac{k}{A}. \tag{14b}$$

We shall now drop the assumption of the validity of Hooke's law (13a), and shall derive the equation of state of a macromolecule $F(\lambda, T)$ using the mechanical model of its chain-like structure. For the sake of simplicity we shall treat it as a one-dimensional system, consisting of a number $z$ of links, which are directed either in the positive or in the negative sense of the $x$-axis, i.e. as a folding ruler.

The hypothesis of free rotation is equivalent in this case to an equal probability of the two opposite directions of each link, and the problem of the determination of the probability of different values of the effective length of the chain turns out to be wholly identical with the problem of the diffusion of a system of particles in one direction (in the absence of external forces), the length of a link $a$ corresponding to an elementary displacement. Taking the respective time as unit, we obtain the expression $D = \frac{1}{2}a^2$ for the diffusion coefficient. The mean square of the displacement of a particle in the direction of the $x$-axis during a time $z$

$$\overline{\lambda^2} = 2Dz = a^2z$$

corresponds to the mean value of the square of the distance $\lambda$ from one end of the chain to the other (this distance may be either positive or negative). We thus take

$$\overline{\lambda^2} = a^2z. \tag{15}$$

If the diffusing particles are initially concentrated in the point $x = 0$ the probability of finding one of them at some later time $t$ in the range between $x$ and $x+dx$ is equal, as is well known, to

$$\frac{1}{\sqrt{(4\pi Dt)}} e^{-x^2/4Dt}\,dx.$$

Replacing $x$ by $\lambda$, $t$ by $z$, and $D$ by $\frac{1}{2}a^2$, we get

$$P(\lambda)\,d\lambda = \frac{1}{\sqrt{(2\pi a^2 z)}} e^{-\lambda^2/2a^2z}\,d\lambda. \tag{16}$$

This formula can be derived directly from the expression

$$P(z_1) = \frac{z!}{z_1!\,z_2!}\left(\frac{1}{2}\right)^z$$

for the probability that out of the $z$ links of the chain $z_1$ links are directed to the right, say, and $z_2 = z-z_1$ to the left, under the assumption that the two opposite directions of each link have the same probability $\frac{1}{2}$. The corresponding value of $\lambda$ is equal to $a(z_1-z_2)$. Putting $z_1 = \frac{1}{2}(z+\zeta)$ and $z_2 = \frac{1}{2}(z-\zeta)$ and assuming that $\zeta \ll z$, it is easy to reduce the preceding expression, with the help of Stirling's formula, to the form (16).

The expression (16) is identical with (14a) if we put in the latter $\bar{\lambda} = 0$ (which is characteristic of the one-dimensional case, both positive and negative values being here admissible and equally probable) and $A = k/\overline{\lambda^2} = k/a^2z'$ in agreement with (14b). This coincidence can be regarded as a justification of the assumption, previously made, of the proportionality between $F$ and $\lambda$. We have accordingly

$$F = AT\lambda = \frac{kT}{a^2z}\lambda. \tag{17}$$

Introducing the mean square value of $\lambda$, $\lambda_0 = \sqrt{(\overline{\lambda^2})} = a\sqrt{z}$, as a measure of the mean absolute value of the length of the molecular chain, and defining the elasticity modulus with the help of the relation

$$F = E\frac{\lambda}{\lambda_0},$$

we obtain for it the expression

$$E = \frac{kT}{\lambda_0} = \frac{kT}{a\sqrt{z}}. \tag{17 a}$$

Quite similar results are obtained in the case of a three-dimensional model of the molecular chain if all the directions of each link (bond) with respect to the preceding one are assumed, for the sake of simplicity, to be equally probable (which is, of course, contrary to the condition of the permanence of the valence angle, but does not alter the fundamental properties of the molecular chain). Making use of the corresponding solution of the three-dimensional diffusion problem, and noting that equation (16) remains valid for each of the three components of the vector $\boldsymbol{\lambda}$, if $a^2$ is replaced by $a^2\overline{\cos^2\theta} = \frac{1}{3}a^2$, we get

$$P(\lambda_x, \lambda_y, \lambda_z)\, d\lambda_x\, d\lambda_y\, d\lambda_z = P(\lambda_x)P(\lambda_y)P(\lambda_z)\, d\lambda_x\, d\lambda_y\, d\lambda_z,$$

that is,

$$Q(\lambda)\, d\lambda = \frac{4\pi\lambda^2\, d\lambda}{(\frac{4}{3}\pi a^2 z)^{\frac{3}{2}}} e^{-3\lambda^2/2a^2z}, \tag{18}$$

where $Q(\lambda)\, d\lambda$ is the probability that the effective length of the chain lies between the limits $\lambda$ and $\lambda + d\lambda$ irrespective of its direction.

The average value of $\lambda$ (which is now an essentially positive quantity) is equal to

$$\bar{\lambda} = a\sqrt{\left(\frac{2}{3\pi}z\right)}, \quad \text{whereas} \quad \overline{\lambda^2} = a^2 z$$

as in the one-dimensional case.

The preceding formula for $Q$ corresponds to the following expression for the entropy

$$S = k \log Q = k\left(-\frac{3\lambda^2}{2a^2z} + 2\log\lambda\right) + \text{const.}, \tag{18 a}$$

whence there follows

$$F = kT\left(\frac{3\lambda}{a^2z} - \frac{2}{\lambda}\right). \tag{19}$$

The normal length of the chain, for which the tension $F$ between its ends vanishes, is thus equal to

$$\lambda_0 = a\sqrt{\frac{2z}{3}},$$

i.e. lies very close to $\bar{\lambda}$. If $\lambda$ does not greatly differ from $\lambda_0$, formula (19) can be replaced by the approximate one

$$F = E\frac{\lambda-\lambda_0}{\lambda_0}, \tag{19a}$$

with an expression for the elasticity modulus

$$E = kT/\lambda_0 = kT/a\surd(\tfrac{2}{3}z) \tag{19b}$$

which differs from (17a) by a factor $\surd\frac{3}{2}$ only.

The preceding result can be obtained in a more straightforward way with the help of the following argument.

Let us suppose that the ends of the chain are pulled in opposite directions parallel to a definite axis with a force $F$. This pulling force is transmitted from the end links to all the inner ones, so that each link of the chain is acted on by a pair of forces $\pm F$, with a torque $Fa\sin\theta$, where $a$ is the length of the link. Under such conditions each link must become partially orientated in the direction of the force in exactly the same way as an electric dipole of the same length under the influence of an external electric field $E = F/e$, where $\pm e$ is the charge of the dipole.

This orientating action of the force is resisted by the heat motion. If each link of the chain is supposed to rotate freely about the points of junction with the neighbouring links, then the mean value of the cosine of the angle $\theta$ is expressed by the Langevin formula

$$\overline{\cos\theta} = L\left(\frac{aF}{kT}\right) = \coth\frac{aF}{kT} - \frac{kT}{aF},$$

or $\overline{\cos\theta} = aF/3kT$ if $aF \ll kT$. Multiplying this expression by $az$, where $z$ is the number of links, we obtain the mean value of the length of the chain in the direction of the extending force

$$\lambda = \frac{za^2F}{3kT}.$$

Rewriting this expression in the form

$$F = \frac{3kT}{a^2z}\lambda,$$

we see that it differs from (19) by the absence of the second term in the brackets only; this difference is explained by the fact that in the present derivation the force $F$ has been assumed to be parallel to a *fixed* direction, whereas in the preceding one its direction was defined to be that of the line connecting the two ends of the chain.

If the extending force is very large, so that the condition $aF \ll kT$ is not fulfilled, the preceding expression must be replaced by

$$\lambda = az\,L\left(\frac{aF}{kT}\right).$$

Hence it is seen that the expression (18 a) for the entropy and consequently the expression (18) for the probability of various configurations of the chain can be applied to the evaluation of the elastic tension produced by the extended chain, as a function of its extension, for small values of the latter only. This is connected with the fact that the expression (18) is only an approximate form of the exact expression for the case of a very long chain. We shall not, however, need this exact expression in the sequel.

Similar results are obtained in the case of a molecular chain, the successive links of which are constrained to make a given angle $\omega$ with respect to each other, while the azimuthal angles $\phi$ between the planes, containing two successive pairs of links, can be varied at random. Formula (18) remains valid in this case if the effective length of a link $a$ is defined by the formula

$$a = l\sqrt{\left(\frac{1+\cos\omega}{1-\cos\omega}\right)},$$

where $l$ is its actual length.

We have considered thus far the configurations of a chain-like macromolecule from the thermodynamical or statistical point of view, i.e. from the point of view of the probability of various configurations. We shall now consider this question from the kinetic point of view, and shall determine the *velocity* with which a given initial distribution of configurations in a solution of chain-like molecules changes with the time, and in particular shall determine the 'relaxation time' which is required for the realization of the final equilibrium distribution, described by Gauss's law (18).

As before, we shall assume the rotation of the links about each other to be free in the sense that the energy of the chain $W$ is independent of its configuration. For the sake of simplicity we shall limit ourselves to the one-dimensional case (model of a folding ruler), and treat its length $\lambda$ as a continuous variable.

One end of all the chains will be supposed to be fixed at a definite point (or plane) $x = 0$, while the other is free to move in the range between $-az$ and $+az$.

Let us denote the number of chains whose free ends are enclosed between $x$ and $x+dx$ at a time $t$ by $n(t,x)$. These free ends can be treated as small molecules diffusing in the solvent without any interaction with each other, and pulled to the origin $x = 0$ by a force $F$ proportional to the distance $x$; according to (17)

$$F = -\frac{kT}{a^2z}x.$$

Under such conditions the variation of the concentration with the time can be represented by the generalized diffusion equation

$$\frac{\partial n}{\partial t} = D\frac{\partial^2 n}{\partial x^2} - \frac{\partial}{\partial x}(qnF), \tag{20}$$

where $q = D/kT$ is the 'mobility' of the free ends. Substituting in this equation the preceding expression for $F$ we get

$$\frac{1}{D}\frac{\partial n}{\partial t} = \frac{\partial^2 n}{\partial x^2} + \frac{1}{a^2z}\frac{\partial(xn)}{\partial x}. \tag{20 a}$$

If this equation is multiplied by $x$ and integrated with respect to $x$ between the limits $-az$ and $+az$, or practically $-\infty$ and $+\infty$, we obtain, making use of the formulae

$$\int x\frac{\partial^2 n}{\partial x^2}\,dx = \int x\,d\frac{\partial n}{\partial x} = \left[x\frac{\partial n}{\partial x}\right]_{-\infty}^{+\infty} - \int \frac{\partial n}{\partial x}\,dx = \left[x\frac{\partial n}{\partial x} - n\right]_{-\infty}^{+\infty} = 0$$

and $$\int x\frac{\partial(nx)}{\partial x}\,dx = [x\,.\,xn]_{-\infty}^{\infty} - \int xn\,dx,$$

the following equation: $$\frac{d\bar{x}}{dt} = -\frac{D}{a^2z}\bar{x}, \tag{20 b}$$

where $$\bar{x}(t) = \frac{\int xn\,dx}{\int n\,dx}$$

is the mean value of the length of the chains at a time $t$.

Equation (20 b) shows that this mean length tends to its normal value $x = 0$ (corresponding to an equal number of free ends on the right and on the left of the fixed ones) according to the law

$$\bar{x} = x_0\,e^{-t/\tau'},$$

where the relaxation time $\tau'$ is given by

$$\tau' = \frac{a^2z}{D}. \tag{21}$$

If a free end of a macromolecule is represented by one of its end monomeric links, then its diffusion coefficient $D$ can be defined by the usual formula referring to small molecules

$$D = \frac{a^2}{6\tau_1}, \tag{21 a}$$

where $\tau_1 = \tau_0 e^{\Delta U'/kT}$ is the relaxation time of the solvent.

The relation (21) can thus be written as follows:

$$\tau' = 6z\tau_1. \tag{21 b}$$

It shows that the relaxation time of polymeric molecules (in the sense defined above) is proportional to their length.

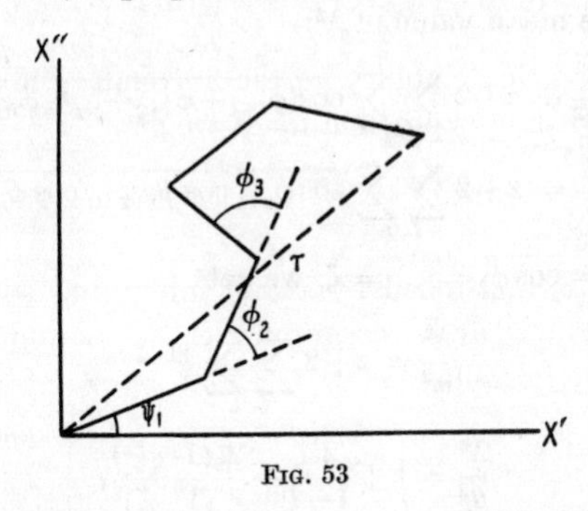


FIG. 53

The preceding calculations refer to the case of absolutely flexible macromolecules. We shall now briefly examine the general case in which the rotation of the links, or rather their twisting with respect to each other, is resisted by the elasticity of the molecular ribbon. The influence of this resistance can be illustrated on a plane model (Fig. 53); the twisting is replaced here by a rotation of the successive links in the plane of the model, the most advantageous configuration, corresponding to the minimum of the potential energy, being an extended one, when they are arranged in a straight line.

We shall not make any special assumptions about the dependence of the potential energy on the angles $\phi_k$ between the successive links (the $k$th and the $(k-1)$th). These angles will be treated as positive if the rotation from one link to the next is anti-clockwise, just as the rotation from the $x'$-axis to the $x''$-axis. The links of the chain can be defined by complex numbers $x_k = x'_k + ix''_k = ae^{i\psi_k}$, where $\psi_k$ is the angle between the $k$th link and the real ($x'$) axis. The square of the effective length of the chain is thus given by the formula

$$\lambda^2 = (x_1+x_2+\ldots+x_z)(x_1^*+x_2^*+\ldots+x_z^*),$$

where $x_k^* = ae^{-i\psi_k}$. The preceding expression can be rewritten in the form

$$\lambda^2 = a^2\left[z+\frac{1}{a^2}\sum_{i<k}\sum (x_i x_k^* + x_i^* x_k)\right].$$

The angle $\psi_k$ is equal to the sum of the angles $\psi_1$, $\phi_2$, $\phi_3$,..., $\phi_k$. We thus have, if $k > i$,

$$x_i x_k^* = a^2 e^{-i(\phi_{i+1}+\phi_{i+2}+...+\phi_k)}.$$

If opposite values of the angles $\phi$ are assumed to be equally probable, so that the mean values of their sines vanish, and if different angles $\phi_i$ and $\phi_k$ are independent of each other, the following expression is obtained for the mean value of $\lambda^2$:

$$\frac{\overline{\lambda^2}}{a^2} = z+2\sum_{i<k}\sum \overline{\cos(\phi_{i+1}+\phi_{i+2}+...+\phi_k)}$$

$$= z+2\sum_{i<k}\sum \overline{\cos\phi_{i+1}}\,\overline{\cos\phi_{i+2}}...\overline{\cos\phi_k}.$$

Putting $\overline{\cos\phi_1} = \overline{\cos\phi_2} = ... = \zeta$, we get

$$\frac{\overline{\lambda^2}}{a^2} = z+2\sum_{i<k}\sum^{k\leqslant z} \zeta^{k-i},$$

that is,

$$\frac{\overline{\lambda^2}}{a^2} = z+\frac{2z\zeta}{1-\zeta}-\frac{2\zeta(1-\zeta^z)}{(1-\zeta)^2},$$

or finally,

$$\frac{\overline{\lambda^2}}{a^2} = z\frac{1+\zeta}{1-\zeta}-2\zeta\frac{1-\zeta^z}{(1-\zeta)^2}. \tag{22}$$

For large values of $z$ the second term of this expression can be neglected compared with the first one, unless the parameter $\zeta$ lies close to 1, i.e. the angles $\phi$ are very small. In the latter case, putting $\zeta = 1-\delta$, where $\delta \ll 1$, we have

$$\zeta^{z-1} \approx 1-(z-1)\delta+\frac{(z-1)(z-2)}{2}\delta^2,$$

and consequently, $\overline{\lambda^2}/a^2 \approx z^2$.

It should be noted that the formula

$$\overline{\lambda^2} = z\frac{1+\zeta}{1-\zeta}a^2 \tag{22 a}$$

coincides with the formula (15) for the linear model ('folding ruler') if the length of a link $a$ is replaced by $\sqrt{\left(\frac{1+\zeta}{1-\zeta}\right)}a$.

In the case of the three-dimensional problem, i.e. of the model of an elastic band which corresponds to a hindered rotation of the links of the carbon chain with fixed values of the angles between them, a rather complicated calculation leads to the following formula:†

$$\overline{\lambda^2} = a^2 z \frac{1+\zeta}{1-\zeta} \frac{1}{1-\cos\omega} \cong a^2 \frac{2\zeta}{1-\zeta} \frac{1}{1-\cos\omega}, \tag{22 b}$$

where $\omega$ is the complement of the valence angle and $\zeta$ the mean value of the cosine of the torsion angle $\epsilon$ between two successive pairs of links ($\epsilon_k$ is the angle between the planes $(k-1, k)$ and $(k, k+1)$, where $k = 2, 3,..., z-1$). The factor $1-\cos\omega$ in the denominator corresponds to the fact that the torsion of the chain leads to its bending only when the consecutive torsion axes (links) are inclined with respect to each other; if, instead of being a zigzag line, as shown in Fig. 53, the carbon backbone of the macromolecule were a straight line ($\omega = 0$), it would not be bent by twisting $\epsilon$ (just as in the case of the torsion of a straight rod). Formula (22 b) is not absolutely exact, for in this case it gives $\lambda = \infty$, instead of $\lambda = az$. So long, however, as $z$ is very large, it remains a good approximation even for small values of the angle $\omega$.

If the potential energy (due to the mutual repulsion of the side groups attached to the carbon backbone) can be represented as a function of the angle of twisting $\epsilon$ by the formula

$$U = \tfrac{1}{2} U_0 (1-\cos\epsilon), \tag{23}$$

where $U_0$ is the energy required for a transition of two successive links from a trans-configuration into a cis-configuration, then $\zeta = \overline{\cos\epsilon}$ is given, as a function of the temperature, by the formula

$$\overline{\cos\epsilon} = \int e^{-U/kT} \cos\epsilon \, d\epsilon \Big/ \int e^{-U/kT} \, d\epsilon$$
$$= \int e^{U_0 \cos\epsilon/2kT} \cos\epsilon \, d\epsilon \Big/ \int e^{U_0 \cos\epsilon/2kT} \, d\epsilon.$$

It differs from the Langevin–Debye formula by the absence of the factor $\sin\epsilon$, in the integrand, which is explained by the fact that the twisting angle $\epsilon$ corresponds to a single rotational degree of freedom (playing the role of an ordinary azimuthal angle), whereas the orientation angle $\theta$ of the Langevin–Debye theory defines the orientation in *space*.

The preceding expression can be evaluated exactly with the help of Bessel's functions of an imaginary argument. We shall limit ourselves, however, to the consideration of two extreme cases, namely of low and high temperatures. The temperature will be defined as low when the

† Cf. Bresler and Frenkel, *Acta Physicochimica, U.R.S.S.* **11**, 487 (1939).

parameter $\alpha = U_0/2kT$ is large compared with 1, and high when it is of the order of 1 or still smaller.

In the former case the angles $\epsilon$ must obviously remain small. We can therefore replace $\cos\epsilon$ by $1-\frac{1}{2}\epsilon^2$, which gives

$$\overline{\cos\epsilon} = \int e^{-\frac{1}{2}\alpha\epsilon^2}\left(1-\frac{\epsilon^2}{2}\right)d\epsilon \Big/ \int e^{-\frac{1}{2}\alpha\epsilon^2}\,d\epsilon.$$

In view of the rapid decrease of the function $e^{-\frac{1}{2}\alpha\epsilon^2}$ with $\epsilon$, the integration limits can be extended from $-\infty$ to $+\infty$, which gives

$$\zeta = \overline{\cos\epsilon} = \left(1-\frac{1}{2\alpha}\right) = 1-\frac{kT}{U_0},$$

that is,

$$1-\zeta \simeq \frac{kT}{U_0},$$

and consequently

$$\overline{\lambda^2} \cong a^2\,\frac{2zU_0}{kT(1-\cos\omega)}. \tag{24}$$

If $U_0 = 3{,}600$ cal./mole, as follows from the experiments of Kistiakowsky, the preceding formulae can be applied to room temperatures ($kT \approx 600$).

In the contrary case ($\alpha < 1$) the rotation (twisting) about the successive links can be treated as practically free, in agreement with Mark–Kuhn's views, and $\overline{\lambda^2}$ can be expressed with sufficient approximation by the formula

$$\overline{\lambda^2} = za^2\,\frac{1+\cos\omega}{1-\cos\omega} \tag{24 a}$$

which does not contain the temperature (and which is obtained from (22 a) if $\zeta$ is replaced by $\cos\omega$).

In the following table the values of $\sqrt{(\overline{\lambda^2})}/a$ calculated according to (24) for room temperature (and $U_0/kT = 6$) are compared for different values of $z$ with those which correspond to the hypothesis of free rotation and are given by (24 a). The latter values must be considered as wrong, if $U_0/kT$ is of the order of a few units.

| $z$ | 16 | 100 | 1,000 |
|---|---|---|---|
| $\sqrt{(\overline{\lambda^2})}/a$ according to (24) | 8 | 22 | 63 |
| $\sqrt{(\overline{\lambda^2})}/a$ according to (24 a) | 14 | 38 | 110 |

It should be remembered that formula (24 a) is valid only for values of $1-\cos\omega$ that are not too small, satisfying the condition $z(1-\cos\omega) \ll 1$. If $\cos\omega \approx 1$, the quantity $\overline{\lambda^2}$ turns out to be proportional not to $z$ but to $z^2$ (a practically rigid chain).

## 7. The Mechanical and Thermodynamical Properties of Rubber-like Substances

High polymeric substances constituted by chain-like molecules display in the condensed state (and also to some extent in solution of a sufficiently high concentration) peculiar mechanical properties, consisting of an extremely high elasticity with respect to extension *without a change of volume*. Thus, for example, a piece of rubber can be extended 10-fold and even more. This fact would be sufficiently remarkable by itself; another remarkable feature of this rubber-like elasticity is the fact that it corresponds to extremely low values of the elasticity modulus. For small extensions the latter (referred to the initial cross-section of the sample) is of the order of 10 kg./cm.$^2$, i.e. about 100,000 times smaller than Young's modulus of ordinary solid bodies.

It must be borne in mind that between the extension of a piece of rubber and that of an ordinary elastic solid there exists a very important difference, which consists in the fact that in the latter case the transverse contraction does not compensate the longitudinal extension, which results in a certain increase of the volume, whereas in the case of the extension of rubber the volume remains practically constant. This difference can be reduced, in a formal way, to the fact that in the case of ordinary elastic solids Poisson's coefficient is smaller than $\frac{1}{2}$ (usually of the order of $\frac{1}{3}$), whereas in the case of rubber and other rubber-like substances it is equal to $\frac{1}{2}$—just as in the case of liquid bodies.

It should be mentioned that in the case of an *all-sided* extension or compression of a piece of rubber, which alters its volume without changing its shape, it behaves in exactly the same way as an ordinary solid or liquid body with a compressibility modulus of the order of $10^5$–$10^6$ kg./cm.$^2$ Its specific high elasticity with a modulus of the order of 10 kg./cm.$^2$ is displayed, consequently, in such deformations only as are reduced to a simple shear, i.e. to a change of shape not accompanied by a change of volume.

We thus see that with respect to high elastic deformation rubber can be likened to a practically incompressible liquid, endowed, however, with a characteristic elasticity of shape. The latter can be described as a 'reversible' or 'relaxational' fluidity which has been examined in § 7 of Ch. IV, and which can be characterized by a relatively small relaxational rigidity modulus $G$ in conjunction with a certain relaxation time $\tau'$, or, more exactly, by two different rigidity moduli $G_1$ and $G_2$, and a viscosity coefficient $\mu_2$ coupled together as shown in the scheme of Fig. 29 (if the ordinary viscosity $\mu_1$, corresponding to an irreversible flow, is treated as infinite). This question has already been discussed in § 7 of Ch. IV from the formal point of view of the general macroscopic theory, with the result that the characteristic distinction of rubber and rubber-like substances consists in the extreme smallness of $G_2$ and $\mu_2$ compared with $G_1$ (the latter being of the same order of magnitude as in ordinary solid bodies) and $\mu_1$ respectively. We must now examine the same question from the point of view of the molecular kinetic theory, starting from the chain-like model of high polymeric molecules which has been considered in the preceding section in connexion with dilute solutions of such molecules in ordinary liquid solvents. Rubber or any rubber-like substance in the pure (condensed) state can be regarded as a solution of chain-like macromolecules in a solvent made up of the same macromolecules. In order to describe quantitatively the properties of such a body, it is not sufficient to know the properties of the individual molecules; it is necessary, moreover, to have some idea of their interrelation and mutual action.

Now, it is clear that in non-vulcanized rubber this interaction must reduce to the van der Waals forces acting between the separate links of different molecules which are in contact with each other. We must obviously imagine that the molecules are interwoven in a chaotic way; nevertheless, under normal conditions, corresponding to a state of statistical equilibrium, the molecules must be curled or folded in exactly the same way as if they were free or dissolved in an ordinary liquid. Hence it follows that each molecule must be in contact with a very large number of other molecules, each link being surrounded by a few (4–6) links, belonging to certain other molecules, which cross each other near the corresponding point in various directions.

In spite of this entanglement the molecules must preserve a certain degree of individual mobility which is necessary to enable them to assume the equilibrium—folded or curled—shape in a finite time $\tau'$, which may be denoted by the term 'structure relaxation time'. The character of the thermal motion of each macromolecule, which ensures the possibility of assuming various configurations consistent with a given length of the separate links and a given valency angle between them, depends on the one hand on the interaction between its successive links (valency forces) and on the other hand between its links and those of the surrounding molecules (van der Waals forces); it must, however, be independent of the way the links of the other molecules are bound with each other. Hence it follows that the relaxation time $\tau'$ of a pure polymeric substance must be approximately the same as for a dilute solution of this substance in a completely depolymerized solvent, i.e. in a liquid constituted by monomeric molecules. It can be calculated accordingly with the help of the formula (21 b) of the preceding section. Putting $z = 1{,}000$ and $\tau_1 = 10^{-11}$—which corresponds to a monomeric liquid at room temperatures—we get $\tau' \approx 10^{-7}$ sec. This figure is in good agreement with the experimental data obtained by Kornfeld for rubber at room temperatures. At a temperature of $-60°$ C., $\tau'$ becomes of the order of 1 sec., so that rubber loses its characteristic high elasticity; it is well known that it becomes brittle as glass after immersion in liquid air.

The 'structure relaxation time' $\tau'$ which determines the rate at which the chain-like macromolecules tend to resume their normal curled shape, or rather the normal (Gaussian) distribution of their effective lengths, must not be confused with Maxwell's relaxation time $\tau$, which determines the viscosity coefficient $\mu_1$ for ordinary irreversible flow according to the formula $\mu_1 = G_1 \tau$. Under ordinary conditions (room temperature) $\tau$ must be enormously larger than $\tau'$, as follows from the extremely high—practically immeasurable—viscosity of rubber. Its fluidity becomes apparent at higher temperatures only; it must, however, be kept in mind that at high temperatures rubber must become practically depolymerized, so that a simple relation between the viscosity $\mu_1$ and the temperature cannot be expected.

Using long-chain paraffins with relatively low values of $z$ Flory has shown experimentally† that the dependence of $\mu$ $(= \mu_1)$ on $T$ can be represented by the usual formula

$$\mu = Ae^{W/kT},$$

where the activation energy $W$ proves to be independent of $z$, while the factor $A$ increases with $z$ exponentially, i.e. according to the formula

$$A = A_0 e^{\alpha z}. \tag{25}$$

The fact that $W$ is independent of $z$ is explained by Eyring and Kauzman‡ with the help of the conception that polymeric molecular chains are not moved as a rigid whole, but 'partially', as a caterpillar, an elementary displacement being due to a relatively small number of links $z_1$ which is independent of $z$, if $z \gg z_1$. Putting $W = Uz_1$, where $U$ is the activation energy for the self-diffusion motion of simple hydro-

† Flory, *J.A.C.S.* **62,** 1057 (1940).
‡ Eyring and Kauzman, *J.A.C.S.* **62,** 3113 (1940).

carbons (as revealed by the viscosity of a monomeric liquid), Eyring obtains for $z_1$ values of the order 20.

The exponential dependence of $A$ on $z$, found by Flory, can be explained on the basis of Einstein's theory of the viscosity of solutions of macromolecules, which has been considered in the preceding section, if a pure polymeric substance is treated as a concentrated solution.

Einstein's formula for the increase of viscosity due to an increase of the concentration of the dissolved substance by the amount $dn$ runs as follows:

$$d\mu = \mu_0 \gamma \omega \, dn,$$

where $\mu_0$ is the value of $\mu$ for $n = 0$.

This result refers to the case of small concentrations only. Its extension to the case of high concentrations can be obtained in the simplest and most natural way if $\mu_0$ is replaced by $\mu$. Since $\gamma$ and $\omega$ are independent of $n$, the integration of the resulting equation gives

$$\mu = \mu_0 e^{\gamma \omega n}.$$

Noting that $\omega$ is the volume occupied by 1 macromolecule and $n$ their number in unit volume of the pure polymer, we get $\omega n = 1$ and consequently

$$\mu = \mu_0 e^{\gamma}. \tag{25 a}$$

Now according to formula (11 a) for rod-like particles we have, if $z$ is of the order of $10^2$ or larger,

$$\gamma = \frac{z}{2 \log z}, \tag{25 b}$$

while Flory's results can be represented by the empirical formula

$$\gamma = \tfrac{1}{4}\sqrt{z}.$$

The discrepancy between this formula and the theoretical formula (25 b) may be due to a partial curling of the molecular chains.

In applying the preceding theory to rubber and other high polymers, it is necessary to take into account the decrease of the degree of polymerization ($z$) with a rise of the temperature. Putting

$$z = z_0 e^{U/kT},$$

where $z_0 \sim 1$, while $U$ is the polymerization energy, we obtain in the preceding formula a complicated dependence of a type found experimentally by Waterton.

From the point of view of a strict thermodynamic theory the rubber-like state of a polymeric substance is not always a stable one. In the sense of § 8, Ch. III, it should be described as 'relatively stable', the absolutely stable state corresponding, within the same temperature range, to an absolute minimum of the free energy, being either a liquid state with a relatively simple molecular structure or a crystalline one.

Let us consider, for example, the case of sulphur. By heating sulphur to a temperature exceeding 252° C. it is transformed from a transparent liquid with a low viscosity into a brown liquid with a very high viscosity. This transformation is explained as follows. In the crystal or in the melt at a temperature below 252° C. the molecules of sulphur are constituted by eight atoms, forming a closed octagon (more exactly, two squares, one of which lies on the top of the other and is rotated with respect to it by an angle of 45°). Above 252° C. these octagons are broken up and become open chains with two free valencies at the ends. Owing to these free valencies such chains are polymerized, i.e. combined 'in series', into chains consisting of a very large number of successively bound atoms ($z = 8z_1$, where $z_1$ is of the order of 10–100–1,000). This polymerization results in an enormous increase of the viscosity.

If now the liquid is rapidly cooled down, it does not return to its original structure, unless kept for a sufficiently long time just below the transformation point (252° C.), but remains in the polymerized state and becomes rubber-like if cooled farther down (to room temperature and even below). This is explained by the fact that the restitution of the original ring-like structure of the sulphur molecules, which is a pre-requisite for its transition into the ordinary (fluid) liquid or crystalline state, requires a breaking up of the polymeric chains, i.e. is connected with a large activation energy $U$, and therefore proceeds at a relatively slow rate. As the temperature is lowered the degree of polymerization $z$ and the viscosity $\mu$ increase so that the overcooled amorphous polymeric sulphur becomes a genuine rubber-like body, unless the temperature is so low that the structure relaxation time $\tau'$ becomes of the order of seconds or minutes and the high elasticity vanishes—just as in frozen rubber.

The preceding conception, which is certainly correct with respect to the rubber-like state of sulphur, may be inapplicable to such high polymeric substances, including ordinary rubber, as can crystallize without a fundamental reconstruction of their molecules, but by a simple straightening out and parallel arrangement of the molecular chains. The actual length of the latter is immaterial for the crystalline structure, the elementary cell containing, as a rule, only a few (two at least) monomeric groups, the end groups of each chain remaining in a somewhat singular—not wholly regular—position. This point of view is borne out not only by an X-ray analysis of the structure of crystallized rubber, but also by the fact that the characteristic crystal structure is partially obtained when ordinary amorphous rubber is stretched to an extent of 200–300 per cent. Such a partial crystallization as a result of extension can be explained, from the molecular-kinetic point of view, by the resulting more or less parallel alinement of the molecular chains, which facilitates a further increase of regularity by way of a spontaneous rearrangement due to the thermal motion. It can also be explained from the thermodynamic point of view as a result of a rise of the crystallization point owing to the application of the extending force, in accordance with the equation

$$\frac{dT}{dF} = -\frac{T\Delta L}{Q}, \tag{26}$$

where $\Delta L$ is the change of length due to crystallization under a given value of the extending force $F$, and $Q$ the resulting latent heat. This equation is obtained in the same way as that of Clausius–Clapeyron, if the specific thermodynamic potentials of the two phases $\phi_i$ $(i = 1, 2)$ are treated as functions of $T$ and $F$, in conjunction with the relation $L_i = \partial\phi_i/\partial F$, which follows from the expression $F\,dL$ for the work done by the system when extended by the amount $dL$ by an external force $F$ (the latter being reckoned positive in the case of a pull). The corresponding change of the free energy $\Psi$ is therefore given by $d\Psi = F\,dL$, or in the general case by

$$d\Psi = F\,dL - S\,dT,$$

where $S$ is the entropy; defining the thermodynamic potential by the formula

$$\Phi = \Psi - LF$$

we thus get

$$d\Phi = -L\,dF - S\,dT,$$

whence $L = -\partial\Phi/\partial F$. The equilibrium between the amorphous and the crystallized phase is defined by the condition

$$\phi_1(T, F) = \phi_2(T, F),$$

from which (26) directly follows by differentiation, in conjunction with $Q = T\Delta S$. $Q$ is positive if a transition from the crystallized to the amorphous phase is considered. This transition (melting) under a constant value of $F$ corresponds to a decrease of the length ($\Delta L < 0$), so that $dT/dF > 0$.

Equation (26) has not yet been checked quantitatively, for this requires a careful measurement both of $\Delta L$ and of $Q$. It should be borne in mind, further, that rubber is not a strictly homogeneous substance. It consists of a large number of macromolecules of different lengths (degrees of polymerization); hence it follows that it must be characterized not by a definite crystallization point, but rather by a certain range of temperature, corresponding (for a given value of $F$) to a *gradual* crystallization.

This result is in agreement with the experimental facts as revealed not only by the X-ray analysis, but also by the gradual hardening of rubber with increase of its extension (the fully crystallized substance is wholly devoid of the characteristic high elasticity).

From the point of view given above it follows that the extension of rubber must be accompanied by its heating, as a result of the (gradual) evolution of the latent heat of crystallization. This inference is also in agreement with the experimental facts, the heating of rubber and other rubber-like substances on extension being in striking contrast to the cooling of ordinary solid bodies under similar conditions.†

## 8. The Elasticity of Rubber-like Substances

In spite of this agreement, the preceding theory can hardly be regarded as fully satisfactory, for it leaves out of account the characteristic *mechanical* properties of rubber, namely its high elasticity, and does not correlate these mechanical properties with the thermomechanical ones.

Now it is possible to obtain an explanation of the latter without recourse to the crystallization process, but on the basis of that picture of the structure and thermal motion of the chain-like macromolecules which has been developed in § 5 for the case of solutions and which has been shown in the preceding section to be applicable, with certain modifications, to the case of pure polymers in the rubber-like state.

From the molecular-kinetic point of view the characteristic properties of this state are due to the tendency of the chain-like macromolecules, as a result of their intramolecular thermal motion, to assume curled (folded) shapes, corresponding to a decrease of the effective length $\bar{\lambda}$ compared with its maximum value in the fully extended state ($\lambda_{\max} = az$). The only difference between the behaviour of such molecules in a dilute solution and in the condensed phase of a pure polymer consists in the fact that in the former case a macromolecule can be extended either by kinetic forces, due to the viscous flow of the solvent with a

† The singularity of these conditions is merely apparent. When an ordinary solid body is extended its volume is increased, and the accompanying cooling is connected with the resulting increase of the potential energy, whereas in the case of rubber the volume, and consequently the potential energy of the molecular forces, are practically unaffected by the extension.

certain velocity gradient, or by statical forces of electrical origin, applied (in opposite directions) to its ends, whereas in the latter case, owing to the practically infinite viscosity of the polymer, such statical forces can be produced and transmitted by the mutual (van der Waals) interaction between the macromolecules.

When a dilute solution of polymeric molecules in an ordinary liquid solvent is extended in one direction, for instance by pressing the solution through a narrow opening, the macromolecules must get orientated and extended in the direction of flow—owing to the resulting viscous stresses—but only for the duration of this flow, returning to their usual disorientated and curled arrangement as soon as the liquid comes to rest or, more exactly, after a certain relaxation time $\tau'$, which has been considered above. If, on the other hand, we extend a piece of rubber by applying a pulling force $F$ (or rather two such forces of opposite directions) to its ends, the resulting orientation and extension of the macromolecules preserves a constant magnitude, corresponding to an equilibrium between the external pull and the internal forces, due to the curling tendency of the macromolecules, i.e. to their intramolecular thermal motion. It may seem, at first sight, that this assertion contradicts the theoretical conclusion, reached in the preceding section, that the relaxation time $\tau'$, in the case of a condensed polymer, must be of the same order of magnitude as in a dilute solution of its macromolecules, for the latter should in both cases return to their irregular disorientated and curled arrangement within practically the same lapse of time ($10^{-7}$ sec. for rubber at room temperature).

This would be true, however, if in both cases no extending force were exerted on the macromolecules by the surrounding molecules after the deformation has reached its final value. This condition is actually realized in the case of dilute solutions, where each macromolecule is surrounded by ordinary simple molecules, and where the viscosity is therefore relatively small. In a condensed polymer, on the other hand, the viscosity is so large that the centres of gravity of the macromolecules cannot be rearranged in a finite length of time. Now, without such a 'translational rearrangement' an effective inner rearrangement of the macromolecules which should alter their effective length or degree of orientation is impossible. So far as this inner rearrangement is concerned, they behave in the same way as if they were imbedded in a simple solvent but kept under constant pulling forces, which are determined by the resulting deformation of the sample.

This kinetic origin of the pulling force in extended rubber and other rubber-like substances can be illustrated with the help of the working of a centrifugal regulator (Fig. 54), which corresponds to two consecutive links of a molecular chain. If the regulator is revolving freely with a linear velocity $v$, a centrifugal force $mv^2/r$ arises in a direction perpendicular to the axis of revolution ($r$ is the distance from the latter of the moving mass $m$).

Let $\theta$ denote the angle between the axis of revolution (which corresponds to the average direction of the chain axis near a given point)

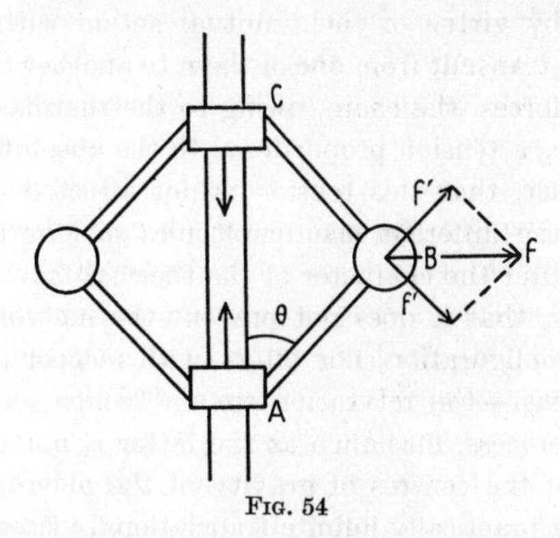


FIG. 54

and the two adjacent links, represented in Fig. 54 by the arms $AB$ and $BC$ of the regulator. The force $f$ is equivalent to two forces, acting in the direction $AB$ and $CB$, and equal to

$$f' = \frac{f}{2 \sin \theta}.$$

Resolving them into two components in a direction perpendicular and parallel to the axis of revolution, we obtain for the latter the expression

$$f'_{11} = f' \cos \theta = \tfrac{1}{2} f \cot \theta = \frac{mv^2}{2r} \cot \theta,$$

or, since $r = a \sin \theta$ ($a = AB = BC$),

$$f'_{11} = \frac{mv^2}{2a} \frac{\cos \theta}{\sin^2 \theta}.$$

This force, or rather these two forces, acting in opposite directions on the points $A$ and $C$, tend to bring them closer together, and thus correspond to a pull along the axis of the molecule, the magnitude of the pull being proportional to the kinetic energy of revolution $\frac{1}{2}mv^2$, that is, consequently, to the temperature, if this revolution represents the thermal motion of the two links.

This result is not altered if the free rotation (which cannot take place in reality) is replaced by rotational oscillations, to which the thermal motion of the separate links must be reduced, if their mutual action with more distant links of the same macromolecule, or with those belonging to the neighbouring macromolecules, is taken into account (since the magnitude of the centrifugal force $mv^2/r$ depends on the square of the velocity irrespective of its direction).

We thus see that if the ends of a molecular chain are kept at a fixed distance apart, by virtue of their mutual action with other macromolecules, which transmit from one of them to another the pull exerted by the external forces, the chain, owing to the thermal oscillations of its links, produces a tension proportional to the absolute temperature. It is clear, further, that this tension is not affected by the mutual action between the different macromolecules so long as this mutual action does not alter the character of the thermal motion. It must be remarked, finally, that it does not prevent the macromolecules from changing their configuration, nor alter—with respect to the order of magnitude, at least—the relaxation time $\tau'$ which characterizes the kinetics of this process, inasmuch as the latter is not connected with such a motion of the centres of gravity of the macromolecules as is prevented by the practically infinite translational viscosity.

A detailed analysis of this question cannot be achieved until a clearer understanding is gained of the relationship between the translational motion of the centres of gravity of complex molecules and the associated variation of their orientations and inner configurations (in the case of flexible macromolecules), which has been indicated in its broad features in Ch. V.

Leaving this question aside, we shall now investigate the quantitative aspect of the theory of the mechanical and thermomechanical properties of rubber and similar substances on the basis of thermodynamical considerations, which have been introduced in their application to individual chain-like macromolecules in § 5.

These considerations were set forth originally by Meyer in 1932 and by Wöhlisch (who, however, treated the molecular chains as rigid), and have been subsequently developed by Kuhn, Mark, Guth, and the present author.†

Meyer and Wöhlisch did not take into account the possibility of a partial crystallization of rubber as a result of a large extension, and

† Meyer, Suvich, and Valko, *Koll. Z.* **59**, 208 (1932); Wöhlisch, *Verh. d. Physiol. Mediz. Ger., Würzburg*, **1**, 53 (1927); *Z. f. Biologie*, **87**, 353 (1928).

assumed, further, that its internal (potential) energy $W$ is not changed so long as its volume is not altered by such an extension. Hence it follows that the elastic force resisting the deformation is connected not with an increase of the potential energy, as in the case of ordinary solid and liquid bodies, but with a decrease of the entropy, just as in the case of ideal gases. In fact, denoting the free energy of a piece of rubber by $\Psi = W - TS$, where $S = -\partial\Psi/\partial T$ is its entropy, we can determine the force arising when it is extended to a length $L$ at constant volume and temperature by the formula

$$F = \left(\frac{\partial\Psi}{\partial L}\right)_{V,T}.$$

If the energy $W$ does not depend on $L$, being a function of $V$ and $T$ only, this formula is reduced to

$$F = -T\left(\frac{\partial S}{\partial L}\right)_{V,T}. \tag{26 a}$$

Since $F$ has a positive value, the entropy must decrease with increase of the length. Hence it follows that an adiabatic extension of rubber must be accompanied by an evolution of structural heat, even if the rubber remains in the amorphous state. A similar effect is found in gases which are *cooled* by an adiabatic expansion. In this case the cooling is due to the transformation of the energy of thermal motion into external work, as a result of the increase of the volume. The molecular mechanism of this cooling or heating effect is explained by considering the change of the velocities of the gas molecule when they are reflected by the wall of a moving piston. In the case of stretched rubber the external forces amount to a pull, and the work done by them when the corresponding piece of rubber is further extended adiabatically is transformed into heat. The corresponding molecular mechanism can be illustrated by the example of the centrifugal regulator considered above: when the distance $AC$ (Fig. 54) is increased, which corresponds to a stretching of the molecular chain, i.e. when the distance $r$ from the axis of revolution is decreased, the velocity of revolution must increase (as a consequence of the law of conservation of angular momentum $mr^2v$), and vice versa.

The thermomechanical effect can be determined quantitatively with the help of the equation

$$T\,dS = dW - F\,dL + p\,dV, \tag{26 b}$$

which, if $V$ and $S$ are kept constant (adiabatic extension), is reduced to

$$dW = F\,dL,$$

or since $dW = c_v dT$ (where $c_v$ is the specific heat at constant volume)

$$dT = \frac{F}{c_v} dL. \tag{26 c}$$

The experimental data obtained by Meyer for small extensions are in good agreement with this formula. It is possible, however, that for larger extensions (exceeding 100 per cent., say) the situation is complicated by a partial crystallization such as has been previously considered. From the general expression

$$d\Psi = -S\,dT - p\,dV + F\,dL$$

for the differential of the free energy, there follows the relation

$$\left(\frac{\partial F}{\partial T}\right)_{V,L} = -\left(\frac{\partial S}{\partial L}\right)_{V,T},$$

which, in conjunction with (26), shows that the entropy is independent of the temperature and that the force $F$ is directly proportional to the latter. The available experimental data are not sufficiently accurate to check this point exactly, the more so because the range of temperatures in which the high elasticity of rubber is manifested is relatively limited. They do not, however, contradict the theoretical relationship.

Since for small extensions $L - L_0$ (where $L_0$ is the normal length of the sample under consideration) the force $F$ must be directly proportional to it, it follows from (26 a) that the entropy can be represented as a function of $L$ by the quadratic expression

$$S = -\tfrac{1}{2}A(L - L_0)^2.$$

We thus see that, starting from the hypothesis of the independence of the energy of a piece of rubber on its shape (length), we obtain results quite similar to those which have been found in § 5 for individual macromolecules in dilute solution. This is explained simply by the fact that so long as the energy of the mutual action of the macromolecules constituting a piece of rubber remains constant (along with its volume), its thermal and mechanical properties can be treated as additive. This refers, in particular, to the entropy $S$, which can be defined as the sum of the entropies of the individual macromolecules $s$, or the product of the mean value of $s$ and the number of molecules $N$.

For a quantitative determination of this entropy it is necessary to make a certain assumption about the configurations of the macromolecules in the unstrained sample. Let us assume, for the sake of simplicity, that the latter has in this case the shape of a sphere with a diameter $L_0$, and that the average effective length of the molecules is equal to $\lambda_0 = a\sqrt{z}$ (which corresponds, strictly speaking, to the one-dimensional model of a folding ruler).

We shall assume further that when the sample is stretched to a length $L$, the effective length of the molecules (in the corresponding direction) is increased on the average in the same ratio

$$\frac{\lambda}{\lambda_0} = \frac{L}{L_0}.$$

This corresponds to a decrease of the entropy of each macromolecule by the amount

$$-\frac{k(\lambda-\lambda_0)^2}{a^2 z} = -\frac{k(\lambda-\lambda_0)^2}{\lambda_0^2}$$

according to (14), and consequently to a decrease of the entropy of the whole body by the amount

$$S - S_0 = -Nk\frac{(L-L_0)^2}{L_0^2}.$$

Hence, according to (26a), we obtain the following expression for the resulting elastic tension:

$$F = \frac{2RT}{L_0^2}(L-L_0), \tag{27}$$

where $R = kN$.

The ratio of $F$ to the initial value of the cross-section of the sample $\frac{1}{4}\pi L_0^2$ can be defined as the normal stress, and the proportionality coefficient between it and the relative extension $(L-L_0)/L_0$

$$E = \frac{2RT}{\frac{1}{4}\pi L_0^3}$$

as the initial value of the elasticity (Young's) modulus. Noting that $\frac{1}{6}\pi L_0^3 = V$ we get

$$E = \frac{4}{3}\frac{RT}{V} \tag{27 a}$$

or

$$E = \frac{4}{3}\frac{nkT}{z},$$

where $n$ is the number of monomeric links in all the molecules contained in unit volume. Hence it follows that the elasticity modulus of a piece of rubber is equal (approximately) to the pressure which it would exert at the same temperature and concentration in a gaseous state without being depolymerized.

Putting $n = 10^{22}$ (which corresponds to the usual concentration of ordinary 'micromolecules' in a condensed body) and $T = 300°$ K. ($kT = 4.10^{-14}$) we get

$$E = \frac{3\times10^8}{z}\frac{\text{dyne}}{\text{cm.}^2} = \frac{3\times10^2}{z}\frac{\text{kg.}}{\text{cm.}^2},$$

which for $z \approx 100$ gives a value of the order of a few kg./cm.²

This result agrees in respect of the order of magnitude with the experimental data. A quantitative agreement can hardly be expected having regard to the roughly simplified character of the calculation.

A better approximation to the actual conditions can be obtained if the molecular chains are treated as three-dimensional systems. If no restrictions are imposed on the values of the angles between the successive links, the entropy of a macromolecule can be determined as a function of its effective length by the formula (18 a). Multiplying it by $N$ and replacing $kN$ by $R$ and $\lambda$ by $\lambda_0 L/L_0$, we get, if $\lambda_0$ is identified with $a\sqrt{(2/3)}$,

$$S = R\left(-\frac{L^2}{L_0^2}+2\log\frac{L}{L_0}\right), \tag{28}$$

whence

$$F = 2RT\left(\frac{L}{L_0^2}-\frac{1}{L}\right). \tag{28 a}$$

This expression corresponds to the definition of $L_0$ as the equilibrium value of $L$ for which $F$ vanishes. For small values of the difference $L-L_0$ it reduces to

$$F = \frac{4RT}{L_0^2}(L-L_0),$$

which differs from (27) by a factor 2 only and corresponds, accordingly, to an 'initial' elasticity modulus

$$E = \frac{8}{3}\frac{RT}{V}. \tag{28 b}$$

The expression (28) has, among other advantages, that of representing in an apparently correct way the asymmetry of the relation between deformation and force for deformations of opposite sign, i.e. extensions and compressions (one-sided). It is, moreover, not restricted to small deformations, as is the expression (27).

The preceding derivation of $E$ is based on the assumption that the individual molecules of rubber are lengthened in the direction of the pulling force by the same fractional amount as the whole body constituted by them. Now, it is clear that this relation cannot hold exactly. In fact, those molecules which are initially extended in the direction of the applied pull cannot be extended any more.

The relation between the deformation of the individual molecules and that of the whole body can be stated in the following more rigorous way.†

In the unstretched state the arrangement of the molecules is described by the simple Gauss law

$$dP_0 = Ce^{-\gamma^2(x^2+y^2+z^2)}\,dxdydz, \tag{29}$$

where $C = (\gamma/\sqrt{\pi})^3$. Let us now assume that when the body is extended in the longitudinal direction in the ratio $\alpha = L/L_0$ and simultaneously compressed in the transverse direction in the ratio $\sqrt{\alpha}$ (so that its volume remains unaltered) the preceding isotropic Gaussian distribution is replaced by the following anisotropic one:

$$dP = Ce^{-\gamma^2[(x^2/\alpha^2)+\alpha(y^2+z^2)]}\,dxdydz. \tag{29 a}$$

The physical meaning of this assumption is the same as that of the simple assumption made before as to the proportionality between the extension of the individual molecules and that of the whole body; it has, however, the advantage of taking into account the *statistical* character of the distribution of the molecules both in the normal and in the stretched state of the body. The entropy of an individual molecule as a function of $x$, $y$, $z$ is given in both cases by the same expression

$$s = k\log\frac{dP_0}{dxdydz} = k\log C - k\gamma^2(x^2+y^2+z^2).$$

The total entropy of the whole body in the normal state is thus equal to

$$S_0 = \int s\,dP_0,$$

while in the stretched state it is given by

$$S = \int s\,dP.$$

Substituting here the preceding expressions for $dP_0$ and $dP$, we obtain after an easy calculation

$$S - S_0 = Nk\left[\frac{3}{2} - \left(\frac{\alpha^2}{2} + \frac{1}{\alpha}\right)\right],$$

that is,

$$S - S_0 = \frac{R}{2}\left[3 - \frac{L^2}{L_0^2} - \frac{2L_0}{L}\right]. \tag{30}$$

This expression differs from (28) by the substitution of the ratio

† Cf. W. Kuhn, *Koll. Z.* **68**, 2 (1934); **76**, 258 (1936), and also Wall, *J. Chem. Phys.* **10**, 1932 (1942).

$L_0/L$ for the logarithmic term $\log(L_0/L)$. Using the equation (26) we obtain from (30) the following expression for the pulling force

$$F = RT\left(\frac{L}{L_0^2}-\frac{L_0}{L^2}\right), \tag{30 a}$$

which is practically identical with (28 a).

The introduction of the restriction about the constant value of the valence angle does not alter the preceding results substantially, the 'effective' length of a link $a$ being simply defined as $l\sqrt{\left(\frac{1+\cos\omega}{1-\cos\omega}\right)}$. The preceding theory must, however, be modified much more seriously if we wish to allow for the hindered rotation (twisting) of the separate links of the chain, due to the mutual repulsion of the side groups attached to the backbone carbon atoms and characterized by the activation energy $U_0$ of the cis-configuration with respect to the normal trans-configuration.

The elasticity modulus can be found in this case most simply with the help of the analogy, already used, between the geometry of the configurations of a molecular chain and the kinematics of diffusion.

Putting
$$\overline{\lambda^2} = 6Dz,$$
where the number of links $z$ stands for the time $t$, and using equation (22 b) we get

$$D = \frac{a^2}{3(1-\zeta)(1-\cos\omega)}.$$

The average length of the chain stretched by an external force $f$ can be determined with the help of the expression

$$\overline{\Delta} = \frac{D}{kT}fz$$

for the average displacement of a particle during the time $z$ under the influence of the force $f$ ($D/kT$ is the mobility of the particle). The elasticity modulus is determined by the ratio $f/\overline{\Delta}$, which in our case turns out to be

$$\frac{3kT(1-\cos\omega)(1-\zeta)}{za^2} = \frac{3(1-\cos\omega)}{za^2U_0}k^2T^2,$$

whereas in the case of free rotation it is equal to

$$\frac{kT}{a^2z}\frac{1-\cos\omega}{1+\cos\omega}.$$

It is thus seen that the existence of an activation energy $U_0$ for rotation (twisting) leads to a *decrease* of the elasticity modulus by a factor $\frac{3kT}{U_0}(1+\cos\omega)$, if $U_0 \gg kT$; it should be noticed that under such conditions this modulus proves to be proportional to the second power of the temperature instead of the first.

Rubber is usually obtained from caoutchouc, both natural and synthetic, by a process of *vulcanization*, which consists in the introduction of sulphur atoms, binding together different chains, if the latter contain double bonds, according to this scheme:

$$\mathrm{RC{=}CR_1 + RC{=}CR_1 + S} \longrightarrow \begin{matrix} \mathrm{RC} & & \mathrm{CR} \\ | & \mathrm{S} & | \\ \mathrm{R_1C} & & \mathrm{CR_1} \end{matrix}$$

The number of such side bonds in each molecular chain depends on the number of unsaturated links (containing double bonds) and on the number of sulphur atoms. In the case of vulcanized rubber it is usually of the order of 1 per cent.

The vulcanization leads to a strong increase of the (translational) viscosity of rubber and to an increase of its 'hardness', i.e. of its elasticity modulus. With a further increase of the sulphur content the chain molecules become fastened to each other in a practically three-dimensional framework, which corresponds to a complete disappearance of the characteristic rubber-like elasticity. By over-vulcanizing rubber a hard body with ordinary mechanical properties—ebonite—is obtained.

The cause of these changes is simply explained if it is assumed that the portions of each molecular chain, contained between two consecutive points where it is bound to two other chains, behave in exactly the same way as free molecular chains of the corresponding reduced length, bound with each other by van der Waals forces. In fact, it has been shown above that the elasticity modulus of a piece of rubber is inversely proportional to the degree of polymerization $z$. Now, if each chain is tied up to other chains, crossing it, by sulphur atoms in $s$ equidistant points, it is equivalent, so far as the elasticity modulus is concerned, to $s$ chains consisting of $z' = z/s$ links each, so that the elasticity of the sample must suffer an $s$-fold increase.

This idea was applied by the author in 1938 to the explanation of the mechanism of muscular contraction.†

The muscles are formed by a substance—myosin—essentially similar to rubber with respect to its molecular structure, the myosin molecules being chain-like macromolecules formed by the polymerization or rather

† J. Frenkel, *Acta Phys. Chim. U.S.S.R.* **9**, 251 (1938).

condensation of amino-acids. This circumstance immediately explains the analogy between the mechanical and thermomechanical properties of rubber and of muscles in the normal, non-excited, state. It is well known, for example, that the elasticity modulus of a relaxed muscle for such deformations as leave its volume unaltered is of the order of 10 kg./cm.$^2$, i.e. of the same order of magnitude as that of ordinary soft rubber. When the muscle is extended by an external force (while remaining in the relaxed state) it is heated, exactly as is rubber, while its contraction (without excitation) is accompanied by cooling.

The specific peculiarity of muscle, with respect to rubber, consists in the fact that it can be brought from the normal (soft) to an excited (hard) state, this transition usually leading to contraction (unless the length of the muscle is kept constant by some external force). It seems natural to assume that the mechanism of this excitation is similar to that of vulcanization, i.e. consists in the binding up of the myosin chains by the molecules of some substance contained in the muscle.† This process differs from ordinary vulcanization by its reversibility, enabling the muscle to relax as a result of the rupture of the side bonds which arise in the process of excitation. The fact that the latter is accompanied by the contraction is easily explained, if it is assumed that even in the relaxed state the muscles are somewhat extended by the bones or other tissues supporting them.‡ This extension $\Delta L$ corresponds in the relaxed state to a certain force $E\,\Delta L/L$ which is balanced by an external pull $F$. If now $E$ is increased, as a result of a process similar to vulcanization, this balance is destroyed and the muscle must contract. Its hardening is a direct indication of the accompanying increase of the elasticity modulus.

The fact that myosin molecules can pass from an extended to a contracted state has been established experimentally by Astbury with the help of X-ray analysis.§ The contracted form is described by Astbury as corresponding to a curling of three consecutive links, with preservation of the value of the valence angles, into nearly closed rings as shown in Fig. 55*a* (Fig. 55*b* refers to the extended form).

Such a picture would be inconsistent with the kinetic theory of the origin of muscular force if the contraction was supposed to be wholly

† This substance is probably phosphoric acid, or, more exactly a more complicated substance, changing from one form to another by the addition or subtraction of a $H_2PO_3$ radical.

‡ This assumption seems to be in agreement with the experimental facts even in those cases where the muscles are supported by connecting tissue.

§ Astbury, *Proc. Roy. Soc.* A, **170**, 69 (1939).

uniform, as assumed by Astbury. It seems, however, that the X-ray diagrams obtained by him can be interpreted just as well on the hypothesis that a certain fraction only of the monomeric links, constituting the polymeric myosin chain (each link consisting in its turn of three elementary carbon links —$CH_2$—CNH—COH), are curled according to Astbury's scheme while the other links preserve their extended configuration. If a myosin chain consists of $z$ links, out of which $3x$ links are curled, while the other $z-3x$ remain straight, it has a certain length $L(z,x)$ which is approximately equal to

$$(z-3x)a+xa = (z-2x)a,$$

where $a$ is the length of a monomeric link. Now this condition can be realized by a number of different configurations corresponding to different positions of the curled portions along the chain. The number $P(z,x)$ of such equivalent configurations, corresponding to given values of $z$ and $x$, is easily seen to increase with $x$ up to a certain maximum value. In order to get an idea of this dependence we shall simplify the problem by assuming each link to become curled separately. In this case the number of equivalent configurations would be given by

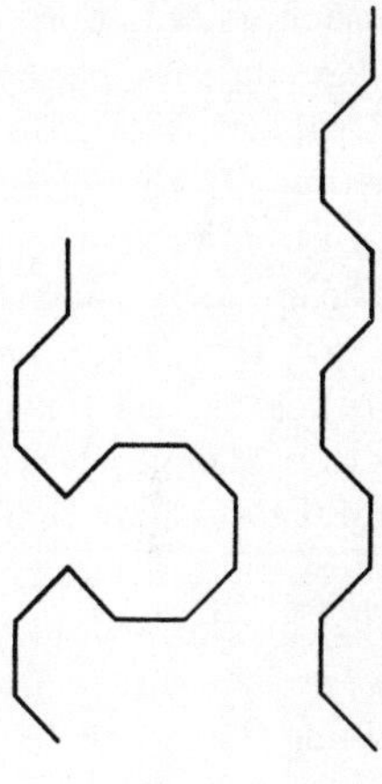

a b

FIG. 55

$$P(z,x) = \frac{z!}{x!(z-x)!},$$

and would reach a maximum value for $x = \frac{1}{2}z$. The logarithm of $P(z,x)$ multiplied by $k$ is a measure of the entropy, corresponding to a length $L(x) = a(z-x)$ of the molecule (if the length of a curled link is compared with a 'straight' one). Introducing the free energy of the chain $\Psi - TS$ and treating its energy $W$ as independent of $x$ (which seems to be contrary to Astbury's views), we obtain for the dependence between the tension and the length $L$ a relation of the same form as that previously examined in the case of rubber on the basis of the model of a 'folding ruler'. The situation is not substantially altered if a certain relatively small activation energy $U_0$ (per link) is introduced for a transition from an extended to a curled form, the resulting correction being similar to that which corresponds to the model of a chain-like molecule with hindered rotation (twisting).

# INDEX

# CATALOG OF DOVER BOOKS

# BOOKS EXPLAINING SCIENCE AND MATHEMATICS

**THE COMMON SENSE OF THE EXACT SCIENCES, W. K. Clifford.** Introduction by James Newman, edited by Karl Pearson. For 70 years this has been a guide to classical scientific and mathematical thought. Explains with unusual clarity basic concepts, such as extension of meaning of symbols, characteristics of surface boundaries, properties of plane figures, vectors, Cartesian method of determining position, etc. Long preface by Bertrand Russell. Bibliography of Clifford. Corrected, 130 diagrams redrawn. 249pp. 5⅜ x 8.
T61 Paperbound **$1.60**

**SCIENCE THEORY AND MAN, Erwin Schrödinger.** This is a complete and unabridged reissue of SCIENCE AND THE HUMAN TEMPERAMENT plus an additional essay: "What is an Elementary Particle?" Nobel Laureate Schrödinger discusses such topics as nature of scientific method, the nature of science, chance and determinism, science and society, conceptual models for physical entities, elementary particles and wave mechanics. Presentation is popular and may be followed by most people with little or no scientific training. "Fine practical preparation for a time when laws of nature, human institutions . . . are undergoing a critical examination without parallel," Waldemar Kaempffert, N. Y. TIMES. 192pp. 5⅜ x 8.
T428 Paperbound **$1.35**

**PIONEERS OF SCIENCE, O. Lodge.** Eminent scientist-expositor's authoritative, yet elementary survey of great scientific theories. Concentrating on individuals—Copernicus, Brahe, Kepler, Galileo, Descartes, Newton, Laplace, Herschel, Lord Kelvin, and other scientists—the author presents their discoveries in historical order adding biographical material on each man and full, specific explanations of their achievements. The clear and complete treatment of the post-Newtonian astronomers is a feature seldom found in other books on the subject. Index. 120 illustrations. xv + 404pp. 5⅜ x 8.
T716 Paperbound **$1.50**

**THE EVOLUTION OF SCIENTIFIC THOUGHT FROM NEWTON TO EINSTEIN, A. d'Abro.** Einstein's special and general theories of relativity, with their historical implications, are analyzed in non-technical terms. Excellent accounts of the contributions of Newton, Riemann, Weyl, Planck, Eddington, Maxwell, Lorentz and others are treated in terms of space and time, equations of electromagnetics, finiteness of the universe, methodology of science. 21 diagrams. 482pp. 5⅜ x 8.
T2 Paperound **$2.00**

**THE RISE OF THE NEW PHYSICS, A. d'Abro.** A half-million word exposition, formerly titled THE DECLINE OF MECHANISM, for readers not versed in higher mathematics. The only thorough explanation, in everyday language, of the central core of modern mathematical physical theory, treating both classical and modern theoretical physics, and presenting in terms almost anyone can understand the equivalent of 5 years of study of mathematical physics. Scientifically impeccable coverage of mathematical-physical thought from the Newtonian system up through the electronic theories of Dirac and Heisenberg and Fermi's statistics. Combines both history and exposition; provides a broad yet unified and detailed view, with constant comparison of classical and modern views on phenomena and theories. "A must for anyone doing serious study in the physical sciences," JOURNAL OF THE FRANKLIN INSTITUTE. "Extraordinary faculty . . . to explain ideas and theories of theoretical physics in the language of daily life," ISIS. First part of set covers philosophy of science, drawing upon the practice of Newton, Maxwell, Poincaré, Einstein, others, discussing modes of thought, experiment, interpretations of causality, etc. In the second part, 100 pages explain grammar and vocabulary of mathematics, with discussions of functions, groups, series, Fourier series, etc. The remainder is devoted to concrete, detailed coverage of both classical and quantum physics, explaining such topics as analytic mechanics, Hamilton's principle, wave theory of light, electromagnetic waves, groups of transformations, thermodynamics, phase rule, Brownian movement, kinetics, special relativity, Planck's original quantum theory, Bohr's atom, Zeeman effect, Broglie's wave mechanics, Heisenberg's uncertainty, Eigen-values, matrices, scores of other important topics. Discoveries and theories are covered for such men as Alembert, Born, Cantor, Debye, Euler, Foucault, Galois, Gauss, Hadamard, Kelvin, Kepler, Laplace, Maxwell, Pauli, Rayleigh, Volterra, Weyl, Young, more than 180 others. Indexed. 97 illustrations. ix + 982pp. 5⅜ x 8.
T3 Volume 1, Paperbound **$2.00**
T4 Volume 2, Paperbound **$2.00**

**CONCERNING THE NATURE OF THINGS, Sir William Bragg.** Christmas lectures delivered at the Royal Society by Nobel laureate. Why a spinning ball travels in a curved track; how uranium is transmuted to lead, etc. Partial contents: atoms, gases, liquids, crystals, metals, etc. No scientific background needed; wonderful for intelligent child. 32pp. of photos, 57 figures. xii + 232pp. 5⅜ x 8.
T31 Paperbound **$1.35**

**THE UNIVERSE OF LIGHT, Sir William Bragg.** No scientific training needed to read Nobel Prize winner's expansion of his Royal Institute Christmas Lectures. Insight into nature of light, methods and philosophy of science. Explains lenses, reflection, color, resonance, polarization, x-rays, the spectrum, Newton's work with prisms, Huygens' with polarization, Crookes' with cathode ray, etc. Leads into clear statement of 2 major historical theories of light, corpuscle and wave. Dozens of experiments you can do. 199 illus., including 2 full-page color plates. 293pp. 5⅜ x 8.
S538 Paperbound **$1.85**

**PHYSICS, THE PIONEER SCIENCE, L. W. Taylor.** First thorough text to place all important physical phenomena in cultural-historical framework; remains best work of its kind. Exposition of physical laws, theories developed chronologically, with great historical, illustrative experiments diagrammed, described, worked out mathematically. Excellent physics text for self-study as well as class work. Vol. 1: Heat, Sound: motion, acceleration, gravitation, conservation of energy, heat engines, rotation, heat, mechanical energy, etc. 211 illus. 407pp. 5⅜ x 8. Vol. 2: Light, Electricity: images, lenses, prisms, magnetism, Ohm's law, dynamos, telegraph, quantum theory, decline of mechanical view of nature, etc. Bibliography. 13 table appendix. Index. 551 illus. 2 color plates. 508pp. 5⅜ x 8.
Vol. 1 S565 Paperbound **$2.00**
Vol. 2 S566 Paperbound **$2.00**
The set **$4.00**

**FROM EUCLID TO EDDINGTON: A STUDY OF THE CONCEPTIONS OF THE EXTERNAL WORLD, Sir Edmund Whittaker.** A foremost British scientist traces the development of theories of natural philosophy from the western rediscovery of Euclid to Eddington, Einstein, Dirac, etc. The inadequacy of classical physics is contrasted with present day attempts to understand the physical world through relativity, non-Euclidean geometry, space curvature, wave mechanics, etc. 5 major divisions of examination: Space; Time and Movement; the Concepts of Classical Physics; the Concepts of Quantum Mechanics; the Eddington Universe. 212pp. 5⅜ x 8. T491 Paperbound **$1.35**

**THE STORY OF ATOMIC THEORY AND ATOMIC ENERGY, J. G. Feinberg.** Wider range of facts on physical theory, cultural implications, than any other similar source. Completely non-technical. Begins with first atomic theory, 600 B.C., goes through A-bomb, developments to 1959. Avogadro, Rutherford, Bohr, Einstein, radioactive decay, binding energy, radiation danger, future benefits of nuclear power, dozens of other topics, told in lively, related, informal manner. Particular stress on European atomic research. "Deserves special mention . . . authoritative," Saturday Review. Formerly "The Atom Story." New chapter to 1959. Index. 34 illustrations. 251pp. 5⅜ x 8. T625 Paperbound **$1.45**

**THE STRANGE STORY OF THE QUANTUM, AN ACCOUNT FOR THE GENERAL READER OF THE GROWTH OF IDEAS UNDERLYING OUR PRESENT ATOMIC KNOWLEDGE, B. Hoffmann.** Presents lucidly and expertly, with barest amount of mathematics, the problems and theories which led to modern quantum physics. Dr. Hoffmann begins with the closing years of the 19th century, when certain trifling discrepancies were noticed, and with illuminating analogies and examples takes you through the brilliant concepts of Planck, Einstein, Pauli, de Broglie, Bohr, Schroedinger, Heisenberg, Dirac, Sommerfeld, Feynman, etc. This edition includes a new, long postscript carrying the story through 1958. "Of the books attempting an account of the history and contents of our modern atomic physics which have come to my attention, this is the best," H. Margenau, Yale University, in "American Journal of Physics." 32 tables and line illustrations. Index. 275pp. 5⅜ x 8. T518 Paperbound **$1.45**

**SPACE AND TIME, Emile Borel.** An entirely non-technical introduction to relativity, by world-renowned mathematician, Sorbonne Professor. (Notes on basic mathematics are included separately.) This book has never been surpassed for insight, and extraordinary clarity of thought, as it presents scores of examples, analogies, arguments, illustrations, which explain such topics as: difficulties due to motion; gravitation a force of inertia; geodesic lines; wave-length and difference of phase; x-rays and crystal structure; the special theory of relativity; and much more. Indexes. 4 appendixes. 15 figures. xvi + 243pp. 5⅜ x 8.
T592 Paperbound **$1.45**

**THE RESTLESS UNIVERSE, Max Born.** New enlarged version of this remarkably readable account by a Nobel laureate. Moving from sub-atomic particles to universe, the author explains in very simple terms the latest theories of wave mechanics. Partial contents: air and its relatives, electrons & ions, waves & particles, electronic structure of the atom, nuclear physics. Nearly 1000 illustrations, including 7 animated sequences. 325pp. 6 x 9.
T412 Paperbound **$2.00**

**SOAP SUBBLES, THEIR COLOURS AND THE FORCES WHICH MOULD THEM, C. V. Boys.** Only complete edition, half again as much material as any other. Includes Boys' hints on performing his experiments, sources of supply. Dozens of lucid experiments show complexities of liquid films, surface tension, etc. Best treatment ever written. Introduction. 83 illustrations. Color plate. 202pp. 5⅜ x 8. T542 Paperbound **95¢**

**SPINNING TOPS AND GYROSCOPIC MOTION, John Perry.** Well-known classic of science still unsurpassed for lucid, accurate, delightful exposition. How quasi-rigidity is induced in flexible and fluid bodies by rapid motions; why gyrostat falls, top rises; nature and effect on climatic conditions of earth's precessional movement; effect of internal fluidity on rotating bodies, etc. Appendixes describe practical uses to which gyroscopes have been put in ships, compasses, monorail transportation. 62 figures. 128pp. 5⅜ x 8. T416 Paperbound **$1.00**

**MATTER & LIGHT, THE NEW PHYSICS, L. de Broglie.** Non-technical papers by a Nobel laureate explain electromagnetic theory, relativity, matter, light and radiation, wave mechanics, quantum physics, philosophy of science. Einstein, Planck, Bohr, others explained so easily that no mathematical training is needed for all but 2 of the 21 chapters. Unabridged. Index. 300pp. 5⅜ x 8. T35 Paperbound **$1.60**

## Mechanics, dynamics, thermodynamics, elasticity

**MECHANICS VIA THE CALCULUS, P. W. Norris, W. S. Legge.** Covers almost everything, from linear motion to vector analysis: equations determining motion, linear methods, compounding of simple harmonic motions, Newton's laws of motion, Hooke's law, the simple pendulum, motion of a particle in 1 plane, centers of gravity, virtual work, friction, kinetic energy of rotating bodies, equilibrium of strings, hydrostatics, sheering stresses, elasticity, etc. 550 problems. 3rd revised edition. xii + 367pp. 6 x 9. S207 Clothbound **$3.95**

**THEORETICAL MECHANICS: AN INTRODUCTION TO MATHEMATICAL PHYSICS, J. S. Ames, F. D. Murnaghan.** A mathematically rigorous development of theoretical mechanics for the advanced student, with constant practical applications. Used in hundreds of advanced courses. An unusually thorough coverage of gyroscopic and baryscopic material, detailed analyses of the Corilis acceleration, applications of Lagrange's equations, motion of the double pendulum, Hamilton-Jacobi partial differential equations, group velocity and dispersion, etc. Special relativity is also included. 159 problems. 44 figures. ix + 462pp. 5⅜ x 8. S461 Paperbound **$2.00**

**THEORETICAL MECHANICS: STATICS AND THE DYNAMICS OF A PARTICLE, W. D. MacMillan.** Used for over 3 decades as a self-contained and extremely comprehensive advanced undergraduate text in mathematical physics, physics, astronomy, and deeper foundations of engineering. Early sections require only a knowledge of geometry; later, a working knowledge of calculus. Hundreds of basic problems, including projectiles to the moon, escape velocity, harmonic motion, ballistics, falling bodies, transmission of power, stress and strain, elasticity, astronomical problems. 340 practice problems plus many fully worked out examples make it possible to test and extend principles developed in the text. 200 figures. xvii + 430pp. 5⅜ x 8. S467 Paperbound **$2.00**

**THEORETICAL MECHANICS: THE THEORY OF THE POTENTIAL, W. D. MacMillan.** A comprehensive, well balanced presentation of potential theory, serving both as an introduction and a reference work with regard to specific problems, for physicists and mathematicians. No prior knowledge of integral relations is assumed, and all mathematical material is developed as it becomes necessary. Includes: Attraction of Finite Bodies; Newtonian Potential Function; Vector Fields, Green and Gauss Theorems; Attractions of Surfaces and Lines; Surface Distribution of Matter; Two-Layer Surfaces; Spherical Harmonics; Ellipsoidal Harmonics; etc. "The great number of particular cases . . . should make the book valuable to geophysicists and others actively engaged in practical applications of the potential theory," Review of Scientific Instruments. Index. Bibliography. xiii + 469pp. 5⅜ x 8. S486 Paperbound **$2.25**

**THEORETICAL MECHANICS: DYNAMICS OF RIGID BODIES, W. D. MacMillan.** Theory of dynamics of a rigid body is developed, using both the geometrical and analytical methods of instruction. Begins with exposition of algebra of vectors, it goes through momentum principles, motion in space, use of differential equations and infinite series to solve more sophisticated dynamics problems. Partial contents: moments of inertia, systems of free particles, motion parallel to a fixed plane, rolling motion, method of periodic solutions, much more. 82 figs. 199 problems. Bibliography. Indexes. xii + 476pp. 5⅜ x 8. S641 Paperbound **$2.00**

**MATHEMATICAL FOUNDATIONS OF STATISTICAL MECHANICS, A. I. Khinchin.** Offering a precise and rigorous formulation of problems, this book supplies a thorough and up-to-date exposition. It provides analytical tools needed to replace cumbersome concepts, and furnishes for the first time a logical step-by-step introduction to the subject. Partial contents: geometry & kinematics of the phase space, ergodic problem, reduction to theory of probability, application of central limit problem, ideal monatomic gas, foundation of thermo-dynamics, dispersion and distribution of sum functions. Key to notations. Index. viii + 179pp. 5⅜ x 8. S147 Paperbound **$1.35**

**ELEMENTARY PRINCIPLES IN STATISTICAL MECHANICS, J. W. Gibbs.** Last work of the great Yale mathematical physicist, still one of the most fundamental treatments available for advanced students and workers in the field. Covers the basic principle of conservation of probability of phase, theory of errors in the calculated phases of a system, the contributions of Clausius, Maxwell, Boltzmann, and Gibbs himself, and much more. Includes valuable comparison of statistical mechanics with thermodynamics: Carnot's cycle, mechanical definitions of entropy, etc. xvi + 208pp. 5⅜ x 8. S707 Paperbound **$1.45**

**THE DYNAMICS OF PARTICLES AND OF RIGID, ELASTIC, AND FLUID BODIES; BEING LECTURES ON MATHEMATICAL PHYSICS, A. G. Webster.** The reissuing of this classic fills the need for a comprehensive work on dynamics. A wide range of topics is covered in unusually great depth, applying ordinary and partial differential equations. Part I considers laws of motion and methods applicable to systems of all sorts; oscillation, resonance, cyclic systems, etc. Part 2 is a detailed study of the dynamics of rigid bodies. Part 3 introduces the theory of potential; stress and strain, Newtonian potential functions, gyrostatics, wave and vortex motion, etc. Further contents: Kinematics of a point; Lagrange's equations; Hamilton's principle; Systems of vectors; Statics and dynamics of deformable bodies; much more, not easily found together in one volume. Unabridged reprinting of 2nd edition. 20 pages of notes on differential equations and the higher analysis. 203 illustrations. Selected bibliography. Index. xi + 588pp. 5⅜ x 8. S522 Paperbound **$2.35**

**A TREATISE ON DYNAMICS OF A PARTICLE, E. J. Routh.** Elementary text on dynamics for beginning mathematics or physics student. Unusually detailed treatment from elementary definitions to motion in 3 dimensions, emphasizing concrete aspects. Much unique material important in recent applications. Covers impulsive forces, rectilinear and constrained motion in 2 dimensions, harmonic and parabolic motion, degrees of freedom, closed orbits, the conical pendulum, the principle of least action, Jacobi's method, and much more. Index. 559 problems, many fully worked out, incorporated into text. xiii + 418pp. 5⅜ x 8.
S696 Paperbound **$2.25**

**DYNAMICS OF A SYSTEM OF RIGID BODIES (Elementary Section), E. J. Routh.** Revised 7th edition of this standard reference. This volume covers the dynamical principles of the subject, and its more elementary applications: finding moments of inertia by integration, foci of inertia, d'Alembert's principle, impulsive forces, motion in 2 and 3 dimensions, Lagrange's equations, relative indicatrix, Euler's theorem, large tautochronous motions, etc. Index. 55 figures. Scores of problems. xv + 443pp. 5⅜ x 8. S664 Paperbound **$2.35**

**DYNAMICS OF A SYSTEM OF RIGID BODIES (Advanced Section), E. J. Routh.** Revised 6th edition of a classic reference aid. Much of its material remains unique. Partial contents: moving axes, relative motion, oscillations about equilibrium, motion. Motion of a body under no forces, any forces. Nature of motion given by linear equations and conditions of stability. Free, forced vibrations, constants of integration, calculus of finite differences, variations, precession and nutation, motion of the moon, motion of string, chain, membranes. 64 figures. 498pp. 5⅜ x 8. S229 Paperbound **$2.35**

**DYNAMICAL THEORY OF GASES, James Jeans.** Divided into mathematical and physical chapters for the convenience of those not expert in mathematics, this volume discusses the mathematical theory of gas in a steady state, thermodynamics, Boltzmann and Maxwell, kinetic theory, quantum theory, exponentials, etc. 4th enlarged edition, with new material on quantum theory, quantum dynamics, etc. Indexes. 28 figures. 444pp. 6⅛ x 9¼.
S136 Paperbound **$2.45**

**FOUNDATIONS OF POTENTIAL THEORY, O. D. Kellogg.** Based on courses given at Harvard this is suitable for both advanced and beginning mathematicians. Proofs are rigorous, and much material not generally avialable elsewhere is included. Partial contents: forces of gravity, fields of force, divergence theorem, properties of Newtonian potentials at points of free space, potentials as solutions of Laplace's equations, harmonic functions, electrostatics, electric images, logarithmic potential, etc. One of Grundlehren Series. ix + 384pp. 5⅜ x 8.
S144 Paperbound **$1.98**

**THERMODYNAMICS, Enrico Fermi.** Unabridged reproduction of 1937 edition. Elementary in treatment; remarkable for clarity, organization. Requires no knowledge of advanced math beyond calculus, only familiarity with fundamentals of thermometry, calorimetry. Partial Contents: Thermodynamic systems; First & Second laws of thermodynamics; Entropy; Thermodynamic potentials: phase rule, reversible electric cell; Gaseous reactions: van't Hoff reaction box, principle of LeChatelier; Thermodynamics of dilute solutions: osmotic & vapor pressures, boiling & freezing points; Entropy constant. Index. 25 problems. 24 illustrations. x + 160pp. 5⅜ x 8. S361 Paperbound **$1.75**

**THE THERMODYNAMICS OF ELECTRICAL PHENOMENA IN METALS and A CONDENSED COLLECTION OF THERMODYNAMIC FORMULAS, P. W. Bridgman.** Major work by the Nobel Prizewinner: stimulating conceptual introduction to aspects of the electron theory of metals, giving an intuitive understanding of fundamental relationships concealed by the formal systems of Onsager and others. Elementary mathematical formulations show clearly the fundamental thermodynamical relationships of the electric field, and a complete phenomenological theory of metals is created. This is the work in which Bridgman announced his famous "thermomotive force" and his distinction between "driving" and "working" electromotive force. We have added in this Dover edition the author's long unavailable tables of thermodynamic formulas, extremely valuable for the speed of reference they allow. Two works bound as one. Index. 33 figures. Bibliography. xviii + 256pp. 5⅜ x 8. S723 Paperbound **$1.65**

**REFLECTIONS ON THE MOTIVE POWER OF FIRE, by Sadi Carnot,** and other papers on the 2nd law of thermodynamics by E. Clapeyron and R. Clausius. Carnot's "Reflections" laid the groundwork of modern thermodynamics. Its non-technical, mostly verbal statements examine the relations between heat and the work done by heat in engines, establishing conditions for the economical working of these engines. The papers by Clapeyron and Clausius here reprinted added further refinements to Carnot's work, and led to its final acceptance by physicists. Selections from posthumous manuscripts of Carnot are also included. All papers in English. New introduction by E. Mendoza. 12 illustrations. xxii + 152pp. 5⅜ x 8.
S661 Paperbound **$1.50**

**TREATISE ON THERMODYNAMICS, Max Planck.** Based on Planck's original papers this offers a uniform point of view for the entire field and has been used as an introduction for students who have studied elementary chemistry, physics, and calculus. Rejecting the earlier approaches of Helmholtz and Maxwell, the author makes no assumptions regarding the nature of heat, but begins with a few empirical facts, and from these deduces new physical and chemical laws. 3rd English edition of this standard text by a Nobel laureate. xvi + 297pp. 5⅜ x 8. S219 Paperbound **$1.75**

**THE THEORY OF HEAT RADIATION, Max Planck.** A pioneering work in thermodynamics, providing basis for most later work. Nobel Laureate Planck writes on Deductions from Electrodynamics and Thermodynamics, Entropy and Probability, Irreversible Radiation Processes, etc. Starts with simple experimental laws of optics, advances to problems of spectral distribution of energy and irreversibility. Bibliography. 7 illustrations, xiv + 224pp. 5⅜ x 8.
S546 Paperbound **$1.50**

**A HISTORY OF THE THEORY OF ELASTICITY AND THE STRENGTH OF MATERIALS, I. Todhunter and K. Pearson.** For over 60 years a basic reference, unsurpassed in scope or authority. Both a history of the mathematical theory of elasticity from Galileo, Hooke, and Mariotte to Saint Venant, Kirchhoff, Clebsch, and Lord Kelvin and a detailed presentation of every important mathematical contribution during this period. Presents proofs of thousands of theorems and laws, summarizes every relevant treatise, many unavailable elsewhere. Practically a book apiece is devoted to modern founders: Saint Venant, Lame, Boussinesq, Rankine, Lord Kelvin, F. Neumann, Kirchhoff, Clebsch. Hundreds of pages of technical and physical treatises on specific applications of elasticity to particular materials. Indispensable for the mathematician, physicist, or engineer working with elasticity. Unabridged, corrected reprint of original 3-volume 1886-1893 edition. Three volume set. Two indexes. Appendix to Vol. I. Total of 2344pp. 5⅜ x 8⅜.
S914–916 The set, Clothbound **$12.50**

**THE MATHEMATICAL THEORY OF ELASTICITY, A. E. H. Love.** A wealth of practical illustration combined with thorough discussion of fundamentals—theory, application, special problems and solutions. Partial Contents: Analysis of Strain & Stress, Elasticity of Solid Bodies, Elasticity of Crystals, Vibration of Spheres, Cylinders, Propagation of Waves in Elastic Solid Media, Torsion, Theory of Continuous Beams, Plates. Rigorous treatment of Volterra's theory of dislocations, 2-dimensional elastic systems, other topics of modern interest. "For years the standard treatise on elasticity," AMERICAN MATHEMATICAL MONTHLY. 4th revised edition. Index. 76 figures. xviii + 643pp. 6⅛ x 9¼.
S174 Paperbound **$2.95**

**RAYLEIGH'S PRINCIPLE AND ITS APPLICATIONS TO ENGINEERING, G. Temple & W. Bickley.** Rayleigh's principle developed to provide upper and lower estimates of true value of fundamental period of a vibrating system, or condition of stability of elastic systems. Illustrative examples; rigorous proofs in special chapters. Partial contents: Energy method of discussing vibrations, stability. Perturbation theory, whirling of uniform shafts. Criteria of elastic stability. Application of energy method. Vibrating systems. Proof, accuracy, successive approximations, application of Rayleigh's principle. Synthetic theorems. Numerical, graphical methods. Equilibrium configurations, Ritz's method. Bibliography. Index. 22 figures. ix + 156pp. 5⅜ x 8.
S307 Paperbound **$1.50**

**INVESTIGATIONS ON THE THEORY OF THE BROWNIAN MOVEMENT, Albert Einstein.** Reprints from rare European journals. 5 basic papers, including the Elementary Theory of the Brownian Movement, written at the request of Lorentz to provide a simple explanation. Translated by A. D. Cowper. Annotated, edited by R. Fürth. 33pp. of notes elucidate, give history of previous investigations. Author, subject indexes. 62 footnotes. 124pp. 5⅜ x 8.
S304 Paperbound **$1.25**

See also: **FUNDAMENTAL FORMULAS OF PHYSICS, D. H. Menzel.**

## ENGINEERING

**THEORY OF FLIGHT, Richard von Mises.** Remains almost unsurpassed as balanced, well-written account of fundamental fluid dynamics, and situations in which air compressibility effects are unimportant. Stressing equally theory and practice, avoiding formidable mathematical structure, it conveys a full understanding of physical phenomena and mathematical concepts. Contains perhaps the best introduction to general theory of stability. "Outstanding," Scientific, Medical, and Technical Books. New introduction by K. H. Hohenemser. Bibliographical, historical notes. Index. 408 illustrations. xvi + 620pp. 5⅜ x 8⅜.
S541 Paperbound **$2.85**

**THEORY OF WING SECTIONS, I. H. Abbott, A. E. von Doenhoff.** Concise compilation of subsonic aerodynamic characteristics of modern NASA wing sections, with description of their geometry, associated theory. Primarily reference work for engineers, students, it gives methods, data for using wing-section data to predict characteristics. Particularly valuable: chapters on thin wings, airfoils; complete summary of NACA's experimental observations, system of construction families of airfoils. 350pp. of tables on Basic Thickness Forms, Mean Lines, Airfoil Ordinates, Aerodynamic Characteristics of Wing Sections. Index. Bibliography. 191 illustrations. Appendix. 705pp. 5⅜ x 8.
S558 Paperbound **$2.95**

**SUPERSONIC AERODYNAMICS, E. R. C. Miles.** Valuable theoretical introduction to the supersonic domain, with emphasis on mathematical tools and principles, for practicing aerodynamicists and advanced students in aeronautical engineering. Covers fundamental theory, divergence theorem and principles of circulation, compressible flow and Helmholtz laws, the Prandtl-Busemann graphic method for 2-dimensional flow, oblique shock waves, the Taylor-Maccoll method for cones in supersonic flow, the Chaplygin method for 2-dimensional flow, etc. Problems range from practical engineering problems to development of theoretical results. "Rendered outstanding by the unprecedented scope of its contents . . . has undoubtedly filled a vital gap," AERONAUTICAL ENGINEERING REVIEW. Index. 173 problems, answers. 106 diagrams. 7 tables. xii + 255pp. 5⅜ x 8.
S214 Paperbound **$1.45**

**K. Pearson; THEORY AND OPERATION OF THE SLIDE RULE, J. P. Ellis; DIFFERENTIAL EQUATIONS FOR ENGINEERS, P. Franklin; MATHEMATICAL METHODS FOR SCIENTISTS AND ENGINEERS, L. P. Smith; APPLIED MATHEMATICS FOR RADIO AND COMMUNICATIONS ENGINEERS, C. E. Smith; MATHEMATICS OF MODERN ENGINEERING, E. G. Keller, R. E. Doherty; THEORY OF FUNCTIONS AS APPLIED TO ENGINEERING PROBLEMS, R. Rothe, F. Ollendorff, K. Pohlhausen.**

# CHEMISTRY AND PHYSICAL CHEMISTRY

**ORGANIC CHEMISTRY, F. C. Whitmore.** The entire subject of organic chemistry for the practicing chemist and the advanced student. Storehouse of facts, theories, processes found elsewhere only in specialized journals. Covers aliphatic compounds (500 pages on the properties and synthetic preparation of hydrocarbons, halides, proteins, ketones, etc.), alicyclic compounds, aromatic compounds, heterocyclic compounds, organophosphorus and organometallic compounds. Methods of synthetic preparation analyzed critically throughout. Includes much of biochemical interest. "The scope of this volume is astonishing," INDUSTRIAL AND ENGINEERING CHEMISTRY. 12,000-reference index. 2387-item bibliography. Total of x + 1005pp. 5⅜ x 8. Two volume set.
S700 Vol I Paperbound **$2.00**
S701 Vol II Paperbound **$2.00**
The set **$4.00**

**THE PRINCIPLES OF ELECTROCHEMISTRY, D. A. MacInnes.** Basic equations for almost every subfield of electrochemistry from first principles, referring at all times to the soundest and most recent theories and results; unusually useful as text or as reference. Covers coulometers and Faraday's Law, electrolytic conductance, the Debye-Hueckel method for the theoretical calculation of activity coefficients, concentration cells, standard electrode potentials, thermodynamic ionization constants, pH, potentiometric titrations, irreversible phenomena, Planck's equation, and much more. "Excellent treatise," AMERICAN CHEMICAL SOCIETY JOURNAL. "Highly recommended," CHEMICAL AND METALLURGICAL ENGINEERING. 2 Indices. Appendix. 585-item bibliography. 137 figures. 94 tables. ii + 478pp. 5⅝ x 8⅜.
S52 Paperbound **$2.35**

**THE CHEMISTRY OF URANIUM: THE ELEMENT, ITS BINARY AND RELATED COMPOUNDS, J. J. Katz and E. Rabinowitch.** Vast post-World War II collection and correlation of thousands of AEC reports and published papers in a useful and easily accessible form, still the most complete and up-to-date compilation. Treats "dry uranium chemistry," occurrences, preparation, properties, simple compounds, isotopic composition, extraction from ores, spectra, alloys, etc. Much material available only here. Index. Thousands of evaluated bibliographical references. 324 tables, charts, figures. xxi + 609pp. 5⅜ x 8. S757 Paperbound **$2.95**

**KINETIC THEORY OF LIQUIDS, J. Frenkel.** Regarding the kinetic theory of liquids as a generalization and extension of the theory of solid bodies, this volume covers all types of arrangements of solids, thermal displacements of atoms, interstitial atoms and ions, orientational and rotational motion of molecules, and transition between states of matter. Mathematical theory is developed close to the physical subject matter. 216 bibliographical footnotes. 55 figures. xi + 485pp. 5⅜ x 8. S94 Clothbound **$3.95**
S95 Paperbound **$2.45**

**POLAR MOLECULES, Pieter Debye.** This work by Nobel laureate Debye offers a complete guide to fundamental electrostatic field relations, polarizability, molecular structure. Partial contents: electric intensity, displacement and force, polarization by orientation, molar polarization and molar refraction, halogen-hydrides, polar liquids, ionic saturation, dielectric constant, etc. Special chapter considers quantum theory. Indexed. 172pp. 5⅜ x 8.
S64 Paperbound **$1.50**

**ELASTICITY, PLASTICITY AND STRUCTURE OF MATTER, R. Houwink.** Standard treatise on rheological aspects of different technically important solids such as crystals, resins, textiles, rubber, clay, many others. Investigates general laws for deformations; determines divergences from these laws for certain substances. Covers general physical and mathematical aspects of plasticity, elasticity, viscosity. Detailed examination of deformations, internal structure of matter in relation to elastic and plastic behavior, formation of solid matter from a fluid, conditions for elastic and plastic behavior of matter. Treats glass, asphalt, gutta percha, balata, proteins, baker's dough, lacquers, sulphur, others. 2nd revised, enlarged edition. Extensive revised bibliography in over 500 footnotes. Index. Table of symbols. 214 figures. xviii + 368pp. 6 x 9¼. S385 Paperbound **$2.45**

**THE PHASE RULE AND ITS APPLICATION, Alexander Findlay.** Covering chemical phenomena of 1, 2, 3, 4, and multiple component systems, this "standard work on the subject" (NATURE, London), has been completely revised and brought up to date by A. N. Campbell and N. O. Smith. Brand new material has been added on such matters as binary, tertiary liquid equilibria, solid solutions in ternary systems, quinary systems of salts and water. Completely revised to triangular coordinates in ternary systems, clarified graphic representation, solid models, etc. 9th revised edition. Author, subject indexes. 236 figures. 505 footnotes, mostly bibliographic. xii + 494pp. 5⅜ x 8. S91 Paperbound **$2.45**

**TERNARY SYSTEMS: INTRODUCTION TO THE THEORY OF THREE COMPONENT SYSTEMS, G. Masing.** Furnishes detailed discussion of representative types of 3-components systems, both in solid models (particularly metallic alloys) and isothermal models. Discusses mechanical mixture without compounds and without solid solutions; unbroken solid solution series; solid solutions with solubility breaks in two binary systems; iron-silicon-aluminum alloys; allotropic forms of iron in ternary system; other topics. Bibliography. Index. 166 illustrations. 178pp. 5⅝ x 8⅜. S631 Paperbound **$1.45**

**THE STORY OF ALCHEMY AND EARLY CHEMISTRY, J. M. Stillman.** An authoritative, scholarly work, highly readable, of development of chemical knowledge from 4000 B.C. to downfall of phlogiston theory in late 18th century. Every important figure, many quotations. Brings alive curious, almost incredible history of alchemical beliefs, practices, writings of Arabian Prince Oneeyade, Vincent of Beauvais, Geber, Zosimos, Paracelsus, Vitruvius, scores more. Studies work, thought of Black, Cavendish, Priestley, Van Helmont, Bergman, Lavoisier, Newton, etc. Index. Bibliography. 579pp. 5⅜ x 8. S628 Paperbound **$2.45**

See also: **ATOMIC SPECTRA AND ATOMIC STRUCTURE, G. Herzberg; INVESTIGATIONS ON THE THEORY OF THE BROWNIAN MOVEMENT, A. Einstein; TREATISE ON THERMODYNAMICS, M. Planck.**

## ASTRONOMY AND ASTROPHYSICS

**AN ELEMENTARY SURVEY OF CELESTIAL MECHANICS, Y. Ryabov.** Elementary exposition of gravitational theory and celestial mechanics. Historical introduction and coverage of basic principles, including: the elliptic, the orbital plane, the 2- and 3-body problems, the discovery of Neptune, planetary rotation, the length of the day, the shapes of galaxies, satellites (detailed treatment of Sputnik I), etc. First American reprinting of successful Russian popular exposition. Elementary algebra and trigonometry helpful, but not necessary; presentation chiefly verbal. Appendix of theorem proofs. 58 figures. 165pp. 5⅜ x 8. T756 Paperbound **$1.25**

**THE SKY AND ITS MYSTERIES, E. A. Beet.** One of most lucid books on mysteries of universe; deals with astronomy from earliest observations to latest theories of expansion of universe, source of stellar energy, birth of planets, origin of moon craters, possibility of life on other planets. Discusses effects of sunspots on weather; distances, ages of several stars; master plan of universe; methods and tools of astronomers; much more. "Eminently readable book," London Times. Extensive bibliography. Over 50 diagrams. 12 full-page plates, fold-out star map. Introduction. Index, 238pp. 5¼ x 7½. T627 Clothbound **$3.00**

**THE REALM OF THE NEBULAE, E. Hubble.** One of the great astronomers of our time records his formulation of the concept of "island universes," and its impact on astronomy. Such topics are covered as the velocity-distance relation; classification, nature, distances, general field of nebulae; cosmological theories; nebulae in the neighborhood of the Milky Way. 39 photos of nebulae, nebulae clusters, spectra of nebulae, and velocity distance relations shown by spectrum comparison. "One of the most progressive lines of astronomical research," The Times (London). New introduction by A. Sandage. 55 illustrations.. Index. iv + 201pp. 5⅜ x 8. S455 Paperbound **$1.50**

**OUT OF THE SKY, H. H. Nininger.** A non-technical but comprehensive introduction to "meteoritics", the young science concerned with all aspects of the arrival of matter from outer space. Written by one of the world's experts on meteorites, this work shows how, despite difficulties of observation and sparseness of data, a considerable body of knowledge has arisen. It defines meteors and meteorites; studies fireball clusters and processions, meteorite composition, size, distribution, showers, explosions, origins, craters, and much more. A true connecting link between astronomy and geology. More than 175 photos, 22 other illustrations. References. Bibliography of author's publications on meteorites. Index. viii + 336pp. 5⅜ x 8. T519 Paperbound **$1.85**

**SATELLITES AND SCIENTIFIC RESEARCH, D. King-Hele.** Non-technical account of the manmade satellites and the discoveries they have yielded up to the spring of 1959. Brings together information hitherto published only in hard-to-get scientific journals. Includes the life history of a typical satellite, methods of tracking, new information on the shape of the earth, zones of radiation, etc. Over 60 diagrams and 6 photographs. Mathematical appendix. Bibliography of over 100 items. Index. xii + 180pp. 5⅜ x 8½. T703 Clothbound **$4.00**

**HOW TO MAKE A TELESCOPE, Jean Texereau.** Enables the most inexperienced to choose, design, and build an f/6 or f/8 Newtonian type reflecting telescope, with an altazimuth Couder mounting, suitable for lunar, planetary, and stellar observation. A practical step-by-step course covering every operation and every piece of equipment. Basic principles of geometric and physical optics are discussed (though unnecessary to construction), and the merits of reflectors and refractors compared. A thorough discussion of eyepieces, finders, grinding, installation, testing, using the instrument, etc. 241 figures and 38 photos show almost every operation and tool. Potential errors are anticipated as much as possible. Foreword by A. Couder. Bibliography and sources of supply listing. Index. xiii + 191pp. 6¼ x 10. T464 Clothbound **$3.50**

# LANGUAGE AND TRAVEL AIDS FOR SCIENTISTS

## Trubner foreign language manuals

These unusual books are members of the famous Trubner series of colloquial manuals. They have been written to provide adults with a sound colloquial knowledge of a foreign language, and are suited for either class use or self-study. Each book is a complete course in itself, with progressive, easy to follow lessons. Phonetics, grammar, and syntax are covered, while hundreds of phrases and idioms, reading texts, exercises, and vocabulary are included. These books are unusual in being neither skimpy nor overdetailed in grammatical matters, and in presenting up-to-date, colloquial, and practical phrase material. Bilingual presentation is stressed, to make thorough self-study easier for the reader.

**COLLOQUIAL HINDUSTANI, A. H. Harley,** formerly Nizam's Reader in Urdu, U. of London. 30 pages on phonetics and scripts (devanagari & Arabic-Persian) are followed by 29 lessons, including material on English and Arabic-Persian influences. Key to all exercises. Vocabulary. 5 x 7½. 147pp. Clothbound **$1.75**

**COLLOQUIAL GERMAN, P. F. Doring.** Intensive thorough coverage of grammar in easily-followed form. Excellent for brush-up, with hundreds of colloquial phrases. 34 pages of bilingual texts. 224pp. 5 x 7½. Clothbound **$1.75**

**COLLOQUIAL ARABIC. DeLacy O'Leary.** Foremost Islamic scholar covers language of Egypt, Syria, Palestine, & Northern Arabia. Extremely clear coverage of complex Arabic verbs & noun plurals; also cultural aspects of language. Vocabulary. xviii + 192pp. 5 x 7½. Clothbound **$1.75**

**COLLOQUIAL PERSIAN, L. P. Elwell-Sutton.** Best introduction to modern Persian, with 90 page grammatical section followed by conversations, 35 page vocabulary. 139pp. Clothbound **$1.75**

**COLLOQUIAL SPANISH, W. R. Patterson.** Castilian grammar and colloquial language, loaded with bilingual phrases and colloquialisms. Excellent for review or self-study. 164pp. 5 x 7½. Clothbound **$1.75**

**COLLOQUIAL RUMANIAN, G. Nandris,** Professor of University of London. Extremely thorough coverage of phonetics, grammar, syntax; also included 70 page reader, and 70 page vocabulary. Probably the best grammar for this increasingly important language. 340pp. 5 x 7½. Clothbound **$2.50**

**COLLOQUIAL FRENCH, W. R. Patterson.** 16th revised edition of this extremely popular manual. Grammar explained with model clarity, and hundreds of useful expressions and phrases; exercises, reading texts, etc. Appendixes of new useful words and phrases. 223pp. 5 x 7½. Clothbound **$1.75**

**COLLOQUIAL CZECH, J. Schwarz,** former headmaster of Lingua Institute, Prague. Full easily followed coverage of grammar, hundreds of immediately useable phrases, texts. Perhaps the best Czech grammar in print. "An absolutely successful textbook," JOURNAL OF CZECHOSLOVAK FORCES IN GREAT BRITAIN. 252pp. 5 x 7½. Clothbound **$3.00**

**COLLOQUIAL ITALIAN, A. L. Hayward.** Excellent self-study course in grammar, vocabulary, idioms, and reading. Easy progressive lessons will give a good working knowledge of Italian in the shortest possible time. 5 x 7½. Clothbound **$1.75**

**AN ENGLISH-FRENCH-GERMAN-SPANISH WORD FREQUENCY DICTIONARY, H. S. Eaton.** An indispensable language study aid, this is a semantic frequency list of the 6000 most frequently used words in 4 languages—24,000 words in all. The lists, based on concepts rather than words alone, and containing all modern, exact, and idomatic vocabulary, are arranged side by side to form a unique 4-language dictionary. A simple key indicates the importance of the individual words within each language. Over 200 pages of separate indexes for each language enable you to locate individual words at a glance. Formerly "Semantic Frequency List." 2 Appendixes. xxi + 441pp. 6 x 9. T738 Paperbound **$2.45**



*Dover publishes books on art, music, philosophy, literature, languages, history, social sciences, psychology, handcrafts, orientalia, puzzles and entertainments, chess, pets and gardens, books explaining science, intermediate and higher mathematics mathematical physics, engineering, biological sciences, earth sciences, classics of science, etc. Write to:*

*Dept. catrr.*
*Dover Publications, Inc.*
*180 Varick Street, N. Y. 14, N. Y.*